Tables of the
Negative Binomial Probability Distribution

Tables of the
Negative Binomial Probability Distribution

Eric Williamson & Michael H Bretherton

John Wiley & Sons London New York

Library of Congress
Catalog Card Number 63-23217

Designed and printed at
The Kynoch Press, Birmingham, England

Contents

Preface

During the last decade, due to the advent of the electronic computer, an ever-increasing collection of numerical tables has reached the market. Virtually all the important mathematical and statistical functions have been tabulated, along with many specialized collections of tables. One notable omission, however, has been the tabulation of the Negative Binomial Probability Distribution, the importance of which is becoming increasingly apparent.

Frequently, in the practical application of statistics, a discrete probability distribution is required to describe events which appear to occur at random, e.g. the arrivals of customers at a service point, the frequencies of accidents in a factory, etc. In cases such as these, it is common practice to suppose that the frequencies of the events follow a Poisson distribution. The assumption inherent in the Poisson series, however, is that the probability of an event remains constant, which in practice is rarely true. Any variation in the expectation of an event—in particular, any tendency for one event to increase the probability of another—will increase the variance of the distribution relative to the mean, and a negative binomial distribution will invariably better describe the data.

The present work contains 1,480 negative binomial tables covering, fairly comprehensively, distributions having mean values between 0·1 and 10, and including some beyond this range. It is anticipated that the tables will frequently be used for the fitting of negative binomial distributions to observed data. To assist in this procedure a section has been included on the estimation of the parameters, mention being made of the maximum-likelihood method. Several references are given for further reading on the subject.

Practitioners in many branches of statistics have recognised areas where the theory of the negative binomial distribution may be applied but have in the past resorted to approximations. It is the authors' hope that this volume will prove an asset to those concerned with the application of the theory to practical problems.

The first application of the negative binomial probability distribution was brought to the notice of statisticians by Yule (1910)*. Suppose that we have a population subjected to recurrent exposures to a disease, and suppose that during an exposure each member of the population has an equal probability p of contracting the disease. After n exposures, the proportions who have contracted the disease 0, 1, 2, ... times will be given by

$$q^n, \; npq^{n-1}, \; \frac{n(n-1)}{2!} p^2 q^{n-2}, \ldots$$

i.e. terms of the positive binomial series $(q+p)^n$. If k unfavourable exposures to the disease are fatal to the individual, the proportion surviving after n exposures will be given by the first k terms of the binomial $(q+p)^n$. The proportion dying during the nth exposure will consist of those who contracted the disease $(k-1)$ times in the first $(n-1)$ exposures and who contract it again during the nth exposure, i.e. it will be

$$\binom{n-1}{k-1} p^{k-1} q^{n-k} \times p = \binom{n-1}{k-1} p^k q^{n-k}$$

and since deaths do not commence until the kth exposure, the proportion of deaths at the kth, $(k+1)$th ... exposure will be

$$p^k \left\{ 1, \; kq, \; k(k+1)\frac{q^2}{2!}, \ldots \right\}$$

i.e. successive terms in the expansion of $p^k (1-q)^{-k}$, a binomial with a negative index.

Thus the proportions of the original population dying during successive exposures are given by successive terms of the negative binomial distribution, the first deaths occurring at the kth exposure.

Most of the practical applications of the negative binomial distribution are due to its derivation as a generalized form of the Poisson distribution,

$$\frac{e^{-\lambda} \lambda^r}{r!}$$

The condition of the Poisson law that the probability of an event is small implies that we should expect the

---

*Mention was first made of the distribution by Montmort (1713).

Poisson distribution capable of describing the frequencies of rare events, so long as the expectation λ remains constant from trial to trial. The classical example of this is the data of L. von Bortkiewicz showing the probability of a cavalryman being killed by the kick of a horse in the course of a year. Table 1 shows, in the second column, the frequency of the number of deaths per corps per year.

Comparison with the original data shows that the Poisson frequencies given in the third column

Table 1

The number of men in ten Prussian army corps killed by a horse kick in the twenty years 1875–94 (Bortkiewicz, 1898)

Number of deaths	Observed frequency	Poisson distribution with same mean
0	109	108·7
1	65	66·3
2	22	20·2
3	3	4·1
4	1	0·6
5 and over	0	0·1
	200	**200**

The mean number of deaths per corps per year is 0·61. The variance is 0·608.

Table 2

Accidents to 647 women in 5 weeks, working on high explosive shells (Greenwood and Yule, 1920)

Number of accidents	Observed frequency	Poisson distribution with same mean	Negative binomial distribution with same mean and variance
0	447	406	442
1	132	189	140
2	42	45	45
3	21	7	14
4	3	1	5
5 and over	2	0·1	2
	647	**648·1**	**648**

The mean number of accidents per person is 0·47. The variance is 0·69.

provide a remarkably good fit. The variance is very close to the mean, which also accords with the theory.

The Poisson frequencies in the third column of Table 2, on the other hand, provide a poor fit to the observed frequencies of accidents given in column 2.

We can account for this discrepancy by assuming that people may be unequally exposed to the risk of accident. Individuals vary in the degree of skill they employ and in the amount of care they exercise, and even a given individual's liability to accident will vary from time to time depending on such factors as stress, fatigue, etc. Suppose, then, that this variation in risk is represented by different values of λ in the Poisson distribution

$$\frac{e^{-\lambda}\lambda^r}{r!}$$

then if λ is distributed with a gamma type probability density function*

$$dF = \frac{c^k}{\Gamma(k)}\,e^{-c\lambda}\,\lambda^{k-1}\,d\lambda$$

the frequency of r accidents will be given by

$$\int_0^\infty \frac{c^k}{\Gamma(k)}\,e^{-c\lambda}\,\lambda^{k-1} \cdot \frac{e^{-\lambda}\lambda^r}{r!}\,d\lambda$$

or the coefficient of t^r in

$$\frac{c^k}{\Gamma(k)}\int_0^\infty e^{-c\lambda}\,\lambda^{k-1}\,e^{-\lambda+\lambda t}\,d\lambda$$

which, on substitution of $\lambda = \dfrac{u}{c+1-t}$, becomes

$$\frac{c^k}{\Gamma(k)(c+1-t)^k}\int_0^\infty u^{k-1}\,e^{-u}\,du = \frac{c^k}{(c+1-t)^k}$$

Thus the frequency of r events is given by the coefficient of t^r in

$$\left(\frac{c}{c+1}\right)^k\left(\frac{c+1-t}{c+1}\right)^{-k} = \left(\frac{c}{c+1}\right)^k\left(1-\frac{t}{c+1}\right)^{-k}$$

The frequency of 0, 1, 2, . . . accidents is therefore

$$\left(\frac{c}{c+1}\right)^k\left\{1,\ \frac{k}{c+1},\ \frac{k(k+1)}{2!\,(c+1)^2},\cdots\right\}$$

which, on putting $\dfrac{c}{c+1} = p$ and $\dfrac{1}{c+1} = q$, gives successive terms of the negative binomial distribution $p^k(1-q)^{-k}$. If now we compute the mean and variance of the observed data and equate these with the first two moments of the negative binomial distribution (see section 4a) we obtain the frequencies recorded in the fourth column of Table 2, which are seen to provide a much closer fit to the observed data.

It will be shown later (see section 2) that the mean of the negative binomial distribution is kq/p and the variance is kq/p^2. Thus as p is necessarily less than unity, the variance is always greater than the mean, while for the Poisson distribution the variance is equal to the mean. Any variation in the Poisson parameter, e.g. any tendency for one event to increase the probability of another event, will increase the variance of the distribution relative to the mean, and a negative binomial distribution will invariably better fit the data.

---

* The choice of this particular distribution function is somewhat arbitrary. A positively skew distribution is preferred to the normal distribution, as λ may be supposed to take values from zero up to and including large positive values. The gamma (or Pearson Type III) distribution function covers a wide range of distributions, from constant ($k \to \infty$) to negative exponential ($k = 1$), and includes all intermediate choices of variability.

9

2. Properties of the Negative Binomial

Writing the negative binomial distribution in the form $p^k (1-q)^{-k}$, the probability of n events is given by

$$P(n) = \binom{n+k-1}{k-1} p^k q^n \qquad (n = 0, 1, 2, \ldots)$$

i.e. the coefficient of t^n in

$$P(t) = \sum_{n=0}^{\infty} \binom{n+k-1}{k-1} p^k (qt)^n = p^k (1-qt)^{-k}$$

which is the frequency generating function.

Thus the moment generating function is

$$M(t) = p^k (1-qe^t)^{-k}$$

which by definition $= \displaystyle\sum_{r=0}^{\infty} \mu_r' \frac{t^r}{r!}$

The moments of the distribution are more easily obtained from the cumulant generating function

$$K(t) = \log M(t) = \log\{p^k (1-qe^t)^{-k}\}$$

$$= -k \log \left(\frac{1-qe^t}{p} \right)$$

$$= -k \log \left\{ 1 - \frac{q}{p} (e^t - 1) \right\}$$

$$= k \left\{ \frac{q}{p} \left(t + \frac{t^2}{2!} + \frac{t^3}{3!} + \ldots \right) + \frac{q^2}{2p^2} \left(t + \frac{t^2}{2!} + \frac{t^3}{3!} + \ldots \right)^2 \right.$$

$$\left. + \frac{q^3}{3p^3} \left(t + \frac{t^2}{2!} + \frac{t^3}{3!} + \ldots \right)^3 + \ldots \right\}$$

Identifying coefficients of $t^r/r!$ we obtain

$$\kappa_1 = \frac{kq}{p} = \text{mean}$$

$$\kappa_2 = \frac{kq}{p^2} = \text{variance}$$

$$\kappa_3 = \frac{kq(1+q)}{p^3} = \mu_3$$

$$\kappa_4 = \frac{kq(1+4q+q^2)}{p^4} = \mu_4 - 3\mu_2^2$$

$$\beta_1 = \frac{\mu_3^2}{\mu_2^3} = \frac{(1+q)^2}{kq}$$

which is a measure of the skewness of the distribution.

$$\beta_2 = \frac{\mu_4}{\mu_2^2} = 3 + \frac{1+4q+q^2}{kq}$$

which is a measure of the kurtosis.

Both β_1 and $(\beta_2 - 3)$ are of order $1/k$, and so as k becomes large, the distribution tends to symmetry and zero kurtosis.

The negative binomial distribution is unimodel. The probability of n events is greater than the probability of $(n-1)$ events so long as

$$\binom{n+k-1}{k-1} p^k q^n > \binom{n+k-2}{k-1} p^k q^{n-1} \qquad (n > 0)$$

i.e. as long as

$$\frac{(n+k-1)!}{(n+k-2)!} \times \frac{(n-1)!}{n!} > \frac{1}{q}$$

or $\qquad \dfrac{n}{n+k-1} < q$

Hence the frequency increases until the highest integral value of n for which $n < q(n+k-1)$, after which the frequency declines again. If for some integral value of n the equality

$$q = \frac{n}{n+k-1}$$

is satisfied, then the probability of n events is equal to the probability of $(n-1)$ events.

Example. Consider the distribution with parameters $p = 0{\cdot}2$, $k = 2{\cdot}0$. The nth term is the greatest, where n is the largest integer which satisfies

i.e. $\qquad \begin{aligned} & n < q(n+k-1) \\ & n < 0{\cdot}8(n+1) \text{ from which we obtain} \\ & n < 4 \end{aligned}$

But as an integral value of n satisfies the equality, the probability of three events is the same as the probability of four events. This can be verified from the tables.

Having derived the negative binomial distribution as a generalized Poisson series, it is not surprising to find that the Poisson distribution is obtained as a limiting form of $p^k (1-q)^{-k}$. Consider the case where q is small, so that k tends to infinity while kq/p remains finite and equal to m.

Thus $\qquad p = \dfrac{k}{k+m} \qquad$ and $\qquad q = \dfrac{m}{k+m}$

3. Description of the Tables

The general term of the negative binomial distribution

$$P(n) = \frac{(n+k-1)!}{n!\,(k-1)!}\, p^k q^n$$

$$= \frac{(n+k-1)!}{n!\,(k-1)!}\left(1+\frac{m}{k}\right)^{-k}\frac{m^n}{(k+m)^n}$$

which on rearrangement becomes

$$\frac{(n+k-1)}{k+m}\frac{(n+k-2)}{k+m}\cdots\frac{k}{k+m}\times\left(1+\frac{m}{k}\right)^{-k}\frac{m^n}{n!}$$

and as $k \to \infty$, $P(n) \to \dfrac{e^{-m}\,m^n}{n!}$

which is the general term of the Poisson distribution.

Computation

The terms of the negative binomial distribution are formed by the expansion of $p^k(1-q)^{-k}$, which yields successive terms

$$p^k\left\{1,\ kq,\ k(k+1)\frac{q^2}{2!},\ k(k+1)(k+2)\frac{q^3}{3!},\ \ldots\right\}$$

The probability of n events

$$P(n) = \binom{n+k-1}{k-1} p^k q^n$$

The term p^k is first computed, this corresponding to the probability that $n = 0$. The second term, $P(1)$, is obtained from the first by multiplying by the factor kq; and, in general, the $(n+1)$th term, $P(n)$, is obtained from the nth term, $P(n-1)$, by multiplying by $\frac{q}{n}(n+k-1)$.

The cumulative probability

$$F(n) = \sum_{r=0}^{n} \binom{r+k-1}{k-1} p^k q^r$$

corresponds to the probability of n or less events, and is obtained by summing the first $(n+1)$ individual terms of the distribution.

The tables were computed on a Ferranti "Pegasus" computer. The computation of the individual and cumulative terms was continued until at least 99·99% of the distribution had been tabulated, i.e. until $F(n)$ exceeded 0·999900, at which point the tabulation of the distribution was terminated. The program calculated the values to an accuracy of nine decimal places and printed them, after rounding to six figures.

Range

The problem of which values of the parameters p and k to include in the tables is not an easy one. The parameter p must lie between 0 and 1, but the only restriction on k is that it must be positive. Unlike the positive binomial, k is not necessarily an integer. The criteria governing the values of the parameters chosen have been the purely practical considerations of, on the one hand, having a range wide enough to cover a large number of applications without the need for too much interpolation by the user of the tables, and, on the other hand, keeping the work down to reasonable proportions. The aim has been to tabulate, as comprehensively as

possible, distributions having mean values between 0·1 and 10.

The result is a work of 1,480 distributions covering the following values of the parameters p and k:

$p = 0·05$ $k = 0·1(0·1)0·5$
$p = 0·10$ $k = 0·1(0·1)1·0$
$p = 0·12(0·02)0·20$ $k = 0·1(0·1)2·5$
$p = 0·22(0·02)0·40$ $k = 0·1(0·1)2·5(0·5)5·0$
$p = 0·42(0·02)0·60$ $k = 0·1(0·1)2·5(0·5)10·0$
$p = 0·62(0·02)0·80$ $k = 0·2(0·2)5·0(1)20$
$p = 0·82(0·02)0·90$ $k = 0·5(0·5)10·0(2)50$
$p = 0·95$ $k = 2(2)50(10)200$

In this section, several methods of fitting the negative binomial distribution to large samples are mentioned. Readers desiring a more detailed knowledge of these methods should refer to Fisher (1941), Haldane (1941), Anscombe (1950), or Bliss and Fisher (1953).

(a) Method of Moments

As has already been shown in this introduction, the mean, M, of the negative binomial distribution is given by kq/p and the variance, V, by kq/p^2. If the first two moments are estimated from the sample moments, then the ratio of the mean to the variance provides an estimate of p; i.e. if the mean of the sample is m and the variance is s^2, then m/s^2 estimates p. As $m = kq/p$, and noting that $q = 1 - p$, an estimate of k is given by $k = mp/(1 - p)$.

The efficiency of estimating p and k by this method is derived by Fisher (1941), and in terms of the parameters used here the reciprocal of the efficiency is given by

$$\frac{1}{E} = 1 + 2\left\{\frac{1}{3}q\frac{2}{(k+2)} + \frac{1}{4}q^2\frac{2.3}{(k+2)(k+3)} \right.$$
$$\left. + \frac{1}{5}q^3\frac{2.3.4}{(k+2)(k+3)(k+4)} + \dots\right\}$$

(b) Maximum-likelihood Method

The maximum-likelihood method of fitting the distribution has been discussed by several writers, e.g. Haldane (1941), Anscombe (1950) and Sichel (1951). The maximum likelihood equations are reproduced below.

Let r_n be the observed frequency of n events and z the highest value of n observed. The total number of observations, N, is given by

$$N = \sum_{n=0}^{z} r_n$$

and the mean of the sample by

$$m = \frac{1}{N}\sum_{n=0}^{z} nr_n$$

The likelihood is given by

$$\prod_{n=0}^{z} [P(n)]^{r_n}$$

and hence the logarithm of the likelihood, L, is given by

$$L = \sum_{n=0}^{z} r_n \log P(n)$$

$$= r_0 k \log p + \sum_{n=1}^{z} r_n \left\{ \sum_{s=0}^{n-1} \log (k+s) - \log n! \right.$$
$$\left. + k \log p + n \log (1-p) \right\}$$

Differentiating this with respect to p, we obtain

$$\frac{\partial L}{\partial p} = \sum_{n=0}^{z} r_n \left(\frac{k}{p} - \frac{n}{(1-p)} \right) = \frac{Nk}{p} - \frac{\sum n r_n}{(1-p)}$$

which, on equating to zero for a maximum, and substituting m for

$$\frac{1}{N} \sum n r_n$$

and q for $(1-p)$, yields

$$m = \frac{kq}{p} \qquad \dots\dots(1)$$

The mean of the sample, m, is therefore the maximum likelihood estimator of the distribution mean M. If now L is differentiated with respect to k, then

$$\frac{\partial L}{\partial k} = r_0 \log p + \sum_{n=1}^{z} r_n \left\{ \sum_{s=0}^{n-1} \frac{1}{(k+s)} + \log p \right\}$$

Equating to zero gives

$$\sum_{n=1}^{z} r_n \sum_{s=0}^{n-1} \frac{1}{(k+s)} = N \log \frac{1}{p}$$

Eliminating p from this equation by equation (1) yields

$$N \log \left(1 + \frac{m}{k} \right) - \frac{r_1 + r_2 + r_3 + \dots + r_n}{k}$$
$$- \frac{r_2 + r_3 + \dots + r_n}{(k+1)} - \dots - \frac{r_n}{(k+z-1)} = 0$$

The solution of this equation other than $k = \infty$ provides an estimate of k. The iterative process of Newton–Raphson (e.g. Hartree, 1958) may be employed. Using as the initial value the value of k obtained by the method of moments, this method has been found to give k to six decimal places after three or four iterations. However, this method could give a spurious result: for example, if a value of k much greater than the root is taken as an initial value, then the method may give either successively larger values of k (tending to the infinite root) or give a meaningless negative value. If, on the other hand, the process starts with a value of k less than the root, then, in the experience of the authors, the required root will be obtained. The number of iterations needed will, of course, depend on the initial value of k. For large values of z this method may be long and tedious.

Other authors, Wise (1946) and Sichel (1951), have expressed the second maximum likelihood equation in terms of the digamma function $F(x)$, where

$$F(x) = \frac{d}{dx} \log \Gamma(x+1)$$

They then solve the equations, using tables of this function. It is claimed that the work involved is far less by this method when z is large.

(c) Estimation of k from the Proportion of Zeros

If r_0 is the observed number of zeros, then an estimate of k (cf. Anscombe, 1950) is

$$\frac{r_0}{N} = \left(1 + \frac{m}{k} \right)^{-k}$$

Taking logarithms of both sides and putting

$$a = -\log r_0 / N$$

yields
$$\frac{a}{k} = \log \left(1 + \frac{m}{k} \right)$$

This expression is similar to the one derived from the maximum likelihood equations and can be solved in a similar manner.

(d) Efficiency of Estimation

Several methods have been put forward for fitting the negative binomial distribution to large samples. It is now necessary to see under what conditions each method is of use.

Concerning the estimation of m, it can be shown that, for large samples, the sample mean is a fully efficient estimator of the distribution mean. However, the efficiencies of the estimators of k vary considerably.

13

References

Figure 1 shows the relative efficiencies of (*a*) the method of moments, and (*c*) the method of estimating *k* from the proportion of zeros, compared with the maximum-likelihood method. From this diagram a decision can be made regarding which method to use, bearing in mind the relative difficulties of the methods and the purpose of fitting the distribution.

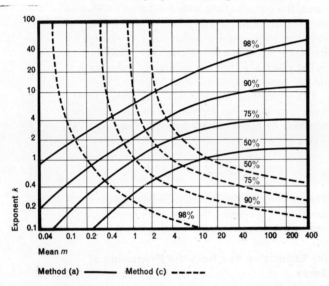

Method (a) ———— **Method (c)** -----

Figure 1 Large-sample efficiencies of estimations of *k* (*Anscombe, 1950*)

1. ANSCOMBE, F. J. (1948). The Transformation of Poisson, binomial, and negative binomial data, *Biometrika*, **35**, 246.

2. ANSCOMBE, F. J. (1949). The statistical analysis of insect counts based on the negative binomial distribution, *Biometrics*, **5**, 165.

3. ANSCOMBE, F. J. (1950). Sampling theory of the negative binomial and logarithmic series distributions, *Biometrika*, **37**, 358.

4. BLISS, C. I. and FISHER, R. A. (1953). Fitting the negative binomial distribution to biological data, and Note on the efficient fitting of the negative binomial, *Biometrics*, **9**, 176.

5. BORTKIEWICZ, L. VON (1898). *Das Gesetz der kleinen Zahlen*. Teubner, Leipzig.

6. FISHER, R. A. (1941). The negative binomial distribution, *Ann. Eugen*, **11**, 182.

7. FISHER, R. A., CORBET, A. S. and WILLIAMS, C. B. (1943). The relation between the number of species and the number of individuals in a random sample of an animal population, *J. Animal Ecol.* **12**, 42.

8. GREENWOOD, M. and YULE, G. U. (1920). An inquiry into the nature of frequency distributions representative of multiple happenings, with particular reference to the occurrence of multiple attacks of disease or of repeated accidents, *J. R. statist. Soc.*, **83**, 255.

9. HALDANE, J. B. S. (1941). The fitting of binomial distributions, *Ann. Eugen.*, **11**, 179.

10. HARTREE, D. R. (1958), *Numerical Analysis* (2nd ed.). The Clarendon Press, Oxford.

11. JEFFREYS, H. (1939). *Theory of Probability*. The Clarendon Press, Oxford.

12. KATTI, S. K. and GURLAND, J. (1962). Efficiency of certain methods of estimation for the negative binomial and the Neyman type A distributions, *Biometrika*, **49**, 215.

13. KENDALL, M. G. and STUART, A. (1958, 1961). *The Advanced Theory of Statistics* (Vols. 1 and 2). Griffin, London.

14. MONTMORT, P. R. DE (1713). *Essai d'analyse sur les jeux de hazards* (2nd ed.). Chez Laurent Le Conte, Quay des Augustins à la ville de Montpellier.

15. NEWBOLD, E. M. (1927). Practical applications of the statistics of repeated events, particularly to industrial accidents, *J. R. statist. Soc.*, **90**, 487.

16. PEARSON, K. (1905). Das Fehlergesetz und seine Verallgemeinerungen durch Fechner und Pearson: A rejoinder, *Biometrika*, **4**, 169.

17. QUENOUILLE, M. H. (1949). A relation between the logarithmic, Poisson, and negative binomial series, *Biometrics*, **5**, 162.

18. SICHEL, H. E. (1951). The estimation of the parameters of a negative binomial distribution, with special reference to psychological data, *Psychometrika*, **16**, 107.

19. "STUDENT" (1919). An explanation of deviations from Poisson's law in practice, *Biometrika*, **12**, 211.

20. TAYLOR, C. J. (1961). The application of the negative binomial distribution to stock control problems, *Operat. Res. Quart.*, **12**, 81.

21. WHITAKER, L. (1914). On Poisson's law of small numbers, *Biometrika*, **10**, 36.

22. WILKS, S. S. (1946). *Mathematical Statistics.* Princeton University Press, New Jersey.

23. WISE, M. E. (1946). The use of the negative binomial distribution in an industrial sampling problem, *J. R. statist. Soc. (Supplement)*, **8**, 202.

24. YULE, G. U. (1910). On the distribution of deaths with age when the causes of death act cumulatively, and similar frequency distributions, *J. R. statist. Soc.*, **73**, 26.

k=0·1
Mean=1·90
Variance=38·00

n	P(n)	F(n)
0	0.741134	0.741134
1	0.070408	0.811542
2	0.036788	0.848330
3	0.024464	0.872794
4	0.018012	0.890806
5	0.014031	0.904837
6	0.011330	0.916167
7	0.009380	0.925547
8	0.007908	0.933455
9	0.006762	0.940217
10	0.005845	0.946062
11	0.005099	0.951161
12	0.004481	0.955641
13	0.003962	0.959603
14	0.003522	0.963125
15	0.003145	0.966270
16	0.002820	0.969090
17	0.002537	0.971626
18	0.002290	0.973916
19	0.002072	0.975988
20	0.001880	0.977868
21	0.001709	0.979577
22	0.001557	0.981135
23	0.001422	0.982556
24	0.001300	0.983856
25	0.001190	0.985047
26	0.001092	0.986138
27	0.001003	0.987141
28	0.000922	0.988063
29	0.000849	0.988911
30	0.000782	0.989693
31	0.000721	0.990415
32	0.000666	0.991081
33	0.000615	0.991696
34	0.000569	0.992265
35	0.000527	0.992792
36	0.000488	0.993280
37	0.000452	0.993732
38	0.000419	0.994152
39	0.000389	0.994541
40	0.000362	0.994903
41	0.000336	0.995239
42	0.000312	0.995551
43	0.000290	0.995841
44	0.000270	0.996112
45	0.000252	0.996363
46	0.000234	0.996598
47	0.000218	0.996816
48	0.000204	0.997020
49	0.000190	0.997210
50	0.000177	0.997387
51	0.000165	0.997552
52	0.000154	0.997706
53	0.000144	0.997850
54	0.000135	0.997985
55	0.000126	0.998111
56	0.000118	0.998228
57	0.000110	0.998338
58	0.000103	0.998441
59	0.000096	0.998537
60	0.000090	0.998627
61	0.000084	0.998712
62	0.000079	0.998791
63	0.000074	0.998864
64	0.000069	0.998934
65	0.000065	0.998998
66	0.000061	0.999059
67	0.000057	0.999116
68	0.000053	0.999169
69	0.000050	0.999219
70	0.000047	0.999266
71	0.000044	0.999310
72	0.000041	0.999352
73	0.000039	0.999390
74	0.000036	0.999427
75	0.000034	0.999461
76	0.000032	0.999493
77	0.000030	0.999523
78	0.000028	0.999551
79	0.000027	0.999578
80	0.000025	0.999603
81	0.000023	0.999626
82	0.000022	0.999648
83	0.000021	0.999669
84	0.000019	0.999688
85	0.000018	0.999706
86	0.000017	0.999724
87	0.000016	0.999740
88	0.000015	0.999755
89	0.000014	0.999769
90	0.000013	0.999783
91	0.000013	0.999795
92	0.000012	0.999807
93	0.000011	0.999818
94	0.000011	0.999829
95	0.000010	0.999839
96	0.000009	0.999848
97	0.000009	0.999857
98	0.000008	0.999865
99	0.000008	0.999873
100	0.000007	0.999880
101	0.000007	0.999887
102	0.000006	0.999893
103	0.000006	0.999899
104	0.000006	0.999905

k=0·2
Mean=3·80
Variance=76·00

n	P(n)	F(n)
0	0.549280	0.549280
1	0.104363	0.653644
2	0.059487	0.713131
3	0.041443	0.754573
4	0.031496	0.786070
5	0.025134	0.811204
6	0.020694	0.831898
7	0.017412	0.849310
8	0.014888	0.864197
9	0.012886	0.877083
10	0.011262	0.888346
11	0.009921	0.898267
12	0.008797	0.907064
13	0.007843	0.914906
14	0.007025	0.921931
15	0.006318	0.928249
16	0.005702	0.933950
17	0.005162	0.939112
18	0.004686	0.943797
19	0.004264	0.948061
20	0.003889	0.951950
21	0.003554	0.955504
22	0.003253	0.958757
23	0.002983	0.961740
24	0.002739	0.964479
25	0.002519	0.966998
26	0.002320	0.969318
27	0.002138	0.971456
28	0.001973	0.973429
29	0.001823	0.975252
30	0.001686	0.976938
31	0.001560	0.978498
32	0.001445	0.979942
33	0.001339	0.981282
34	0.001242	0.982524
35	0.001153	0.983678
36	0.001071	0.984749
37	0.000996	0.985745
38	0.000926	0.986671
39	0.000862	0.987533
40	0.000802	0.988335
41	0.000747	0.989082
42	0.000696	0.989779
43	0.000649	0.990428
44	0.000606	0.991034
45	0.000565	0.991599
46	0.000528	0.992126
47	0.000493	0.992619
48	0.000460	0.993079
49	0.000430	0.993509
50	0.000402	0.993911
51	0.000376	0.994287
52	0.000352	0.994639
53	0.000329	0.994968
54	0.000308	0.995275
55	0.000288	0.995564
56	0.000270	0.995834
57	0.000253	0.996086
58	0.000237	0.996323
59	0.000222	0.996545
60	0.000208	0.996753
61	0.000195	0.996948
62	0.000183	0.997131
63	0.000172	0.997303
64	0.000161	0.997464

n	P(n)	F(n)
65	0.000151	0.997615
66	0.000142	0.997757
67	0.000133	0.997890
68	0.000125	0.998015
69	0.000117	0.998132
70	0.000110	0.998242
71	0.000103	0.998346
72	0.000097	0.998443
73	0.000091	0.998534
74	0.000086	0.998620
75	0.000081	0.998701
76	0.000076	0.998776
77	0.000071	0.998848
78	0.000067	0.998915
79	0.000063	0.998978
80	0.000059	0.999037
81	0.000056	0.999093
82	0.000052	0.999145
83	0.000049	0.999195
84	0.000046	0.999241
85	0.000044	0.999285
86	0.000041	0.999326
87	0.000039	0.999365
88	0.000036	0.999401
89	0.000034	0.999435
90	0.000032	0.999468
91	0.000030	0.999498
92	0.000029	0.999527
93	0.000027	0.999554
94	0.000025	0.999579
95	0.000024	0.999603
96	0.000023	0.999626
97	0.000021	0.999647
98	0.000020	0.999667
99	0.000019	0.999686
100	0.000018	0.999703
101	0.000017	0.999720
102	0.000016	0.999736
103	0.000015	0.999751
104	0.000014	0.999765
105	0.000013	0.999778
106	0.000012	0.999791
107	0.000012	0.999802
108	0.000011	0.999813
109	0.000010	0.999824
110	0.000010	0.999834
111	0.000009	0.999843
112	0.000009	0.999852
113	0.000008	0.999860
114	0.000008	0.999868
115	0.000007	0.999875
116	0.000007	0.999882
117	0.000007	0.999889
118	0.000006	0.999895
119	0.000006	0.999901

$k = 0.3$
Mean = 5.70
Variance = 114.00

n	P(n)	F(n)
0	0.407091	0.407091
1	0.116021	0.523111
2	0.071643	0.594754
3	0.052180	0.646934
4	0.040896	0.687830
5	0.033412	0.721242
6	0.028038	0.749280
7	0.023973	0.773253
8	0.020781	0.794034
9	0.018207	0.812241
10	0.016086	0.828327
11	0.014309	0.842636
12	0.012801	0.855436
13	0.011506	0.866942
14	0.010384	0.877326
15	0.009404	0.886730
16	0.008543	0.895273
17	0.007782	0.903055
18	0.007105	0.910161
19	0.006501	0.916662
20	0.005960	0.922622
21	0.005473	0.928096
22	0.005034	0.933130
23	0.004637	0.937767
24	0.004277	0.942044
25	0.003949	0.945993
26	0.003651	0.949643
27	0.003378	0.953021
28	0.003129	0.956150
29	0.002901	0.959051
30	0.002691	0.961743
31	0.002499	0.964242
32	0.002322	0.966564
33	0.002159	0.968724
34	0.002009	0.970733
35	0.001871	0.972603
36	0.001742	0.974346
37	0.001624	0.975970
38	0.001514	0.977484
39	0.001413	0.978897
40	0.001319	0.980216
41	0.001231	0.981447
42	0.001150	0.982597
43	0.001075	0.983672
44	0.001005	0.984677
45	0.000940	0.985617
46	0.000879	0.986497
47	0.000823	0.987320
48	0.000770	0.988090
49	0.000721	0.988811
50	0.000676	0.989487
51	0.000633	0.990120
52	0.000593	0.990714
53	0.000556	0.991270
54	0.000522	0.991792

n	P(n)	F(n)
55	0.000489	0.992281
56	0.000459	0.992740
57	0.000431	0.993170
58	0.000404	0.993575
59	0.000379	0.993954
60	0.000356	0.994310
61	0.000335	0.994645
62	0.000314	0.994959
63	0.000295	0.995254
64	0.000277	0.995532
65	0.000261	0.995792
66	0.000245	0.996037
67	0.000230	0.996268
68	0.000217	0.996484
69	0.000204	0.996688
70	0.000192	0.996879
71	0.000180	0.997059
72	0.000169	0.997229
73	0.000159	0.997388
74	0.000150	0.997538
75	0.000141	0.997680
76	0.000133	0.997813
77	0.000125	0.997938
78	0.000118	0.998056
79	0.000111	0.998166
80	0.000104	0.998271
81	0.000098	0.998369
82	0.000093	0.998462
83	0.000087	0.998549
84	0.000082	0.998631
85	0.000077	0.998709
86	0.000073	0.998782
87	0.000069	0.998851
88	0.000065	0.998916
89	0.000061	0.998977
90	0.000058	0.999034
91	0.000054	0.999089
92	0.000051	0.999140
93	0.000048	0.999188
94	0.000046	0.999234
95	0.000043	0.999276
96	0.000040	0.999317
97	0.000038	0.999355
98	0.000036	0.999391
99	0.000034	0.999425
100	0.000032	0.999457
101	0.000030	0.999487
102	0.000029	0.999516
103	0.000027	0.999543
104	0.000025	0.999568
105	0.000024	0.999592
106	0.000023	0.999615
107	0.000021	0.999636
108	0.000020	0.999656
109	0.000019	0.999675
110	0.000018	0.999693
111	0.000017	0.999710
112	0.000016	0.999726
113	0.000015	0.999741
114	0.000014	0.999755

n	P(n)	F(n)
115	0.000013	0.999769
116	0.000013	0.999782
117	0.000012	0.999794
118	0.000011	0.999805
119	0.000011	0.999816
120	0.000010	0.999826
121	0.000010	0.999835
122	0.000009	0.999844
123	0.000009	0.999853
124	0.000008	0.999861
125	0.000008	0.999869
126	0.000007	0.999876
127	0.000007	0.999883
128	0.000006	0.999889
129	0.000006	0.999895
130	0.000006	0.999901

k = 0·4
Mean = 7·60
Variance = 152·00

n	P(n)	F(n)
0	0.301709	0.301709
1	0.114649	0.416358
2	0.076242	0.492600
3	0.057944	0.550544
4	0.046790	0.597333
5	0.039116	0.636449
6	0.033444	0.669894
7	0.029049	0.698942
8	0.025527	0.724469
9	0.022634	0.747103
10	0.020212	0.767314
11	0.018154	0.785468
12	0.016384	0.801852
13	0.014846	0.816698
14	0.013500	0.830198
15	0.012312	0.842509
16	0.011257	0.853767
17	0.010317	0.864084
18	0.009475	0.873558
19	0.008717	0.882275
20	0.008032	0.890307
21	0.007413	0.897720
22	0.006850	0.904570
23	0.006338	0.910908
24	0.005870	0.916778
25	0.005443	0.922221
26	0.005051	0.927272
27	0.004692	0.931965
28	0.004362	0.936327
29	0.004058	0.940385
30	0.003778	0.944163
31	0.003520	0.947683
32	0.003281	0.950964
33	0.003060	0.954025
34	0.002856	0.956881

n	P(n)	F(n)
35	0.002667	0.959548
36	0.002491	0.962039
37	0.002328	0.964367
38	0.002177	0.966544
39	0.002036	0.968580
40	0.001905	0.970486
41	0.001784	0.972270
42	0.001670	0.973940
43	0.001565	0.975505
44	0.001466	0.976971
45	0.001374	0.978345
46	0.001289	0.979633
47	0.001208	0.980842
48	0.001134	0.981976
49	0.001064	0.983039
50	0.000999	0.984038
51	0.000937	0.984975
52	0.000880	0.985856
53	0.000827	0.986682
54	0.000777	0.987459
55	0.000730	0.988189
56	0.000686	0.988875
57	0.000645	0.989520
58	0.000606	0.990126
59	0.000570	0.990696
60	0.000536	0.991232
61	0.000504	0.991736
62	0.000474	0.992211
63	0.000446	0.992657
64	0.000420	0.993077
65	0.000395	0.993473
66	0.000372	0.993845
67	0.000350	0.994195
68	0.000330	0.994525
69	0.000311	0.994836
70	0.000293	0.995129
71	0.000276	0.995405
72	0.000260	0.995664
73	0.000245	0.995909
74	0.000231	0.996140
75	0.000217	0.996357
76	0.000205	0.996562
77	0.000193	0.996755
78	0.000182	0.996937
79	0.000172	0.997109
80	0.000162	0.997271
81	0.000153	0.997423
82	0.000144	0.997567
83	0.000136	0.997703
84	0.000128	0.997831
85	0.000121	0.997951
86	0.000114	0.998065
87	0.000107	0.998173
88	0.000101	0.998274
89	0.000096	0.998370
90	0.000090	0.998460
91	0.000085	0.998545
92	0.000080	0.998626
93	0.000076	0.998702
94	0.000072	0.998773

n	P(n)	F(n)
95	0.000068	0.998841
96	0.000064	0.998905
97	0.000060	0.998965
98	0.000057	0.999022
99	0.000054	0.999076
100	0.000051	0.999126
101	0.000048	0.999174
102	0.000045	0.999220
103	0.000043	0.999262
104	0.000040	0.999303
105	0.000038	0.999341
106	0.000036	0.999377
107	0.000034	0.999411
108	0.000032	0.999443
109	0.000030	0.999473
110	0.000029	0.999502
111	0.000027	0.999529
112	0.000026	0.999555
113	0.000024	0.999579
114	0.000023	0.999602
115	0.000022	0.999624
116	0.000020	0.999644
117	0.000019	0.999663
118	0.000018	0.999682
119	0.000017	0.999699
120	0.000016	0.999715
121	0.000015	0.999731
122	0.000015	0.999745
123	0.000014	0.999759
124	0.000013	0.999772
125	0.000012	0.999784
126	0.000012	0.999796
127	0.000011	0.999807
128	0.000010	0.999817
129	0.000010	0.999827
130	0.000009	0.999837
131	0.000009	0.999845
132	0.000008	0.999854
133	0.000008	0.999862
134	0.000007	0.999869
135	0.000007	0.999876
136	0.000007	0.999883
137	0.000006	0.999889
138	0.000006	0.999895
139	0.000006	0.999901

k = 0·5
Mean = 9·50
Variance = 190·00

n	P(n)	F(n)
0	0.223607	0.223607
1	0.106213	0.329820
2	0.075677	0.405497
3	0.059911	0.465408
4	0.049801	0.515209
5	0.042580	0.557789
6	0.037080	0.594868
7	0.032710	0.627578
8	0.029132	0.656710
9	0.026138	0.682848

10	0.023590	0.706438	70	0.000415	0.992942	130	0.000014	0.999750
11	0.021391	0.727829	71	0.000392	0.993334	131	0.000013	0.999763
12	0.019475	0.747305	72	0.000369	0.993703	132	0.000013	0.999776
13	0.017790	0.765094	73	0.000349	0.994052	133	0.000012	0.999788
14	0.016297	0.781391	74	0.000329	0.994381	134	0.000011	0.999799
15	0.014966	0.796357	75	0.000310	0.994691	135	0.000011	0.999810
16	0.013773	0.810130	76	0.000293	0.994984	136	0.000010	0.999820
17	0.012700	0.822830	77	0.000276	0.995261	137	0.000010	0.999830
18	0.011730	0.834559	78	0.000261	0.995521	138	0.000009	0.999839
19	0.010850	0.845409	79	0.000246	0.995768	139	0.000009	0.999847
20	0.010050	0.855459	80	0.000233	0.996000	140	0.000008	0.999855
21	0.009320	0.864779	81	0.000220	0.996220	141	0.000008	0.999863
22	0.008653	0.873431	82	0.000207	0.996427	142	0.000007	0.999870
23	0.008041	0.881473	83	0.000196	0.996623	143	0.000007	0.999877
24	0.007480	0.888953	84	0.000185	0.996808	144	0.000007	0.999884
25	0.006964	0.895917	85	0.000175	0.996983	145	0.000006	0.999890
26	0.006489	0.902406	86	0.000165	0.997148	146	0.000006	0.999896
27	0.006050	0.908456	87	0.000156	0.997303	147	0.000006	0.999901
28	0.005645	0.914100	88	0.000147	0.997450			
29	0.005270	0.919371	89	0.000139	0.997589			
30	0.004923	0.924294	90	0.000131	0.997721			
31	0.004602	0.928895	91	0.000124	0.997845			
32	0.004303	0.933199	92	0.000117	0.997962			
33	0.004026	0.937225	93	0.000111	0.998073			
34	0.003769	0.940993	94	0.000105	0.998177			
35	0.003529	0.944522	95	0.000099	0.998276			
36	0.003306	0.947828	96	0.000093	0.998370			
37	0.003098	0.950927	97	0.000088	0.998458			
38	0.002905	0.953831	98	0.000083	0.998542			
39	0.002724	0.956555	99	0.000079	0.998621			
40	0.002555	0.959111	100	0.000075	0.998695			
41	0.002398	0.961509	101	0.000071	0.998766			
42	0.002251	0.963760	102	0.000067	0.998832			
43	0.002114	0.965873	103	0.000063	0.998895			
44	0.001985	0.967858	104	0.000060	0.998955			
45	0.001865	0.969723	105	0.000056	0.999011			
46	0.001752	0.971476	106	0.000053	0.999065			
47	0.001647	0.973123	107	0.000050	0.999115			
48	0.001548	0.974671	108	0.000048	0.999163			
49	0.001456	0.976127	109	0.000045	0.999208			
50	0.001369	0.977497	110	0.000043	0.999250			
51	0.001288	0.978785	111	0.000040	0.999290			
52	0.001212	0.979997	112	0.000038	0.999329			
53	0.001141	0.981137	113	0.000036	0.999365			
54	0.001073	0.982211	114	0.000034	0.999399			
55	0.001011	0.983221	115	0.000032	0.999431			
56	0.000951	0.984173	116	0.000030	0.999461			
57	0.000896	0.985069	117	0.000029	0.999490			
58	0.000844	0.985912	118	0.000027	0.999518			
59	0.000795	0.986707	119	0.000026	0.999543			
60	0.000749	0.987456	120	0.000024	0.999568			
61	0.000705	0.988161	121	0.000023	0.999591			
62	0.000665	0.988826	122	0.000022	0.999613			
63	0.000627	0.989453	123	0.000021	0.999633			
64	0.000591	0.990043	124	0.000020	0.999653			
65	0.000557	0.990600	125	0.000019	0.999671			
66	0.000525	0.991125	126	0.000018	0.999689			
67	0.000495	0.991620	127	0.000017	0.999706			
68	0.000467	0.992087	128	0.000016	0.999721			
69	0.000440	0.992527	129	0.000015	0.999736			

	k = 0·3	
55	0.000017	0.999865
56	0.000015	0.999880
57	0.000013	0.999893
58	0.000012	0.999905

k = 0·1
Mean = 0·90
Variance = 9·00

k = 0·2
Mean = 1·80
Variance = 18·00

k = 0·3
Mean = 2·70
Variance = 27·00

n	P(n)	F(n)	n	P(n)	F(n)	n	P(n)	F(n)
0	0.794328	0.794328	0	0.630957	0.630957	0	0.501187	0.501187
1	0.071490	0.865818	1	0.113572	0.744530	1	0.135321	0.636508
2	0.035387	0.901205	2	0.061329	0.805859	2	0.079163	0.715670
3	0.022294	0.923499	3	0.040477	0.846336	3	0.054622	0.770292
4	0.015550	0.939049	4	0.029144	0.875479	4	0.040557	0.810849
5	0.011476	0.950525	5	0.022033	0.897512	5	0.031391	0.842240
6	0.008779	0.959304	6	0.017185	0.914697	6	0.024956	0.867196
7	0.006885	0.966190	7	0.013699	0.928397	7	0.020214	0.887411
8	0.005500	0.971689	8	0.011096	0.939493	8	0.016601	0.904012
9	0.004455	0.976144	9	0.009099	0.948592	9	0.013779	0.917790
10	0.003648	0.979792	10	0.007534	0.956126	10	0.011533	0.929323
11	0.003015	0.982807	11	0.006287	0.962413	11	0.009719	0.939042
12	0.002510	0.985317	12	0.005281	0.967695	12	0.008237	0.947279
13	0.002103	0.987420	13	0.004461	0.972156	13	0.007014	0.954293
14	0.001771	0.989190	14	0.003785	0.975941	14	0.005997	0.960290
15	0.001498	0.990688	15	0.003225	0.979166	15	0.005145	0.965436
16	0.001272	0.991961	16	0.002757	0.981923	16	0.004428	0.969864
17	0.001084	0.993045	17	0.002365	0.984288	17	0.003821	0.973685
18	0.000927	0.993972	18	0.002034	0.986322	18	0.003305	0.976991
19	0.000795	0.994767	19	0.001753	0.988076	19	0.002865	0.979856
20	0.000683	0.995451	20	0.001515	0.989590	20	0.002489	0.982345
21	0.000589	0.996039	21	0.001311	0.990902	21	0.002165	0.984510
22	0.000508	0.996547	22	0.001137	0.992039	22	0.001887	0.986396
23	0.000439	0.996987	23	0.000988	0.993027	23	0.001646	0.988042
24	0.000381	0.997367	24	0.000860	0.993887	24	0.001433	0.989481
25	0.000330	0.997697	25	0.000749	0.994636	25	0.001258	0.990739
26	0.000287	0.997984	26	0.000653	0.995289	26	0.001102	0.991841
27	0.000250	0.998234	27	0.000571	0.995860	27	0.000966	0.992807
28	0.000217	0.998451	28	0.000499	0.996359	28	0.000848	0.993655
29	0.000190	0.998641	29	0.000437	0.996795	29	0.000745	0.994399
30	0.000166	0.998807	30	0.000382	0.997177	30	0.000654	0.995054
31	0.000145	0.998951	31	0.000335	0.997513	31	0.000576	0.995629
32	0.000127	0.999078	32	0.000294	0.997807	32	0.000507	0.996136
33	0.000111	0.999188	33	0.000258	0.998065	33	0.000446	0.996583
34	0.000097	0.999286	34	0.000227	0.998292	34	0.000394	0.996976
35	0.000085	0.999371	35	0.000200	0.998492	35	0.000347	0.997323
36	0.000075	0.999445	36	0.000176	0.998668	36	0.000306	0.997630
37	0.000066	0.999511	37	0.000155	0.998823	37	0.000270	0.997900
38	0.000058	0.999568	38	0.000136	0.998959	38	0.000239	0.998139
39	0.000051	0.999619	39	0.000120	0.999079	39	0.000211	0.998350
40	0.000045	0.999664	40	0.000105	0.999185	40	0.000187	0.998537
41	0.000039	0.999703	41	0.000094	0.999279	41	0.000165	0.998702
42	0.000035	0.999737	42	0.000083	0.999361	42	0.000146	0.998848
43	0.000030	0.999768	43	0.000073	0.999434	43	0.000129	0.998978
44	0.000027	0.999795	44	0.000064	0.999499	44	0.000115	0.999092
45	0.000024	0.999818	45	0.000057	0.999556	45	0.000102	0.999194
46	0.000021	0.999839	46	0.000050	0.999606	46	0.000090	0.999284
47	0.000018	0.999858	47	0.000045	0.999650	47	0.000080	0.999364
48	0.000016	0.999874	48	0.000039	0.999690	48	0.000071	0.999434
49	0.000014	0.999888	49	0.000035	0.999725	49	0.000063	0.999497
50	0.000013	0.999901	50	0.000031	0.999756			
			51	0.000027	0.999783			
			52	0.000024	0.999807			
			53	0.000022	0.999829			
			54	0.000019	0.999848			

n	P(n)	F(n)
50	0.000056	0.999553
51	0.000049	0.999602
52	0.000044	0.999646
53	0.000039	0.999685
54	0.000035	0.999720
55	0.000031	0.999751
56	0.000027	0.999778
57	0.000024	0.999803
58	0.000022	0.999824
59	0.000019	0.999843
60	0.000017	0.999860
61	0.000015	0.999876
62	0.000014	0.999889
63	0.000012	0.999901

k = 0·4
Mean = 3·60
Variance = 36·00

n	P(n)	F(n)
0	0.398107	0.398107
1	0.143319	0.541426
2	0.090291	0.631716
3	0.065009	0.696726
4	0.049732	0.746458
5	0.039388	0.785846
6	0.031904	0.817750
7	0.026253	0.844002
8	0.021855	0.865858
9	0.018358	0.884216
10	0.015531	0.899747
11	0.013216	0.912963
12	0.011299	0.924262
13	0.009700	0.933962
14	0.008356	0.942318
15	0.007220	0.949538
16	0.006254	0.955792
17	0.005430	0.961222
18	0.004724	0.965946
19	0.004117	0.970063
20	0.003594	0.973657
21	0.003143	0.976800
22	0.002751	0.979551
23	0.002411	0.981963
24	0.002116	0.984079
25	0.001859	0.985937
26	0.001634	0.987572
27	0.001438	0.989010
28	0.001267	0.990276
29	0.001116	0.991393
30	0.000985	0.992377
31	0.000869	0.993246
32	0.000767	0.994014
33	0.000678	0.994692
34	0.000600	0.995292
35	0.000530	0.995822
36	0.000469	0.996291
37	0.000416	0.996707
38	0.000368	0.997075
39	0.000326	0.997401
40	0.000289	0.997690
41	0.000256	0.997947
42	0.000228	0.998174
43	0.000202	0.998376
44	0.000179	0.998555
45	0.000159	0.998715
46	0.000141	0.998856
47	0.000126	0.998982
48	0.000112	0.999093
49	0.000099	0.999192
50	0.000088	0.999281
51	0.000078	0.999359
52	0.000070	0.999429
53	0.000062	0.999491
54	0.000055	0.999546
55	0.000049	0.999596
56	0.000044	0.999640
57	0.000039	0.999679
58	0.000035	0.999713
59	0.000031	0.999744
60	0.000028	0.999772
61	0.000025	0.999796
62	0.000022	0.999818
63	0.000020	0.999838
64	0.000017	0.999855
65	0.000016	0.999871
66	0.000014	0.999885
67	0.000012	0.999897
68	0.000011	0.999908

k = 0·5
Mean = 4·50
Variance = 45·00

n	P(n)	F(n)
0	0.316228	0.316228
1	0.142302	0.458530
2	0.096054	0.554584
3	0.072041	0.626625
4	0.056732	0.683357
5	0.045953	0.729310
6	0.037911	0.767221
7	0.031683	0.798904
8	0.026732	0.825637
9	0.022723	0.848359
10	0.019428	0.867787
11	0.016690	0.884477
12	0.014395	0.898872
13	0.012458	0.911330
14	0.010811	0.922141
15	0.009406	0.931547
16	0.008201	0.939748
17	0.007164	0.946912
18	0.006268	0.953180
19	0.005493	0.958673
20	0.004820	0.963493
21	0.004235	0.967727
22	0.003725	0.971452
23	0.003279	0.974731
24	0.002890	0.977621
25	0.002549	0.980170
26	0.002250	0.982420
27	0.001987	0.984407
28	0.001757	0.986164
29	0.001554	0.987718
30	0.001375	0.989093
31	0.001218	0.990310
32	0.001079	0.991389
33	0.000956	0.992345
34	0.000848	0.993193
35	0.000752	0.993945
36	0.000668	0.994613
37	0.000593	0.995205
38	0.000526	0.995732
39	0.000468	0.996200
40	0.000416	0.996615
41	0.000370	0.996985
42	0.000329	0.997313
43	0.000292	0.997606
44	0.000260	0.997866
45	0.000231	0.998097
46	0.000206	0.998303
47	0.000183	0.998487
48	0.000163	0.998650
49	0.000146	0.998796
50	0.000130	0.998926
51	0.000116	0.999041
52	0.000103	0.999144
53	0.000092	0.999236
54	0.000082	0.999318
55	0.000073	0.999391
56	0.000065	0.999456
57	0.000058	0.999514
58	0.000052	0.999566
59	0.000046	0.999612
60	0.000041	0.999654
61	0.000037	0.999691
62	0.000033	0.999724
63	0.000029	0.999753
64	0.000026	0.999779
65	0.000023	0.999803
66	0.000021	0.999824
67	0.000019	0.999842
68	0.000017	0.999859
69	0.000015	0.999874
70	0.000013	0.999887
71	0.000012	0.999899
72	0.000011	0.999910

k = 0·6
Mean = 5·40
Variance = 54·00

n	P(n)	F(n)
0	0.251189	0.251189
1	0.135642	0.386831
2	0.097662	0.484493
3	0.076176	0.560669
4	0.061703	0.622372

n	P(n)	F(n)
5	0.051090	0.673462
6	0.042916	0.716378
7	0.036417	0.752795
8	0.031137	0.783931
9	0.026777	0.810709
10	0.023136	0.833844
11	0.020065	0.853909
12	0.017456	0.871366
13	0.015227	0.886593
14	0.013313	0.899906
15	0.011662	0.911569
16	0.010234	0.921802
17	0.008994	0.930796
18	0.007914	0.938710
19	0.006973	0.945683
20	0.006150	0.951833
21	0.005430	0.957263
22	0.004798	0.962061
23	0.004243	0.966304
24	0.003755	0.970059
25	0.003325	0.973385
26	0.002947	0.976331
27	0.002613	0.978944
28	0.002318	0.981262
29	0.002057	0.983320
30	0.001827	0.985147
31	0.001623	0.986770
32	0.001443	0.988212
33	0.001283	0.989495
34	0.001141	0.990636
35	0.001015	0.991651
36	0.000903	0.992554
37	0.000804	0.993358
38	0.000716	0.994074
39	0.000638	0.994712
40	0.000568	0.995280
41	0.000507	0.995787
42	0.000452	0.996238
43	0.000403	0.996641
44	0.000359	0.997000
45	0.000320	0.997320
46	0.000286	0.997606
47	0.000255	0.997861
48	0.000228	0.998089
49	0.000203	0.998292
50	0.000181	0.998473
51	0.000162	0.998635
52	0.000145	0.998780
53	0.000129	0.998909
54	0.000115	0.999024
55	0.000103	0.999127
56	0.000092	0.999219
57	0.000082	0.999302
58	0.000074	0.999375
59	0.000066	0.999441
60	0.000059	0.999500
61	0.000053	0.999553
62	0.000047	0.999600
63	0.000042	0.999642
64	0.000038	0.999679
65	0.000034	0.999713
66	0.000030	0.999743
67	0.000027	0.999770
68	0.000024	0.999794
69	0.000022	0.999816
70	0.000019	0.999835
71	0.000017	0.999852
72	0.000015	0.999868
73	0.000014	0.999881
74	0.000012	0.999894
75	0.000011	0.999905

k = 0·7
Mean = 6·30
Variance = 63·00

n	P(n)	F(n)
0	0.199526	0.199526
1	0.125702	0.325228
2	0.096162	0.421389
3	0.077891	0.499280
4	0.064844	0.564125
5	0.054858	0.618983
6	0.046904	0.665887
7	0.040404	0.706291
8	0.035000	0.741291
9	0.030450	0.771741
10	0.026583	0.798324
11	0.023272	0.821596
12	0.020421	0.842018
13	0.017955	0.859973
14	0.015813	0.875786
15	0.013947	0.889733
16	0.012317	0.902051
17	0.010890	0.912940
18	0.009638	0.922578
19	0.008537	0.931115
20	0.007568	0.938683
21	0.006714	0.945397
22	0.005960	0.951357
23	0.005294	0.956651
24	0.004705	0.961356
25	0.004184	0.965540
26	0.003722	0.969262
27	0.003313	0.972574
28	0.002949	0.975523
29	0.002627	0.978150
30	0.002341	0.980491
31	0.002086	0.982577
32	0.001860	0.984437
33	0.001659	0.986096
34	0.001480	0.987575
35	0.001320	0.988896
36	0.001178	0.990074
37	0.001052	0.991126
38	0.000939	0.992065
39	0.000839	0.992904
40	0.000749	0.993653
41	0.000669	0.994323
42	0.000598	0.994921
43	0.000535	0.995456
44	0.000478	0.995934
45	0.000427	0.996361
46	0.000382	0.996743
47	0.000342	0.997084
48	0.000306	0.997390
49	0.000273	0.997663
50	0.000244	0.997908
51	0.000219	0.998126
52	0.000196	0.998322
53	0.000175	0.998497
54	0.000157	0.998654
55	0.000140	0.998794
56	0.000126	0.998920
57	0.000112	0.999032
58	0.000101	0.999133
59	0.000090	0.999223
60	0.000081	0.999304
61	0.000072	0.999376
62	0.000065	0.999441
63	0.000058	0.999499
64	0.000052	0.999551
65	0.000047	0.999598
66	0.000042	0.999639
67	0.000037	0.999677
68	0.000033	0.999710
69	0.000030	0.999740
70	0.000027	0.999767
71	0.000024	0.999791
72	0.000022	0.999813
73	0.000019	0.999832
74	0.000017	0.999849
75	0.000016	0.999865
76	0.000014	0.999879
77	0.000012	0.999891
78	0.000011	0.999903

k = 0·8
Mean = 7·20
Variance = 72·00

n	P(n)	F(n)
0	0.158489	0.158489
1	0.114112	0.272602
2	0.092431	0.365033
3	0.077642	0.442675
4	0.066384	0.509059
5	0.057356	0.566414
6	0.049899	0.616314
7	0.043626	0.659940
8	0.038282	0.698222
9	0.033688	0.731911
10	0.029713	0.761624
11	0.026256	0.787879
12	0.023236	0.811115
13	0.020591	0.831706
14	0.018267	0.849973

n	P(n)	F(n)
15	0.016221	0.866194
16	0.014416	0.880611
17	0.012822	0.893433
18	0.011412	0.904845
19	0.010162	0.915007
20	0.009055	0.924062
21	0.008072	0.932134
22	0.007198	0.939332
23	0.006422	0.945754
24	0.005732	0.951486
25	0.005117	0.956604
26	0.004570	0.961174
27	0.004083	0.965257
28	0.003648	0.968905
29	0.003261	0.972166
30	0.002915	0.975081
31	0.002607	0.977688
32	0.002331	0.980019
33	0.002086	0.982104
34	0.001866	0.983970
35	0.001670	0.985640
36	0.001494	0.987135
37	0.001338	0.988472
38	0.001198	0.989670
39	0.001072	0.990742
40	0.000960	0.991702
41	0.000860	0.992562
42	0.000770	0.993333
43	0.000690	0.994023
44	0.000618	0.994641
45	0.000554	0.995195
46	0.000496	0.995691
47	0.000445	0.996136
48	0.000399	0.996535
49	0.000357	0.996892
50	0.000320	0.997212
51	0.000287	0.997500
52	0.000257	0.997757
53	0.000231	0.997988
54	0.000207	0.998195
55	0.000186	0.998381
56	0.000166	0.998547
57	0.000149	0.998696
58	0.000134	0.998830
59	0.000120	0.998950
60	0.000108	0.999058
61	0.000097	0.999155
62	0.000087	0.999241
63	0.000078	0.999319
64	0.000070	0.999389
65	0.000063	0.999451
66	0.000056	0.999508
67	0.000050	0.999558
68	0.000045	0.999603
69	0.000041	0.999644
70	0.000036	0.999680
71	0.000033	0.999713
72	0.000029	0.999742
73	0.000026	0.999769
74	0.000024	0.999792
75	0.000021	0.999814
76	0.000019	0.999833
77	0.000017	0.999850
78	0.000015	0.999865
79	0.000014	0.999879
80	0.000012	0.999891
81	0.000011	0.999902

k = 0·9
Mean = 8·10
Variance = 81·00

n	P(n)	F(n)
0	0.125893	0.125893
1	0.101973	0.227865
2	0.087187	0.315052
3	0.075853	0.390905
4	0.066561	0.457466
5	0.058706	0.516172
6	0.051955	0.568127
7	0.046092	0.614219
8	0.040964	0.655183
9	0.036458	0.691641
10	0.032484	0.724125
11	0.028970	0.753095
12	0.025856	0.778951
13	0.023091	0.802042
14	0.020634	0.822675
15	0.018446	0.841121
16	0.016498	0.857619
17	0.014761	0.872380
18	0.013211	0.885591
19	0.011827	0.897418
20	0.010591	0.908010
21	0.009487	0.917497
22	0.008499	0.925996
23	0.007616	0.933612
24	0.006826	0.940438
25	0.006119	0.946557
26	0.005486	0.952042
27	0.004919	0.956961
28	0.004411	0.961372
29	0.003956	0.965329
30	0.003549	0.968878
31	0.003184	0.972061
32	0.002856	0.974918
33	0.002563	0.977481
34	0.002300	0.979780
35	0.002064	0.981844
36	0.001852	0.983697
37	0.001663	0.985359
38	0.001492	0.986852
39	0.001340	0.988192
40	0.001203	0.989394
41	0.001080	0.990474
42	0.000970	0.991444
43	0.000871	0.992314
44	0.000782	0.993096
45	0.000702	0.993798
46	0.000630	0.994428
47	0.000566	0.994995
48	0.000508	0.995503
49	0.000457	0.995960
50	0.000410	0.996370
51	0.000368	0.996738
52	0.000331	0.997069
53	0.000297	0.997367
54	0.000267	0.997634
55	0.000240	0.997874
56	0.000216	0.998089
57	0.000194	0.998283
58	0.000174	0.998457
59	0.000156	0.998613
60	0.000140	0.998754
61	0.000126	0.998880
62	0.000113	0.998994
63	0.000102	0.999095
64	0.000092	0.999187
65	0.000082	0.999269
66	0.000074	0.999343
67	0.000066	0.999410
68	0.000060	0.999469
69	0.000054	0.999523
70	0.000048	0.999571
71	0.000043	0.999615
72	0.000039	0.999654
73	0.000035	0.999689
74	0.000031	0.999720
75	0.000028	0.999748
76	0.000025	0.999774
77	0.000023	0.999797
78	0.000021	0.999817
79	0.000018	0.999836
80	0.000017	0.999852
81	0.000015	0.999867
82	0.000013	0.999881
83	0.000012	0.999893
84	0.000011	0.999904

k = 1·0
Mean = 9·00
Variance = 90·00

n	P(n)	F(n)
0	0.100000	0.100000
1	0.090000	0.190000
2	0.081000	0.271000
3	0.072900	0.343900
4	0.065610	0.409510
5	0.059049	0.468559
6	0.053144	0.521703
7	0.047830	0.569533
8	0.043047	0.612580
9	0.038742	0.651322
10	0.034868	0.686189
11	0.031381	0.717570
12	0.028243	0.745813
13	0.025419	0.771232
14	0.022877	0.794109

n	P(n)	F(n)	n	P(n)	F(n)	n	P(n)	F(n)
15	0.020589	0.814698	40	0.001478	0.986697	65	0.000106	0.999045
16	0.018530	0.833228	41	0.001330	0.988027	66	0.000096	0.999140
17	0.016677	0.849905	42	0.001197	0.989225	67	0.000086	0.999226
18	0.015009	0.864915	43	0.001078	0.990302	68	0.000077	0.999304
19	0.013509	0.878423	44	0.000970	0.991272	69	0.000070	0.999373
20	0.012158	0.890581	45	0.000873	0.992145	70	0.000063	0.999436
21	0.010942	0.901523	46	0.000786	0.992930	71	0.000056	0.999492
22	0.009848	0.911371	47	0.000707	0.993637	72	0.000051	0.999543
23	0.008863	0.920234	48	0.000636	0.994274	73	0.000046	0.999589
24	0.007977	0.928210	49	0.000573	0.994846	74	0.000041	0.999630
25	0.007179	0.935389	50	0.000515	0.995362	75	0.000037	0.999667
26	0.006461	0.941850	51	0.000464	0.995825	76	0.000033	0.999700
27	0.005815	0.947665	52	0.000417	0.996243	77	0.000030	0.999730
28	0.005233	0.952899	53	0.000376	0.996619	78	0.000027	0.999757
29	0.004710	0.957609	54	0.000338	0.996957	79	0.000024	0.999782
30	0.004239	0.961848	55	0.000304	0.997261	80	0.000022	0.999803
31	0.003815	0.965663	56	0.000274	0.997535	81	0.000020	0.999823
32	0.003434	0.969097	57	0.000247	0.997781	82	0.000018	0.999841
33	0.003090	0.972187	58	0.000222	0.998003	83	0.000016	0.999857
34	0.002781	0.974968	59	0.000200	0.998203	84	0.000014	0.999871
35	0.002503	0.977472	60	0.000180	0.998383	85	0.000013	0.999884
36	0.002253	0.979724	61	0.000162	0.998544	86	0.000012	0.999895
37	0.002028	0.981752	62	0.000146	0.998690	87	0.000010	0.999906
38	0.001825	0.983577	63	0.000131	0.998821			
39	0.001642	0.985219	64	0.000118	0.998939			

k=0.1
Mean=0.73
Variance=6.11

n	P(n)	F(n)	n	P(n)	F(n)	n	P(n)	F(n)
0	0.808943	0.808943	25	0.000192	0.998874	5	0.020422	0.917666
1	0.071187	0.880130	26	0.000163	0.999037	6	0.015575	0.933241
2	0.034455	0.914585	27	0.000139	0.999176	7	0.012140	0.945381
3	0.021224	0.935809	28	0.000118	0.999294	8	0.009615	0.954996
4	0.014475	0.950284	29	0.000101	0.999394	9	0.007709	0.962705
5	0.010445	0.960729	30	0.000086	0.999480	10	0.006241	0.968946
6	0.007813	0.968541	31	0.000073	0.999554	11	0.005093	0.974039
7	0.005991	0.974533	32	0.000063	0.999617	12	0.004183	0.978221
8	0.004679	0.979212	33	0.000054	0.999670	13	0.003454	0.981676
9	0.003706	0.982918	34	0.000046	0.999716	14	0.002866	0.984542
10	0.002968	0.985886	35	0.000039	0.999756	15	0.002388	0.986930
11	0.002398	0.988284	36	0.000034	0.999790	16	0.001996	0.988926
12	0.001952	0.990236	37	0.000029	0.999819	17	0.001674	0.990600
13	0.001599	0.991834	38	0.000025	0.999844	18	0.001408	0.992007
14	0.001316	0.993151	39	0.000021	0.999865	19	0.001187	0.993194
15	0.001089	0.994240	40	0.000018	0.999884	20	0.001002	0.994196
16	0.000904	0.995144	41	0.000016	0.999900	21	0.000848	0.995045
17	0.000754	0.995898	42	0.000014	0.999913	22	0.000720	0.995764
18	0.000630	0.996528				23	0.000611	0.996375
19	0.000528	0.997056				24	0.000520	0.996895

k=0.2
Mean=1.47
Variance=12.22

n	P(n)	F(n)	n	P(n)	F(n)
20	0.000444	0.997500	25	0.000443	0.997338
21	0.000374	0.997874	26	0.000378	0.997716
22	0.000316	0.998190	27	0.000323	0.998038
23	0.000267	0.998457	28	0.000276	0.998314
24	0.000226	0.998683	29	0.000236	0.998550
0	0.654389	0.654389	30	0.000202	0.998752
1	0.115173	0.769562	31	0.000173	0.998925
2	0.060811	0.830373	32	0.000149	0.999074
3	0.039243	0.869616	33	0.000128	0.999202
4	0.027627	0.897244	34	0.000110	0.999311

35	0.000094	0.999406	40	0.000080	0.999478	40	0.000127	0.999162
36	0.000081	0.999487	41	0.000069	0.999547	41	0.000110	0.999272
37	0.000070	0.999557	42	0.000060	0.999607	42	0.000095	0.999367
38	0.000060	0.999617	43	0.000052	0.999659	43	0.000083	0.999450
39	0.000052	0.999669	44	0.000045	0.999704	44	0.000072	0.999522
40	0.000045	0.999714	45	0.000039	0.999743	45	0.000062	0.999584
41	0.000039	0.999752	46	0.000034	0.999777	46	0.000054	0.999638
42	0.000033	0.999785	47	0.000029	0.999806	47	0.000047	0.999685
43	0.000029	0.999814	48	0.000025	0.999832	48	0.000041	0.999726
44	0.000025	0.999839	49	0.000022	0.999854	49	0.000035	0.999761
45	0.000021	0.999861	50	0.000019	0.999873	50	0.000031	0.999792
46	0.000019	0.999879	51	0.000017	0.999889	51	0.000027	0.999819
47	0.000016	0.999895	52	0.000014	0.999904	52	0.000023	0.999842
48	0.000014	0.999909				53	0.000020	0.999863
						54	0.000018	0.999880
						55	0.000015	0.999896
						56	0.000013	0.999909

$k = 0.3$
Mean $= 2.20$
Variance $= 18.33$

$k = 0.4$
Mean $= 2.93$
Variance $= 24.44$

$k = 0.5$
Mean $= 3.67$
Variance $= 30.56$

n	$P(n)$	$F(n)$	n	$P(n)$	$F(n)$	n	$P(n)$	$F(n)$
0	0.529364	0.529364	0	0.428225	0.428225	0	0.346410	0.346410
1	0.139752	0.669116	1	0.150735	0.578961	1	0.152420	0.498831
2	0.079938	0.749054	2	0.092853	0.671814	2	0.100598	0.599428
3	0.053932	0.802986	3	0.065369	0.737182	3	0.073772	0.673200
4	0.039154	0.842140	4	0.048896	0.786078	4	0.056804	0.730004
5	0.029632	0.871772	5	0.037865	0.823943	5	0.044989	0.774993
6	0.023034	0.894806	6	0.029989	0.853932	6	0.036291	0.811284
7	0.018243	0.913049	7	0.024128	0.878060	7	0.029655	0.840938
8	0.014649	0.927698	8	0.019640	0.897700	8	0.024465	0.865404
9	0.011889	0.939587	9	0.016131	0.913832	9	0.020333	0.885737
10	0.009730	0.949316	10	0.013344	0.927175	10	0.016999	0.902736
11	0.008017	0.957333	11	0.011102	0.938277	11	0.014279	0.917015
12	0.006644	0.963977	12	0.009281	0.947559	12	0.012042	0.929057
13	0.005532	0.969508	13	0.007791	0.955349	13	0.010189	0.939246
14	0.004624	0.974133	14	0.006562	0.961911	14	0.008646	0.947892
15	0.003880	0.978012	15	0.005543	0.967455	15	0.007355	0.955247
16	0.003265	0.981277	16	0.004695	0.972150	16	0.006270	0.961518
17	0.002755	0.984032	17	0.003986	0.976136	17	0.005356	0.966873
18	0.002330	0.986361	18	0.003391	0.979527	18	0.004582	0.971455
19	0.001975	0.988336	19	0.002890	0.982417	19	0.003926	0.975381
20	0.001677	0.990013	20	0.002467	0.984883	20	0.003369	0.978750
21	0.001426	0.991439	21	0.002109	0.986992	21	0.002894	0.981643
22	0.001215	0.992655	22	0.001805	0.988797	22	0.002489	0.984132
23	0.001037	0.993692	23	0.001547	0.990344	23	0.002142	0.986274
24	0.000886	0.994577	24	0.001327	0.991671	24	0.001846	0.988120
25	0.000758	0.995335	25	0.001140	0.992811	25	0.001592	0.989712
26	0.000649	0.995984	26	0.000980	0.993791	26	0.001374	0.991086
27	0.000556	0.996540	27	0.000843	0.994634	27	0.001187	0.992273
28	0.000477	0.997018	28	0.000726	0.995360	28	0.001026	0.993299
29	0.000410	0.997427	29	0.000626	0.995986	29	0.000887	0.994186
30	0.000352	0.997780	30	0.000540	0.996526	30	0.000768	0.994953
31	0.000303	0.998083	31	0.000466	0.996992	31	0.000665	0.995618
32	0.000261	0.998343	32	0.000402	0.997394	32	0.000576	0.996194
33	0.000225	0.998568	33	0.000347	0.997741	33	0.000499	0.996693
34	0.000194	0.998762	34	0.000300	0.998042	34	0.000433	0.997125
35	0.000167	0.998929	35	0.000260	0.998302			
36	0.000144	0.999073	36	0.000225	0.998526			
37	0.000124	0.999197	37	0.000195	0.998721			
38	0.000107	0.999304	38	0.000169	0.998890			
39	0.000093	0.999397	39	0.000146	0.999036			

n	P(n)	F(n)
35	0.000375	0.997501
36	0.000326	0.997826
37	0.000283	0.998109
38	0.000245	0.998354
39	0.000213	0.998568
40	0.000185	0.998753
41	0.000161	0.998914
42	0.000140	0.999054
43	0.000122	0.999176
44	0.000106	0.999282
45	0.000092	0.999374
46	0.000080	0.999454
47	0.000070	0.999524
48	0.000061	0.999585
49	0.000053	0.999638
50	0.000046	0.999684
51	0.000040	0.999725
52	0.000035	0.999760
53	0.000031	0.999790
54	0.000027	0.999817
55	0.000023	0.999840
56	0.000020	0.999861
57	0.000018	0.999878
58	0.000015	0.999894
59	0.000013	0.999907

k = 0·6
Mean = 4·40
Variance = 36·67

n	P(n)	F(n)
0	0.280226	0.280226
1	0.147959	0.428186
2	0.104163	0.532349
3	0.079442	0.611791
4	0.062918	0.674709
5	0.050938	0.725648
6	0.041837	0.767485
7	0.034713	0.802198
8	0.029020	0.831218
9	0.024403	0.855621
10	0.020615	0.876237
11	0.017482	0.893718
12	0.014871	0.908590
13	0.012684	0.921274
14	0.010843	0.932117
15	0.009287	0.941404
16	0.007969	0.949373
17	0.006847	0.956220
18	0.005892	0.962112
19	0.005076	0.967188
20	0.004377	0.971565
21	0.003779	0.975343
22	0.003265	0.978608
23	0.002823	0.981431
24	0.002443	0.983874
25	0.002115	0.985989
26	0.001833	0.987822
27	0.001589	0.989411
28	0.001378	0.990789
29	0.001196	0.991985

n	P(n)	F(n)
30	0.001039	0.993024
31	0.000902	0.993926
32	0.000784	0.994710
33	0.000682	0.995392
34	0.000593	0.995985
35	0.000516	0.996500
36	0.000449	0.996949
37	0.000391	0.997339
38	0.000340	0.997680
39	0.000296	0.997976
40	0.000258	0.998234
41	0.000225	0.998459
42	0.000196	0.998655
43	0.000171	0.998826
44	0.000149	0.998975
45	0.000130	0.999105
46	0.000113	0.999218
47	0.000099	0.999317
48	0.000086	0.999403
49	0.000075	0.999479
50	0.000066	0.999544
51	0.000057	0.999602
52	0.000050	0.999652
53	0.000044	0.999696
54	0.000038	0.999734
55	0.000033	0.999767
56	0.000029	0.999797
57	0.000026	0.999822
58	0.000022	0.999844
59	0.000019	0.999864
60	0.000017	0.999881
61	0.000015	0.999896
62	0.000013	0.999909

k = 0·7
Mean = 5·13
Variance = 42·78

n	P(n)	F(n)
0	0.226687	0.226687
1	0.139639	0.366326
2	0.104450	0.470777
3	0.082725	0.553501
4	0.067338	0.620839
5	0.055702	0.676541
6	0.046567	0.723107
7	0.039222	0.762330
8	0.033221	0.795551
9	0.028260	0.823812
10	0.024123	0.847935
11	0.020649	0.868584
12	0.017717	0.886301
13	0.015231	0.901532
14	0.013116	0.914649
15	0.011312	0.925960
16	0.009767	0.935728
17	0.008444	0.944171
18	0.007307	0.951478
19	0.006328	0.957806

n	P(n)	F(n)
20	0.005485	0.963292
21	0.004758	0.968050
22	0.004130	0.972180
23	0.003587	0.975767
24	0.003117	0.978884
25	0.002710	0.981594
26	0.002357	0.983952
27	0.002052	0.986003
28	0.001786	0.987789
29	0.001555	0.989345
30	0.001355	0.990700
31	0.001181	0.991881
32	0.001029	0.992910
33	0.000898	0.993808
34	0.000783	0.994591
35	0.000683	0.995274
36	0.000596	0.995870
37	0.000520	0.996391
38	0.000454	0.996845
39	0.000397	0.997242
40	0.000346	0.997588
41	0.000303	0.997891
42	0.000264	0.998155
43	0.000231	0.998386
44	0.000202	0.998588
45	0.000177	0.998765
46	0.000154	0.998919
47	0.000135	0.999054
48	0.000118	0.999172
49	0.000103	0.999275
50	0.000090	0.999366
51	0.000079	0.999445
52	0.000069	0.999514
53	0.000060	0.999574
54	0.000053	0.999627
55	0.000046	0.999674
56	0.000041	0.999714
57	0.000035	0.999750
58	0.000031	0.999781
59	0.000027	0.999808
60	0.000024	0.999832
61	0.000021	0.999852
62	0.000018	0.999871
63	0.000016	0.999887
64	0.000014	0.999901

k = 0·8
Mean = 5·87
Variance = 48·89

n	P(n)	F(n)
0	0.183377	0.183377
1	0.129097	0.312475
2	0.102245	0.414720
3	0.083977	0.498697
4	0.070205	0.568902
5	0.059309	0.628211
6	0.050452	0.678664
7	0.043130	0.721793
8	0.037005	0.758799
9	0.031841	0.790640

n	P(n)	F(n)
10	0.027460	0.818099
11	0.023725	0.841824
12	0.020530	0.862354
13	0.017789	0.880143
14	0.015430	0.895573
15	0.013398	0.908971
16	0.011643	0.920613
17	0.010125	0.930738
18	0.008811	0.939549
19	0.007672	0.947221
20	0.006684	0.953905
21	0.005826	0.959731
22	0.005080	0.964811
23	0.004432	0.969242
24	0.003867	0.973110
25	0.003376	0.976486
26	0.002948	0.979434
27	0.002575	0.982009
28	0.002250	0.984259
29	0.001966	0.986225
30	0.001719	0.987943
31	0.001503	0.989446
32	0.001314	0.990760
33	0.001149	0.991910
34	0.001006	0.992915
35	0.000880	0.993795
36	0.000770	0.994565
37	0.000674	0.995239
38	0.000590	0.995829
39	0.000516	0.996345
40	0.000452	0.996798
41	0.000396	0.997194
42	0.000347	0.997540
43	0.000304	0.997844
44	0.000266	0.998110
45	0.000233	0.998343
46	0.000204	0.998548
47	0.000179	0.998727
48	0.000157	0.998884
49	0.000137	0.999021
50	0.000120	0.999141
51	0.000106	0.999247
52	0.000093	0.999340
53	0.000081	0.999421
54	0.000071	0.999492
55	0.000062	0.999554
56	0.000055	0.999609
57	0.000048	0.999657
58	0.000042	0.999699
59	0.000037	0.999736
60	0.000032	0.999768
61	0.000028	0.999797
62	0.000025	0.999822
63	0.000022	0.999844
64	0.000019	0.999863
65	0.000017	0.999880
66	0.000015	0.999894
67	0.000013	0.999907

k = 0.9
Mean = 6·60
Variance = 55·00

n	P(n)	F(n)
0	0.148342	0.148342
1	0.117487	0.265828
2	0.098219	0.364047
3	0.083551	0.447598
4	0.071687	0.519286
5	0.061823	0.581109
6	0.053497	0.634606
7	0.046405	0.681011
8	0.040326	0.721338
9	0.035093	0.756430
10	0.030573	0.787003
11	0.026659	0.813663
12	0.023265	0.836927
13	0.020316	0.857243
14	0.017750	0.874993
15	0.015516	0.890509
16	0.013569	0.904077
17	0.011870	0.915948
18	0.010388	0.926335
19	0.009093	0.935428
20	0.007962	0.943390
21	0.006973	0.950363
22	0.006108	0.956472
23	0.005352	0.961824
24	0.004690	0.966514
25	0.004111	0.970625
26	0.003604	0.974228
27	0.003159	0.977388
28	0.002770	0.980158
29	0.002430	0.982588
30	0.002131	0.984719
31	0.001869	0.986588
32	0.001640	0.988228
33	0.001439	0.989666
34	0.001262	0.990928
35	0.001108	0.992036
36	0.000972	0.993008
37	0.000853	0.993861
38	0.000749	0.994609
39	0.000657	0.995267
40	0.000577	0.995843
41	0.000506	0.996350
42	0.000445	0.996794
43	0.000390	0.997185
44	0.000343	0.997527
45	0.000301	0.997828
46	0.000264	0.998092
47	0.000232	0.998324
48	0.000204	0.998528
49	0.000179	0.998707
50	0.000157	0.998864
51	0.000138	0.999002
52	0.000121	0.999123
53	0.000106	0.999230
54	0.000094	0.999323

n	P(n)	F(n)
55	0.000082	0.999406
56	0.000072	0.999478
57	0.000063	0.999541
58	0.000056	0.999597
59	0.000049	0.999646
60	0.000043	0.999689
61	0.000038	0.999726
62	0.000033	0.999760
63	0.000029	0.999789
64	0.000026	0.999814
65	0.000023	0.999837
66	0.000020	0.999857
67	0.000017	0.999874
68	0.000015	0.999889
69	0.000013	0.999903

k = 1.0
Mean = 7·33
Variance = 61·11

n	P(n)	F(n)
0	0.120000	0.120000
1	0.105600	0.225600
2	0.092928	0.318528
3	0.081777	0.400305
4	0.071963	0.472268
5	0.063328	0.535596
6	0.055728	0.591324
7	0.049041	0.640365
8	0.043156	0.683522
9	0.037977	0.721499
10	0.033420	0.754919
11	0.029410	0.784329
12	0.025881	0.810209
13	0.022775	0.832984
14	0.020042	0.853026
15	0.017637	0.870663
16	0.015520	0.886183
17	0.013658	0.899841
18	0.012019	0.911860
19	0.010577	0.922437
20	0.009308	0.931745
21	0.008191	0.939935
22	0.007208	0.947143
23	0.006343	0.953486
24	0.005582	0.959068
25	0.004912	0.963980
26	0.004322	0.968302
27	0.003804	0.972106
28	0.003347	0.975453
29	0.002946	0.978399
30	0.002592	0.980991
31	0.002281	0.983272
32	0.002007	0.985279
33	0.001766	0.987046
34	0.001555	0.988600
35	0.001368	0.989968
36	0.001204	0.991172
37	0.001059	0.992231
38	0.000932	0.993164
39	0.000820	0.993984

n	P(n)	F(n)
40	0.000722	0.994706
41	0.000635	0.995341
42	0.000559	0.995900
43	0.000492	0.996392
44	0.000433	0.996825
45	0.000381	0.997206
46	0.000335	0.997541
47	0.000295	0.997836
48	0.000260	0.998096
49	0.000228	0.998325
50	0.000201	0.998526
51	0.000177	0.998703
52	0.000156	0.998858
53	0.000137	0.998995
54	0.000121	0.999116
55	0.000106	0.999222
56	0.000093	0.999315
57	0.000082	0.999397
58	0.000072	0.999470
59	0.000064	0.999533
60	0.000056	0.999589
61	0.000049	0.999639
62	0.000043	0.999682
63	0.000038	0.999720
64	0.000034	0.999754
65	0.000030	0.999783
66	0.000026	0.999809
67	0.000023	0.999832
68	0.000020	0.999852
69	0.000018	0.999870
70	0.000016	0.999886
71	0.000014	0.999899
72	0.000012	0.999911

k=1·1
Mean=8·07
Variance=67·22

n	P(n)	F(n)
0	0.097073	0.097073
1	0.093967	0.191040
2	0.086825	0.277865
3	0.078953	0.356819
4	0.071216	0.428034
5	0.063923	0.491958
6	0.057190	0.549148
7	0.051046	0.600194
8	0.045482	0.645676
9	0.040469	0.686145
10	0.035969	0.722114
11	0.031940	0.754054
12	0.028342	0.782396
13	0.025133	0.807529
14	0.022275	0.829803
15	0.019732	0.849536
16	0.017473	0.867009
17	0.015467	0.882475
18	0.013686	0.896162
19	0.012107	0.908269

n	P(n)	F(n)
20	0.010708	0.918977
21	0.009468	0.928445
22	0.008369	0.936814
23	0.007397	0.944211
24	0.006537	0.950748
25	0.005775	0.956523
26	0.005102	0.961625
27	0.004506	0.966131
28	0.003980	0.970110
29	0.003514	0.973624
30	0.003103	0.976727
31	0.002739	0.979466
32	0.002418	0.981884
33	0.002134	0.984019
34	0.001884	0.985902
35	0.001662	0.987565
36	0.001467	0.989032
37	0.001294	0.990326
38	0.001142	0.991468
39	0.001008	0.992476
40	0.000889	0.993365
41	0.000784	0.994149
42	0.000692	0.994841
43	0.000610	0.995451
44	0.000538	0.995989
45	0.000475	0.996464
46	0.000419	0.996882
47	0.000369	0.997251
48	0.000325	0.997577
49	0.000287	0.997864
50	0.000253	0.998117
51	0.000223	0.998340
52	0.000197	0.998537
53	0.000173	0.998710
54	0.000153	0.998863
55	0.000135	0.998998
56	0.000119	0.999117
57	0.000105	0.999222
58	0.000092	0.999314
59	0.000081	0.999395
60	0.000072	0.999467
61	0.000063	0.999530
62	0.000056	0.999586
63	0.000049	0.999635
64	0.000043	0.999679
65	0.000038	0.999717
66	0.000034	0.999750
67	0.000030	0.999780
68	0.000026	0.999806
69	0.000023	0.999829
70	0.000020	0.999850
71	0.000018	0.999867
72	0.000016	0.999883
73	0.000014	0.999897
74	0.000012	0.999909

k=1·2
Mean=8·80
Variance=73·33

n	P(n)	F(n)
0	0.078527	0.078527
1	0.082924	0.161451
2	0.080271	0.241722
3	0.075347	0.317069
4	0.069621	0.386690
5	0.063717	0.450407
6	0.057940	0.508347
7	0.052444	0.560791
8	0.047305	0.608096
9	0.042553	0.650649
10	0.038196	0.688845
11	0.034223	0.723068
12	0.030618	0.753686
13	0.027359	0.781045
14	0.024420	0.805465
15	0.021776	0.827240
16	0.019402	0.846643
17	0.017275	0.863918
18	0.015371	0.879288
19	0.013669	0.892957
20	0.012149	0.905106
21	0.010793	0.915898
22	0.009584	0.925482
23	0.008507	0.933989
24	0.007549	0.941538
25	0.006696	0.948234
26	0.005938	0.954172
27	0.005264	0.959436
28	0.004665	0.964101
29	0.004134	0.968235
30	0.003662	0.971897
31	0.003243	0.975141
32	0.002872	0.978013
33	0.002543	0.980555
34	0.002251	0.982806
35	0.001992	0.984798
36	0.001763	0.986561
37	0.001560	0.988120
38	0.001380	0.989500
39	0.001220	0.990720
40	0.001079	0.991799
41	0.000954	0.992754
42	0.000844	0.993597
43	0.000746	0.994343
44	0.000659	0.995003
45	0.000583	0.995586
46	0.000515	0.996101
47	0.000455	0.996556
48	0.000402	0.996959
49	0.000356	0.997314
50	0.000314	0.997628
51	0.000277	0.997906
52	0.000245	0.998151
53	0.000217	0.998367
54	0.000191	0.998559

n	P(n)	F(n)
55	0.000169	0.998728
56	0.000149	0.998877
57	0.000132	0.999009
58	0.000116	0.999125
59	0.000103	0.999228
60	0.000091	0.999318
61	0.000080	0.999398
62	0.000071	0.999469
63	0.000062	0.999531
64	0.000055	0.999586
65	0.000049	0.999635
66	0.000043	0.999678
67	0.000038	0.999716
68	0.000033	0.999749
69	0.000030	0.999779
70	0.000026	0.999805
71	0.000023	0.999828
72	0.000020	0.999848
73	0.000018	0.999866
74	0.000016	0.999882
75	0.000014	0.999896
76	0.000012	0.999908

k = 1·3
Mean = 9·53
Variance = 79·44

n	P(n)	F(n)
0	0.063524	0.063524
1	0.072671	0.136195
2	0.073543	0.209738
3	0.071190	0.280928
4	0.067346	0.348273
5	0.062820	0.411093
6	0.058046	0.469139
7	0.053269	0.522408
8	0.048635	0.571043
9	0.044225	0.615268
10	0.040086	0.655354
11	0.036238	0.691591
12	0.032686	0.724278
13	0.029428	0.753705
14	0.026451	0.780157
15	0.023743	0.803899
16	0.021285	0.825185
17	0.019062	0.844246
18	0.017054	0.861300
19	0.015244	0.876544
20	0.013616	0.890161
21	0.012153	0.902314
22	0.010841	0.913155
23	0.009664	0.922819
24	0.008611	0.931430
25	0.007669	0.939099
26	0.006826	0.945925
27	0.006074	0.951999
28	0.005402	0.957401
29	0.004803	0.962204
30	0.004269	0.966473
31	0.003793	0.970266
32	0.003369	0.973636
33	0.002992	0.976628
34	0.002656	0.979284
35	0.002357	0.981641
36	0.002092	0.983733
37	0.001856	0.985589
38	0.001646	0.987234
39	0.001460	0.988694
40	0.001294	0.989988
41	0.001147	0.991135
42	0.001017	0.992152
43	0.000901	0.993053
44	0.000798	0.993851
45	0.000707	0.994558
46	0.000626	0.995184
47	0.000555	0.995739
48	0.000491	0.996230
49	0.000435	0.996665
50	0.000385	0.997050
51	0.000341	0.997391
52	0.000302	0.997692
53	0.000267	0.997959
54	0.000236	0.998195
55	0.000209	0.998404
56	0.000185	0.998589
57	0.000164	0.998753
58	0.000145	0.998897
59	0.000128	0.999025
60	0.000113	0.999138
61	0.000100	0.999239
62	0.000088	0.999327
63	0.000078	0.999405
64	0.000069	0.999474
65	0.000061	0.999536
66	0.000054	0.999590
67	0.000048	0.999637
68	0.000042	0.999680
69	0.000037	0.999717
70	0.000033	0.999750
71	0.000029	0.999779
72	0.000026	0.999805
73	0.000023	0.999828
74	0.000020	0.999848
75	0.000018	0.999866
76	0.000016	0.999881
77	0.000014	0.999895
78	0.000012	0.999907

k = 1·4
Mean = 10·27
Variance = 85·56

n	P(n)	F(n)
0	0.051387	0.051387
1	0.063309	0.114696
2	0.066854	0.181550
3	0.066676	0.248226
4	0.064542	0.312768
5	0.061341	0.374109
6	0.057579	0.431688
7	0.053565	0.485252
8	0.049494	0.534746
9	0.045490	0.580236
10	0.041633	0.621869
11	0.037969	0.659838
12	0.034526	0.694365
13	0.031318	0.725683
14	0.028347	0.754030
15	0.025611	0.779641
16	0.023101	0.802742
17	0.020807	0.823549
18	0.018717	0.842267
19	0.016818	0.859085
20	0.015096	0.874181
21	0.013537	0.887718
22	0.012129	0.899847
23	0.010860	0.910707
24	0.009716	0.920423
25	0.008687	0.929109
26	0.007762	0.936871
27	0.006932	0.943803
28	0.006187	0.949990
29	0.005520	0.955509
30	0.004922	0.960431
31	0.004387	0.964818
32	0.003909	0.968728
33	0.003482	0.972209
34	0.003100	0.975309
35	0.002759	0.978068
36	0.002455	0.980523
37	0.002184	0.982707
38	0.001942	0.984649
39	0.001726	0.986375
40	0.001534	0.987910
41	0.001363	0.989273
42	0.001211	0.990484
43	0.001076	0.991560
44	0.000955	0.992516
45	0.000848	0.993364
46	0.000753	0.994117
47	0.000668	0.994785
48	0.000593	0.995378
49	0.000526	0.995904
50	0.000467	0.996370
51	0.000414	0.996784
52	0.000367	0.997151
53	0.000325	0.997477
54	0.000288	0.997765
55	0.000256	0.998021
56	0.000227	0.998247
57	0.000201	0.998448
58	0.000178	0.998626
59	0.000158	0.998784
60	0.000140	0.998923
61	0.000124	0.999047
62	0.000110	0.999157
63	0.000097	0.999254
64	0.000086	0.999340

n	P(n)	F(n)
65	0.000076	0.999416
66	0.000067	0.999483
67	0.000060	0.999543
68	0.000053	0.999595
69	0.000047	0.999642
70	0.000041	0.999683
71	0.000037	0.999720
72	0.000032	0.999752
73	0.000029	0.999781
74	0.000025	0.999806
75	0.000022	0.999829
76	0.000020	0.999849
77	0.000018	0.999866
78	0.000016	0.999882
79	0.000014	0.999895
80	0.000012	0.999907

k = 1·5
Mean = 11·00
Variance = 91·67

n	P(n)	F(n)
0	0.041569	0.041569
1	0.054871	0.096441
2	0.060359	0.156799
3	0.061968	0.218767
4	0.061348	0.280116
5	0.059385	0.339501
6	0.056614	0.396115
7	0.053379	0.449494
8	0.049909	0.499403
9	0.046360	0.545763
10	0.042837	0.588600
11	0.039410	0.628009
12	0.036126	0.664135
13	0.033013	0.697148
14	0.030089	0.727238
15	0.027361	0.754599
16	0.024830	0.779429
17	0.022493	0.801922
18	0.020344	0.822266
19	0.018374	0.840640
20	0.016573	0.857213
21	0.014932	0.872145
22	0.013438	0.885583
23	0.012083	0.897666
24	0.010854	0.908521
25	0.009743	0.918264
26	0.008739	0.927003
27	0.007832	0.934835
28	0.007016	0.941851
29	0.006280	0.948131
30	0.005619	0.953750
31	0.005024	0.958774
32	0.004490	0.963264
33	0.004011	0.967276
34	0.003582	0.970858
35	0.003197	0.974055
36	0.002853	0.976907
37	0.002544	0.979452
38	0.002268	0.981720
39	0.002022	0.983742
40	0.001801	0.985543
41	0.001605	0.987147
42	0.001429	0.988576
43	0.001272	0.989848
44	0.001132	0.990980
45	0.001007	0.991988
46	0.000896	0.992884
47	0.000797	0.993680
48	0.000709	0.994389
49	0.000630	0.995019
50	0.000560	0.995579
51	0.000498	0.996076
52	0.000442	0.996518
53	0.000393	0.996911
54	0.000349	0.997260
55	0.000310	0.997569
56	0.000275	0.997844
57	0.000244	0.998088
58	0.000217	0.998305
59	0.000192	0.998497
60	0.000171	0.998668
61	0.000151	0.998819
62	0.000134	0.998954
63	0.000119	0.999073
64	0.000106	0.999178
65	0.000094	0.999272
66	0.000083	0.999355
67	0.000074	0.999429
68	0.000065	0.999494
69	0.000058	0.999552
70	0.000051	0.999603
71	0.000045	0.999648
72	0.000040	0.999689
73	0.000036	0.999724
74	0.000032	0.999756
75	0.000028	0.999784
76	0.000025	0.999809
77	0.000022	0.999831
78	0.000019	0.999850
79	0.000017	0.999867
80	0.000015	0.999883
81	0.000014	0.999896
82	0.000012	0.999908

k = 1·6
Mean = 11·73
Variance = 97·78

n	P(n)	F(n)
0	0.033627	0.033627
1	0.047347	0.080974
2	0.054165	0.135139
3	0.057198	0.192337
4	0.057885	0.250222
5	0.057051	0.307273
6	0.055225	0.362498
7	0.052764	0.415262
8	0.049915	0.465177
9	0.046853	0.512030
10	0.043705	0.555735
11	0.040558	0.596293
12	0.037476	0.633769
13	0.034501	0.668269
14	0.031662	0.699931
15	0.028977	0.728908
16	0.026456	0.755364
17	0.024103	0.779466
18	0.021917	0.801384
19	0.019896	0.821280
20	0.018034	0.839314
21	0.016323	0.855638
22	0.014756	0.870394
23	0.013324	0.883719
24	0.012019	0.895737
25	0.010830	0.906568
26	0.009751	0.916318
27	0.008771	0.925089
28	0.007884	0.932973
29	0.007081	0.940055
30	0.006356	0.946411
31	0.005702	0.952113
32	0.005112	0.957225
33	0.004580	0.961805
34	0.004102	0.965906
35	0.003671	0.969577
36	0.003285	0.972862
37	0.002937	0.975799
38	0.002626	0.978425
39	0.002346	0.980771
40	0.002096	0.982867
41	0.001871	0.984738
42	0.001670	0.986408
43	0.001490	0.987898
44	0.001329	0.989227
45	0.001185	0.990412
46	0.001057	0.991469
47	0.000942	0.992411
48	0.000839	0.993250
49	0.000747	0.993997
50	0.000666	0.994663
51	0.000593	0.995256
52	0.000528	0.995783
53	0.000470	0.996253
54	0.000418	0.996670
55	0.000372	0.997042
56	0.000331	0.997373
57	0.000294	0.997667
58	0.000261	0.997928
59	0.000232	0.998160
60	0.000206	0.998367
61	0.000183	0.998550
62	0.000163	0.998713
63	0.000145	0.998858
64	0.000129	0.998987

n	P(n)	F(n)
65	0.000114	0.999101
66	0.000101	0.999203
67	0.000090	0.999293
68	0.000080	0.999373
69	0.000071	0.999444
70	0.000063	0.999507
71	0.000056	0.999562
72	0.000050	0.999612
73	0.000044	0.999656
74	0.000039	0.999695
75	0.000035	0.999730
76	0.000031	0.999761
77	0.000027	0.999788
78	0.000024	0.999812
79	0.000021	0.999833
80	0.000019	0.999852
81	0.000017	0.999869
82	0.000015	0.999884
83	0.000013	0.999897
84	0.000012	0.999909

k = 1·7
Mean = 12·47
Variance = 103·89

n	P(n)	F(n)
0	0.027202	0.027202
1	0.040695	0.067897
2	0.048346	0.116243
3	0.052471	0.168714
4	0.054255	0.222969
5	0.054429	0.277397
6	0.053485	0.330883
7	0.051774	0.382656
8	0.049547	0.432204
9	0.046993	0.479197
10	0.044249	0.523445
11	0.041417	0.564862
12	0.038573	0.603435
13	0.035772	0.639206
14	0.033053	0.672259
15	0.030444	0.702704
16	0.027963	0.730666
17	0.025621	0.756287
18	0.023423	0.779710
19	0.021372	0.801082
20	0.019465	0.820547
21	0.017700	0.838247
22	0.016072	0.854319
23	0.014574	0.868893
24	0.013199	0.882092
25	0.011940	0.894032
26	0.010790	0.904823
27	0.009742	0.914564
28	0.008787	0.923351
29	0.007919	0.931270
30	0.007132	0.938402
31	0.006417	0.944819
32	0.005771	0.950590
33	0.005186	0.955776
34	0.004658	0.960434
35	0.004181	0.964615
36	0.003751	0.968366
37	0.003363	0.971729
38	0.003014	0.974743
39	0.002700	0.977442
40	0.002417	0.979860
41	0.002164	0.982024
42	0.001936	0.983959
43	0.001731	0.985691
44	0.001548	0.987238
45	0.001383	0.988622
46	0.001236	0.989857
47	0.001104	0.990961
48	0.000985	0.991946
49	0.000880	0.992826
50	0.000785	0.993611
51	0.000700	0.994311
52	0.000624	0.994935
53	0.000557	0.995492
54	0.000496	0.995988
55	0.000442	0.996430
56	0.000394	0.996824
57	0.000351	0.997175
58	0.000313	0.997488
59	0.000278	0.997766
60	0.000248	0.998014
61	0.000221	0.998235
62	0.000196	0.998431
63	0.000175	0.998606
64	0.000155	0.998761
65	0.000138	0.998899
66	0.000123	0.999022
67	0.000109	0.999132
68	0.000097	0.999229
69	0.000086	0.999315
70	0.000077	0.999392
71	0.000068	0.999460
72	0.000061	0.999521
73	0.000054	0.999575
74	0.000048	0.999623
75	0.000042	0.999665
76	0.000038	0.999703
77	0.000034	0.999736
78	0.000030	0.999766
79	0.000026	0.999792
80	0.000023	0.999816
81	0.000021	0.999837
82	0.000018	0.999855
83	0.000016	0.999872
84	0.000015	0.999886
85	0.000013	0.999899
86	0.000011	0.999911

k = 1·8
Mean = 13·20
Variance = 110·00

n	P(n)	F(n)
0	0.022005	0.022005
1	0.034856	0.056862
2	0.042943	0.099805
3	0.047867	0.147672
4	0.050548	0.198219
5	0.051599	0.249818
6	0.051461	0.301280
7	0.050462	0.351741
8	0.048847	0.400588
9	0.046806	0.447394
10	0.044485	0.491879
11	0.041993	0.533872
12	0.039418	0.573290
13	0.036822	0.610113
14	0.034255	0.644368
15	0.031752	0.676120
16	0.029339	0.705459
17	0.027033	0.732493
18	0.024847	0.757340
19	0.022786	0.780125
20	0.020854	0.800979
21	0.019050	0.820029
22	0.017374	0.837403
23	0.015821	0.853224
24	0.014386	0.867610
25	0.013065	0.880675
26	0.011851	0.892526
27	0.010738	0.903264
28	0.009719	0.912983
29	0.008789	0.921772
30	0.007941	0.929713
31	0.007168	0.936881
32	0.006466	0.943346
33	0.005828	0.949174
34	0.005249	0.954423
35	0.004725	0.959148
36	0.004250	0.963398
37	0.003821	0.967219
38	0.003433	0.970652
39	0.003083	0.973735
40	0.002767	0.976503
41	0.002483	0.978986
42	0.002227	0.981212
43	0.001996	0.983208
44	0.001788	0.984996
45	0.001602	0.986598
46	0.001434	0.988032
47	0.001283	0.989315
48	0.001148	0.990463
49	0.001027	0.991490
50	0.000918	0.992408
51	0.000821	0.993229
52	0.000733	0.993962
53	0.000655	0.994617
54	0.000585	0.995202

n	P(n)	F(n)
55	0.000522	0.995725
56	0.000466	0.996191
57	0.000416	0.996607
58	0.000371	0.996978
59	0.000331	0.997309
60	0.000295	0.997604
61	0.000263	0.997867
62	0.000235	0.998102
63	0.000209	0.998311
64	0.000186	0.998497
65	0.000166	0.998663
66	0.000148	0.998811
67	0.000132	0.998942
68	0.000117	0.999059
69	0.000104	0.999164
70	0.000093	0.999256
71	0.000083	0.999339
72	0.000074	0.999413
73	0.000065	0.999478
74	0.000058	0.999536
75	0.000052	0.999588
76	0.000046	0.999634
77	0.000041	0.999675
78	0.000036	0.999711
79	0.000032	0.999744
80	0.000029	0.999772
81	0.000026	0.999798
82	0.000023	0.999820
83	0.000020	0.999841
84	0.000018	0.999859
85	0.000016	0.999874
86	0.000014	0.999889
87	0.000013	0.999901

k = 1·9
Mean = 13·93
Variance = 116·11

n	P(n)	F(n)
0	0.017801	0.017801
1	0.029763	0.047564
2	0.037978	0.085542
3	0.043447	0.128989
4	0.046836	0.175825
5	0.048634	0.224459
6	0.049218	0.273676
7	0.048880	0.322557
8	0.047854	0.370410
9	0.046322	0.416733
10	0.044432	0.461165
11	0.042300	0.503465
12	0.040016	0.543480
13	0.037652	0.581132
14	0.035263	0.616395
15	0.032894	0.649289
16	0.030575	0.679863
17	0.028330	0.708194
18	0.026177	0.734371
19	0.024127	0.758497
20	0.022187	0.780685
21	0.020361	0.801046
22	0.018651	0.819697
23	0.017055	0.836752
24	0.015571	0.852324
25	0.014196	0.866520
26	0.012925	0.879445
27	0.011753	0.891198
28	0.010675	0.901873
29	0.009686	0.911559
30	0.008779	0.920338
31	0.007950	0.928288
32	0.007193	0.935481
33	0.006502	0.941983
34	0.005873	0.947857
35	0.005302	0.953158
36	0.004782	0.957940
37	0.004310	0.962250
38	0.003883	0.966134
39	0.003496	0.969630
40	0.003146	0.972775
41	0.002829	0.975604
42	0.002543	0.978147
43	0.002285	0.980431
44	0.002051	0.982483
45	0.001841	0.984324
46	0.001652	0.985977
47	0.001482	0.987458
48	0.001328	0.988787
49	0.001190	0.989977
50	0.001066	0.991044
51	0.000955	0.991999
52	0.000855	0.992854
53	0.000765	0.993619
54	0.000685	0.994303
55	0.000612	0.994916
56	0.000547	0.995463
57	0.000489	0.995952
58	0.000437	0.996390
59	0.000391	0.996780
60	0.000349	0.997129
61	0.000312	0.997441
62	0.000278	0.997719
63	0.000248	0.997968
64	0.000222	0.998189
65	0.000198	0.998387
66	0.000176	0.998563
67	0.000157	0.998721
68	0.000140	0.998861
69	0.000125	0.998986
70	0.000111	0.999097
71	0.000099	0.999197
72	0.000088	0.999285
73	0.000079	0.999364
74	0.000070	0.999434
75	0.000063	0.999497
76	0.000056	0.999552
77	0.000050	0.999602
78	0.000044	0.999646
79	0.000039	0.999685
80	0.000035	0.999720
81	0.000031	0.999751
82	0.000028	0.999779
83	0.000025	0.999804
84	0.000022	0.999825
85	0.000019	0.999845
86	0.000017	0.999862
87	0.000015	0.999878
88	0.000014	0.999891
89	0.000012	0.999903

k = 2·0
Mean = 14·67
Variance = 122·22

n	P(n)	F(n)
0	0.014400	0.014400
1	0.025344	0.039744
2	0.033454	0.073198
3	0.039253	0.112451
4	0.043178	0.155629
5	0.045596	0.201225
6	0.046812	0.248037
7	0.047079	0.295116
8	0.046609	0.341725
9	0.045573	0.387298
10	0.044115	0.431412
11	0.042350	0.473762
12	0.040374	0.514136
13	0.038262	0.552398
14	0.036075	0.588473
15	0.033863	0.622336
16	0.031662	0.653998
17	0.029501	0.683499
18	0.027403	0.710902
19	0.025384	0.736287
20	0.023455	0.759741
21	0.021623	0.781365
22	0.019893	0.801258
23	0.018267	0.819525
24	0.016745	0.836271
25	0.015325	0.851596
26	0.014005	0.865600
27	0.012781	0.878381
28	0.011649	0.890030
29	0.010604	0.900634
30	0.009643	0.910277
31	0.008759	0.919036
32	0.007949	0.926985
33	0.007207	0.934193
34	0.006529	0.940722
35	0.005910	0.946631
36	0.005345	0.951976
37	0.004831	0.956807
38	0.004363	0.961170
39	0.003938	0.965107
40	0.003552	0.968659
41	0.003202	0.971861
42	0.002885	0.974746
43	0.002598	0.977343
44	0.002338	0.979681

n	P(n)	F(n)
45	0.002103	0.981784
46	0.001891	0.983675
47	0.001699	0.985374
48	0.001527	0.986901
49	0.001371	0.988272
50	0.001230	0.989502
51	0.001104	0.990606
52	0.000990	0.991597
53	0.000888	0.992484
54	0.000796	0.993280
55	0.000713	0.993993
56	0.000639	0.994632
57	0.000572	0.995204
58	0.000512	0.995716
59	0.000458	0.996174
60	0.000410	0.996584
61	0.000367	0.996950
62	0.000328	0.997278
63	0.000293	0.997571
64	0.000262	0.997833
65	0.000234	0.998067
66	0.000209	0.998276
67	0.000187	0.998463
68	0.000167	0.998630
69	0.000149	0.998778
70	0.000133	0.998911
71	0.000119	0.999030
72	0.000106	0.999136
73	0.000094	0.999230
74	0.000084	0.999314
75	0.000075	0.999389
76	0.000067	0.999456
77	0.000060	0.999516
78	0.000053	0.999569
79	0.000047	0.999616
80	0.000042	0.999659
81	0.000038	0.999696
82	0.000033	0.999730
83	0.000030	0.999760
84	0.000027	0.999786
85	0.000024	0.999810
86	0.000021	0.999831
87	0.000019	0.999850
88	0.000017	0.999866
89	0.000015	0.999881
90	0.000013	0.999894
91	0.000012	0.999906

k=2·1
Mean = 15·40
Variance = 128·33

n	P(n)	F(n)
0	0.011649	0.011649
1	0.021527	0.033176
2	0.029363	0.062539
3	0.035314	0.097852
4	0.039622	0.137474

n	P(n)	F(n)
5	0.042538	0.180012
6	0.044296	0.224308
7	0.045106	0.269415
8	0.045151	0.314566
9	0.044590	0.359156
10	0.043555	0.402711
11	0.042161	0.444872
12	0.040503	0.485375
13	0.038658	0.524033
14	0.036692	0.560726
15	0.034657	0.595383
16	0.032595	0.627978
17	0.030540	0.658518
18	0.028517	0.687035
19	0.026548	0.713583
20	0.024647	0.738230
21	0.022826	0.761056
22	0.021091	0.782147
23	0.019448	0.801595
24	0.017898	0.819493
25	0.016444	0.835937
26	0.015083	0.851019
27	0.013813	0.864833
28	0.012633	0.877466
29	0.011539	0.889005
30	0.010527	0.899532
31	0.009592	0.909124
32	0.008731	0.917855
33	0.007940	0.925795
34	0.007213	0.933008
35	0.006547	0.939554
36	0.005937	0.945492
37	0.005380	0.950872
38	0.004872	0.955743
39	0.004408	0.960151
40	0.003986	0.964137
41	0.003601	0.967738
42	0.003252	0.970991
43	0.002935	0.973926
44	0.002648	0.976573
45	0.002387	0.978960
46	0.002151	0.981111
47	0.001937	0.983048
48	0.001743	0.984791
49	0.001569	0.986360
50	0.001411	0.987771
51	0.001268	0.989039
52	0.001140	0.990179
53	0.001024	0.991203
54	0.000919	0.992122
55	0.000825	0.992947
56	0.000740	0.993687
57	0.000664	0.994351
58	0.000596	0.994947
59	0.000534	0.995481
60	0.000478	0.995959
61	0.000429	0.996388
62	0.000384	0.996772
63	0.000344	0.997115
64	0.000308	0.997423

n	P(n)	F(n)
65	0.000275	0.997698
66	0.000246	0.997944
67	0.000220	0.998165
68	0.000197	0.998362
69	0.000176	0.998538
70	0.000157	0.998695
71	0.000141	0.998836
72	0.000126	0.998962
73	0.000112	0.999074
74	0.000100	0.999174
75	0.000090	0.999264
76	0.000080	0.999344
77	0.000071	0.999415
78	0.000064	0.999479
79	0.000057	0.999535
80	0.000051	0.999586
81	0.000045	0.999631
82	0.000040	0.999672
83	0.000036	0.999707
84	0.000032	0.999739
85	0.000029	0.999768
86	0.000025	0.999794
87	0.000023	0.999816
88	0.000020	0.999836
89	0.000018	0.999854
90	0.000016	0.999870
91	0.000014	0.999885
92	0.000013	0.999897
93	0.000011	0.999909

k=2·2
Mean = 16·13
Variance = 134·44

n	P(n)	F(n)
0	0.009423	0.009423
1	0.018243	0.027667
2	0.025687	0.053353
3	0.031646	0.084999
4	0.036203	0.121202
5	0.039505	0.160707
6	0.041717	0.202423
7	0.043004	0.245428
8	0.043520	0.288948
9	0.043404	0.332352
10	0.042779	0.375131
11	0.041752	0.416883
12	0.040416	0.457300
13	0.038849	0.496149
14	0.037118	0.533267
15	0.035277	0.568544
16	0.033372	0.601916
17	0.031440	0.633356
18	0.029512	0.662868
19	0.027611	0.690479
20	0.025755	0.716234
21	0.023960	0.740194
22	0.022235	0.762428
23	0.020587	0.783016
24	0.019023	0.802038

33

n	P(n)	F(n)
25	0.017544	0.819582
26	0.016151	0.835733
27	0.014844	0.850577
28	0.013623	0.864200
29	0.012484	0.876684
30	0.011426	0.888110
31	0.010444	0.898553
32	0.009535	0.908088
33	0.008696	0.916784
34	0.007923	0.924707
35	0.007211	0.931918
36	0.006557	0.938475
37	0.005957	0.944433
38	0.005408	0.949841
39	0.004906	0.954746
40	0.004446	0.959192
41	0.004027	0.963220
42	0.003645	0.966865
43	0.003297	0.970163
44	0.002981	0.973143
45	0.002693	0.975836
46	0.002432	0.978268
47	0.002195	0.980463
48	0.001980	0.982442
49	0.001785	0.984227
50	0.001608	0.985835
51	0.001448	0.987284
52	0.001304	0.988588
53	0.001174	0.989761
54	0.001056	0.990817
55	0.000949	0.991766
56	0.000853	0.992619
57	0.000767	0.993386
58	0.000689	0.994075
59	0.000618	0.994693
60	0.000555	0.995248
61	0.000498	0.995746
62	0.000447	0.996193
63	0.000401	0.996594
64	0.000359	0.996953
65	0.000322	0.997275
66	0.000288	0.997563
67	0.000258	0.997821
68	0.000231	0.998053
69	0.000207	0.998260
70	0.000185	0.998445
71	0.000166	0.998611
72	0.000148	0.998760
73	0.000133	0.998892
74	0.000119	0.999011
75	0.000106	0.999117
76	0.000095	0.999212
77	0.000085	0.999297
78	0.000076	0.999373
79	0.000068	0.999440
80	0.000060	0.999501
81	0.000054	0.999555
82	0.000048	0.999603
83	0.000043	0.999646
84	0.000038	0.999685
85	0.000034	0.999719
86	0.000031	0.999749
87	0.000027	0.999777
88	0.000024	0.999801
89	0.000022	0.999823
90	0.000019	0.999842
91	0.000017	0.999859
92	0.000015	0.999875
93	0.000014	0.999889
94	0.000012	0.999901

k=2·3
Mean=16·87
Variance=140·56

n	P(n)	F(n)
0	0.007623	0.007623
1	0.015429	0.023051
2	0.022402	0.045454
3	0.028257	0.073711
4	0.032947	0.106658
5	0.036532	0.143190
6	0.039114	0.182304
7	0.040812	0.223117
8	0.041751	0.264868
9	0.042048	0.306916
10	0.041813	0.348728
11	0.041144	0.389872
12	0.040129	0.430001
13	0.038845	0.468845
14	0.037357	0.506203
15	0.035724	0.541926
16	0.033991	0.575917
17	0.032199	0.608117
18	0.030382	0.638499
19	0.028565	0.667064
20	0.026772	0.693836
21	0.025017	0.718853
22	0.023316	0.742169
23	0.021678	0.763847
24	0.020110	0.783957
25	0.018617	0.802574
26	0.017202	0.819776
27	0.015867	0.835643
28	0.014611	0.850254
29	0.013434	0.863688
30	0.012334	0.876022
31	0.011309	0.887332
32	0.010356	0.897688
33	0.009473	0.907161
34	0.008655	0.915816
35	0.007899	0.923715
36	0.007202	0.930917
37	0.006561	0.937477
38	0.005971	0.943448
39	0.005429	0.948878
40	0.004933	0.953811
41	0.004479	0.958290
42	0.004063	0.962353
43	0.003684	0.966037
44	0.003338	0.969375
45	0.003022	0.972397
46	0.002734	0.975131
47	0.002473	0.977604
48	0.002235	0.979839
49	0.002019	0.981858
50	0.001823	0.983681
51	0.001645	0.985326
52	0.001484	0.986810
53	0.001338	0.988148
54	0.001206	0.989354
55	0.001086	0.990440
56	0.000978	0.991418
57	0.000880	0.992298
58	0.000792	0.993090
59	0.000712	0.993802
60	0.000640	0.994443
61	0.000576	0.995018
62	0.000517	0.995535
63	0.000464	0.996000
64	0.000417	0.996417
65	0.000374	0.996791
66	0.000336	0.997127
67	0.000301	0.997428
68	0.000270	0.997698
69	0.000242	0.997940
70	0.000217	0.998158
71	0.000195	0.998352
72	0.000174	0.998527
73	0.000156	0.998683
74	0.000140	0.998823
75	0.000125	0.998948
76	0.000112	0.999060
77	0.000100	0.999160
78	0.000090	0.999250
79	0.000080	0.999330
80	0.000072	0.999402
81	0.000064	0.999466
82	0.000057	0.999523
83	0.000051	0.999574
84	0.000046	0.999620
85	0.000041	0.999661
86	0.000037	0.999698
87	0.000033	0.999730
88	0.000029	0.999760
89	0.000026	0.999786
90	0.000023	0.999809
91	0.000021	0.999830
92	0.000019	0.999848
93	0.000017	0.999865
94	0.000015	0.999879
95	0.000013	0.999892
96	0.000012	0.999904

k = 2·4
Mean = 17·60
Variance = 146·67

n	P(n)	F(n)
0	0.006166	0.006166
1	0.013024	0.019190
2	0.019483	0.038673
3	0.025146	0.063820
4	0.029874	0.093693
5	0.033650	0.127343
6	0.036521	0.163865
7	0.038567	0.202431
8	0.039878	0.242309
9	0.040551	0.282860
10	0.040681	0.323541
11	0.040356	0.363897
12	0.039656	0.403553
13	0.038656	0.442209
14	0.037419	0.479627
15	0.036002	0.515629
16	0.034454	0.550082
17	0.032816	0.582899
18	0.031124	0.614023
19	0.029407	0.643430
20	0.027690	0.671120
21	0.025992	0.697112
22	0.024328	0.721440
23	0.022712	0.744152
24	0.021152	0.765305
25	0.019657	0.784961
26	0.018229	0.803190
27	0.016873	0.820064
28	0.015591	0.835655
29	0.014383	0.850037
30	0.013247	0.863285
31	0.012184	0.875469
32	0.011191	0.886660
33	0.010266	0.896926
34	0.009406	0.906332
35	0.008608	0.914940
36	0.007870	0.922810
37	0.007188	0.929998
38	0.006558	0.936556
39	0.005978	0.942534
40	0.005445	0.947979
41	0.004955	0.952934
42	0.004506	0.957440
43	0.004094	0.961535
44	0.003718	0.965253
45	0.003373	0.968626
46	0.003059	0.971685
47	0.002772	0.974457
48	0.002511	0.976967
49	0.002272	0.979240
50	0.002056	0.981295
51	0.001859	0.983154
52	0.001680	0.984834
53	0.001517	0.986351
54	0.001370	0.987721

n	P(n)	F(n)
55	0.001236	0.988957
56	0.001115	0.990071
57	0.001005	0.991077
58	0.000906	0.991983
59	0.000816	0.992799
60	0.000735	0.993534
61	0.000662	0.994195
62	0.000595	0.994791
63	0.000536	0.995326
64	0.000482	0.995808
65	0.000433	0.996241
66	0.000389	0.996630
67	0.000350	0.996979
68	0.000314	0.997293
69	0.000282	0.997575
70	0.000253	0.997828
71	0.000227	0.998055
72	0.000204	0.998259
73	0.000183	0.998441
74	0.000164	0.998605
75	0.000147	0.998752
76	0.000132	0.998884
77	0.000118	0.999002
78	0.000106	0.999107
79	0.000095	0.999202
80	0.000085	0.999286
81	0.000076	0.999362
82	0.000068	0.999430
83	0.000061	0.999491
84	0.000054	0.999545
85	0.000049	0.999594
86	0.000043	0.999637
87	0.000039	0.999676
88	0.000035	0.999711
89	0.000031	0.999742
90	0.000028	0.999770
91	0.000025	0.999794
92	0.000022	0.999817
93	0.000020	0.999836
94	0.000018	0.999854
95	0.000016	0.999870
96	0.000014	0.999884
97	0.000013	0.999896
98	0.000011	0.999908

k = 2·5
Mean = 18·33
Variance = 152·78

n	P(n)	F(n)
0	0.004988	0.004988
1	0.010974	0.015963
2	0.016900	0.032863
3	0.022309	0.055171
4	0.026993	0.082165
5	0.030880	0.113045
6	0.033968	0.147013
7	0.036298	0.183311
8	0.037931	0.221242
9	0.038943	0.260185

n	P(n)	F(n)
10	0.039410	0.299594
11	0.039410	0.339004
12	0.039016	0.378020
13	0.038295	0.416315
14	0.037311	0.453626
15	0.036117	0.489743
16	0.034762	0.524505
17	0.033290	0.557795
18	0.031737	0.589532
19	0.030133	0.619665
20	0.028506	0.648171
21	0.026877	0.675047
22	0.025264	0.700312
23	0.023683	0.723994
24	0.022143	0.746138
25	0.020655	0.766793
26	0.019225	0.786018
27	0.017858	0.803876
28	0.016557	0.820433
29	0.015324	0.835757
30	0.014159	0.849916
31	0.013063	0.862979
32	0.012034	0.875013
33	0.011072	0.886085
34	0.010173	0.896257
35	0.009336	0.905593
36	0.008558	0.914151
37	0.007836	0.921987
38	0.007168	0.929155
39	0.006550	0.935705
40	0.005981	0.941686
41	0.005455	0.947141
42	0.004972	0.952113
43	0.004528	0.956642
44	0.004121	0.960762
45	0.003747	0.964509
46	0.003405	0.967914
47	0.003092	0.971006
48	0.002806	0.973812
49	0.002545	0.976357
50	0.002307	0.978664
51	0.002090	0.980753
52	0.001892	0.982645
53	0.001712	0.984357
54	0.001548	0.985905
55	0.001400	0.987305
56	0.001265	0.988570
57	0.001142	0.989712
58	0.001031	0.990743
59	0.000931	0.991674
60	0.000839	0.992513
61	0.000757	0.993270
62	0.000682	0.993952
63	0.000615	0.994566
64	0.000553	0.995120
65	0.000498	0.995618
66	0.000448	0.996066
67	0.000403	0.996470
68	0.000363	0.996833
69	0.000326	0.997159

n	P(n)	F(n)	n	P(n)	F(n)	n	P(n)	F(n)
70	0.000293	0.997452	80	0.000099	0.999153	90	0.000033	0.999724
71	0.000264	0.997716	81	0.000089	0.999242	91	0.000029	0.999753
72	0.000237	0.997953	82	0.000080	0.999322	92	0.000026	0.999780
73	0.000213	0.998165	83	0.000072	0.999394	93	0.000024	0.999803
74	0.000191	0.998356	84	0.000064	0.999458	94	0.000021	0.999824
75	0.000171	0.998527	85	0.000057	0.999515	95	0.000019	0.999843
76	0.000154	0.998681	86	0.000051	0.999567	96	0.000017	0.999860
77	0.000138	0.998819	87	0.000046	0.999613	97	0.000015	0.999875
78	0.000124	0.998943	88	0.000041	0.999654	98	0.000013	0.999883
79	0.000111	0.999054	89	0.000037	0.999691	99	0.000012	0.999901

$k=0.1$
Mean $=0.61$
Variance $=4.39$

n	P(n)	F(n)
0	0.821510	0.821510
1	0.070650	0.892160
2	0.033417	0.925577
3	0.020117	0.945694
4	0.013408	0.959103
5	0.009455	0.968558
6	0.006912	0.975470
7	0.005180	0.980650
8	0.003954	0.984604
9	0.003060	0.987664
10	0.002395	0.990058
11	0.001891	0.991950
12	0.001504	0.993454
13	0.001204	0.994658
14	0.000969	0.995627
15	0.000783	0.996410
16	0.000636	0.997046
17	0.000518	0.997564
18	0.000423	0.997987
19	0.000347	0.998334
20	0.000285	0.998618
21	0.000234	0.998853
22	0.000193	0.999046
23	0.000160	0.999206
24	0.000132	0.999338
25	0.000110	0.999447
26	0.000091	0.999538
27	0.000076	0.999614
28	0.000063	0.999677
29	0.000052	0.999729
30	0.000044	0.999773
31	0.000037	0.999810
32	0.000031	0.999840
33	0.000026	0.999866
34	0.000021	0.999887
35	0.000018	0.999905

$k=0.2$
Mean $=1.23$
Variance $=8.78$

n	P(n)	F(n)
0	0.674879	0.674879
1	0.116079	0.790958
2	0.059897	0.850854
3	0.037775	0.888629
4	0.025989	0.914619
5	0.018775	0.933393
6	0.013993	0.947386
7	0.010659	0.958045
8	0.008250	0.966295
9	0.006464	0.972760
10	0.005115	0.977874
11	0.004079	0.981953
12	0.003274	0.985227
13	0.002642	0.987869
14	0.002142	0.990011
15	0.001744	0.991755
16	0.001425	0.993181
17	0.001168	0.994348
18	0.000960	0.995308
19	0.000791	0.996099
20	0.000653	0.996751
21	0.000540	0.997291
22	0.000447	0.997739
23	0.000371	0.998110
24	0.000309	0.998419
25	0.000257	0.998676
26	0.000214	0.998890
27	0.000179	0.999069
28	0.000149	0.999219
29	0.000125	0.999344
30	0.000105	0.999448
31	0.000088	0.999536
32	0.000073	0.999609
33	0.000062	0.999671
34	0.000052	0.999723
35	0.000044	0.999766
36	0.000037	0.999803
37	0.000031	0.999834
38	0.000026	0.999859
39	0.000022	0.999881

n	P(n)	F(n)
40	0.000018	0.999900
41	0.000016	0.999915

k = 0·3
Mean = 1·84
Variance = 13·16

n	P(n)	F(n)
0	0.554419	0.554419
1	0.143040	0.697460
2	0.079959	0.777419
3	0.052720	0.830139
4	0.037405	0.867544
5	0.027665	0.895208
6	0.021016	0.916224
7	0.016266	0.932491
8	0.012765	0.945256
9	0.010124	0.955380
10	0.008097	0.963477
11	0.006520	0.969997
12	0.005280	0.975278
13	0.004297	0.979574
14	0.003510	0.983085
15	0.002878	0.985963
16	0.002367	0.988330
17	0.001952	0.990281
18	0.001613	0.991895
19	0.001336	0.993231
20	0.001109	0.994340
21	0.000922	0.995262
22	0.000768	0.996029
23	0.000640	0.996669
24	0.000534	0.997204
25	0.000447	0.997650
26	0.000374	0.998024
27	0.000313	0.998337
28	0.000263	0.998600
29	0.000220	0.998820
30	0.000185	0.999005
31	0.000156	0.999161
32	0.000131	0.999292
33	0.000110	0.999402
34	0.000093	0.999495
35	0.000078	0.999573
36	0.000066	0.999639
37	0.000056	0.999694
38	0.000047	0.999741
39	0.000040	0.999781
40	0.000034	0.999815
41	0.000028	0.999843
42	0.000024	0.999867
43	0.000020	0.999887
44	0.000017	0.999904

k = 0·4
Mean = 2·46
Variance = 17·55

n	P(n)	F(n)
0	0.455461	0.455461
1	0.156679	0.612140
2	0.094321	0.706460
3	0.064893	0.771353
4	0.047436	0.818789
5	0.035900	0.854689
6	0.027787	0.882475
7	0.021848	0.904324
8	0.017380	0.921704
9	0.013951	0.935654
10	0.011278	0.946932
11	0.009170	0.956102
12	0.007492	0.963593
13	0.006145	0.969739
14	0.005059	0.974797
15	0.004176	0.978974
16	0.003457	0.982431
17	0.002868	0.985299
18	0.002384	0.987683
19	0.001986	0.989669
20	0.001657	0.991325
21	0.001384	0.992709
22	0.001158	0.993867
23	0.000970	0.994837
24	0.000813	0.995650
25	0.000682	0.996332
26	0.000573	0.996905
27	0.000482	0.997388
28	0.000406	0.997793
29	0.000342	0.998135
30	0.000288	0.998423
31	0.000243	0.998666
32	0.000205	0.998871
33	0.000173	0.999044
34	0.000145	0.999190
35	0.000124	0.999314
36	0.000105	0.999418
37	0.000088	0.999507
38	0.000075	0.999582
39	0.000063	0.999645
40	0.000054	0.999699
41	0.000045	0.999744
42	0.000039	0.999783
43	0.000033	0.999815
44	0.000028	0.999843
45	0.000024	0.999867
46	0.000020	0.999887
47	0.000017	0.999904

k = 0·5
Mean = 3·07
Variance = 21·94

n	P(n)	F(n)
0	0.374166	0.374166
1	0.160891	0.535057
2	0.103775	0.638832
3	0.074372	0.713204
4	0.055965	0.769169
5	0.043317	0.812486
6	0.034148	0.846634
7	0.027270	0.873903
8	0.021986	0.895890
9	0.017858	0.913747
10	0.014590	0.928337
11	0.011977	0.940314
12	0.009871	0.950185
13	0.008162	0.958347
14	0.006769	0.965116
15	0.005627	0.970744
16	0.004688	0.975432
17	0.003913	0.979345
18	0.003272	0.982617
19	0.002740	0.985357
20	0.002297	0.987654
21	0.001929	0.989583
22	0.001621	0.991204
23	0.001364	0.992568
24	0.001148	0.993716
25	0.000968	0.994684
26	0.000816	0.995500
27	0.000689	0.996189
28	0.000582	0.996771
29	0.000492	0.997263
30	0.000416	0.997679
31	0.000352	0.998031
32	0.000298	0.998329
33	0.000252	0.998582
34	0.000214	0.998795
35	0.000181	0.998977
36	0.000154	0.999131
37	0.000130	0.999261
38	0.000111	0.999372
39	0.000094	0.999466
40	0.000080	0.999545
41	0.000068	0.999613
42	0.000058	0.999671
43	0.000049	0.999720
44	0.000042	0.999761
45	0.000035	0.999797
46	0.000030	0.999827
47	0.000026	0.999853
48	0.000022	0.999874
49	0.000019	0.999893
50	0.000016	0.999909

	k=0·6 Mean=3·69 Variance=26·33			k=0·7 Mean=4·30 Variance=30·71			55	0.000015	0.999914

k=0·6
Mean=3·69
Variance=26·33

n	P(n)	F(n)
0	0.307381	0.307381
1	0.158609	0.465989
2	0.109123	0.575112
3	0.081333	0.656445
4	0.062952	0.719396
5	0.049807	0.769204
6	0.039979	0.809182
7	0.032417	0.841599
8	0.026485	0.868084
9	0.021765	0.889848
10	0.017969	0.907817
11	0.014891	0.922708
12	0.012380	0.935088
13	0.010319	0.945407
14	0.008621	0.954027
15	0.007216	0.961244
16	0.006051	0.967294
17	0.005081	0.972375
18	0.004273	0.976648
19	0.003597	0.980245
20	0.003032	0.983277
21	0.002558	0.985834
22	0.002160	0.987994
23	0.001825	0.989819
24	0.001543	0.991362
25	0.001306	0.992668
26	0.001106	0.993774
27	0.000937	0.994711
28	0.000794	0.995505
29	0.000674	0.996179
30	0.000572	0.996750
31	0.000485	0.997236
32	0.000412	0.997648
33	0.000350	0.997998
34	0.000298	0.998295
35	0.000253	0.998548
36	0.000215	0.998763
37	0.000183	0.998946
38	0.000156	0.999102
39	0.000133	0.999235
40	0.000113	0.999347
41	0.000096	0.999444
42	0.000082	0.999525
43	0.000070	0.999595
44	0.000059	0.999655
45	0.000051	0.999705
46	0.000043	0.999749
47	0.000037	0.999785
48	0.000031	0.999817
49	0.000027	0.999844
50	0.000023	0.999866
51	0.000020	0.999886
52	0.000017	0.999903

k=0·7
Mean=4·30
Variance=30·71

n	P(n)	F(n)
0	0.252516	0.252516
1	0.152015	0.404531
2	0.111123	0.515654
3	0.086009	0.601663
4	0.068420	0.670084
5	0.055311	0.725394
6	0.045189	0.770584
7	0.037197	0.807781
8	0.030790	0.838570
9	0.025597	0.864167
10	0.021353	0.885520
11	0.017863	0.903382
12	0.014978	0.918360
13	0.012584	0.930943
14	0.010590	0.941533
15	0.008925	0.950459
16	0.007532	0.957990
17	0.006363	0.964354
18	0.005381	0.969735
19	0.004555	0.974289
20	0.003858	0.978147
21	0.003271	0.981418
22	0.002774	0.984192
23	0.002355	0.986547
24	0.002000	0.988547
25	0.001699	0.990246
26	0.001444	0.991691
27	0.001228	0.992919
28	0.001045	0.993964
29	0.000890	0.994854
30	0.000757	0.995611
31	0.000645	0.996256
32	0.000550	0.996806
33	0.000468	0.997274
34	0.000399	0.997673
35	0.000340	0.998014
36	0.000290	0.998304
37	0.000248	0.998552
38	0.000211	0.998763
39	0.000180	0.998943
40	0.000154	0.999097
41	0.000131	0.999228
42	0.000112	0.999340
43	0.000096	0.999436
44	0.000082	0.999518
45	0.000070	0.999588
46	0.000060	0.999648
47	0.000051	0.999699
48	0.000044	0.999742
49	0.000037	0.999780
50	0.000032	0.999811
51	0.000027	0.999839
52	0.000023	0.999862
53	0.000020	0.999882
54	0.000017	0.999899
55	0.000015	0.999914

k=0·8
Mean=4·91
Variance=35·10

n	P(n)	F(n)
0	0.207445	0.207445
1	0.142722	0.350167
2	0.110467	0.460634
3	0.088668	0.549302
4	0.072442	0.621743
5	0.059808	0.681551
6	0.049720	0.731272
7	0.041538	0.772809
8	0.034829	0.807639
9	0.029288	0.836927
10	0.024684	0.861610
11	0.020842	0.882452
12	0.017625	0.900078
13	0.014925	0.915002
14	0.012652	0.927654
15	0.010735	0.938389
16	0.009117	0.947507
17	0.007748	0.955255
18	0.006590	0.961845
19	0.005607	0.967452
20	0.004774	0.972226
21	0.004067	0.976293
22	0.003466	0.979759
23	0.002954	0.982713
24	0.002520	0.985233
25	0.002150	0.987382
26	0.001834	0.989217
27	0.001566	0.990783
28	0.001337	0.992120
29	0.001142	0.993262
30	0.000976	0.994237
31	0.000834	0.995071
32	0.000712	0.995783
33	0.000609	0.996392
34	0.000521	0.996913
35	0.000445	0.997358
36	0.000381	0.997738
37	0.000326	0.998064
38	0.000279	0.998343
39	0.000238	0.998581
40	0.000204	0.998785
41	0.000175	0.998959
42	0.000149	0.999109
43	0.000128	0.999237
44	0.000109	0.999346
45	0.000094	0.999440
46	0.000080	0.999520
47	0.000069	0.999589
48	0.000059	0.999648
49	0.000050	0.999698

n	P(n)	F(n)
50	0.000043	0.999741
51	0.000037	0.999778
52	0.000032	0.999810
53	0.000027	0.999837
54	0.000023	0.999860
55	0.000020	0.999880
56	0.000017	0.999897
57	0.000015	0.999912

k=0·9
Mean=5·53
Variance=39·49

n	P(n)	F(n)
0	0.170418	0.170418
1	0.131903	0.302321
2	0.107765	0.410086
3	0.089589	0.499675
4	0.075120	0.574795
5	0.063311	0.638107
6	0.053540	0.691647
7	0.045387	0.737034
8	0.038545	0.775578
9	0.032780	0.808359
10	0.027909	0.836268
11	0.023784	0.860051
12	0.020283	0.880335
13	0.017310	0.897644
14	0.014780	0.912424
15	0.012626	0.925050
16	0.010790	0.935841
17	0.009225	0.945066
18	0.007890	0.952955
19	0.006749	0.959705
20	0.005775	0.965480
21	0.004943	0.970423
22	0.004232	0.974655
23	0.003624	0.978279
24	0.003103	0.981382
25	0.002658	0.984040
26	0.002277	0.986317
27	0.001951	0.988269
28	0.001672	0.989941
29	0.001433	0.991374
30	0.001228	0.992602
31	0.001053	0.993655
32	0.000903	0.994557
33	0.000774	0.995331
34	0.000664	0.995995
35	0.000569	0.996564
36	0.000488	0.997052
37	0.000419	0.997471
38	0.000359	0.997830
39	0.000308	0.998138
40	0.000264	0.998402
41	0.000227	0.998628
42	0.000194	0.998823
43	0.000167	0.998990
44	0.000143	0.999133

n	P(n)	F(n)
45	0.000123	0.999256
46	0.000105	0.999361
47	0.000090	0.999452
48	0.000078	0.999529
49	0.000067	0.999596
50	0.000057	0.999653
51	0.000049	0.999702
52	0.000042	0.999744
53	0.000036	0.999780
54	0.000031	0.999812
55	0.000027	0.999838
56	0.000023	0.999861
57	0.000020	0.999881
58	0.000017	0.999898
59	0.000014	0.999912

k=1·0
Mean=6·14
Variance=43·88

n	P(n)	F(n)
0	0.140000	0.140000
1	0.120400	0.260400
2	0.103544	0.363944
3	0.089048	0.452992
4	0.076581	0.529573
5	0.065860	0.595433
6	0.056639	0.652072
7	0.048710	0.700782
8	0.041891	0.742673
9	0.036026	0.778698
10	0.030982	0.809681
11	0.026645	0.836325
12	0.022914	0.859240
13	0.019706	0.878946
14	0.016948	0.895894
15	0.014575	0.910469
16	0.012534	0.923003
17	0.010780	0.933783
18	0.009270	0.943053
19	0.007973	0.951026
20	0.006856	0.957882
21	0.005897	0.963779
22	0.005071	0.968850
23	0.004361	0.973211
24	0.003751	0.976961
25	0.003225	0.980187
26	0.002774	0.982960
27	0.002386	0.985346
28	0.002052	0.987398
29	0.001764	0.989162
30	0.001517	0.990679
31	0.001305	0.991984
32	0.001122	0.993106
33	0.000965	0.994071
34	0.000830	0.994901
35	0.000714	0.995615
36	0.000614	0.996229
37	0.000528	0.996757
38	0.000454	0.997211
39	0.000390	0.997602

n	P(n)	F(n)
40	0.000336	0.997937
41	0.000289	0.998226
42	0.000248	0.998474
43	0.000214	0.998688
44	0.000184	0.998872
45	0.000158	0.999030
46	0.000136	0.999166
47	0.000117	0.999282
48	0.000100	0.999383
49	0.000086	0.999469
50	0.000074	0.999544
51	0.000064	0.999607
52	0.000055	0.999662
53	0.000047	0.999710
54	0.000041	0.999750
55	0.000035	0.999785
56	0.000030	0.999815
57	0.000026	0.999841
58	0.000022	0.999863
59	0.000019	0.999883
60	0.000016	0.999899
61	0.000014	0.999913

k=1·1
Mean=6·76
Variance=48·27

n	P(n)	F(n)
0	0.115011	0.115011
1	0.108801	0.223812
2	0.098247	0.322059
3	0.087309	0.409368
4	0.076963	0.486331
5	0.067512	0.553843
6	0.059028	0.612871
7	0.051489	0.664360
8	0.044834	0.709194
9	0.038986	0.748180
10	0.033863	0.782043
11	0.029387	0.811430
12	0.025483	0.836913
13	0.022084	0.858997
14	0.019128	0.878125
15	0.016560	0.894685
16	0.014331	0.909016
17	0.012397	0.921413
18	0.010720	0.932133
19	0.009268	0.941401
20	0.008010	0.949412
21	0.006922	0.956333
22	0.005980	0.962313
23	0.005165	0.967478
24	0.004460	0.971938
25	0.003851	0.975790
26	0.003325	0.979114
27	0.002870	0.981984
28	0.002477	0.984461
29	0.002138	0.986599

n		
30	0.001844	0.988443
31	0.001591	0.990035
32	0.001373	0.991407
33	0.001184	0.992592
34	0.001021	0.993613
35	0.000881	0.994494
36	0.000760	0.995254
37	0.000655	0.995909
38	0.000565	0.996474
39	0.000487	0.996961
40	0.000420	0.997380
41	0.000362	0.997742
42	0.000312	0.998055
43	0.000269	0.998323
44	0.000232	0.998555
45	0.000200	0.998755
46	0.000172	0.998927
47	0.000148	0.999076
48	0.000128	0.999204
49	0.000110	0.999314
50	0.000095	0.999409
51	0.000082	0.999491
52	0.000071	0.999561
53	0.000061	0.999622
54	0.000052	0.999675
55	0.000045	0.999720
56	0.000039	0.999759
57	0.000033	0.999792
58	0.000029	0.999821
59	0.000025	0.999846
60	0.000021	0.999867
61	0.000018	0.999886
62	0.000016	0.999901

k=1·2
Mean=7·37
Variance=52·65

n	P(n)	F(n)
0	0.094483	0.094483
1	0.097506	0.191989
2	0.092241	0.284231
3	0.084616	0.368846
4	0.076408	0.445254
5	0.068339	0.513594
6	0.060731	0.574325
7	0.053721	0.628046
8	0.047355	0.675401
9	0.041630	0.717031
10	0.036518	0.753549
11	0.031977	0.785525
12	0.027958	0.813484
13	0.024414	0.837898
14	0.021296	0.859193
15	0.018559	0.877752
16	0.016160	0.893912
17	0.014061	0.907973
18	0.012227	0.920200
19	0.010626	0.930826
20	0.009230	0.940055
21	0.008013	0.948069
22	0.006954	0.955022
23	0.006032	0.961055
24	0.005231	0.966286
25	0.004535	0.970820
26	0.003930	0.974750
27	0.003405	0.978155
28	0.002949	0.981104
29	0.002554	0.983657
30	0.002211	0.985868
31	0.001913	0.987782
32	0.001656	0.989437
33	0.001433	0.990870
34	0.001239	0.992110
35	0.001072	0.993181
36	0.000927	0.994108
37	0.000802	0.994910
38	0.000693	0.995603
39	0.000599	0.996202
40	0.000518	0.996720
41	0.000447	0.997167
42	0.000387	0.997554
43	0.000334	0.997888
44	0.000289	0.998176
45	0.000249	0.998425
46	0.000215	0.998641
47	0.000186	0.998827
48	0.000161	0.998987
49	0.000139	0.999126
50	0.000120	0.999246
51	0.000103	0.999349
52	0.000089	0.999438
53	0.000077	0.999515
54	0.000066	0.999582
55	0.000057	0.999639
56	0.000050	0.999689
57	0.000043	0.999731
58	0.000037	0.999768
59	0.000032	0.999800
60	0.000027	0.999828
61	0.000024	0.999851
62	0.000020	0.999872
63	0.000018	0.999889
64	0.000015	0.999905

k=1·3
Mean=7·99
Variance=57·04

n	P(n)	F(n)
0	0.077619	0.077619
1	0.086778	0.164396
2	0.085823	0.250220
3	0.081189	0.331408
4	0.075059	0.406467
5	0.068424	0.474891
6	0.061787	0.536678
7	0.055414	0.592091
8	0.049443	0.641534
9	0.043938	0.685473
10	0.038921	0.724393
11	0.034385	0.758778
12	0.030310	0.789088
13	0.026668	0.815756
14	0.023426	0.839182
15	0.020549	0.859731
16	0.018004	0.877735
17	0.015756	0.893492
18	0.013776	0.907268
19	0.012035	0.919303
20	0.010505	0.929808
21	0.009164	0.938971
22	0.007988	0.946960
23	0.006959	0.953919
24	0.006060	0.959979
25	0.005274	0.965253
26	0.004588	0.969841
27	0.003990	0.973830
28	0.003468	0.977298
29	0.003013	0.980311
30	0.002617	0.982928
31	0.002273	0.985201
32	0.001973	0.987174
33	0.001712	0.988885
34	0.001485	0.990371
35	0.001288	0.991659
36	0.001117	0.992776
37	0.000969	0.993745
38	0.000840	0.994584
39	0.000728	0.995312
40	0.000630	0.995942
41	0.000546	0.996488
42	0.000473	0.996961
43	0.000410	0.997371
44	0.000355	0.997726
45	0.000307	0.998033
46	0.000266	0.998298
47	0.000230	0.998528
48	0.000199	0.998728
49	0.000172	0.998900
50	0.000149	0.999049
51	0.000129	0.999178
52	0.000112	0.999289
53	0.000096	0.999386
54	0.000083	0.999469
55	0.000072	0.999541
56	0.000062	0.999604
57	0.000054	0.999657
58	0.000047	0.999704
59	0.000040	0.999744
60	0.000035	0.999779
61	0.000030	0.999809
62	0.000026	0.999835
63	0.000022	0.999858
64	0.000019	0.999877
65	0.000017	0.999894
66	0.000014	0.999908

k=1·4
Mean=8·60
Variance=61·43

n	P(n)	F(n)
0	0.063765	0.063765
1	0.076773	0.140537
2	0.079229	0.219766
3	0.077222	0.296988
4	0.073052	0.370040
5	0.067851	0.437891
6	0.062242	0.500133
7	0.056587	0.556720
8	0.051098	0.607817
9	0.045897	0.653715
10	0.041050	0.694765
11	0.036587	0.731352
12	0.032514	0.763866
13	0.028822	0.792688
14	0.025495	0.818183
15	0.022511	0.840694
16	0.019843	0.860537
17	0.017467	0.878004
18	0.015355	0.893359
19	0.013483	0.906842
20	0.011828	0.918670
21	0.010366	0.929035
22	0.009076	0.938112
23	0.007941	0.946053
24	0.006943	0.952997
25	0.006067	0.959064
26	0.005298	0.964362
27	0.004624	0.968985
28	0.004033	0.973018
29	0.003516	0.976535
30	0.003064	0.979599
31	0.002669	0.982268
32	0.002324	0.984593
33	0.002023	0.986616
34	0.001760	0.988376
35	0.001531	0.989908
36	0.001332	0.991239
37	0.001157	0.992397
38	0.001006	0.993402
39	0.000874	0.994276
40	0.000759	0.995036
41	0.000659	0.995695
42	0.000572	0.996267
43	0.000497	0.996764
44	0.000431	0.997195
45	0.000374	0.997569
46	0.000324	0.997893
47	0.000281	0.998175
48	0.000244	0.998419
49	0.000212	0.998631
50	0.000183	0.998814
51	0.000159	0.998973
52	0.000138	0.999111
53	0.000119	0.999230
54	0.000103	0.999334
55	0.000090	0.999423
56	0.000078	0.999501
57	0.000067	0.999568
58	0.000058	0.999626
59	0.000050	0.999677
60	0.000044	0.999720
61	0.000038	0.999758
62	0.000033	0.999791
63	0.000028	0.999819
64	0.000024	0.999843
65	0.000021	0.999865
66	0.000018	0.999883
67	0.000016	0.999899
68	0.000014	0.999912

k=1·5
Mean=9·21
Variance=65·82

n	P(n)	F(n)
0	0.052383	0.052383
1	0.067574	0.119958
2	0.072642	0.192600
3	0.072885	0.265484
4	0.070516	0.336000
5	0.066708	0.402708
6	0.062150	0.464858
7	0.057266	0.522124
8	0.052327	0.574451
9	0.047501	0.621953
10	0.042894	0.664847
11	0.038565	0.703412
12	0.034548	0.737960
13	0.030854	0.768814
14	0.027482	0.796297
15	0.024423	0.820719
16	0.021660	0.842379
17	0.019175	0.861554
18	0.016949	0.878503
19	0.014960	0.893463
20	0.013187	0.906650
21	0.011611	0.918260
22	0.010212	0.928472
23	0.008973	0.937446
24	0.007878	0.945324
25	0.006910	0.952234
26	0.006057	0.958291
27	0.005306	0.963597
28	0.004644	0.968241
29	0.004063	0.972305
30	0.003552	0.975857
31	0.003104	0.978961
32	0.002711	0.981673
33	0.002367	0.984040
34	0.002066	0.986106
35	0.001802	0.987908
36	0.001571	0.989479
37	0.001369	0.990848
38	0.001193	0.992042
39	0.001039	0.993081
40	0.000905	0.993986
41	0.000788	0.994774
42	0.000686	0.995459
43	0.000596	0.996056
44	0.000519	0.996575
45	0.000451	0.997026
46	0.000392	0.997418
47	0.000341	0.997759
48	0.000296	0.998055
49	0.000257	0.998312
50	0.000224	0.998536
51	0.000194	0.998730
52	0.000169	0.998898
53	0.000146	0.999045
54	0.000127	0.999172
55	0.000110	0.999282
56	0.000096	0.999378
57	0.000083	0.999460
58	0.000072	0.999532
59	0.000062	0.999595
60	0.000054	0.999649
61	0.000047	0.999696
62	0.000041	0.999737
63	0.000035	0.999772
64	0.000031	0.999802
65	0.000026	0.999829
66	0.000023	0.999852
67	0.000020	0.999872
68	0.000017	0.999889
69	0.000015	0.999904

k=1·6
Mean=9·83
Variance=70·20

n	P(n)	F(n)
0	0.043033	0.043033
1	0.059214	0.102247
2	0.066201	0.168448
3	0.068320	0.236768
4	0.067568	0.304336
5	0.065082	0.369417
6	0.061567	0.430984
7	0.057486	0.488470
8	0.053146	0.541616
9	0.048752	0.590369
10	0.044443	0.634812
11	0.040306	0.675117
12	0.036396	0.711513
13	0.032745	0.744258
14	0.029368	0.773626
15	0.026266	0.799892
16	0.023436	0.823329
17	0.020867	0.844195
18	0.018543	0.862739
19	0.016451	0.879189
20	0.014572	0.893762
21	0.012890	0.906652
22	0.011388	0.918040
23	0.010049	0.928089
24	0.008858	0.936947

n	P(n)	F(n)	n	P(n)	F(n)	n	P(n)	F(n)
25	0.007801	0.944748	5	0.063054	0.338060	65	0.000040	0.999734
26	0.006864	0.951612	6	0.060553	0.398613	66	0.000035	0.999769
27	0.006034	0.957645	7	0.057283	0.455897	67	0.000030	0.999800
28	0.005300	0.962946	8	0.053574	0.509471	68	0.000026	0.999826
29	0.004653	0.967598	9	0.049657	0.559128	69	0.000023	0.999849
30	0.004081	0.971680	10	0.045695	0.604823	70	0.000020	0.999869
31	0.003578	0.975257	11	0.041798	0.646621	71	0.000017	0.999886
32	0.003135	0.978392	12	0.038043	0.684665	72	0.000015	0.999901
33	0.002745	0.981137	13	0.034479	0.719144			
34	0.002402	0.983539	14	0.031135	0.750278			

k = 1·8
Mean = 11·06
Variance = 78·98

n	P(n)	F(n)	n	P(n)	F(n)	n	P(n)	F(n)
35	0.002101	0.985640	15	0.028025	0.778304	0	0.029042	0.029042
36	0.001837	0.987478	16	0.025156	0.803460	1	0.044957	0.074000
37	0.001606	0.989083	17	0.022525	0.825985	2	0.054129	0.128128
38	0.001403	0.990486	18	0.020125	0.846110	3	0.058964	0.187093
39	0.001225	0.991711	19	0.017945	0.864055	4	0.060851	0.247944
40	0.001069	0.992780	20	0.015973	0.880028	5	0.060705	0.308649
41	0.000933	0.993713	21	0.014195	0.894222	6	0.059167	0.367816
42	0.000814	0.994527	22	0.012596	0.906818	7	0.056699	0.424515
43	0.000710	0.995236	23	0.011162	0.917980	8	0.053637	0.478152
44	0.000619	0.995855	24	0.009879	0.927860	9	0.050228	0.528381
45	0.000539	0.996394	25	0.008734	0.936594	10	0.046652	0.575033
46	0.000470	0.996863	26	0.007714	0.944307	11	0.043039	0.618072
47	0.000409	0.997273	27	0.006806	0.951113	12	0.039481	0.657552
48	0.000356	0.997629	28	0.005999	0.957112	13	0.036043	0.693595
49	0.000310	0.997939	29	0.005284	0.962396	14	0.032768	0.726364
50	0.000270	0.998209	30	0.004650	0.967046	15	0.029684	0.756047
51	0.000235	0.998443	31	0.004089	0.971136	16	0.026804	0.782852
52	0.000204	0.998648	32	0.003594	0.974729	17	0.024136	0.806988
53	0.000178	0.998825	33	0.003156	0.977886	18	0.021680	0.828668
54	0.000154	0.998980	34	0.002770	0.980656	19	0.019430	0.848098
55	0.000134	0.999114	35	0.002430	0.983086	20	0.017378	0.865476
56	0.000117	0.999231	36	0.002131	0.985217	21	0.015514	0.880990
57	0.000101	0.999332	37	0.001867	0.987083	22	0.013828	0.894818
58	0.000088	0.999421	38	0.001635	0.988719	23	0.012305	0.907123
59	0.000077	0.999497	39	0.001431	0.990150	24	0.010935	0.918058
60	0.000067	0.999564	40	0.001253	0.991403	25	0.009705	0.927764
61	0.000058	0.999621	41	0.001096	0.992498	26	0.008603	0.936367
62	0.000050	0.999672	42	0.000958	0.993456	27	0.007618	0.943985
63	0.000044	0.999715	43	0.000837	0.994293	28	0.006739	0.950724
64	0.000038	0.999753	44	0.000731	0.995025	29	0.005955	0.956679
65	0.000033	0.999786	45	0.000639	0.995664	30	0.005258	0.961937
66	0.000028	0.999814	46	0.000558	0.996221	31	0.004639	0.966576
67	0.000025	0.999839	47	0.000487	0.996708	32	0.004089	0.970665
68	0.000021	0.999860	48	0.000425	0.997133	33	0.003602	0.974267
69	0.000019	0.999879	49	0.000371	0.997504	34	0.003170	0.977437
70	0.000016	0.999895	50	0.000323	0.997827	35	0.002789	0.980226
71	0.000014	0.999909	51	0.000282	0.998108	36	0.002452	0.982678
			52	0.000246	0.998354	37	0.002154	0.984832
			53	0.000214	0.998568	38	0.001891	0.986723
			54	0.000186	0.998754	39	0.001660	0.988383

k = 1·7
Mean = 10·44
Variance = 74·59

n	P(n)	F(n)	n	P(n)	F(n)	n	P(n)	F(n)
			55	0.000162	0.998916	40	0.001456	0.989840
			56	0.000141	0.999058	41	0.001277	0.991116
			57	0.000123	0.999181	42	0.001119	0.992235
			58	0.000107	0.999288	43	0.000980	0.993216
			59	0.000093	0.999381	44	0.000858	0.994074
0	0.035352	0.035352	60	0.000081	0.999462			
1	0.051685	0.087037	61	0.000071	0.999533			
2	0.060006	0.147044	62	0.000061	0.999594			
3	0.063647	0.210690	63	0.000053	0.999647			
4	0.064315	0.275005	64	0.000046	0.999694			

n	P(n)	F(n)
45	0.000751	0.994825
46	0.000657	0.995482
47	0.000575	0.996057
48	0.000503	0.996560
49	0.000439	0.996999
50	0.000384	0.997383
51	0.000335	0.997718
52	0.000293	0.998011
53	0.000256	0.998267
54	0.000223	0.998490
55	0.000195	0.998685
56	0.000170	0.998854
57	0.000148	0.999003
58	0.000129	0.999132
59	0.000113	0.999244
60	0.000098	0.999342
61	0.000085	0.999428
62	0.000074	0.999502
63	0.000065	0.999567
64	0.000056	0.999623
65	0.000049	0.999672
66	0.000043	0.999715
67	0.000037	0.999752
68	0.000032	0.999785
69	0.000028	0.999813
70	0.000025	0.999838
71	0.000021	0.999859
72	0.000019	0.999877
73	0.000016	0.999893
74	0.000014	0.999907

k=1·9
Mean=11·67
Variance=83·37

n	P(*n*)	F(*n*)
0	0.023859	0.023859
1	0.038985	0.062843
2	0.048614	0.111457
3	0.054351	0.165808
4	0.057258	0.223066
5	0.058106	0.281172
6	0.057467	0.338638
7	0.055775	0.394414
8	0.053363	0.447777
9	0.050481	0.498258
10	0.047321	0.545580
11	0.044026	0.589606
12	0.040702	0.630308
13	0.037427	0.667735
14	0.034257	0.701991
15	0.031228	0.733220
16	0.028367	0.761586
17	0.025687	0.787274
18	0.023195	0.810469
19	0.020893	0.831362
20	0.018777	0.850139
21	0.016840	0.866978
22	0.015075	0.882053
23	0.013472	0.895525
24	0.012020	0.907545
25	0.010709	0.918254
26	0.009529	0.927783
27	0.008468	0.936251
28	0.007517	0.943768
29	0.006665	0.950432
30	0.005904	0.956336
31	0.005225	0.961561
32	0.004620	0.966180
33	0.004081	0.970261
34	0.003603	0.973864
35	0.003178	0.977042
36	0.002801	0.979843
37	0.002468	0.982311
38	0.002173	0.984484
39	0.001912	0.986395
40	0.001681	0.988076
41	0.001477	0.989554
42	0.001298	0.990851
43	0.001139	0.991991
44	0.001000	0.992991
45	0.000877	0.993868
46	0.000769	0.994637
47	0.000674	0.995311
48	0.000591	0.995901
49	0.000517	0.996419
50	0.000453	0.996871
51	0.000396	0.997268
52	0.000347	0.997614
53	0.000303	0.997918
54	0.000265	0.998183
55	0.000232	0.998415
56	0.000203	0.998617
57	0.000177	0.998794
58	0.000154	0.998948
59	0.000135	0.999083
60	0.000118	0.999201
61	0.000103	0.999304
62	0.000090	0.999394
63	0.000078	0.999472
64	0.000068	0.999540
65	0.000059	0.999599
66	0.000052	0.999651
67	0.000045	0.999696
68	0.000039	0.999736
69	0.000034	0.999770
70	0.000030	0.999800
71	0.000026	0.999826
72	0.000023	0.999849
73	0.000020	0.999868
74	0.000017	0.999886
75	0.000015	0.999900

k=2·0
Mean=12·29
Variance=87·76

n	P(*n*)	F(*n*)
0	0.019600	0.019600
1	0.033712	0.053312
2	0.043488	0.096800
3	0.049867	0.146667
4	0.053607	0.200274
5	0.055322	0.255596
6	0.055507	0.311103
7	0.054555	0.365658
8	0.052782	0.418440
9	0.050436	0.468876
10	0.047713	0.516589
11	0.044763	0.561352
12	0.041704	0.603056
13	0.038625	0.641681
14	0.035590	0.677271
15	0.032648	0.709918
16	0.029832	0.739750
17	0.027165	0.766915
18	0.024659	0.791574
19	0.022323	0.813897
20	0.020158	0.834055
21	0.018161	0.852216
22	0.016329	0.868545
23	0.014653	0.883198
24	0.013127	0.896325
25	0.011741	0.908066
26	0.010485	0.918551
27	0.009351	0.927902
28	0.008329	0.936232
29	0.007410	0.943642
30	0.006585	0.950227
31	0.005846	0.956073
32	0.005185	0.961258
33	0.004594	0.965852
34	0.004067	0.969919
35	0.003598	0.973516
36	0.003180	0.976696
37	0.002809	0.979505
38	0.002479	0.981983
39	0.002187	0.984170
40	0.001927	0.986097
41	0.001698	0.987795
42	0.001495	0.989290
43	0.001316	0.990606
44	0.001157	0.991763
45	0.001017	0.992781
46	0.000894	0.993674
47	0.000785	0.994460
48	0.000689	0.995149
49	0.000605	0.995754
50	0.000531	0.996284
51	0.000465	0.996750
52	0.000408	0.997157
53	0.000357	0.997515
54	0.000313	0.997828

n	P(n)	F(n)
55	0.000274	0.998102
56	0.000240	0.998342
57	0.000210	0.998552
58	0.000184	0.998735
59	0.000161	0.998896
60	0.000140	0.999036
61	0.000123	0.999159
62	0.000107	0.999266
63	0.000094	0.999360
64	0.000082	0.999442
65	0.000071	0.999513
66	0.000062	0.999576
67	0.000054	0.999630
68	0.000048	0.999678
69	0.000041	0.999719
70	0.000036	0.999755
71	0.000032	0.999787
72	0.000028	0.999814
73	0.000024	0.999838
74	0.000021	0.999859
75	0.000018	0.999878
76	0.000016	0.999893
77	0.000014	0.999907

$k = 2.1$
Mean $= 12.90$
Variance $= 92.14$

n	P(n)	F(n)
0	0.016102	0.016102
1	0.029079	0.045181
2	0.038763	0.083944
3	0.045559	0.129503
4	0.049956	0.179459
5	0.052414	0.231873
6	0.053340	0.285213
7	0.053081	0.338293
8	0.051926	0.390219
9	0.050114	0.440334
10	0.047839	0.488173
11	0.045256	0.533429
12	0.042488	0.575917
13	0.039631	0.615548
14	0.036761	0.652309
15	0.033933	0.686242
16	0.031188	0.717430
17	0.028558	0.745988
18	0.026060	0.772048
19	0.023709	0.795757
20	0.021512	0.817269
21	0.019469	0.836738
22	0.017581	0.854318
23	0.015842	0.870161
24	0.014249	0.884410
25	0.012793	0.897203
26	0.011468	0.908670
27	0.010264	0.918934
28	0.009174	0.928108
29	0.008189	0.936297
30	0.007300	0.943597
31	0.006501	0.950099
32	0.005783	0.955882
33	0.005139	0.961021
34	0.004563	0.965584
35	0.004047	0.969631
36	0.003587	0.973219
37	0.003177	0.976395
38	0.002811	0.979206
39	0.002486	0.981692
40	0.002196	0.983888
41	0.001940	0.985828
42	0.001712	0.987540
43	0.001510	0.989049
44	0.001331	0.990380
45	0.001173	0.991553
46	0.001032	0.992585
47	0.000909	0.993494
48	0.000799	0.994293
49	0.000703	0.994996
50	0.000618	0.995614
51	0.000543	0.996157
52	0.000477	0.996633
53	0.000418	0.997052
54	0.000367	0.997419
55	0.000322	0.997741
56	0.000282	0.998024
57	0.000248	0.998271
58	0.000217	0.998488
59	0.000190	0.998678
60	0.000166	0.998845
61	0.000146	0.998990
62	0.000128	0.999118
63	0.000112	0.999229
64	0.000098	0.999327
65	0.000085	0.999413
66	0.000075	0.999487
67	0.000065	0.999552
68	0.000057	0.999609
69	0.000050	0.999659
70	0.000044	0.999703
71	0.000038	0.999741
72	0.000033	0.999774
73	0.000029	0.999803
74	0.000025	0.999828
75	0.000022	0.999850
76	0.000019	0.999870
77	0.000017	0.999886
78	0.000015	0.999901

$k = 2.2$
Mean $= 13.51$
Variance $= 96.53$

n	P(n)	F(n)
0	0.013228	0.013228
1	0.025027	0.038254
2	0.034437	0.072691
3	0.041462	0.114153
4	0.046354	0.160507
5	0.049432	0.209939
6	0.051014	0.260953
7	0.051393	0.312346
8	0.050828	0.363174
9	0.049540	0.412714
10	0.047717	0.460431
11	0.045513	0.505944
12	0.043056	0.548999
13	0.040446	0.589445
14	0.037765	0.627210
15	0.035076	0.662286
16	0.032428	0.694714
17	0.029856	0.724570
18	0.027388	0.751958
19	0.025041	0.777000
20	0.022828	0.799827
21	0.020754	0.820581
22	0.018822	0.839403
23	0.017031	0.856434
24	0.015379	0.871813
25	0.013861	0.885674
26	0.012471	0.898145
27	0.011201	0.909346
28	0.010046	0.919392
29	0.008997	0.928390
30	0.008047	0.936437
31	0.007188	0.943625
32	0.006414	0.950039
33	0.005716	0.955755
34	0.005090	0.960845
35	0.004527	0.965372
36	0.004023	0.969395
37	0.003572	0.972967
38	0.003169	0.976136
39	0.002809	0.978945
40	0.002488	0.981434
41	0.002203	0.983636
42	0.001948	0.985585
43	0.001722	0.987307
44	0.001522	0.988829
45	0.001344	0.990172
46	0.001186	0.991358
47	0.001046	0.992403
48	0.000922	0.993325
49	0.000812	0.994137
50	0.000715	0.994852
51	0.000630	0.995482
52	0.000554	0.996036
53	0.000487	0.996523
54	0.000428	0.996951
55	0.000376	0.997327
56	0.000331	0.997658
57	0.000290	0.997948
58	0.000255	0.998203
59	0.000224	0.998427
60	0.000196	0.998623
61	0.000172	0.998795
62	0.000151	0.998946
63	0.000132	0.999078
64	0.000116	0.999193

n	P(n)	F(n)
65	0.000101	0.999295
66	0.000089	0.999384
67	0.000078	0.999461
68	0.000068	0.999529
69	0.000060	0.999589
70	0.000052	0.999641
71	0.000046	0.999686
72	0.000040	0.999726
73	0.000035	0.999761
74	0.000030	0.999792
75	0.000027	0.999818
76	0.000023	0.999841
77	0.000020	0.999862
78	0.000018	0.999879
79	0.000015	0.999895
80	0.000013	0.999908

k = 2.3
Mean = 14.13
Variance = 100.92

n	P(n)	F(n)
0	0.010867	0.010867
1	0.021494	0.032361
2	0.030500	0.062861
3	0.037597	0.100458
4	0.042841	0.143299
5	0.046423	0.189722
6	0.048574	0.238296
7	0.049531	0.287827
8	0.049519	0.337346
9	0.048738	0.386084
10	0.047363	0.433447
11	0.045546	0.478993
12	0.043413	0.522407
13	0.041069	0.563476
14	0.038599	0.602075
15	0.036072	0.638146
16	0.033542	0.671689
17	0.031052	0.702741
18	0.028634	0.731375
19	0.026310	0.757685
20	0.024097	0.781782
21	0.022007	0.803789
22	0.020044	0.823833
23	0.018212	0.842045
24	0.016511	0.858555
25	0.014938	0.873493
26	0.013489	0.886982
27	0.012159	0.899140
28	0.010942	0.910083
29	0.009832	0.919915
30	0.008822	0.928736
31	0.007905	0.936641
32	0.007074	0.943716
33	0.006324	0.950040
34	0.005646	0.955686
35	0.005036	0.960722
36	0.004488	0.965210
37	0.003995	0.969205
38	0.003553	0.972758
39	0.003158	0.975915
40	0.002804	0.978719
41	0.002488	0.981207
42	0.002206	0.983412
43	0.001954	0.985367
44	0.001730	0.987097
45	0.001531	0.988628
46	0.001354	0.989982
47	0.001197	0.991178
48	0.001057	0.992235
49	0.000933	0.993168
50	0.000823	0.993992
51	0.000726	0.994718
52	0.000640	0.995358
53	0.000564	0.995922
54	0.000497	0.996418
55	0.000437	0.996855
56	0.000385	0.997240
57	0.000338	0.997579
58	0.000298	0.997876
59	0.000262	0.998138
60	0.000230	0.998367
61	0.000202	0.998569
62	0.000177	0.998747
63	0.000156	0.998902
64	0.000136	0.999039
65	0.000120	0.999158
66	0.000105	0.999263
67	0.000092	0.999355
68	0.000081	0.999436
69	0.000071	0.999507
70	0.000062	0.999569
71	0.000054	0.999623
72	0.000047	0.999670
73	0.000042	0.999712
74	0.000036	0.999748
75	0.000032	0.999780
76	0.000028	0.999808
77	0.000024	0.999832
78	0.000021	0.999854
79	0.000019	0.999872
80	0.000016	0.999888
81	0.000014	0.999903

k = 2.4
Mean = 14.74
Variance = 105.31

n	P(n)	F(n)
0	0.008927	0.008927
1	0.018425	0.027352
2	0.026938	0.054290
3	0.033978	0.088268
4	0.039448	0.127716
5	0.043425	0.171141
6	0.046059	0.217200
7	0.047533	0.264732
8	0.048032	0.312764
9	0.047733	0.360497
10	0.046797	0.407295
11	0.045368	0.452663
12	0.043568	0.496231
13	0.041504	0.537735
14	0.039263	0.576998
15	0.036917	0.613915
16	0.034527	0.648442
17	0.032139	0.680581
18	0.029789	0.710370
19	0.027506	0.737876
20	0.025311	0.763187
21	0.023219	0.786406
22	0.021239	0.807645
23	0.019377	0.827022
24	0.017636	0.844658
25	0.016017	0.860675
26	0.014516	0.875191
27	0.013131	0.888322
28	0.011857	0.900180
29	0.010690	0.910870
30	0.009622	0.920492
31	0.008649	0.929140
32	0.007763	0.936904
33	0.006960	0.943863
34	0.006232	0.950095
35	0.005574	0.955669
36	0.004980	0.960649
37	0.004445	0.965094
38	0.003963	0.969057
39	0.003531	0.972588
40	0.003143	0.975730
41	0.002795	0.978525
42	0.002484	0.981009
43	0.002206	0.983215
44	0.001957	0.985172
45	0.001736	0.986908
46	0.001538	0.988446
47	0.001362	0.989808
48	0.001206	0.991013
49	0.001066	0.992080
50	0.000943	0.993022
51	0.000833	0.993856
52	0.000736	0.994591
53	0.000649	0.995241
54	0.000573	0.995814
55	0.000505	0.996319
56	0.000445	0.996764
57	0.000392	0.997157
58	0.000346	0.997503
59	0.000304	0.997807
60	0.000268	0.998075
61	0.000236	0.998310
62	0.000207	0.998518
63	0.000182	0.998700
64	0.000160	0.998860

n	P(n)	F(n)
65	0.000141	0.999001
66	0.000124	0.999124
67	0.000108	0.999233
68	0.000095	0.999328
69	0.000084	0.999411
70	0.000073	0.999485
71	0.000064	0.999549
72	0.000056	0.999605
73	0.000049	0.999654
74	0.000043	0.999698
75	0.000038	0.999736
76	0.000033	0.999769
77	0.000029	0.999798
78	0.000025	0.999823
79	0.000022	0.999846
80	0.000019	0.999865
81	0.000017	0.999882
82	0.000015	0.999897
83	0.000013	0.999910

$k = 2.5$
Mean $= 15.36$
Variance $= 109.69$

n	P(n)	F(n)
0	0.007334	0.007334
1	0.015767	0.023101
2	0.023730	0.046831
3	0.030612	0.077442
4	0.036198	0.113640
5	0.040469	0.154110
6	0.043505	0.197615
7	0.045431	0.243046
8	0.046397	0.289443
9	0.046551	0.335994
10	0.046039	0.382033
11	0.044993	0.427026
12	0.043531	0.470557
13	0.041756	0.512313
14	0.039758	0.552071
15	0.037611	0.589682
16	0.035378	0.625059
17	0.033109	0.658169
18	0.030847	0.689015
19	0.028623	0.717638
20	0.026462	0.744100
21	0.024382	0.768482
22	0.022399	0.790881
23	0.020519	0.811400
24	0.018749	0.830149
25	0.017092	0.847241
26	0.015547	0.862788
27	0.014113	0.876901
28	0.012788	0.889689
29	0.011566	0.901255
30	0.010444	0.911699
31	0.009417	0.921116
32	0.008478	0.929594
33	0.007622	0.937216
34	0.006845	0.944061
35	0.006139	0.950200
36	0.005499	0.955699
37	0.004921	0.960620
38	0.004399	0.965019
39	0.003929	0.968947
40	0.003505	0.972453
41	0.003125	0.975578
42	0.002783	0.978361
43	0.002477	0.980838
44	0.002203	0.983042
45	0.001958	0.984999
46	0.001739	0.986738
47	0.001543	0.988281
48	0.001368	0.989649
49	0.001213	0.990862
50	0.001074	0.991936
51	0.000951	0.992887
52	0.000842	0.993729
53	0.000744	0.994473
54	0.000658	0.995131
55	0.000581	0.995712
56	0.000513	0.996225
57	0.000453	0.996678
58	0.000400	0.997078
59	0.000352	0.997430
60	0.000311	0.997741
61	0.000274	0.998015
62	0.000241	0.998256
63	0.000212	0.998468
64	0.000187	0.998655
65	0.000164	0.998819
66	0.000145	0.998964
67	0.000127	0.999091
68	0.000112	0.999203
69	0.000098	0.999301
70	0.000086	0.999387
71	0.000076	0.999463
72	0.000066	0.999529
73	0.000058	0.999588
74	0.000051	0.999639
75	0.000045	0.999684
76	0.000039	0.999723
77	0.000035	0.999758
78	0.000030	0.999788
79	0.000027	0.999814
80	0.000023	0.999838
81	0.000020	0.999858
82	0.000018	0.999876
83	0.000016	0.999891
84	0.000014	0.999905

k = 0·1
Mean = 0·53
Variance = 3·28

n	P(n)	F(n)
0	0.832553	0.832553
1	0.069934	0.902488
2	0.032310	0.934797
3	0.018998	0.953796
4	0.012368	0.966163
5	0.008519	0.974682
6	0.006083	0.980765
7	0.004452	0.985217
8	0.003319	0.988536
9	0.002509	0.991046
10	0.001918	0.992964
11	0.001479	0.994443
12	0.001150	0.995593
13	0.000899	0.996492
14	0.000706	0.997198
15	0.000558	0.997756
16	0.000442	0.998198
17	0.000352	0.998550
18	0.000281	0.998830
19	0.000225	0.999055
20	0.000180	0.999235
21	0.000145	0.999380
22	0.000117	0.999497
23	0.000094	0.999591
24	0.000076	0.999667
25	0.000062	0.999729
26	0.000050	0.999779
27	0.000041	0.999820
28	0.000033	0.999853
29	0.000027	0.999879
30	0.000022	0.999901

k = 0·2
Mean = 1·05
Variance = 6·56

n	P(n)	F(n)
0	0.693145	0.693145
1	0.116448	0.809593
2	0.058690	0.868283
3	0.036153	0.904436
4	0.024295	0.928731
5	0.017142	0.945873
6	0.012480	0.958353
7	0.009285	0.967638
8	0.007019	0.974657
9	0.005372	0.980030
10	0.004152	0.984181
11	0.003234	0.987415
12	0.002535	0.989950
13	0.001999	0.991949
14	0.001583	0.993531

15	0.001259	0.994790
16	0.001004	0.995795
17	0.000804	0.996599
18	0.000645	0.997244
19	0.000519	0.997763
20	0.000419	0.998182
21	0.000338	0.998520
22	0.000274	0.998794
23	0.000222	0.999016
24	0.000180	0.999197
25	0.000147	0.999343
26	0.000119	0.999463
27	0.000097	0.999560
28	0.000079	0.999639
29	0.000065	0.999704
30	0.000053	0.999757
31	0.000043	0.999800
32	0.000036	0.999836
33	0.000029	0.999865
34	0.000024	0.999889
35	0.000020	0.999909

k = 0·3
Mean = 1·58
Variance = 9·84

n	P(n)	F(n)
0	0.577080	0.577080
1	0.145424	0.722504
2	0.079402	0.801906
3	0.051135	0.853040
4	0.035436	0.888477
5	0.025599	0.914076
6	0.018995	0.933070
7	0.014360	0.947430
8	0.011007	0.958437
9	0.008527	0.966964
10	0.006661	0.973625
11	0.005239	0.978864
12	0.004144	0.983008
13	0.003294	0.986302
14	0.002628	0.988930
15	0.002105	0.991035
16	0.001691	0.992726
17	0.001362	0.994087
18	0.001099	0.995187
19	0.000889	0.996076
20	0.000721	0.996797
21	0.000585	0.997383
22	0.000476	0.997859
23	0.000388	0.998246
24	0.000316	0.998563
25	0.000258	0.998821
26	0.000211	0.999032
27	0.000173	0.999205
28	0.000141	0.999346
29	0.000116	0.999462

30	0.000095	0.999557
31	0.000078	0.999635
32	0.000064	0.999699
33	0.000053	0.999752
34	0.000043	0.999795
35	0.000036	0.999831
36	0.000029	0.999861
37	0.000024	0.999885
38	0.000020	0.999905

k = 0·4
Mean = 2·10
Variance = 13·13

n	P(n)	F(n)
0	0.480450	0.480450
1	0.161431	0.641881
2	0.094922	0.736802
3	0.063787	0.800590
4	0.045544	0.846134
5	0.033666	0.879800
6	0.025452	0.905252
7	0.019547	0.924798
8	0.015188	0.939986
9	0.011907	0.951894
10	0.009402	0.961296
11	0.007467	0.968763
12	0.005959	0.974721
13	0.004774	0.979495
14	0.003838	0.983334
15	0.003095	0.986429
16	0.002503	0.988932
17	0.002028	0.990960
18	0.001647	0.992607
19	0.001340	0.993946
20	0.001091	0.995038
21	0.000891	0.995928
22	0.000728	0.996656
23	0.000595	0.997251
24	0.000488	0.997739
25	0.000400	0.998139
26	0.000328	0.998467
27	0.000269	0.998736
28	0.000221	0.998958
29	0.000182	0.999140
30	0.000150	0.999290
31	0.000124	0.999413
32	0.000102	0.999515
33	0.000084	0.999599
34	0.000069	0.999668
35	0.000057	0.999726
36	0.000047	0.999773
37	0.000039	0.999812
38	0.000032	0.999844
39	0.000027	0.999871
40	0.000022	0.999893
41	0.000018	0.999911

k = 0·5
Mean = 2·62
Variance = 16·41

n	P(n)	F(n)
0	0.400000	0.400000
1	0.168000	0.568000
2	0.105840	0.673840
3	0.074088	0.747928
4	0.054455	0.802383
5	0.041168	0.843550
6	0.031699	0.875250
7	0.024725	0.899975
8	0.019471	0.919446
9	0.015447	0.934893
10	0.012327	0.947220
11	0.009884	0.957104
12	0.007957	0.965061
13	0.006426	0.971487
14	0.005205	0.976692
15	0.004227	0.980919
16	0.003440	0.984359
17	0.002804	0.987163
18	0.002290	0.989453
19	0.001873	0.991326
20	0.001534	0.992860
21	0.001258	0.994118
22	0.001033	0.995151
23	0.000849	0.995999
24	0.000698	0.996697
25	0.000575	0.997272
26	0.000473	0.997745
27	0.000390	0.998135
28	0.000322	0.998457
29	0.000266	0.998723
30	0.000220	0.998943
31	0.000181	0.999124
32	0.000150	0.999274
33	0.000124	0.999398
34	0.000103	0.999501
35	0.000085	0.999586
36	0.000070	0.999656
37	0.000058	0.999715
38	0.000048	0.999763
39	0.000040	0.999803
40	0.000033	0.999837
41	0.000028	0.999864
42	0.000023	0.999887
43	0.000019	0.999906

k = 0·6
Mean = 3·15
Variance = 19·69

n	P(n)	F(n)
0	0.333021	0.333021
1	0.167843	0.500864
2	0.112790	0.613654
3	0.082111	0.695766
4	0.062076	0.757842
5	0.047972	0.805814
6	0.037610	0.843425
7	0.029787	0.873212
8	0.023770	0.896983
9	0.019080	0.916062
10	0.015386	0.931448
11	0.012454	0.943902
12	0.010113	0.954015
13	0.008233	0.962248
14	0.006718	0.968967
15	0.005493	0.974460
16	0.004499	0.978959
17	0.003690	0.982649
18	0.003031	0.985679
19	0.002492	0.988172
20	0.002052	0.990223
21	0.001691	0.991914
22	0.001394	0.993308
23	0.001151	0.994459
24	0.000951	0.995409
25	0.000786	0.996195
26	0.000650	0.996845
27	0.000538	0.997383
28	0.000445	0.997828
29	0.000369	0.998197
30	0.000306	0.998502
31	0.000253	0.998756
32	0.000210	0.998966
33	0.000174	0.999141
34	0.000145	0.999285
35	0.000120	0.999406
36	0.000100	0.999506
37	0.000083	0.999589
38	0.000069	0.999658
39	0.000057	0.999715
40	0.000048	0.999763
41	0.000040	0.999802
42	0.000033	0.999835
43	0.000027	0.999863
44	0.000023	0.999886
45	0.000019	0.999905

k = 0·7
Mean = 3·68
Variance = 22·97

n	P(n)	F(n)
0	0.277258	0.277258
1	0.163028	0.440286
2	0.116402	0.556687
3	0.088000	0.644687
4	0.068376	0.713063
5	0.053990	0.767052
6	0.043084	0.810136
7	0.034639	0.844775
8	0.028006	0.872781
9	0.022741	0.895522
10	0.018529	0.914051
11	0.015140	0.929191
12	0.012400	0.941591
13	0.010175	0.951766
14	0.008364	0.960130
15	0.006885	0.967016
16	0.005675	0.972691
17	0.004683	0.977374
18	0.003868	0.981242
19	0.003198	0.984440
20	0.002646	0.987086
21	0.002191	0.989277
22	0.001815	0.991092
23	0.001505	0.992597
24	0.001248	0.993846
25	0.001036	0.994882
26	0.000860	0.995742
27	0.000715	0.996456
28	0.000594	0.997050
29	0.000494	0.997544
30	0.000411	0.997954
31	0.000341	0.998296
32	0.000284	0.998580
33	0.000237	0.998817
34	0.000197	0.999013
35	0.000164	0.999177
36	0.000137	0.999314
37	0.000114	0.999428
38	0.000095	0.999523
39	0.000079	0.999602
40	0.000066	0.999668
41	0.000055	0.999723
42	0.000046	0.999769
43	0.000038	0.999807
44	0.000032	0.999839
45	0.000027	0.999865
46	0.000022	0.999887
47	0.000019	0.999906

k = 0·8
Mean = 4·20
Variance = 26·25

n	P(n)	F(n)
0	0.230832	0.230832
1	0.155119	0.385951
2	0.117270	0.503221
3	0.091940	0.595161
4	0.073368	0.668529
5	0.059164	0.727693
6	0.048041	0.775734
7	0.039202	0.814935
8	0.032106	0.847041
9	0.026370	0.873411
10	0.021708	0.895118
11	0.017903	0.913021
12	0.014788	0.927809
13	0.012231	0.940040
14	0.010127	0.950167

n	P(n)	F(n)		n	P(n)	F(n)		n	P(n)	F(n)
15	0.008393	0.958560		20	0.004068	0.979161		20	0.004894	0.974304
16	0.006962	0.965522		21	0.003401	0.982562		21	0.004111	0.978415
17	0.005779	0.971301		22	0.002844	0.985406		22	0.003454	0.981869
18	0.004801	0.976102		23	0.002378	0.987784		23	0.002901	0.984770
19	0.003990	0.980092		24	0.001990	0.989774		24	0.002437	0.987207
20	0.003318	0.983411		25	0.001665	0.991438		25	0.002047	0.989254
21	0.002761	0.986171		26	0.001393	0.992831		26	0.001719	0.990973
22	0.002298	0.988469		27	0.001166	0.993997		27	0.001444	0.992417
23	0.001914	0.990383		28	0.000976	0.994972		28	0.001213	0.993631
24	0.001594	0.991977		29	0.000817	0.995789		29	0.001019	0.994650
25	0.001328	0.993305		30	0.000684	0.996473		30	0.000856	0.995506
26	0.001107	0.994412		31	0.000572	0.997045		31	0.000719	0.996225
27	0.000923	0.995335		32	0.000479	0.997525		32	0.000604	0.996829
28	0.000770	0.996105		33	0.000401	0.997926		33	0.000507	0.997336
29	0.000642	0.996747		34	0.000336	0.998262		34	0.000426	0.997762
30	0.000536	0.997283		35	0.000282	0.998544		35	0.000358	0.998120
31	0.000447	0.997730		36	0.000236	0.998780		36	0.000301	0.998421
32	0.000373	0.998104		37	0.000198	0.998977		37	0.000253	0.998674
33	0.000312	0.998415		38	0.000166	0.999143		38	0.000212	0.998886
34	0.000260	0.998676		39	0.000139	0.999282		39	0.000178	0.999064
35	0.000217	0.998893		40	0.000116	0.999398		40	0.000150	0.999214
36	0.000182	0.999075		41	0.000097	0.999495		41	0.000126	0.999340
37	0.000152	0.999226		42	0.000082	0.999577		42	0.000106	0.999445
38	0.000127	0.999353		43	0.000068	0.999645		43	0.000089	0.999534
39	0.000106	0.999459		44	0.000057	0.999703		44	0.000075	0.999609
40	0.000089	0.999548		45	0.000048	0.999751		45	0.000063	0.999671
41	0.000074	0.999622		46	0.000040	0.999791		46	0.000053	0.999724
42	0.000062	0.999684		47	0.000034	0.999825		47	0.000044	0.999768
43	0.000052	0.999735		48	0.000028	0.999853		48	0.000037	0.999805
44	0.000043	0.999779		49	0.000024	0.999877		49	0.000031	0.999836
45	0.000036	0.999815		50	0.000020	0.999897		50	0.000026	0.999863
46	0.000030	0.999845		51	0.000017	0.999913		51	0.000022	0.999885
47	0.000025	0.999870						52	0.000018	0.999903
48	0.000021	0.999891								
49	0.000018	0.999909								

k=0.9
Mean=4.73
Variance=29.53

k=1.0
Mean=5.25
Variance=32.81

k=1.1
Mean=5.78
Variance=36.09

n	P(n)	F(n)		n	P(n)	F(n)		n	P(n)	F(n)
0	0.192180	0.192180		0	0.160000	0.160000		0	0.133209	0.133209
1	0.145288	0.337468		1	0.134400	0.294400		1	0.123085	0.256293
2	0.115940	0.453408		2	0.112896	0.407296		2	0.108561	0.364854
3	0.094143	0.547551		3	0.094833	0.502129		3	0.094231	0.459085
4	0.077103	0.624654		4	0.079659	0.581788		4	0.081133	0.540217
5	0.063471	0.688126		5	0.066914	0.648702		5	0.069514	0.609732
6	0.052427	0.740553		6	0.056208	0.704910		6	0.059365	0.669097
7	0.043410	0.783963		7	0.047214	0.752124		7	0.050579	0.719676
8	0.036008	0.819971		8	0.039660	0.791784		8	0.043018	0.762694
9	0.029911	0.849882		9	0.033315	0.825099		9	0.036536	0.799230
10	0.024874	0.874756		10	0.027984	0.853083		10	0.030997	0.830227
11	0.020704	0.895461		11	0.023507	0.876590		11	0.026275	0.856502
12	0.017247	0.912707		12	0.019746	0.896335		12	0.022255	0.878757
13	0.014376	0.927083		13	0.016586	0.912922		13	0.018838	0.897594
14	0.011989	0.939072		14	0.013933	0.926854		14	0.015937	0.913531
15	0.010004	0.949076		15	0.011703	0.938558		15	0.013476	0.927007
16	0.008351	0.957427		16	0.009831	0.948388		16	0.011391	0.938397
17	0.006973	0.964400		17	0.008258	0.956646		17	0.009624	0.948022
18	0.005825	0.970225		18	0.006937	0.963583		18	0.008129	0.956151
19	0.004867	0.975093		19	0.005827	0.969410		19	0.006865	0.963016

n	P(n)	F(n)
20	0.005795	0.968811
21	0.004891	0.973702
22	0.004127	0.977829
23	0.003482	0.981311
24	0.002937	0.984248
25	0.002477	0.986725
26	0.002089	0.988814
27	0.001761	0.990575
28	0.001484	0.992059
29	0.001251	0.993310
30	0.001055	0.994365
31	0.000889	0.995254
32	0.000749	0.996002
33	0.000631	0.996633
34	0.000532	0.997165
35	0.000448	0.997613
36	0.000377	0.997990
37	0.000318	0.998307
38	0.000268	0.998575
39	0.000225	0.998800
40	0.000190	0.998990
41	0.000160	0.999150
42	0.000135	0.999284
43	0.000113	0.999398
44	0.000095	0.999493
45	0.000080	0.999573
46	0.000068	0.999641
47	0.000057	0.999698
48	0.000048	0.999746
49	0.000040	0.999786
50	0.000034	0.999820
51	0.000029	0.999848
52	0.000024	0.999872
53	0.000020	0.999893
54	0.000017	0.999910

k=1·2
Mean=6·30
Variance=39·38

n	P(n)	F(n)
0	0.110903	0.110903
1	0.111790	0.222694
2	0.103294	0.325988
3	0.092552	0.418540
4	0.081631	0.500170
5	0.071313	0.571483
6	0.061899	0.633382
7	0.053481	0.686863
8	0.046047	0.732910
9	0.039539	0.772449
10	0.033877	0.806326
11	0.028974	0.835300
12	0.024744	0.860044
13	0.021105	0.881149
14	0.017981	0.899130
15	0.015306	0.914436
16	0.013017	0.927453
17	0.011063	0.938517
18	0.009396	0.947913
19	0.007976	0.955889

n	P(n)	F(n)
20	0.006767	0.962656
21	0.005738	0.968394
22	0.004864	0.973258
23	0.004121	0.977379
24	0.003491	0.980870
25	0.002956	0.983826
26	0.002502	0.986328
27	0.002117	0.988445
28	0.001791	0.990236
29	0.001515	0.991751
30	0.001281	0.993032
31	0.001083	0.994115
32	0.000915	0.995030
33	0.000774	0.995804
34	0.000654	0.996457
35	0.000552	0.997010
36	0.000466	0.997476
37	0.000394	0.997870
38	0.000333	0.998203
39	0.000281	0.998483
40	0.000237	0.998721
41	0.000200	0.998921
42	0.000169	0.999090
43	0.000143	0.999232
44	0.000120	0.999352
45	0.000101	0.999454
46	0.000086	0.999539
47	0.000072	0.999612
48	0.000061	0.999673
49	0.000051	0.999724
50	0.000043	0.999767
51	0.000037	0.999804
52	0.000031	0.999835
53	0.000026	0.999861
54	0.000022	0.999883
55	0.000018	0.999901

k=1·3
Mean=6·83
Variance=42·66

n	P(n)	F(n)
0	0.092333	0.092333
1	0.100827	0.193160
2	0.097399	0.290559
3	0.089997	0.380556
4	0.081267	0.461824
5	0.072360	0.534184
6	0.063822	0.598006
7	0.055908	0.653914
8	0.048724	0.702637
9	0.042292	0.744930
10	0.036591	0.781521
11	0.031575	0.813096
12	0.027186	0.840282
13	0.023363	0.863645
14	0.020046	0.883691

n	P(n)	F(n)
15	0.017175	0.900866
16	0.014698	0.915563
17	0.012564	0.928127
18	0.010730	0.938857
19	0.009155	0.948012
20	0.007806	0.955818
21	0.006650	0.962468
22	0.005663	0.968130
23	0.004819	0.972949
24	0.004098	0.977047
25	0.003484	0.980531
26	0.002960	0.983491
27	0.002514	0.986005
28	0.002135	0.988140
29	0.001812	0.989951
30	0.001537	0.991488
31	0.001303	0.992792
32	0.001105	0.993897
33	0.000937	0.994834
34	0.000794	0.995628
35	0.000673	0.996300
36	0.000570	0.996870
37	0.000482	0.997352
38	0.000408	0.997761
39	0.000346	0.998106
40	0.000293	0.998399
41	0.000248	0.998646
42	0.000209	0.998856
43	0.000177	0.999033
44	0.000150	0.999183
45	0.000127	0.999310
46	0.000107	0.999417
47	0.000091	0.999507
48	0.000077	0.999584
49	0.000065	0.999648
50	0.000055	0.999703
51	0.000046	0.999749
52	0.000039	0.999788
53	0.000033	0.999821
54	0.000028	0.999849
55	0.000024	0.999873
56	0.000020	0.999893
57	0.000017	0.999909

k=1·4
Mean=7·35
Variance=45·94

n	P(n)	F(n)
0	0.076872	0.076872
1	0.090401	0.167273
2	0.091125	0.258398
3	0.086751	0.345149
4	0.080158	0.425306
5	0.072719	0.498025
6	0.065156	0.563181
7	0.057859	0.621040
8	0.051031	0.672072
9	0.044772	0.716843

P(n)	F(n)
0.039112	0.755956
0.034049	0.790005
0.029555	0.819559
0.025590	0.845149
0.022110	0.867259
0.019067	0.886326
0.016417	0.902743
0.014115	0.916858
0.012120	0.928977
0.010395	0.939372
0.008906	0.948279
0.007624	0.955903
0.006521	0.962423
0.005572	0.967996
0.004759	0.972755
0.004061	0.976816
0.003464	0.980280
0.002953	0.983233
0.002516	0.985749
0.002143	0.987892
0.001824	0.989715
0.001552	0.991267
0.001320	0.992587
0.001122	0.993709
0.000954	0.994662
0.000810	0.995472
0.000688	0.996160
0.000584	0.996745
0.000496	0.997241
0.000421	0.997661
0.000357	0.998018
0.000303	0.998321
0.000257	0.998578
0.000218	0.998796
0.000185	0.998980
0.000156	0.999137
0.000133	0.999269
0.000112	0.999382
0.000095	0.999477
0.000081	0.999557
0.000068	0.999625
0.000058	0.999683
0.000049	0.999732
0.000041	0.999773
0.000035	0.999808
0.000030	0.999838
0.000025	0.999863
0.000021	0.999884
0.000018	0.999902

$k = 1.5$
Mean = 7·88
Variance = 49·22

P(n)	F(n)
0.064000	0.064000
0.080640	0.144640
0.084672	0.229312
0.082979	0.312291
0.078415	0.390705

n	P(n)	F(n)
5	0.072455	0.463161
6	0.065934	0.529095
7	0.059341	0.588436
8	0.052962	0.641397
9	0.046959	0.688357
10	0.041418	0.729775
11	0.036373	0.766147
12	0.031826	0.797974
13	0.027762	0.825736
14	0.024153	0.849889
15	0.020965	0.870854
16	0.018161	0.889014
17	0.015704	0.904718
18	0.013558	0.918276
19	0.011688	0.929964
20	0.010063	0.940027
21	0.008655	0.948682
22	0.007435	0.956117
23	0.006381	0.962498
24	0.005472	0.967970
25	0.004688	0.972658
26	0.004014	0.976672
27	0.003434	0.980106
28	0.002936	0.983042
29	0.002509	0.985551
30	0.002143	0.987694
31	0.001829	0.989523
32	0.001560	0.991083
33	0.001330	0.992413
34	0.001134	0.993547
35	0.000966	0.994514
36	0.000823	0.995336
37	0.000701	0.996037
38	0.000596	0.996633
39	0.000507	0.997140
40	0.000431	0.997572
41	0.000367	0.997939
42	0.000312	0.998250
43	0.000265	0.998515
44	0.000225	0.998740
45	0.000191	0.998932
46	0.000162	0.999094
47	0.000138	0.999232
48	0.000117	0.999349
49	0.000099	0.999448
50	0.000084	0.999532
51	0.000071	0.999603
52	0.000061	0.999664
53	0.000051	0.999715
54	0.000044	0.999759
55	0.000037	0.999796
56	0.000031	0.999827
57	0.000027	0.999854
58	0.000022	0.999876
59	0.000019	0.999895
60	0.000016	0.999911

$k = 1.6$
Mean = 8·40
Variance = 52·50

n	P(n)	F(n)
0	0.053283	0.053283
1	0.071613	0.124896
2	0.078201	0.203098
3	0.078827	0.281924
4	0.076147	0.358071
5	0.071639	0.429710
6	0.066194	0.495904
7	0.060369	0.556274
8	0.054513	0.610787
9	0.048844	0.659631
10	0.043491	0.703122
11	0.038525	0.741647
12	0.033979	0.775626
13	0.029860	0.805485
14	0.026157	0.831642
15	0.022851	0.854493
16	0.019914	0.874408
17	0.017319	0.891726
18	0.015033	0.906759
19	0.013026	0.919785
20	0.011270	0.931055
21	0.009737	0.940792
22	0.008403	0.949195
23	0.007242	0.956437
24	0.006236	0.962673
25	0.005364	0.968036
26	0.004609	0.972646
27	0.003958	0.976603
28	0.003396	0.979999
29	0.002912	0.982911
30	0.002495	0.985406
31	0.002136	0.987542
32	0.001828	0.989370
33	0.001563	0.990933
34	0.001336	0.992269
35	0.001142	0.993411
36	0.000975	0.994386
37	0.000832	0.995219
38	0.000710	0.995929
39	0.000606	0.996535
40	0.000516	0.997051
41	0.000440	0.997491
42	0.000375	0.997866
43	0.000319	0.998186
44	0.000272	0.998458
45	0.000232	0.998689
46	0.000197	0.998886
47	0.000168	0.999054
48	0.000143	0.999196
49	0.000121	0.999318
50	0.000103	0.999421
51	0.000088	0.999508
52	0.000074	0.999583
53	0.000063	0.999646
54	0.000054	0.999700

n	P(n)	F(n)
55	0.000046	0.999745
56	0.000039	0.999784
57	0.000033	0.999817
58	0.000028	0.999845
59	0.000024	0.999868
60	0.000020	0.999888
61	0.000017	0.999905

k = 1·7
Mean = 8·93
Variance = 55·78

n	P(n)	F(n)
0	0.044361	0.044361
1	0.063348	0.107709
2	0.071837	0.179546
3	0.074423	0.253968
4	0.073455	0.327423
5	0.070341	0.397764
6	0.065980	0.463744
7	0.060965	0.524709
8	0.055692	0.580400
9	0.050419	0.630820
10	0.045317	0.676137
11	0.040489	0.716625
12	0.035994	0.752620
13	0.031863	0.784483
14	0.028104	0.812587
15	0.024709	0.837295
16	0.021663	0.858959
17	0.018946	0.877905
18	0.016534	0.894439
19	0.014400	0.908839
20	0.012520	0.921359
21	0.010867	0.932226
22	0.009419	0.941644
23	0.008152	0.949797
24	0.007048	0.956845
25	0.006086	0.962931
26	0.005250	0.968180
27	0.004524	0.972704
28	0.003895	0.976600
29	0.003351	0.979951
30	0.002881	0.982831
31	0.002474	0.985306
32	0.002124	0.987430
33	0.001822	0.989252
34	0.001562	0.990813
35	0.001338	0.992152
36	0.001146	0.993298
37	0.000981	0.994278
38	0.000839	0.995118
39	0.000717	0.995835
40	0.000613	0.996448
41	0.000524	0.996972
42	0.000447	0.997420
43	0.000382	0.997802
44	0.000326	0.998127

n	P(n)	F(n)
45	0.000278	0.998406
46	0.000237	0.998643
47	0.000202	0.998845
48	0.000172	0.999017
49	0.000147	0.999164
50	0.000125	0.999289
51	0.000106	0.999395
52	0.000091	0.999486
53	0.000077	0.999563
54	0.000066	0.999629
55	0.000056	0.999685
56	0.000047	0.999732
57	0.000040	0.999772
58	0.000034	0.999807
59	0.000029	0.999836
60	0.000025	0.999861
61	0.000021	0.999882
62	0.000018	0.999900
63	0.000015	0.999915

k = 1·8
Mean = 9·45
Variance = 59·06

n	P(n)	F(n)
0	0.036933	0.036933
1	0.055843	0.092776
2	0.065671	0.158447
3	0.069874	0.228321
4	0.070433	0.298755
5	0.068630	0.367385
6	0.065336	0.432720
7	0.061154	0.493875
8	0.056507	0.550381
9	0.051685	0.602066
10	0.046888	0.648955
11	0.042251	0.691205
12	0.037857	0.729062
13	0.033756	0.762818
14	0.029976	0.792794
15	0.026523	0.819317
16	0.023393	0.842709
17	0.020575	0.863284
18	0.018051	0.881335
19	0.015801	0.897136
20	0.013804	0.910940
21	0.012037	0.922977
22	0.010479	0.933456
23	0.009108	0.942564
24	0.007906	0.950470
25	0.006854	0.957324
26	0.005934	0.963258
27	0.005132	0.968390
28	0.004434	0.972825
29	0.003828	0.976652
30	0.003301	0.979953
31	0.002844	0.982798
32	0.002449	0.985247
33	0.002107	0.987354
34	0.001812	0.989165

n	P(n)	F(n)
35	0.001556	0.99072
36	0.001336	0.99205
37	0.001147	0.99320
38	0.000984	0.99418
39	0.000843	0.99503
40	0.000723	0.99575
41	0.000619	0.99637
42	0.000530	0.99690
43	0.000453	0.99735
44	0.000388	0.99774
45	0.000331	0.99807
46	0.000283	0.99835
47	0.000242	0.99860
48	0.000207	0.99880
49	0.000176	0.99898
50	0.000151	0.99913
51	0.000128	0.99926
52	0.000110	0.99937
53	0.000093	0.99946
54	0.000080	0.99954
55	0.000068	0.99961
56	0.000058	0.99967
57	0.000049	0.99972
58	0.000042	0.99976
59	0.000036	0.99979
60	0.000030	0.99982
61	0.000026	0.99985
62	0.000022	0.99987
63	0.000019	0.99989
64	0.000016	0.99991

k = 1·9
Mean = 9·98
Variance = 62·34

n	P(n)	F(n)
0	0.030749	0.03074
1	0.049075	0.07982
2	0.059773	0.13959
3	0.065273	0.20487
4	0.067165	0.27203
5	0.066574	0.33861
6	0.064311	0.40292
7	0.060967	0.46388
8	0.056973	0.52086
9	0.052643	0.57350
10	0.048200	0.62170
11	0.043801	0.66550
12	0.039552	0.70505
13	0.035524	0.74058
14	0.031758	0.77234
15	0.028278	0.8006
16	0.025089	0.82570
17	0.022191	0.84785
18	0.019572	0.86747
19	0.017220	0.88465
20	0.015115	0.89980
21	0.013241	0.91305
22	0.011577	0.92462
23	0.010106	0.93472
24	0.008807	0.94353

n	P(n)	F(n)
5	0.007664	0.951201
6	0.006661	0.957862
7	0.005782	0.963643
8	0.005013	0.968656
9	0.004341	0.972997
10	0.003756	0.976753
11	0.003247	0.980000
12	0.002804	0.982804
13	0.002420	0.985223
14	0.002086	0.987310
15	0.001797	0.989107
16	0.001548	0.990655
17	0.001332	0.991986
18	0.001145	0.993131
19	0.000984	0.994115
20	0.000845	0.994961
21	0.000726	0.995686
22	0.000623	0.996309
23	0.000534	0.996843
24	0.000458	0.997300
25	0.000392	0.997692
26	0.000336	0.998028
27	0.000287	0.998316
28	0.000246	0.998562
29	0.000210	0.998772
30	0.000180	0.998952
31	0.000154	0.999106
32	0.000131	0.999237
33	0.000112	0.999350
34	0.000096	0.999445
35	0.000082	0.999527
36	0.000070	0.999597
37	0.000060	0.999657
38	0.000051	0.999708
39	0.000043	0.999751
40	0.000037	0.999788
41	0.000032	0.999820
42	0.000027	0.999846
43	0.000023	0.999869
44	0.000019	0.999889
45	0.000017	0.999905

k = 2·0
Mean = 10·50
Variance = 65·63

P(n)	F(n)
0.025600	0.025600
0.043008	0.068608
0.054190	0.122798
0.060693	0.183491
0.063728	0.247219
0.064237	0.311456
0.062953	0.374408
0.060435	0.434843
0.057111	0.491954
0.053303	0.545257

n	P(n)	F(n)
10	0.049252	0.594509
11	0.045133	0.639642
12	0.041071	0.680713
13	0.037153	0.717866
14	0.033438	0.751304
15	0.029961	0.781265
16	0.026740	0.808005
17	0.023783	0.831787
18	0.021087	0.852875
19	0.018646	0.871520
20	0.016445	0.887966
21	0.014472	0.902438
22	0.012709	0.915147
23	0.011140	0.926286
24	0.009747	0.936034
25	0.008515	0.944549
26	0.007428	0.951977
27	0.006471	0.958447
28	0.005629	0.964077
29	0.004892	0.968968
30	0.004246	0.973214
31	0.003682	0.976896
32	0.003189	0.980085
33	0.002760	0.982845
34	0.002387	0.985232
35	0.002062	0.987294
36	0.001780	0.989075
37	0.001536	0.990610
38	0.001324	0.991935
39	0.001141	0.993075
40	0.000982	0.994057
41	0.000845	0.994903
42	0.000727	0.995629
43	0.000625	0.996254
44	0.000537	0.996791
45	0.000461	0.997252
46	0.000396	0.997647
47	0.000339	0.997987
48	0.000291	0.998278
49	0.000249	0.998527
50	0.000214	0.998741
51	0.000183	0.998924
52	0.000157	0.999080
53	0.000134	0.999214
54	0.000115	0.999329
55	0.000098	0.999427
56	0.000084	0.999511
57	0.000072	0.999583
58	0.000061	0.999644
59	0.000052	0.999697
60	0.000045	0.999741
61	0.000038	0.999779
62	0.000033	0.999812
63	0.000028	0.999840
64	0.000024	0.999864
65	0.000020	0.999884
66	0.000017	0.999901

k = 2·1
Mean = 11·03
Variance = 68·91

n	P(n)	F(n)
0	0.021313	0.021313
1	0.037597	0.058910
2	0.048951	0.107861
3	0.056196	0.164057
4	0.060186	0.224243
5	0.061678	0.285921
6	0.061308	0.347229
7	0.059592	0.406820
8	0.056940	0.463760
9	0.053675	0.517435
10	0.050047	0.567482
11	0.046243	0.613725
12	0.042405	0.656130
13	0.038634	0.694765
14	0.035003	0.729767
15	0.031558	0.761325
16	0.028332	0.789657
17	0.025338	0.814995
18	0.022585	0.837580
19	0.020070	0.857650
20	0.017786	0.875436
21	0.015723	0.891158
22	0.013867	0.905026
23	0.012206	0.917231
24	0.010723	0.927954
25	0.009403	0.937357
26	0.008233	0.945590
27	0.007197	0.952788
28	0.006283	0.959071
29	0.005478	0.964549
30	0.004770	0.969320
31	0.004149	0.973469
32	0.003605	0.977075
33	0.003129	0.980204
34	0.002714	0.982918
35	0.002351	0.985269
36	0.002035	0.987304
37	0.001761	0.989065
38	0.001522	0.990586
39	0.001314	0.991901
40	0.001134	0.993035
41	0.000978	0.994013
42	0.000843	0.994857
43	0.000727	0.995583
44	0.000626	0.996209
45	0.000538	0.996747
46	0.000463	0.997210
47	0.000398	0.997608
48	0.000342	0.997950
49	0.000294	0.998244
50	0.000252	0.998496
51	0.000216	0.998712
52	0.000186	0.998898
53	0.000159	0.999057
54	0.000136	0.999194

n	P(n)	F(n)
55	0.000117	0.999310
56	0.000100	0.999411
57	0.000086	0.999496
58	0.000073	0.999570
59	0.000063	0.999632
60	0.000054	0.999686
61	0.000046	0.999732
62	0.000039	0.999771
63	0.000034	0.999805
64	0.000029	0.999833
65	0.000024	0.999858
66	0.000021	0.999879
67	0.000018	0.999897
68	0.000015	0.999912

k=2·2
Mean=11·55
Variance=72·19

n	P(n)	F(n)
0	0.017745	0.017745
1	0.032792	0.050536
2	0.044072	0.094609
3	0.051829	0.146438
4	0.056597	0.203035
5	0.058952	0.261986
6	0.059423	0.321410
7	0.058473	0.379882
8	0.056484	0.436367
9	0.053773	0.490140
10	0.050590	0.540730
11	0.047131	0.587861
12	0.043549	0.631410
13	0.039958	0.671369
14	0.036442	0.707810
15	0.033060	0.740871
16	0.029853	0.770724
17	0.026847	0.797571
18	0.024055	0.821625
19	0.021482	0.843108
20	0.019128	0.862235
21	0.016985	0.879221
22	0.015046	0.894267
23	0.013298	0.907565
24	0.011729	0.919294
25	0.010325	0.929619
26	0.009073	0.938692
27	0.007960	0.946653
28	0.006973	0.953626
29	0.006100	0.959726
30	0.005329	0.965055
31	0.004650	0.969705
32	0.004052	0.973757
33	0.003528	0.977284
34	0.003068	0.980352
35	0.002665	0.983017
36	0.002313	0.985331
37	0.002006	0.987337
38	0.001739	0.989075
39	0.001505	0.990581

n	P(n)	F(n)
40	0.001302	0.991883
41	0.001126	0.993009
42	0.000973	0.993982
43	0.000840	0.994822
44	0.000725	0.995547
45	0.000625	0.996172
46	0.000539	0.996711
47	0.000464	0.997175
48	0.000400	0.997575
49	0.000344	0.997918
50	0.000296	0.998214
51	0.000254	0.998469
52	0.000219	0.998687
53	0.000188	0.998875
54	0.000161	0.999036
55	0.000138	0.999175
56	0.000119	0.999293
57	0.000102	0.999395
58	0.000087	0.999482
59	0.000075	0.999557
60	0.000064	0.999621
61	0.000055	0.999676
62	0.000047	0.999723
63	0.000040	0.999764
64	0.000034	0.999798
65	0.000029	0.999827
66	0.000025	0.999853
67	0.000022	0.999874
68	0.000018	0.999893
69	0.000016	0.999908

k=2·3
Mean=12·07
Variance=75·47

n	P(n)	F(n)
0	0.014773	0.014773
1	0.028542	0.043315
2	0.039559	0.082874
3	0.047629	0.130503
4	0.053011	0.183515
5	0.056107	0.239622
6	0.057341	0.296963
7	0.057112	0.354075
8	0.055770	0.409845
9	0.053614	0.463459
10	0.050890	0.514349
11	0.047800	0.562148
12	0.044501	0.606650
13	0.041119	0.647769
14	0.037747	0.685516
15	0.034456	0.719972
16	0.031295	0.751267
17	0.028298	0.779565
18	0.025487	0.805051
19	0.022874	0.827925
20	0.020463	0.848388
21	0.018253	0.866641
22	0.016238	0.882879
23	0.014411	0.897290
24	0.012761	0.910051

n	P(n)	F(n)
25	0.011277	0.921328
26	0.009946	0.931274
27	0.008757	0.940031
28	0.007697	0.947729
29	0.006756	0.954484
30	0.005921	0.960405
31	0.005182	0.965587
32	0.004530	0.970116
33	0.003955	0.974071
34	0.003449	0.977520
35	0.003005	0.980525
36	0.002615	0.983140
37	0.002274	0.985414
38	0.001975	0.987390
39	0.001715	0.989104
40	0.001487	0.990591
41	0.001289	0.991880
42	0.001116	0.992996
43	0.000966	0.993962
44	0.000835	0.994798
45	0.000722	0.995519
46	0.000624	0.996143
47	0.000538	0.996681
48	0.000464	0.997146
49	0.000400	0.997546
50	0.000345	0.997891
51	0.000297	0.998189
52	0.000256	0.998445
53	0.000220	0.998665
54	0.000189	0.998854
55	0.000163	0.999017
56	0.000140	0.999157
57	0.000120	0.999278
58	0.000103	0.999381
59	0.000089	0.999470
60	0.000076	0.999546
61	0.000065	0.999611
62	0.000056	0.999667
63	0.000048	0.999715
64	0.000041	0.999756
65	0.000035	0.999792
66	0.000030	0.999822
67	0.000026	0.999848
68	0.000022	0.999870
69	0.000019	0.999889
70	0.000016	0.999905

k=2·4
Mean=12·60
Variance=78·75

n	P(n)	F(n)
0	0.012300	0.012300
1	0.024796	0.037099
2	0.035408	0.072507
3	0.043623	0.116127
4	0.049469	0.165590

n	P(n)	F(n)
5	0.053189	0.218784
6	0.055104	0.273888
7	0.055544	0.329432
8	0.054822	0.384255
9	0.053214	0.437469
10	0.050958	0.488427
11	0.048252	0.536679
12	0.045261	0.581940
13	0.042113	0.624053
14	0.038913	0.662966
15	0.035738	0.698704
16	0.032646	0.731350
17	0.029681	0.761031
18	0.026871	0.787903
19	0.024235	0.812138
20	0.021783	0.833920
21	0.019517	0.853438
22	0.017438	0.870875
23	0.015539	0.886415
24	0.013814	0.900229
25	0.012254	0.912483
26	0.010848	0.923330
27	0.009584	0.932915
28	0.008453	0.941368
29	0.007444	0.948812
30	0.006545	0.955357
31	0.005746	0.961102
32	0.005038	0.966140
33	0.004411	0.970551
34	0.003858	0.974409
35	0.003370	0.977779
36	0.002941	0.980720
37	0.002564	0.983284
38	0.002233	0.985517
39	0.001943	0.987460
40	0.001689	0.989149
41	0.001468	0.990617
42	0.001274	0.991891
43	0.001105	0.992996
44	0.000958	0.993953
45	0.000829	0.994783
46	0.000718	0.995500
47	0.000621	0.996121
48	0.000537	0.996658
49	0.000464	0.997122
50	0.000401	0.997523
51	0.000346	0.997868
52	0.000298	0.998167
53	0.000257	0.998424
54	0.000222	0.998645
55	0.000191	0.998836
56	0.000164	0.999000
57	0.000141	0.999142
58	0.000122	0.999263
59	0.000105	0.999368
60	0.000090	0.999458
61	0.000077	0.999535
62	0.000066	0.999602
63	0.000057	0.999659
64	0.000049	0.999708
65	0.000042	0.999750
66	0.000036	0.999786
67	0.000031	0.999816
68	0.000026	0.999843
69	0.000023	0.999866
70	0.000019	0.999885
71	0.000017	0.999902

k = 2·5
Mean = 13·12
Variance = 82·03

n	P(n)	F(n)
0	0.010240	0.010240
1	0.021504	0.031744
2	0.031611	0.063355
3	0.039830	0.103185
4	0.046003	0.149188
5	0.050236	0.199424
6	0.052747	0.252171
7	0.053802	0.305973
8	0.053668	0.359641
9	0.052594	0.412236
10	0.050806	0.463042
11	0.048497	0.511539
12	0.045830	0.557368
13	0.042939	0.600307
14	0.039933	0.640240
15	0.036898	0.677138
16	0.033900	0.711039
17	0.030989	0.742027
18	0.028200	0.770227
19	0.025558	0.795785
20	0.023079	0.818864
21	0.020771	0.839635
22	0.018637	0.858272
23	0.016676	0.874948
24	0.014884	0.889831
25	0.013252	0.903084
26	0.011774	0.914858
27	0.010440	0.925298
28	0.009239	0.934537
29	0.008162	0.942699
30	0.007199	0.949898
31	0.006340	0.956238
32	0.005575	0.961813
33	0.004896	0.966709
34	0.004294	0.971003
35	0.003762	0.974765
36	0.003291	0.978057
37	0.002877	0.980933
38	0.002512	0.983445
39	0.002191	0.985637
40	0.001910	0.987546
41	0.001663	0.989209
42	0.001447	0.990656
43	0.001258	0.991913
44	0.001092	0.993006
45	0.000948	0.993954
46	0.000822	0.994776
47	0.000713	0.995489
48	0.000618	0.996107
49	0.000535	0.996641
50	0.000463	0.997104
51	0.000400	0.997504
52	0.000346	0.997849
53	0.000299	0.998148
54	0.000258	0.998406
55	0.000222	0.998628
56	0.000192	0.998820
57	0.000165	0.998985
58	0.000143	0.999128
59	0.000123	0.999251
60	0.000106	0.999356
61	0.000091	0.999447
62	0.000078	0.999526
63	0.000067	0.999593
64	0.000058	0.999651
65	0.000050	0.999700
66	0.000043	0.999743
67	0.000037	0.999780
68	0.000031	0.999811
69	0.000027	0.999838
70	0.000023	0.999862
71	0.000020	0.999881
72	0.000017	0.999899
73	0.000015	0.999913

k = 0·1
Mean = 0·46
Variance = 2·53

n	P(n)	F(n)
0	0.842417	0.842417
1	0.069078	0.911495
2	0.031154	0.942650
3	0.017883	0.960532
4	0.011364	0.971897
5	0.007641	0.979538
6	0.005326	0.984864
7	0.003806	0.988670
8	0.002770	0.991440
9	0.002044	0.993484
10	0.001525	0.995009
11	0.001148	0.996157
12	0.000871	0.997028
13	0.000665	0.997693
14	0.000510	0.998203
15	0.000393	0.998596
16	0.000304	0.998901
17	0.000236	0.999137
18	0.000184	0.999321
19	0.000144	0.999465
20	0.000113	0.999578
21	0.000088	0.999666
22	0.000070	0.999735
23	0.000055	0.999790
24	0.000043	0.999833
25	0.000034	0.999868
26	0.000027	0.999895
27	0.000021	0.999916

k = 0·2
Mean = 0·91
Variance = 5·06

n	P(n)	F(n)
0	0.709667	0.709667
1	0.116385	0.826052
2	0.057262	0.883314
3	0.034433	0.917747
4	0.022588	0.940335
5	0.015559	0.955894
6	0.011057	0.966951
7	0.008031	0.974982
8	0.005927	0.980908
9	0.004428	0.985336
10	0.003340	0.988677
11	0.002540	0.991217
12	0.001944	0.993160
13	0.001496	0.994656
14	0.001157	0.995813
15	0.000898	0.996711
16	0.000699	0.997410
17	0.000546	0.997956
18	0.000428	0.998385
19	0.000336	0.998721

n	P(n)	F(n)
20	0.000265	0.998986
21	0.000209	0.999195
22	0.000165	0.999360
23	0.000131	0.999490
24	0.000104	0.999594
25	0.000082	0.999676
26	0.000065	0.999741
27	0.000052	0.999793
28	0.000041	0.999835
29	0.000033	0.999868
30	0.000026	0.999894
31	0.000021	0.999915

k = 0·3
Mean = 1·37
Variance = 7·59

n	P(n)	F(n)
0	0.597836	0.597836
1	0.147068	0.744903
2	0.078387	0.823290
3	0.049279	0.872569
4	0.033337	0.905907
5	0.023510	0.929416
6	0.017029	0.946445
7	0.012567	0.959012
8	0.009403	0.968416
9	0.007111	0.975527
10	0.005423	0.980950
11	0.004164	0.985114
12	0.003215	0.988329
13	0.002494	0.990823
14	0.001943	0.992766
15	0.001519	0.994286
16	0.001191	0.995477
17	0.000937	0.996413
18	0.000738	0.997151
19	0.000583	0.997734
20	0.000461	0.998195
21	0.000366	0.998561
22	0.000290	0.998851
23	0.000231	0.999082
24	0.000184	0.999266
25	0.000146	0.999412
26	0.000117	0.999529
27	0.000093	0.999622
28	0.000075	0.999697
29	0.000060	0.999757
30	0.000048	0.999805
31	0.000038	0.999843
32	0.000031	0.999874
33	0.000025	0.999898
34	0.000020	0.999918

k = 0·4
Mean = 1·82
Variance = 10·12

n	P(n)	F(n)
0	0.503627	0.503627
1	0.165190	0.668817
2	0.094819	0.763636
3	0.062201	0.825837
4	0.043354	0.869191
5	0.031284	0.900475
6	0.023088	0.923563
7	0.017309	0.940873
8	0.013129	0.954002
9	0.010048	0.964050
10	0.007745	0.971795
11	0.006005	0.977799
12	0.004678	0.982477
13	0.003659	0.986136
14	0.002871	0.989007
15	0.002260	0.991268
16	0.001784	0.993052
17	0.001411	0.994463
18	0.001119	0.995581
19	0.000888	0.996470
20	0.000707	0.997176
21	0.000563	0.997739
22	0.000449	0.998188
23	0.000359	0.998547
24	0.000287	0.998833
25	0.000229	0.999063
26	0.000184	0.999247
27	0.000147	0.999394
28	0.000118	0.999512
29	0.000095	0.999607
30	0.000076	0.999683
31	0.000061	0.999745
32	0.000049	0.999794
33	0.000040	0.999834
34	0.000032	0.999866
35	0.000026	0.999892
36	0.000021	0.999912

k = 0·5
Mean = 2·28
Variance = 12·65

n	P(n)	F(n)
0	0.424264	0.424264
1	0.173948	0.598212
2	0.106978	0.705191
3	0.073102	0.778292
4	0.052451	0.830743
5	0.038708	0.869451
6	0.029096	0.898547
7	0.022154	0.920702
8	0.017031	0.937733
9	0.013190	0.950923

n	P(n)	F(n)
10	0.010275	0.961197
11	0.008042	0.969240
12	0.006320	0.975560
13	0.004983	0.980543
14	0.003940	0.984483
15	0.003123	0.987606
16	0.002481	0.990087
17	0.001975	0.992062
18	0.001574	0.993636
19	0.001257	0.994893
20	0.001005	0.995898
21	0.000804	0.996702
22	0.000645	0.997347
23	0.000517	0.997864
24	0.000415	0.998279
25	0.000334	0.998613
26	0.000268	0.998881
27	0.000216	0.999097
28	0.000174	0.999271
29	0.000140	0.999411
30	0.000113	0.999524
31	0.000091	0.999615
32	0.000074	0.999689
33	0.000059	0.999748
34	0.000048	0.999796
35	0.000039	0.999835
36	0.000031	0.999866
37	0.000025	0.999892
38	0.000021	0.999912

k=0.6
Mean=2.73
Variance=15.19

n	P(n)	F(n)
0	0.357407	0.357407
1	0.175844	0.533252
2	0.115354	0.648606
3	0.081978	0.730584
4	0.060500	0.791084
5	0.045641	0.836725
6	0.034931	0.871656
7	0.027006	0.898662
8	0.021038	0.919700
9	0.016484	0.936185
10	0.012977	0.949161
11	0.010254	0.959415
12	0.008128	0.967543
13	0.006460	0.974003
14	0.005146	0.979148
15	0.004107	0.983255
16	0.003283	0.986539
17	0.002629	0.989168
18	0.002108	0.991276
19	0.001692	0.992968
20	0.001360	0.994328
21	0.001094	0.995421
22	0.000881	0.996302
23	0.000710	0.997012
24	0.000572	0.997584
25	0.000462	0.998045
26	0.000373	0.998418
27	0.000301	0.998719
28	0.000243	0.998963
29	0.000197	0.999159
30	0.000159	0.999319
31	0.000129	0.999448
32	0.000104	0.999552
33	0.000085	0.999636
34	0.000069	0.999705
35	0.000056	0.999760
36	0.000045	0.999806
37	0.000037	0.999842
38	0.000030	0.999872
39	0.000024	0.999896
40	0.000020	0.999915

k=0.7
Mean=3.19
Variance=17.72

n	P(n)	F(n)
0	0.301086	0.301086
1	0.172823	0.473910
2	0.120458	0.594368
3	0.088898	0.683265
4	0.067429	0.750695
5	0.051974	0.802669
6	0.040488	0.843157
7	0.031777	0.874934
8	0.025080	0.900014
9	0.019880	0.919895
10	0.015813	0.935708
11	0.012613	0.948320
12	0.010084	0.958404
13	0.008078	0.966482
14	0.006482	0.972964
15	0.005209	0.978173
16	0.004191	0.982365
17	0.003376	0.985741
18	0.002722	0.988463
19	0.002197	0.990660
20	0.001775	0.992435
21	0.001434	0.993869
22	0.001160	0.995029
23	0.000939	0.995968
24	0.000760	0.996728
25	0.000616	0.997344
26	0.000499	0.997844
27	0.000405	0.998249
28	0.000328	0.998577
29	0.000267	0.998843
30	0.000216	0.999060
31	0.000176	0.999235
32	0.000143	0.999378
33	0.000116	0.999494
34	0.000094	0.999588

k=0.8
Mean=3.64
Variance=20.25

n	P(n)	F(n)
0	0.253640	0.253640
1	0.166388	0.420028
2	0.122794	0.542822
3	0.093979	0.636801
4	0.073209	0.710010
5	0.057630	0.767641
6	0.045682	0.813322
7	0.036389	0.849711
8	0.029093	0.878804
9	0.023326	0.902130
10	0.018745	0.920874
11	0.015091	0.935966
12	0.012169	0.948134
13	0.009825	0.957959
14	0.007941	0.965900
15	0.006425	0.972325
16	0.005203	0.977528
17	0.004216	0.981744
18	0.003419	0.985162
19	0.002774	0.987936
20	0.002252	0.990188
21	0.001829	0.992017
22	0.001486	0.993503
23	0.001208	0.994711
24	0.000982	0.995693
25	0.000799	0.996492
26	0.000650	0.997142
27	0.000529	0.997671
28	0.000431	0.998102
29	0.000351	0.998453
30	0.000286	0.998739
31	0.000233	0.998971
32	0.000190	0.999161
33	0.000155	0.999316
34	0.000126	0.999442
35	0.000103	0.999545
36	0.000084	0.999628
37	0.000068	0.999697
38	0.000056	0.999752
39	0.000045	0.999798
40	0.000037	0.999835
41	0.000030	0.999865
42	0.000025	0.999890
43	0.000020	0.999910

k = 0·9
Mean = 4·10
Variance = 22·78

n	P(n)	F(n)
0	0.213671	0.213671
1	0.157689	0.371360
2	0.122840	0.494200
3	0.097371	0.591571
4	0.077848	0.669419
5	0.062559	0.731978
6	0.050443	0.782421
7	0.040773	0.823193
8	0.033016	0.856209
9	0.026772	0.882981
10	0.021733	0.904714
11	0.017659	0.922374
12	0.014360	0.936734
13	0.011685	0.948418
14	0.009513	0.957931
15	0.007749	0.965680
16	0.006314	0.971994
17	0.005147	0.977141
18	0.004197	0.981339
19	0.003424	0.984762
20	0.002793	0.987556
21	0.002280	0.989835
22	0.001861	0.991696
23	0.001519	0.993215
24	0.001241	0.994456
25	0.001013	0.995469
26	0.000828	0.996297
27	0.000676	0.996973
28	0.000552	0.997525
29	0.000451	0.997977
30	0.000369	0.998346
31	0.000302	0.998647
32	0.000247	0.998894
33	0.000202	0.999095
34	0.000165	0.999260
35	0.000135	0.999395
36	0.000110	0.999505
37	0.000090	0.999595
38	0.000074	0.999669
39	0.000060	0.999729
40	0.000049	0.999778
41	0.000040	0.999819
42	0.000033	0.999851
43	0.000027	0.999878
44	0.000022	0.999901

k = 1·0
Mean = 4·56
Variance = 25·31

n	P(n)	F(n)
0	0.180000	0.180000
1	0.147600	0.327600
2	0.121032	0.448632
3	0.099246	0.547878
4	0.081382	0.629260

k = 0·9 (continued)

n	P(n)	F(n)
5	0.066733	0.695993
6	0.054721	0.750715
7	0.044871	0.795586
8	0.036795	0.832380
9	0.030172	0.862552
10	0.024741	0.887293
11	0.020287	0.907580
12	0.016636	0.924216
13	0.013641	0.937857
14	0.011186	0.949043
15	0.009172	0.958215
16	0.007521	0.965736
17	0.006167	0.971904
18	0.005057	0.976961
19	0.004147	0.981108
20	0.003401	0.984509
21	0.002788	0.987297
22	0.002287	0.989584
23	0.001875	0.991459
24	0.001537	0.992996
25	0.001261	0.994257
26	0.001034	0.995291
27	0.000848	0.996138
28	0.000695	0.996833
29	0.000570	0.997403
30	0.000467	0.997871
31	0.000383	0.998254
32	0.000314	0.998568
33	0.000258	0.998826
34	0.000211	0.999037
35	0.000173	0.999211
36	0.000142	0.999353
37	0.000117	0.999469
38	0.000096	0.999565
39	0.000078	0.999643
40	0.000064	0.999707
41	0.000053	0.999760
42	0.000043	0.999803
43	0.000035	0.999839
44	0.000029	0.999868
45	0.000024	0.999891
46	0.000020	0.999911

k = 1·1
Mean = 5·01
Variance = 27·84

n	P(n)	F(n)
0	0.151635	0.151635
1	0.136775	0.288410
2	0.117763	0.406173
3	0.099785	0.505958
4	0.083869	0.589827
5	0.070148	0.659975
6	0.058480	0.718455
7	0.048639	0.767094
8	0.040382	0.807476
9	0.033481	0.840957
10	0.027729	0.868687
11	0.022945	0.891631
12	0.018971	0.910603
13	0.015676	0.926279
14	0.012946	0.939225
15	0.010687	0.949912
16	0.008818	0.958730
17	0.007273	0.966003
18	0.005997	0.972001
19	0.004944	0.976944
20	0.004074	0.981018
21	0.003357	0.984375
22	0.002765	0.987140
23	0.002277	0.989417
24	0.001875	0.991292
25	0.001544	0.992835
26	0.001271	0.994106
27	0.001046	0.995152
28	0.000861	0.996012
29	0.000708	0.996721
30	0.000583	0.997303
31	0.000479	0.997783
32	0.000394	0.998177
33	0.000324	0.998501
34	0.000267	0.998768
35	0.000219	0.998987
36	0.000180	0.999167
37	0.000148	0.999316
38	0.000122	0.999437
39	0.000100	0.999538
40	0.000082	0.999620
41	0.000068	0.999688
42	0.000056	0.999743
43	0.000046	0.999789
44	0.000038	0.999827
45	0.000031	0.999858
46	0.000025	0.999883
47	0.000021	0.999904

k = 1·2
Mean = 5·47
Variance = 30·37

n	P(n)	F(n)
0	0.127740	0.127740
1	0.125696	0.253436
2	0.113378	0.366814
3	0.099168	0.465982
4	0.085384	0.551366
5	0.072815	0.624181
6	0.061699	0.685879
7	0.052038	0.737918
8	0.043738	0.781656
9	0.036662	0.818319
10	0.030664	0.848983
11	0.025602	0.874585
12	0.021344	0.895929
13	0.017771	0.913700
14	0.014780	0.928480

n	P(n)	F(n)	n	P(n)	F(n)	n	P(n)	F(n)
15	0.012282	0.940761	20	0.005618	0.972601	20	0.006486	0.967627
16	0.010197	0.950958	21	0.004673	0.977274	21	0.005420	0.973047
17	0.008460	0.959418	22	0.003884	0.981158	22	0.004525	0.977573
18	0.007014	0.966432	23	0.003226	0.984384	23	0.003775	0.981348
19	0.005812	0.972244	24	0.002679	0.987063	24	0.003147	0.984495
20	0.004814	0.977057	25	0.002223	0.989286	25	0.002622	0.987117
21	0.003985	0.981042	26	0.001844	0.991130	26	0.002183	0.989301
22	0.003297	0.984339	27	0.001529	0.992658	27	0.001817	0.991117
23	0.002727	0.987066	28	0.001267	0.993925	28	0.001511	0.992628
24	0.002255	0.989321	29	0.001050	0.994975	29	0.001256	0.993885
25	0.001864	0.991185	30	0.000869	0.995844	30	0.001044	0.994928
26	0.001540	0.992725	31	0.000720	0.996564	31	0.000867	0.995795
27	0.001272	0.993997	32	0.000596	0.997160	32	0.000720	0.996515
28	0.001051	0.995048	33	0.000493	0.997653	33	0.000597	0.997113
29	0.000867	0.995916	34	0.000408	0.998060	34	0.000496	0.997608
30	0.000716	0.996632	35	0.000337	0.998398	35	0.000411	0.998019
31	0.000591	0.997223	36	0.000279	0.998677	36	0.000341	0.998360
32	0.000488	0.997710	37	0.000231	0.998907	37	0.000282	0.998642
33	0.000402	0.998113	38	0.000191	0.999098	38	0.000234	0.998876
34	0.000332	0.998444	39	0.000157	0.999255	39	0.000194	0.999070
35	0.000274	0.998718	40	0.000130	0.999385	40	0.000161	0.999231
36	0.000226	0.998944	41	0.000107	0.999492	41	0.000133	0.999364
37	0.000186	0.999130	42	0.000089	0.999581	42	0.000110	0.999474
38	0.000153	0.999283	43	0.000073	0.999654	43	0.000091	0.999565
39	0.000126	0.999409	44	0.000060	0.999715	44	0.000075	0.999641
40	0.000104	0.999514	45	0.000050	0.999765	45	0.000062	0.999703
41	0.000086	0.999599	46	0.000041	0.999806	46	0.000052	0.999754
42	0.000071	0.999670	47	0.000034	0.999840	47	0.000043	0.999797
43	0.000058	0.999728	48	0.000028	0.999868	48	0.000035	0.999832
44	0.000048	0.999776	49	0.000023	0.999891	49	0.000029	0.999862
45	0.000040	0.999816	50	0.000019	0.999910	50	0.000024	0.999886
46	0.000033	0.999848				51	0.000020	0.999906
47	0.000027	0.999875						
48	0.000022	0.999897						
49	0.000018	0.999915						

k=1·3
Mean = 5·92
Variance = 32·90

k=1·4
Mean = 6·38
Variance = 35·43

k=1·5
Mean = 6·83
Variance = 37·96

n	P(n)	F(n)	n	P(n)	F(n)	n	P(n)	F(n)
0	0.107610	0.107610	0	0.090653	0.090653	0	0.076368	0.076368
1	0.114713	0.222323	1	0.104069	0.194722	1	0.093932	0.170300
2	0.108174	0.330497	2	0.102404	0.297127	2	0.096280	0.266580
3	0.097573	0.428070	3	0.095168	0.392295	3	0.092108	0.358688
4	0.086011	0.514081	4	0.085841	0.478136	4	0.084970	0.443658
5	0.074760	0.588841	5	0.076021	0.554157	5	0.076643	0.520301
6	0.064369	0.653210	6	0.066493	0.620650	6	0.068084	0.588385
7	0.055044	0.708254	7	0.057640	0.678290	7	0.059817	0.648202
8	0.046829	0.755083	8	0.049628	0.727918	8	0.052116	0.700318
9	0.039680	0.794763	9	0.042504	0.770422	9	0.045109	0.745427
10	0.033514	0.828277	10	0.036247	0.806669	10	0.038839	0.784265
11	0.028231	0.856507	11	0.030803	0.837473	11	0.033295	0.817561
12	0.023728	0.880235	12	0.026101	0.863573	12	0.028440	0.846000
13	0.019906	0.900141	13	0.022061	0.885635	13	0.024218	0.870218
14	0.016673	0.916814	14	0.018607	0.904242	14	0.020568	0.890786
15	0.013945	0.930759	15	0.015665	0.919906	15	0.017428	0.908213
16	0.011649	0.942408	16	0.013166	0.933072	16	0.014737	0.922951
17	0.009721	0.952129	17	0.011050	0.944123	17	0.012440	0.935391
18	0.008104	0.960233	18	0.009263	0.953385	18	0.010484	0.945875
19	0.006750	0.966983	19	0.007755	0.961140	19	0.008823	0.954698

20	0.007416	0.962114	20	0.008404	0.956045	20	0.009446	0.949404
21	0.006226	0.968340	21	0.007088	0.963132	21	0.008004	0.957408
22	0.005221	0.973561	22	0.005971	0.969103	22	0.006772	0.964180
23	0.004374	0.977936	23	0.005024	0.974127	23	0.005722	0.969902
24	0.003662	0.981597	24	0.004222	0.978349	24	0.004829	0.974730
25	0.003063	0.984660	25	0.003545	0.981894	25	0.004071	0.978801
26	0.002560	0.987220	26	0.002974	0.984869	26	0.003428	0.982229
27	0.002138	0.989358	27	0.002493	0.987362	27	0.002884	0.985112
28	0.001784	0.991142	28	0.002088	0.989450	28	0.002424	0.987536
29	0.001488	0.992630	29	0.001748	0.991198	29	0.002035	0.989571
30	0.001241	0.993871	30	0.001462	0.992659	30	0.001708	0.991279
31	0.001034	0.994905	31	0.001222	0.993881	31	0.001432	0.992711
32	0.000861	0.995766	32	0.001021	0.994902	32	0.001200	0.993911
33	0.000717	0.996483	33	0.000852	0.995754	33	0.001005	0.994916
34	0.000596	0.997079	34	0.000711	0.996465	34	0.000841	0.995757
35	0.000496	0.997575	35	0.000593	0.997058	35	0.000703	0.996461
36	0.000412	0.997988	36	0.000494	0.997553	36	0.000588	0.997049
37	0.000343	0.998330	37	0.000412	0.997965	37	0.000491	0.997540
38	0.000285	0.998615	38	0.000343	0.998308	38	0.000410	0.997950
39	0.000236	0.998852	39	0.000286	0.998594	39	0.000342	0.998293
40	0.000196	0.999048	40	0.000238	0.998832	40	0.000286	0.998578
41	0.000163	0.999211	41	0.000198	0.999030	41	0.000238	0.998817
42	0.000135	0.999346	42	0.000165	0.999194	42	0.000199	0.999015
43	0.000112	0.999458	43	0.000137	0.999331	43	0.000166	0.999181
44	0.000093	0.999551	44	0.000114	0.999445	44	0.000138	0.999319
45	0.000077	0.999628	45	0.000095	0.999539	45	0.000115	0.999434
46	0.000064	0.999692	46	0.000079	0.999618	46	0.000096	0.999529
47	0.000053	0.999745	47	0.000065	0.999683	47	0.000080	0.999609
48	0.000044	0.999789	48	0.000054	0.999737	48	0.000066	0.999675
49	0.000036	0.999826	49	0.000045	0.999782	49	0.000055	0.999730
50	0.000030	0.999856	50	0.000037	0.999819	50	0.000046	0.999776
51	0.000025	0.999881	51	0.000031	0.999850	51	0.000038	0.999814
52	0.000021	0.999901	52	0.000026	0.999876	52	0.000032	0.999846
			53	0.000021	0.999897	53	0.000026	0.999872
			54	0.000018	0.999915	54	0.000022	0.999894
						55	0.000018	0.999912

k=1·6
Mean=7·29
Variance=40·49

n	P(n)	F(n)	n	P(n)	F(n)
0	0.064333	0.064333	0	0.054196	0.054196
1	0.084405	0.148739	1	0.075549	0.129744
2	0.089976	0.238715	2	0.083632	0.213376
3	0.088536	0.327251	3	0.084580	0.297956
4	0.083490	0.410741	4	0.081493	0.379449
5	0.076677	0.487418	5	0.076180	0.455629
6	0.069163	0.556581	6	0.069755	0.525384
7	0.061575	0.618156	7	0.062919	0.588303
8	0.054278	0.672434	8	0.056108	0.644411
9	0.047475	0.719909	9	0.049587	0.693998
10	0.041265	0.761174	10	0.043508	0.737506
11	0.035683	0.796857	11	0.037947	0.775452
12	0.030723	0.827581	12	0.032931	0.808384
13	0.026356	0.853937	13	0.028458	0.836841
14	0.022538	0.876475	14	0.024502	0.861344
15	0.019220	0.895695	15	0.021029	0.882373
16	0.016352	0.912047	16	0.017999	0.900371
17	0.013882	0.925929	17	0.015366	0.915738
18	0.011762	0.937691	18	0.013091	0.928829
19	0.009950	0.947641	19	0.011130	0.939958

(middle column header) k=1·7
Mean=7·74
Variance=43·02

k=1·8
Mean=8·20
Variance=45·56

n	P(n)	F(n)
0	0.045655	0.045655
1	0.067387	0.113042
2	0.077360	0.190403
3	0.080352	0.270754
4	0.079066	0.349820
5	0.075208	0.425028
6	0.069893	0.494921
7	0.063862	0.558783
8	0.057604	0.616387
9	0.051434	0.667821
10	0.045550	0.713370
11	0.040067	0.753437
12	0.035045	0.788483
13	0.030506	0.818989
14	0.026444	0.845433

n	P(n)	F(n)
15	0.022841	0.868273
16	0.019666	0.887939
17	0.016885	0.904824
18	0.014461	0.919285
19	0.012357	0.931642
20	0.010538	0.942180
21	0.008971	0.951151
22	0.007623	0.958774
23	0.006469	0.965243
24	0.005481	0.970724
25	0.004638	0.975362
26	0.003920	0.979282
27	0.003310	0.982592
28	0.002792	0.985384
29	0.002352	0.987736
30	0.001980	0.989717
31	0.001666	0.991383
32	0.001400	0.992783
33	0.001176	0.993959
34	0.000987	0.994946
35	0.000828	0.995773
36	0.000694	0.996467
37	0.000581	0.997049
38	0.000487	0.997535
39	0.000407	0.997943
40	0.000341	0.998283
41	0.000285	0.998568
42	0.000238	0.998806
43	0.000199	0.999005
44	0.000166	0.999171
45	0.000138	0.999309
46	0.000116	0.999425
47	0.000096	0.999521
48	0.000080	0.999601
49	0.000067	0.999668
50	0.000056	0.999724
51	0.000046	0.999771
52	0.000039	0.999809
53	0.000032	0.999841
54	0.000027	0.999868
55	0.000022	0.999891
56	0.000019	0.999909

k=1.9
Mean=8.66
Variance=48.09

n	P(n)	F(n)
0	0.038461	0.038461
1	0.059922	0.098383
2	0.071247	0.169630
3	0.075949	0.245579
4	0.076291	0.321870
5	0.073819	0.395690
6	0.069612	0.465301
7	0.064421	0.529722
8	0.058768	0.588489
9	0.053008	0.641498

n	P(n)	F(n)
10	0.047379	0.688877
11	0.042029	0.730906
12	0.037049	0.767955
13	0.032483	0.800439
14	0.028349	0.828787
15	0.024641	0.853428
16	0.021342	0.874770
17	0.018427	0.893197
18	0.015866	0.909062
19	0.013626	0.922688
20	0.011676	0.934364
21	0.009985	0.944349
22	0.008522	0.952872
23	0.007262	0.960133
24	0.006178	0.966311
25	0.005248	0.971560
26	0.004453	0.976012
27	0.003773	0.979785
28	0.003193	0.982978
29	0.002700	0.985678
30	0.002280	0.987958
31	0.001924	0.989882
32	0.001622	0.991504
33	0.001366	0.992871
34	0.001150	0.994021
35	0.000967	0.994988
36	0.000813	0.995801
37	0.000683	0.996484
38	0.000573	0.997057
39	0.000481	0.997538
40	0.000403	0.997941
41	0.000338	0.998279
42	0.000283	0.998562
43	0.000237	0.998799
44	0.000198	0.998997
45	0.000166	0.999163
46	0.000139	0.999302
47	0.000116	0.999418
48	0.000097	0.999514
49	0.000081	0.999595
50	0.000067	0.999663
51	0.000056	0.999719
52	0.000047	0.999766
53	0.000039	0.999805
54	0.000033	0.999838
55	0.000027	0.999865
56	0.000023	0.999888
57	0.000019	0.999907

k=2.0
Mean=9.11
Variance=50.62

n	P(n)	F(n)
0	0.032400	0.032400
1	0.053136	0.085536
2	0.065357	0.150893
3	0.071457	0.222351
4	0.073244	0.295594

n	P(n)	F(n)
5	0.072072	0.367666
6	0.068949	0.436615
7	0.064615	0.501230
8	0.059607	0.560837
9	0.054309	0.615146
10	0.048986	0.664132
11	0.043821	0.707953
12	0.038927	0.746880
13	0.034376	0.781256
14	0.030202	0.811457
15	0.026416	0.837874
16	0.023015	0.860889
17	0.019983	0.880872
18	0.017296	0.898168
19	0.014929	0.913097
20	0.012854	0.925951
21	0.011042	0.936993
22	0.009466	0.946460
23	0.008100	0.954559
24	0.006919	0.961478
25	0.005900	0.967378
26	0.005024	0.972402
27	0.004272	0.976675
28	0.003629	0.980303
29	0.003078	0.983381
30	0.002608	0.985989
31	0.002208	0.988197
32	0.001867	0.990064
33	0.001577	0.991641
34	0.001331	0.992972
35	0.001123	0.994095
36	0.000946	0.995042
37	0.000797	0.995839
38	0.000671	0.996509
39	0.000564	0.997073
40	0.000474	0.997547
41	0.000398	0.997946
42	0.000334	0.998280
43	0.000281	0.998561
44	0.000235	0.998796
45	0.000197	0.998993
46	0.000165	0.999158
47	0.000138	0.999297
48	0.000116	0.999413
49	0.000097	0.999509
50	0.000081	0.999590
51	0.000068	0.999658
52	0.000057	0.999715
53	0.000047	0.999762
54	0.000040	0.999802
55	0.000033	0.999835
56	0.000028	0.999862
57	0.000023	0.999885
58	0.000019	0.999904

k = 2·1
Mean = 9·57
Variance = 53·15

n	P(n)	F(n)
0	0.027294	0.027294
1	0.047001	0.074295
2	0.059738	0.134033
3	0.066946	0.200980
4	0.069992	0.270972
5	0.070020	0.340993
6	0.067943	0.408936
7	0.064468	0.473404
8	0.060133	0.533537
9	0.055336	0.588873
10	0.050366	0.639239
11	0.045431	0.684670
12	0.040668	0.725338
13	0.036169	0.761507
14	0.031989	0.793496
15	0.028155	0.821651
16	0.024674	0.846326
17	0.021542	0.867868
18	0.018744	0.886611
19	0.016260	0.902871
20	0.014066	0.916938
21	0.012139	0.929076
22	0.010451	0.939528
23	0.008980	0.948508
24	0.007701	0.956209
25	0.006593	0.962802
26	0.005635	0.968437
27	0.004809	0.973245
28	0.004098	0.977343
29	0.003488	0.980831
30	0.002965	0.983796
31	0.002518	0.986314
32	0.002135	0.988449
33	0.001809	0.990258
34	0.001532	0.991790
35	0.001295	0.993086
36	0.001095	0.994180
37	0.000924	0.995105
38	0.000780	0.995885
39	0.000658	0.996542
40	0.000554	0.997096
41	0.000466	0.997563
42	0.000393	0.997955
43	0.000330	0.998285
44	0.000277	0.998563
45	0.000233	0.998796
46	0.000196	0.998992
47	0.000164	0.999156
48	0.000138	0.999294
49	0.000115	0.999409
50	0.000097	0.999506
51	0.000081	0.999587
52	0.000068	0.999655
53	0.000057	0.999712
54	0.000048	0.999759

n	P(n)	F(n)
55	0.000040	0.999799
56	0.000033	0.999832
57	0.000028	0.999860
58	0.000023	0.999883
59	0.000019	0.999903

k = 2·2
Mean = 10·02
Variance = 55·68

n	P(n)	F(n)
0	0.022993	0.022993
1	0.041480	0.064473
2	0.054421	0.118894
3	0.062476	0.181370
4	0.066599	0.247969
5	0.067718	0.315687
6	0.066635	0.382322
7	0.064007	0.446329
8	0.060359	0.506688
9	0.056093	0.562782
10	0.051516	0.614298
11	0.046852	0.661150
12	0.042260	0.703410
13	0.037852	0.741262
14	0.033699	0.774961
15	0.029844	0.804805
16	0.026308	0.831113
17	0.023095	0.854208
18	0.020200	0.874408
19	0.017610	0.892019
20	0.015307	0.907326
21	0.013269	0.920595
22	0.011474	0.932069
23	0.009900	0.941968
24	0.008524	0.950492
25	0.007325	0.957817
26	0.006284	0.964100
27	0.005382	0.969482
28	0.004602	0.974084
29	0.003930	0.978013
30	0.003351	0.981365
31	0.002854	0.984219
32	0.002428	0.986648
33	0.002064	0.988711
34	0.001752	0.990463
35	0.001486	0.991949
36	0.001259	0.993208
37	0.001066	0.994274
38	0.000902	0.995176
39	0.000762	0.995938
40	0.000644	0.996581
41	0.000543	0.997125
42	0.000458	0.997583
43	0.000386	0.997969
44	0.000325	0.998294
45	0.000274	0.998568
46	0.000230	0.998799
47	0.000194	0.998992
48	0.000163	0.999155
49	0.000137	0.999292

n	P(n)	F(n)
50	0.000115	0.999407
51	0.000096	0.999503
52	0.000081	0.999584
53	0.000068	0.999652
54	0.000057	0.999709
55	0.000048	0.999757
56	0.000040	0.999797
57	0.000033	0.999830
58	0.000028	0.999858
59	0.000023	0.999881
60	0.000020	0.999901

k = 2·3
Mean = 10·48
Variance = 58·21

n	P(n)	F(n)
0	0.019370	0.019370
1	0.036532	0.055901
2	0.049427	0.105329
3	0.058093	0.163422
4	0.063119	0.226541
5	0.065214	0.291755
6	0.065062	0.356817
7	0.063259	0.420075
8	0.060301	0.480377
9	0.056590	0.536966
10	0.052436	0.589402
11	0.048079	0.637481
12	0.043696	0.681177
13	0.039414	0.720591
14	0.035320	0.755911
15	0.031473	0.787383
16	0.027904	0.815288
17	0.024631	0.839919
18	0.021656	0.861576
19	0.018973	0.880549
20	0.016569	0.897118
21	0.014428	0.911546
22	0.012530	0.924076
23	0.010855	0.934932
24	0.009384	0.944315
25	0.008095	0.952410
26	0.006970	0.959380
27	0.005990	0.965370
28	0.005140	0.970510
29	0.004404	0.974914
30	0.003768	0.978681
31	0.003219	0.981900
32	0.002747	0.984647
33	0.002341	0.986988
34	0.001993	0.988981
35	0.001695	0.990676
36	0.001440	0.992116
37	0.001222	0.993338
38	0.001037	0.994375
39	0.000878	0.995253

n	P(n)	F(n)
40	0.000744	0.995997
41	0.000629	0.996626
42	0.000532	0.997158
43	0.000449	0.997608
44	0.000379	0.997987
45	0.000320	0.998307
46	0.000270	0.998577
47	0.000227	0.998804
48	0.000192	0.998996
49	0.000161	0.999157
50	0.000136	0.999292
51	0.000114	0.999407
52	0.000096	0.999502
53	0.000081	0.999583
54	0.000068	0.999651
55	0.000057	0.999707
56	0.000048	0.999755
57	0.000040	0.999795
58	0.000033	0.999828
59	0.000028	0.999856
60	0.000024	0.999880
61	0.000020	0.999900
62	0.000016	0.999916

$k = 2.4$
Mean $= 10.93$
Variance $= 60.74$

n	P(n)	F(n)
0	0.016318	0.016318
1	0.032113	0.048430
2	0.044765	0.093196
3	0.053838	0.147034
4	0.059598	0.206632
5	0.062555	0.269186
6	0.063263	0.332450
7	0.062251	0.394701
8	0.059979	0.454680
9	0.056834	0.511514
10	0.053128	0.564642
11	0.049110	0.613751
12	0.044968	0.658719
13	0.040845	0.699564
14	0.036842	0.736406
15	0.033030	0.769436
16	0.029455	0.798891
17	0.026142	0.825032
18	0.023104	0.848136
19	0.020341	0.868477
20	0.017847	0.886324
21	0.015610	0.901934
22	0.013615	0.915549
23	0.011844	0.927393
24	0.010278	0.937671
25	0.008900	0.946572
26	0.007691	0.954263
27	0.006634	0.960897
28	0.005712	0.966608
29	0.004910	0.971518
30	0.004214	0.975732
31	0.003611	0.979343
32	0.003091	0.982434
33	0.002642	0.985076
34	0.002256	0.987332
35	0.001924	0.989256
36	0.001639	0.990895
37	0.001395	0.992289
38	0.001186	0.993475
39	0.001007	0.994482
40	0.000855	0.995337
41	0.000725	0.996062
42	0.000614	0.996676
43	0.000520	0.997196
44	0.000440	0.997636
45	0.000372	0.998008
46	0.000314	0.998322
47	0.000265	0.998588
48	0.000224	0.998812
49	0.000189	0.999001
50	0.000159	0.999160
51	0.000134	0.999294
52	0.000113	0.999407
53	0.000095	0.999502
54	0.000080	0.999582
55	0.000067	0.999650
56	0.000057	0.999706
57	0.000048	0.999754
58	0.000040	0.999794
59	0.000033	0.999827
60	0.000028	0.999855
61	0.000024	0.999879
62	0.000020	0.999899
63	0.000017	0.999915

$k = 2.5$
Mean $= 11.39$
Variance $= 63.27$

n	P(n)	F(n)
0	0.013746	0.013746
1	0.028180	0.041926
2	0.040438	0.082364
3	0.049738	0.132102
4	0.056080	0.188182
5	0.059781	0.247963
6	0.061276	0.309239
7	0.061013	0.370253
8	0.059412	0.429664
9	0.056837	0.486502
10	0.053597	0.540099
11	0.049943	0.590042
12	0.046073	0.636115
13	0.042139	0.678253
14	0.038256	0.716509
15	0.034507	0.751016
16	0.030948	0.781964
17	0.027617	0.809581
18	0.024533	0.834114
19	0.021705	0.855819
20	0.019133	0.874952
21	0.016810	0.891762
22	0.014724	0.906486
23	0.012861	0.919347
24	0.011205	0.930552
25	0.009739	0.940291
26	0.008447	0.948738
27	0.007311	0.956050
28	0.006317	0.962366
29	0.005448	0.967814
30	0.004690	0.972504
31	0.004032	0.976536
32	0.003461	0.979998
33	0.002967	0.982965
34	0.002541	0.985506
35	0.002173	0.987678
36	0.001856	0.989534
37	0.001583	0.991117
38	0.001350	0.992467
39	0.001149	0.993616
40	0.000978	0.994594
41	0.000831	0.995425
42	0.000706	0.996131
43	0.000599	0.996730
44	0.000508	0.997238
45	0.000430	0.997668
46	0.000364	0.998032
47	0.000308	0.998341
48	0.000261	0.998601
49	0.000220	0.998822
50	0.000186	0.999008
51	0.000157	0.999165
52	0.000133	0.999297
53	0.000112	0.999409
54	0.000094	0.999503
55	0.000079	0.999583
56	0.000067	0.999650
57	0.000056	0.999706
58	0.000047	0.999753
59	0.000040	0.999793
60	0.000033	0.999826
61	0.000028	0.999854
62	0.000024	0.999878
63	0.000020	0.999898
64	0.000017	0.999914

k = 0·1
Mean = 0·40
Variance = 2·00

n	P(n)	F(n)
0	0.851340	0.851340
1	0.068107	0.919447
2	0.029967	0.949414
3	0.016782	0.966196
4	0.010405	0.976600
5	0.006825	0.983426
6	0.004641	0.988067
7	0.003236	0.991303
8	0.002297	0.993600
9	0.001654	0.995254
10	0.001204	0.996458
11	0.000885	0.997343
12	0.000655	0.997997
13	0.000487	0.998485
14	0.000365	0.998850
15	0.000274	0.999124
16	0.000207	0.999331
17	0.000157	0.999488
18	0.000119	0.999607
19	0.000091	0.999698
20	0.000069	0.999768
21	0.000053	0.999821
22	0.000041	0.999862
23	0.000031	0.999893
24	0.000024	0.999917

k = 0·2
Mean = 0·80
Variance = 4·00

n	P(n)	F(n)
0	0.724780	0.724780
1	0.115965	0.840744
2	0.055663	0.896407
3	0.032656	0.929063
4	0.020900	0.949963
5	0.014045	0.964007
6	0.009738	0.973745
7	0.006900	0.980645
8	0.004968	0.985612
9	0.003621	0.989233
10	0.002665	0.991899
11	0.001977	0.993875
12	0.001476	0.995352
13	0.001108	0.996460
14	0.000836	0.997296
15	0.000633	0.997929
16	0.000481	0.998410
17	0.000367	0.998777
18	0.000280	0.999057
19	0.000215	0.999272
20	0.000165	0.999437
21	0.000127	0.999564
22	0.000098	0.999662
23	0.000076	0.999738
24	0.000058	0.999796

25	0.000045	0.999841
26	0.000035	0.999876
27	0.000027	0.999904

k = 0·3
Mean = 1·20
Variance = 6·00

n	P(n)	F(n)
0	0.617034	0.617034
1	0.148088	0.765122
2	0.077006	0.842128
3	0.047230	0.889358
4	0.031172	0.920530
5	0.021446	0.941976
6	0.015155	0.957132
7	0.010912	0.968044
8	0.007966	0.976009
9	0.005877	0.981886
10	0.004372	0.986259
11	0.003275	0.989534
12	0.002467	0.992001
13	0.001868	0.993869
14	0.001419	0.995288
15	0.001083	0.996371
16	0.000828	0.997199
17	0.000635	0.997834
18	0.000488	0.998323
19	0.000376	0.998699
20	0.000291	0.998990
21	0.000225	0.999214
22	0.000174	0.999388
23	0.000135	0.999523
24	0.000105	0.999628
25	0.000082	0.999710
26	0.000063	0.999773
27	0.000049	0.999823
28	0.000039	0.999861
29	0.000030	0.999891
30	0.000024	0.999915

k = 0·4
Mean = 1·60
Variance = 8·00

n	P(n)	F(n)
0	0.525306	0.525306
1	0.168098	0.693403
2	0.094135	0.787538
3	0.060246	0.847784
4	0.040967	0.888752
5	0.028841	0.917593
6	0.020766	0.938358
7	0.015189	0.953547
8	0.011240	0.964787
9	0.008392	0.973179

10	0.006311	0.979490
11	0.004773	0.984263
12	0.003628	0.987891
13	0.002768	0.990659
14	0.002120	0.992779
15	0.001628	0.994407
16	0.001253	0.995660
17	0.000967	0.996627
18	0.000748	0.997376
19	0.000580	0.997955
20	0.000450	0.998405
21	0.000350	0.998754
22	0.000272	0.999026
23	0.000212	0.999238
24	0.000165	0.999404
25	0.000129	0.999533
26	0.000101	0.999634
27	0.000079	0.999713
28	0.000062	0.999774
29	0.000048	0.999823
30	0.000038	0.999861
31	0.000030	0.999890
32	0.000023	0.999914

k = 0·5
Mean = 2·00
Variance = 10·00

n	P(n)	F(n)
0	0.447214	0.447214
1	0.178885	0.626099
2	0.107331	0.733430
3	0.071554	0.804984
4	0.050088	0.855072
5	0.036063	0.891136
6	0.026446	0.917582
7	0.019646	0.937228
8	0.014734	0.951962
9	0.011133	0.963095
10	0.008461	0.971556
11	0.006461	0.978017
12	0.004953	0.982970
13	0.003810	0.986781
14	0.002939	0.989720
15	0.002273	0.991993
16	0.001762	0.993755
17	0.001368	0.995123
18	0.001064	0.996187
19	0.000829	0.997016
20	0.000646	0.997662
21	0.000505	0.998167
22	0.000395	0.998561
23	0.000309	0.998870
24	0.000242	0.999112
25	0.000190	0.999302
26	0.000149	0.999451
27	0.000117	0.999568
28	0.000092	0.999660
29	0.000072	0.999732

n	P(n)	F(n)
30	0.000057	0.999788
31	0.000045	0.999833
32	0.000035	0.999868
33	0.000028	0.999896
34	0.000022	0.999918

k = 0·6
Mean = 2·40
Variance = 12·00

n	P(n)	F(n)
0	0.380731	0.380731
1	0.182751	0.563482
2	0.116960	0.680442
3	0.081093	0.761535
4	0.058387	0.819921
5	0.042973	0.862894
6	0.032086	0.894980
7	0.024202	0.919182
8	0.018394	0.937576
9	0.014061	0.951637
10	0.010799	0.962436
11	0.008325	0.970761
12	0.006438	0.977198
13	0.004992	0.982190
14	0.003879	0.986070
15	0.003021	0.989090
16	0.002356	0.991447
17	0.001841	0.993287
18	0.001440	0.994727
19	0.001128	0.995855
20	0.000884	0.996739
21	0.000694	0.997432
22	0.000545	0.997977
23	0.000428	0.998406
24	0.000337	0.998742
25	0.000265	0.999008
26	0.000209	0.999217
27	0.000165	0.999381
28	0.000130	0.999511
29	0.000102	0.999614
30	0.000081	0.999695
31	0.000064	0.999758
32	0.000050	0.999809
33	0.000040	0.999849
34	0.000032	0.999880
35	0.000025	0.999905

k = 0·7
Mean = 2·80
Variance = 14·00

n	P(n)	F(n)
0	0.324131	0.324131
1	0.181514	0.505645
2	0.123429	0.629074
3	0.088869	0.717943
4	0.065763	0.783706
5	0.049454	0.833160
6	0.037585	0.870745
7	0.028779	0.899524
8	0.022160	0.921684
9	0.017137	0.938821
10	0.013298	0.952120
11	0.010349	0.962468
12	0.008072	0.970540
13	0.006308	0.976849
14	0.004939	0.981787
15	0.003872	0.985659
16	0.003039	0.988699
17	0.002389	0.991087
18	0.001879	0.992966
19	0.001480	0.994446
20	0.001166	0.995612
21	0.000919	0.996531
22	0.000725	0.997257
23	0.000573	0.997829
24	0.000453	0.998282
25	0.000358	0.998640
26	0.000283	0.998922
27	0.000224	0.999146
28	0.000177	0.999323
29	0.000140	0.999464
30	0.000111	0.999575
31	0.000088	0.999663
32	0.000070	0.999732
33	0.000055	0.999788
34	0.000044	0.999831
35	0.000035	0.999866
36	0.000028	0.999894
37	0.000022	0.999916

k = 0·8
Mean = 3·20
Variance = 16·00

n	P(n)	F(n)
0	0.275946	0.275946
1	0.176605	0.452551
2	0.127156	0.579707
3	0.094943	0.674650
4	0.072157	0.746807
5	0.055416	0.802223
6	0.042855	0.845079
7	0.033305	0.878383
8	0.025978	0.904361
9	0.020320	0.924681
10	0.015931	0.940613
11	0.012513	0.953126
12	0.009844	0.962969
13	0.007754	0.970723
14	0.006114	0.976838
15	0.004826	0.981664
16	0.003813	0.985477
17	0.003014	0.988491
18	0.002385	0.990876
19	0.001888	0.992763
20	0.001495	0.994258
21	0.001185	0.995443
22	0.000939	0.996382
23	0.000745	0.997127
24	0.000591	0.997718
25	0.000469	0.998187
26	0.000372	0.998559
27	0.000296	0.998854
28	0.000235	0.999089
29	0.000187	0.999276
30	0.000148	0.999424
31	0.000118	0.999542
32	0.000094	0.999635
33	0.000074	0.999710
34	0.000059	0.999769
35	0.000047	0.999816
36	0.000037	0.999854
37	0.000030	0.999884
38	0.000024	0.999907

k = 0·9
Mean = 3·60
Variance = 18·00

n	P(n)	F(n)
0	0.234924	0.234924
1	0.169145	0.404069
2	0.128550	0.532619
3	0.099412	0.632031
4	0.077542	0.709573
5	0.060793	0.770366
6	0.047823	0.818189
7	0.037712	0.855901
8	0.029793	0.885694
9	0.023569	0.909263
10	0.018667	0.927930
11	0.014798	0.942728
12	0.011740	0.954467
13	0.009319	0.963787
14	0.007402	0.971189
15	0.005882	0.977071
16	0.004676	0.981748
17	0.003719	0.985467
18	0.002959	0.988426
19	0.002355	0.990780
20	0.001874	0.992655
21	0.001492	0.994147
22	0.001188	0.995335
23	0.000947	0.996282
24	0.000754	0.997036
25	0.000601	0.997637
26	0.000479	0.998116
27	0.000382	0.998497
28	0.000304	0.998802
29	0.000243	0.999044
30	0.000193	0.999238
31	0.000154	0.999392
32	0.000123	0.999515
33	0.000098	0.999613
34	0.000078	0.999691

n	P(n)	F(n)
35	0.000062	0.999753
36	0.000050	0.999803
37	0.000040	0.999843
38	0.000032	0.999875
39	0.000025	0.999900
40	0.000020	0.999920

k=1·0
Mean = 4·00
Variance = 20·00

n	P(n)	F(n)
0	0.200000	0.200000
1	0.160000	0.360000
2	0.128000	0.488000
3	0.102400	0.590400
4	0.081920	0.672320
5	0.065536	0.737856
6	0.052429	0.790285
7	0.041943	0.832228
8	0.033554	0.865782
9	0.026844	0.892626
10	0.021475	0.914101
11	0.017180	0.931281
12	0.013744	0.945024
13	0.010995	0.956020
14	0.008796	0.964816
15	0.007037	0.971853
16	0.005630	0.977482
17	0.004504	0.981986
18	0.003603	0.985588
19	0.002882	0.988471
20	0.002306	0.990777
21	0.001845	0.992621
22	0.001476	0.994097
23	0.001181	0.995278
24	0.000944	0.996222
25	0.000756	0.996978
26	0.000604	0.997582
27	0.000484	0.998066
28	0.000387	0.998453
29	0.000309	0.998762
30	0.000248	0.999010
31	0.000198	0.999208
32	0.000158	0.999366
33	0.000127	0.999493
34	0.000101	0.999594
35	0.000081	0.999675
36	0.000065	0.999740
37	0.000052	0.999792
38	0.000042	0.999834
39	0.000033	0.999867
40	0.000027	0.999894
41	0.000021	0.999915

k=1·1
Mean = 4·40
Variance = 22·00

n	P(n)	F(n)
0	0.170268	0.170268
1	0.149836	0.320104
2	0.125862	0.445966
3	0.104046	0.550012
4	0.085318	0.635330
5	0.069619	0.704949
6	0.056624	0.761573
7	0.045946	0.807519
8	0.037216	0.844735
9	0.030104	0.874839
10	0.024324	0.899163
11	0.019636	0.918799
12	0.015840	0.934638
13	0.012769	0.947408
14	0.010288	0.957696
15	0.008286	0.965982
16	0.006670	0.972652
17	0.005367	0.978019
18	0.004318	0.982337
19	0.003472	0.985809
20	0.002792	0.988601
21	0.002244	0.990845
22	0.001803	0.992648
23	0.001449	0.994097
24	0.001164	0.995261
25	0.000935	0.996196
26	0.000751	0.996947
27	0.000603	0.997550
28	0.000484	0.998034
29	0.000389	0.998422
30	0.000312	0.998734
31	0.000250	0.998985
32	0.000201	0.999185
33	0.000161	0.999347
34	0.000129	0.999476
35	0.000104	0.999580
36	0.000083	0.999663
37	0.000067	0.999730
38	0.000054	0.999783
39	0.000043	0.999826
40	0.000034	0.999861
41	0.000028	0.999888
42	0.000022	0.999910

k=1·2
Mean = 4·80
Variance = 24·00

n	P(n)	F(n)
0	0.144956	0.144956
1	0.139158	0.284114
2	0.122459	0.406572
3	0.104498	0.511071
4	0.087778	0.598849

n	P(n)	F(n)
5	0.073032	0.671881
6	0.060373	0.732254
7	0.049678	0.781932
8	0.040736	0.822668
9	0.033313	0.855981
10	0.027184	0.883165
11	0.022142	0.905307
12	0.018009	0.923316
13	0.014629	0.937945
14	0.011870	0.949815
15	0.009623	0.959438
16	0.007794	0.967232
17	0.006309	0.973541
18	0.005103	0.978644
19	0.004126	0.982770
20	0.003333	0.986103
21	0.002692	0.988795
22	0.002173	0.990969
23	0.001754	0.992723
24	0.001415	0.994137
25	0.001141	0.995278
26	0.000920	0.996198
27	0.000741	0.996939
28	0.000597	0.997536
29	0.000481	0.998017
30	0.000387	0.998405
31	0.000312	0.998716
32	0.000251	0.998968
33	0.000202	0.999170
34	0.000163	0.999332
35	0.000131	0.999463
36	0.000105	0.999568
37	0.000085	0.999653
38	0.000068	0.999721
39	0.000055	0.999776
40	0.000044	0.999820
41	0.000035	0.999855
42	0.000028	0.999884
43	0.000023	0.999907

k=1·3
Mean = 5·20
Variance = 26·00

n	P(n)	F(n)
0	0.123407	0.123407
1	0.128343	0.251750
2	0.118076	0.369825
3	0.103907	0.473732
4	0.089360	0.563092
5	0.075777	0.638869
6	0.063653	0.702521
7	0.053104	0.755626
8	0.044077	0.799702
9	0.036437	0.836139
10	0.030024	0.866163
11	0.024674	0.890837
12	0.020233	0.911070
13	0.016560	0.927630
14	0.013532	0.941162

n	P(n)	F(n)
15	0.011042	0.952203
16	0.008999	0.961203
17	0.007326	0.968529
18	0.005959	0.974488
19	0.004842	0.979330
20	0.003932	0.983262
21	0.003190	0.986452
22	0.002587	0.989040
23	0.002097	0.991136
24	0.001698	0.992835
25	0.001375	0.994210
26	0.001113	0.995322
27	0.000900	0.996222
28	0.000728	0.996950
29	0.000588	0.997538
30	0.000475	0.998014
31	0.000384	0.998398
32	0.000310	0.998708
33	0.000250	0.998958
34	0.000202	0.999160
35	0.000163	0.999323
36	0.000131	0.999454
37	0.000106	0.999560
38	0.000085	0.999646
39	0.000069	0.999715
40	0.000056	0.999770
41	0.000045	0.999815
42	0.000036	0.999851
43	0.000029	0.999880
44	0.000023	0.999903

k = 1·4
Mean = 5·60
Variance = 28·00

n	P(n)	F(n)
0	0.105061	0.105061
1	0.117668	0.222730
2	0.112962	0.335691
3	0.102419	0.438110
4	0.090128	0.528238
5	0.077871	0.606109
6	0.066450	0.672559
7	0.056198	0.728757
8	0.047206	0.775963
9	0.039443	0.815406
10	0.032817	0.848223
11	0.027208	0.875431
12	0.022492	0.897923
13	0.018547	0.916470
14	0.015262	0.931732
15	0.012535	0.944267
16	0.010279	0.954545
17	0.008416	0.962962
18	0.006883	0.969844
19	0.005622	0.975467
20	0.004588	0.980054
21	0.003740	0.983794
22	0.003046	0.986841
23	0.002480	0.989320
24	0.002017	0.991337
25	0.001639	0.992976
26	0.001332	0.994308
27	0.001081	0.995389
28	0.000877	0.996266
29	0.000711	0.996977
30	0.000577	0.997554
31	0.000467	0.998021
32	0.000379	0.998400
33	0.000306	0.998706
34	0.000248	0.998954
35	0.000201	0.999155
36	0.000162	0.999317
37	0.000131	0.999449
38	0.000106	0.999555
39	0.000086	0.999641
40	0.000069	0.999710
41	0.000056	0.999766
42	0.000045	0.999811
43	0.000037	0.999848
44	0.000029	0.999877
45	0.000024	0.999901

k = 1·5
Mean = 6·00
Variance = 30·00

n	P(n)	F(n)
0	0.089443	0.089443
1	0.107331	0.196774
2	0.107331	0.304105
3	0.100176	0.404281
4	0.090158	0.494439
5	0.079339	0.573779
6	0.068761	0.642539
7	0.058938	0.701477
8	0.050097	0.751574
9	0.042304	0.793878
10	0.035536	0.829414
11	0.029721	0.859134
12	0.024767	0.883902
13	0.020576	0.904478
14	0.017049	0.921526
15	0.014093	0.935619
16	0.011627	0.947247
17	0.009575	0.956822
18	0.007873	0.964695
19	0.006464	0.971159
20	0.005301	0.976460
21	0.004341	0.980801
22	0.003552	0.984353
23	0.002903	0.987257
24	0.002371	0.989628
25	0.001935	0.991563
26	0.001578	0.993140
27	0.001285	0.994426
28	0.001047	0.995472
29	0.000852	0.996324

k = 1·6
Mean = 6·40
Variance = 32·00

n	P(n)	F(n)
0	0.076146	0.076146
1	0.097467	0.173613
2	0.101366	0.274979
3	0.097311	0.372290
4	0.089526	0.461816
5	0.080216	0.542032
6	0.070590	0.612622
7	0.061312	0.673934
8	0.052728	0.726662
9	0.044995	0.771657
10	0.038156	0.809813
11	0.032190	0.842002
12	0.027039	0.869042
13	0.022630	0.891671
14	0.018880	0.910551
15	0.015708	0.926259
16	0.013038	0.939296
17	0.010798	0.950095
18	0.008926	0.959021
19	0.007367	0.966388
20	0.006070	0.972458
21	0.004995	0.977453
22	0.004105	0.981558
23	0.003370	0.984927
24	0.002763	0.987690
25	0.002263	0.989954
26	0.001853	0.991806
27	0.001515	0.993321
28	0.001238	0.994559
29	0.001011	0.995570
30	0.000825	0.996395
31	0.000673	0.997068
32	0.000548	0.997616
33	0.000447	0.998062
34	0.000364	0.998426

Right-hand continuation (k = 1·5 upper section):

n	P(n)	F(n)
30	0.000693	0.997017
31	0.000563	0.997580
32	0.000458	0.998038
33	0.000372	0.998410
34	0.000302	0.998711
35	0.000245	0.998956
36	0.000199	0.999155
37	0.000161	0.999316
38	0.000130	0.999446
39	0.000106	0.999552
40	0.000086	0.999637
41	0.000069	0.999707
42	0.000056	0.999763
43	0.000045	0.999808
44	0.000037	0.999845
45	0.000030	0.999875
46	0.000024	0.999899
47	0.000019	0.999918

n	P(n)	F(n)
35	0.000296	0.998722
36	0.000241	0.998962
37	0.000196	0.999158
38	0.000159	0.999317
39	0.000129	0.999446
40	0.000105	0.999551
41	0.000085	0.999636
42	0.000069	0.999705
43	0.000056	0.999761
44	0.000045	0.999807
45	0.000037	0.999843
46	0.000030	0.999873
47	0.000024	0.999897
48	0.000020	0.999917

n	P(n)	F(n)
40	0.000127	0.999448
41	0.000104	0.999552
42	0.000084	0.999636
43	0.000068	0.999705
44	0.000056	0.999760
45	0.000045	0.999806
46	0.000037	0.999842
47	0.000030	0.999872
48	0.000024	0.999896
49	0.000020	0.999916

n	P(n)	F(n)
45	0.000055	0.999761
46	0.000045	0.999806
47	0.000036	0.999842
48	0.000030	0.999872
49	0.000024	0.999896
50	0.000020	0.999915

k=1·7
Mean=6·80
Variance=34·00

n	P(n)	F(n)
0	0.064826	0.064826
1	0.088164	0.152990
2	0.095217	0.248207
3	0.093947	0.342154
4	0.088310	0.430464
5	0.080539	0.511004
6	0.071948	0.582952
7	0.063314	0.646266
8	0.055084	0.701350
9	0.047494	0.748844
10	0.040655	0.789499
11	0.034594	0.824093
12	0.029289	0.853383
13	0.024693	0.878076
14	0.020742	0.898818
15	0.017368	0.916186
16	0.014502	0.930689
17	0.012080	0.942769
18	0.010040	0.952808
19	0.008328	0.961136
20	0.006895	0.968031
21	0.005700	0.973731
22	0.004705	0.978436
23	0.003879	0.982315
24	0.003193	0.985508
25	0.002626	0.988135
26	0.002158	0.990292
27	0.001771	0.992063
28	0.001452	0.993515
29	0.001190	0.994705
30	0.000974	0.995679
31	0.000797	0.996475
32	0.000651	0.997127
33	0.000532	0.997659
34	0.000434	0.998093
35	0.000355	0.998448
36	0.000289	0.998737
37	0.000236	0.998973
38	0.000192	0.999165
39	0.000156	0.999321

k=1·8
Mean=7·20
Variance=36·00

n	P(n)	F(n)
0	0.055189	0.055189
1	0.079472	0.134662
2	0.089009	0.223671
3	0.090196	0.313867
4	0.086588	0.400455
5	0.080354	0.480808
6	0.072854	0.553662
7	0.064944	0.618607
8	0.057151	0.675758
9	0.049785	0.725542
10	0.043014	0.768556
11	0.036914	0.805470
12	0.031500	0.836970
13	0.026751	0.863721
14	0.022623	0.886344
15	0.019064	0.905408
16	0.016014	0.921422
17	0.013414	0.934836
18	0.011208	0.946044
19	0.009344	0.955388
20	0.007774	0.963162
21	0.006456	0.969618
22	0.005353	0.974971
23	0.004431	0.979402
24	0.003663	0.983065
25	0.003024	0.986090
26	0.002494	0.988583
27	0.002054	0.990638
28	0.001690	0.992328
29	0.001390	0.993717
30	0.001141	0.994859
31	0.000937	0.995795
32	0.000768	0.996563
33	0.000629	0.997193
34	0.000515	0.997708
35	0.000422	0.998130
36	0.000345	0.998474
37	0.000282	0.998756
38	0.000230	0.998986
39	0.000188	0.999174
40	0.000153	0.999328
41	0.000125	0.999453
42	0.000102	0.999555
43	0.000083	0.999638
44	0.000068	0.999706

k=1·9
Mean=7·60
Variance=38·00

n	P(n)	F(n)
0	0.046985	0.046985
1	0.071417	0.118402
2	0.082844	0.201245
3	0.086157	0.287402
4	0.084434	0.371836
5	0.079706	0.451542
6	0.073329	0.524872
7	0.066206	0.591078
8	0.058923	0.650001
9	0.051852	0.701853
10	0.045215	0.747069
11	0.039132	0.786201
12	0.033653	0.819854
13	0.028787	0.848641
14	0.024510	0.873150
15	0.020784	0.893934
16	0.017563	0.911497
17	0.014794	0.926291
18	0.012427	0.938718
19	0.010412	0.949131
20	0.008705	0.957835
21	0.007262	0.965098
22	0.006048	0.971145
23	0.005027	0.976173
24	0.004173	0.980345
25	0.003458	0.983804
26	0.002862	0.986666
27	0.002366	0.989032
28	0.001954	0.990986
29	0.001612	0.992598
30	0.001328	0.993926
31	0.001093	0.995019
32	0.000899	0.995918
33	0.000739	0.996657
34	0.000607	0.997264
35	0.000498	0.997762
36	0.000408	0.998170
37	0.000335	0.998505
38	0.000274	0.998779
39	0.000224	0.999003
40	0.000183	0.999186
41	0.000150	0.999336
42	0.000123	0.999459
43	0.000100	0.999559
44	0.000082	0.999641

n	P(n)	F(n)		n	P(n)	F(n)		n	P(n)	F(n)
45	0.000067	0.999707		45	0.000080	0.999645		45	0.000096	0.999571
46	0.000054	0.999762		46	0.000066	0.999710		46	0.000078	0.999649
47	0.000044	0.999806		47	0.000054	0.999764		47	0.000064	0.999714
48	0.000036	0.999842		48	0.000044	0.999807		48	0.000053	0.999766
49	0.000029	0.999872		49	0.000036	0.999843		49	0.000043	0.999809
50	0.000024	0.999896		50	0.000029	0.999872		50	0.000035	0.999844
51	0.000020	0.999915		51	0.000024	0.999896		51	0.000029	0.999873
				52	0.000019	0.999915		52	0.000023	0.999896
								53	0.000019	0.999915

k = 2·0 Mean = 8·00 Variance = 40·00
k = 2·1 Mean = 8·40 Variance = 42·00
k = 2·2 Mean = 8·80 Variance = 44·00

n	P(n)	F(n)		n	P(n)	F(n)		n	P(n)	F(n)
0	0.040000	0.040000		0	0.034054	0.034054		0	0.028991	0.028991
1	0.064000	0.104000		1	0.057210	0.091264		1	0.051024	0.080016
2	0.076800	0.180800		2	0.070940	0.162204		2	0.065311	0.145327
3	0.081920	0.262720		3	0.077562	0.239766		3	0.073149	0.218476
4	0.081920	0.344640		4	0.079113	0.318878		4	0.076075	0.294550
5	0.078643	0.423283		5	0.077214	0.396093		5	0.075466	0.370016
6	0.073400	0.496684		6	0.073096	0.469189		6	0.072447	0.442464
7	0.067109	0.563792		7	0.067666	0.536855		7	0.067894	0.510357
8	0.060398	0.624190		8	0.061576	0.598431		8	0.062462	0.572820
9	0.053687	0.677877		9	0.055282	0.653712		9	0.056632	0.629452
10	0.047245	0.725122		10	0.049090	0.702802		10	0.050743	0.680194
11	0.041232	0.766354		11	0.043199	0.746002		11	0.045022	0.725217
12	0.035734	0.802088		12	0.037727	0.783729		12	0.039620	0.764837
13	0.030786	0.832874		13	0.032736	0.816465		13	0.034622	0.799458
14	0.026388	0.859263		14	0.028246	0.844711		14	0.030071	0.829530
15	0.022518	0.881781		15	0.024254	0.868965		15	0.025982	0.855511
16	0.019140	0.900921		16	0.020737	0.889702		16	0.022344	0.877855
17	0.016213	0.917134		17	0.017663	0.907366		17	0.019137	0.896992
18	0.013691	0.930825		18	0.014994	0.922360		18	0.016330	0.913323
19	0.011529	0.942354		19	0.012690	0.935050		19	0.013889	0.927212
20	0.009685	0.952038		20	0.010710	0.945760		20	0.011778	0.938990
21	0.008117	0.960155		21	0.009017	0.954777		21	0.009961	0.948951
22	0.006788	0.966943		22	0.007574	0.962351		22	0.008403	0.957355
23	0.005667	0.972610		23	0.006349	0.968700		23	0.007074	0.964428
24	0.004722	0.977333		24	0.005312	0.974012		24	0.005942	0.970370
25	0.003929	0.981262		25	0.004437	0.978449		25	0.004982	0.975352
26	0.003264	0.984526		26	0.003700	0.982149		26	0.004169	0.979521
27	0.002708	0.987234		27	0.003080	0.985229		27	0.003484	0.983005
28	0.002244	0.989478		28	0.002561	0.987790		28	0.002906	0.985911
29	0.001857	0.991334		29	0.002126	0.989916		29	0.002421	0.988332
30	0.001535	0.992869		30	0.001764	0.991680		30	0.002014	0.990347
31	0.001268	0.994137		31	0.001461	0.993141		31	0.001674	0.992021
32	0.001046	0.995183		32	0.001209	0.994350		32	0.001389	0.993410
33	0.000862	0.996045		33	0.000999	0.995349		33	0.001152	0.994562
34	0.000710	0.996755		34	0.000825	0.996174		34	0.000954	0.995516
35	0.000584	0.997339		35	0.000681	0.996856		35	0.000789	0.996305
36	0.000480	0.997819		36	0.000561	0.997417		36	0.000653	0.996958
37	0.000395	0.998214		37	0.000463	0.997880		37	0.000539	0.997497
38	0.000324	0.998538		38	0.000381	0.998260		38	0.000445	0.997942
39	0.000266	0.998804		39	0.000313	0.998573		39	0.000367	0.998309
40	0.000218	0.999022		40	0.000257	0.998831		40	0.000302	0.998611
41	0.000179	0.999200		41	0.000211	0.999042		41	0.000249	0.998860
42	0.000146	0.999347		42	0.000174	0.999216		42	0.000205	0.999065
43	0.000120	0.999466		43	0.000142	0.999358		43	0.000168	0.999233
44	0.000098	0.999564		44	0.000117	0.999475		44	0.000138	0.999371

n	P(n)	F(n)		n	P(n)	F(n)		n	P(n)	F(n)
45	0.000114	0.999485		45	0.000134	0.999385		40	0.000410	0.998070
46	0.000093	0.999578		46	0.000110	0.999496		41	0.000339	0.998409
47	0.000077	0.999655		47	0.000091	0.999587		42	0.000280	0.998690
48	0.000063	0.999718		48	0.000075	0.999661		43	0.000232	0.998921
49	0.000051	0.999769		49	0.000061	0.999722		44	0.000191	0.999112
50	0.000042	0.999811		50	0.000050	0.999773		45	0.000158	0.999270
51	0.000035	0.999846		51	0.000041	0.999814		46	0.000130	0.999400
52	0.000028	0.999874		52	0.000034	0.999848		47	0.000107	0.999507
53	0.000023	0.999897		53	0.000028	0.999875		48	0.000088	0.999595
54	0.000019	0.999916		54	0.000023	0.999898		49	0.000073	0.999668
				55	0.000019	0.999917		50	0.000060	0.999728
								51	0.000049	0.999777
								52	0.000040	0.999817
								53	0.000033	0.999850
								54	0.000027	0.999877
								55	0.000022	0.999899
								56	0.000018	0.999918

k=2·3
Mean=9·20
Variance=46·00

k=2·4
Mean=9·60
Variance=48·00

k=2·5
Mean=10·00
Variance=50·00

n	P(n)	F(n)		n	P(n)	F(n)		n	P(n)	F(n)
0	0.024681	0.024681		0	0.021012	0.021012		0	0.017889	0.017889
1	0.045414	0.070095		1	0.040343	0.061356		1	0.035777	0.053666
2	0.059946	0.130041		2	0.054867	0.116223		2	0.050088	0.103754
3	0.068738	0.198779		3	0.064377	0.180600		3	0.060106	0.163859
4	0.072862	0.271642		4	0.069528	0.250128		4	0.066116	0.229975
5	0.073445	0.345087		5	0.071196	0.321324		5	0.068761	0.298736
6	0.071487	0.416574		6	0.070247	0.391571		6	0.068761	0.367497
7	0.067810	0.484384		7	0.067437	0.459008		7	0.066796	0.434293
8	0.063064	0.547448		8	0.063391	0.522399		8	0.063456	0.497749
9	0.057738	0.605186		9	0.058601	0.581000		9	0.059226	0.556975
10	0.052195	0.657381		10	0.053444	0.634445		10	0.054488	0.611463
11	0.046691	0.704073		11	0.048197	0.682642		11	0.049534	0.660997
12	0.041399	0.745472		12	0.043056	0.725698		12	0.044581	0.705578
13	0.036432	0.781904		13	0.038154	0.763852		13	0.039780	0.745358
14	0.031852	0.813755		14	0.033576	0.797428		14	0.035234	0.780591
15	0.027690	0.841445		15	0.029368	0.826796		15	0.031006	0.811597
16	0.023952	0.865396		16	0.025550	0.852346		16	0.027130	0.838727
17	0.020626	0.886023		17	0.022123	0.874469		17	0.023619	0.862346
18	0.017693	0.903716		18	0.019075	0.893544		18	0.020470	0.882816
19	0.015123	0.918839		19	0.016385	0.909929		19	0.017669	0.900484
20	0.012885	0.931723		20	0.014025	0.923954		20	0.015195	0.915679
21	0.010946	0.942669		21	0.011968	0.935922		21	0.013024	0.928704
22	0.009274	0.951943		22	0.010184	0.946106		22	0.011130	0.939834
23	0.007839	0.959782		23	0.008643	0.954749		23	0.009485	0.949318
24	0.006611	0.966392		24	0.007318	0.962066		24	0.008062	0.957380
25	0.005563	0.971956		25	0.006182	0.968248		25	0.006836	0.964217
26	0.004673	0.976629		26	0.005212	0.973460		26	0.005785	0.970001
27	0.003919	0.980548		27	0.004386	0.977846		27	0.004885	0.974886
28	0.003280	0.983828		28	0.003684	0.981530		28	0.004117	0.979003
29	0.002742	0.986570		29	0.003089	0.984619		29	0.003464	0.982468
30	0.002289	0.988859		30	0.002587	0.987206		30	0.002910	0.985378
31	0.001908	0.990767		31	0.002163	0.989369		31	0.002441	0.987818
32	0.001588	0.992355		32	0.001806	0.991175		32	0.002044	0.989862
33	0.001321	0.993675		33	0.001506	0.992681		33	0.001710	0.991572
34	0.001097	0.994772		34	0.001255	0.993936		34	0.001428	0.992999
35	0.000910	0.995682		35	0.001044	0.994980				
36	0.000754	0.996437		36	0.000868	0.995847				
37	0.000625	0.997061		37	0.000720	0.996568				
38	0.000517	0.997578		38	0.000597	0.997165				
39	0.000427	0.998006		39	0.000495	0.997660				
40	0.000353	0.998358								
41	0.000291	0.998650								
42	0.000240	0.998890								
43	0.000198	0.999088								
44	0.000163	0.999251								

35	0.001191	0.994191
36	0.000993	0.995184
37	0.000826	0.996010
38	0.000687	0.996697
39	0.000571	0.997268
40	0.000474	0.997742
41	0.000393	0.998135
42	0.000326	0.998461
43	0.000270	0.998730
44	0.000223	0.998953
45	0.000184	0.999137
46	0.000152	0.999290
47	0.000126	0.999415
48	0.000104	0.999519
49	0.000086	0.999605
50	0.000070	0.999675
51	0.000058	0.999733
52	0.000048	0.999781
53	0.000039	0.999820
54	0.000032	0.999853
55	0.000027	0.999879
56	0.000022	0.999901

k=0·1
Mean = 0·35
Variance = 1·61

n	P(n)	F(n)
0	0.859493	0.859493
1	0.067040	0.926533
2	0.028760	0.955294
3	0.015703	0.970997
4	0.009493	0.980489
5	0.006071	0.986561
6	0.004025	0.990586
7	0.002736	0.993322
8	0.001894	0.995216
9	0.001330	0.996546
10	0.000944	0.997490
11	0.000676	0.998166
12	0.000488	0.998653
13	0.000354	0.999007
14	0.000258	0.999266
15	0.000189	0.999455
16	0.000139	0.999595
17	0.000103	0.999698
18	0.000076	0.999774
19	0.000057	0.999831
20	0.000042	0.999873
21	0.000032	0.999905

k=0·2
Mean = 0·71
Variance = 3·22

n	P(n)	F(n)
0	0.738728	0.738728
1	0.115242	0.853970
2	0.053933	0.907903
3	0.030850	0.938752
4	0.019250	0.958002
5	0.012613	0.970615
6	0.008526	0.979141
7	0.005890	0.985032
8	0.004135	0.989167
9	0.002939	0.992106
10	0.002109	0.994214
11	0.001525	0.995740
12	0.001110	0.996850
13	0.000813	0.997663
14	0.000598	0.998260
15	0.000441	0.998702
16	0.000327	0.999029
17	0.000243	0.999272
18	0.000181	0.999453
19	0.000135	0.999589
20	0.000101	0.999690
21	0.000076	0.999766
22	0.000057	0.999823
23	0.000043	0.999866
24	0.000032	0.999899

25	0.000025	0.999923

k=0·3
Mean = 1·06
Variance = 4·83

n	P(n)	F(n)
0	0.634931	0.634931
1	0.148574	0.783505
2	0.075327	0.858832
3	0.045046	0.903878
4	0.028987	0.932865
5	0.019444	0.952309
6	0.013397	0.965706
7	0.009405	0.975111
8	0.006694	0.981805
9	0.004815	0.986620
10	0.003493	0.990113
11	0.002551	0.992664
12	0.001874	0.994538
13	0.001383	0.995921
14	0.001025	0.996945
15	0.000762	0.997707
16	0.000568	0.998276
17	0.000425	0.998701
18	0.000319	0.999019
19	0.000239	0.999259

71

n	P(n)	F(n)
20	0.000180	0.999439
21	0.000136	0.999575
22	0.000103	0.999677
23	0.000078	0.999755
24	0.000059	0.999814
25	0.000045	0.999858
26	0.000034	0.999892
27	0.000026	0.999918

k=0.4
Mean=1·42
Variance=6·45

n	P(n)	F(n)
0	0.545719	0.545719
1	0.170264	0.715983
2	0.092964	0.808948
3	0.058010	0.866957
4	0.038460	0.905418
5	0.026399	0.931817
6	0.018532	0.950349
7	0.013216	0.963566
8	0.009535	0.973101
9	0.006942	0.980043
10	0.005090	0.985133
11	0.003753	0.988886
12	0.002781	0.991667
13	0.002069	0.993737
14	0.001545	0.995281
15	0.001157	0.996438
16	0.000868	0.997307
17	0.000653	0.997960
18	0.000493	0.998453
19	0.000372	0.998825
20	0.000282	0.999107
21	0.000213	0.999320
22	0.000162	0.999482
23	0.000123	0.999605
24	0.000094	0.999699
25	0.000071	0.999770
26	0.000054	0.999824
27	0.000041	0.999865
28	0.000032	0.999897
29	0.000024	0.999921

k=0.5
Mean=1·77
Variance=8·06

n	P(n)	F(n)
0	0.469042	0.469042
1	0.182926	0.651968
2	0.107012	0.758980
3	0.069558	0.828537
4	0.047473	0.876010
5	0.033326	0.909337
6	0.023828	0.933165
7	0.017258	0.950423
8	0.012620	0.963043
9	0.009297	0.972340
10	0.006889	0.979229
11	0.005129	0.984358
12	0.003834	0.988193
13	0.002876	0.991068
14	0.002163	0.993231
15	0.001631	0.994862
16	0.001232	0.996094
17	0.000933	0.997027
18	0.000707	0.997734
19	0.000537	0.998271
20	0.000409	0.998680
21	0.000311	0.998991
22	0.000237	0.999228
23	0.000181	0.999409
24	0.000138	0.999548
25	0.000106	0.999653
26	0.000081	0.999734
27	0.000062	0.999796
28	0.000047	0.999843
29	0.000036	0.999880
30	0.000028	0.999907

k=0.6
Mean=2·13
Variance=9·67

n	P(n)	F(n)
0	0.403138	0.403138
1	0.188669	0.591806
2	0.117729	0.709536
3	0.079585	0.789120
4	0.055869	0.844989
5	0.040091	0.885080
6	0.029186	0.914267
7	0.021465	0.935731
8	0.015905	0.951637
9	0.011855	0.963491
10	0.008877	0.972368
11	0.006672	0.979040
12	0.005031	0.984071
13	0.003803	0.987874
14	0.002882	0.990756
15	0.002188	0.992944
16	0.001664	0.994608
17	0.001267	0.995875
18	0.000967	0.996842
19	0.000738	0.997580
20	0.000564	0.998144
21	0.000432	0.998576
22	0.000331	0.998906
23	0.000253	0.999159
24	0.000194	0.999354
25	0.000149	0.999503
26	0.000115	0.999617
27	0.000088	0.999705
28	0.000068	0.999773
29	0.000052	0.999825

n	P(n)	F(n)
30	0.000040	0.999865
31	0.000031	0.999896
32	0.000024	0.999920

k=0.7
Mean=2·48
Variance=11·28

n	P(n)	F(n)
0	0.346494	0.346494
1	0.189186	0.535680
2	0.125430	0.661110
3	0.088052	0.749162
4	0.063530	0.812692
5	0.046580	0.859271
6	0.034516	0.893787
7	0.025768	0.919555
8	0.019346	0.938901
9	0.014587	0.953488
10	0.011036	0.964524
11	0.008373	0.972897
12	0.006368	0.979265
13	0.004852	0.984118
14	0.003704	0.987822
15	0.002831	0.990653
16	0.002167	0.992820
17	0.001660	0.994480
18	0.001274	0.995754
19	0.000978	0.996731
20	0.000751	0.997482
21	0.000578	0.998060
22	0.000444	0.998504
23	0.000342	0.998846
24	0.000263	0.999110
25	0.000203	0.999313
26	0.000157	0.999469
27	0.000121	0.999590
28	0.000093	0.999683
29	0.000072	0.999755
30	0.000056	0.999811
31	0.000043	0.999854
32	0.000033	0.999887
33	0.000026	0.999912

k=0.8
Mean=2·84
Variance=12·89

n	P(n)	F(n)
0	0.297809	0.297809
1	0.185833	0.483642
2	0.130455	0.614097
3	0.094971	0.709068
4	0.070374	0.779442
5	0.052696	0.832137
6	0.039733	0.871870
7	0.030106	0.901976
8	0.022896	0.924871
9	0.017462	0.942333

10	0.013348	0.955681
11	0.010222	0.965903
12	0.007840	0.973743
13	0.006021	0.979764
14	0.004630	0.984394
15	0.003563	0.987956
16	0.002744	0.990701
17	0.002115	0.992816
18	0.001632	0.994448
19	0.001259	0.995707
20	0.000972	0.996680
21	0.000751	0.997431
22	0.000581	0.998011
23	0.000449	0.998460
24	0.000347	0.998808
25	0.000269	0.999076
26	0.000208	0.999284
27	0.000161	0.999445
28	0.000125	0.999570
29	0.000097	0.999667
30	0.000075	0.999742
31	0.000058	0.999800
32	0.000045	0.999845
33	0.000035	0.999879
34	0.000027	0.999906

k=0.9
Mean=3·19
Variance=14·50

n	P(n)	F(n)
0	0.255965	0.255965
1	0.179687	0.435652
2	0.133148	0.568801
3	0.100394	0.669194
4	0.076350	0.745544
5	0.058362	0.803906
6	0.044763	0.848669
7	0.034417	0.883085
8	0.026509	0.909595
9	0.020448	0.930042
10	0.015790	0.945832
11	0.012204	0.958036
12	0.009440	0.967476
13	0.007306	0.974782
14	0.005658	0.980440
15	0.004384	0.984824
16	0.003398	0.988223
17	0.002635	0.990857
18	0.002044	0.992901
19	0.001586	0.994487
20	0.001231	0.995718
21	0.000955	0.996673
22	0.000742	0.997415
23	0.000576	0.997991
24	0.000448	0.998439
25	0.000348	0.998786
26	0.000270	0.999057
27	0.000210	0.999267
28	0.000163	0.999430
29	0.000127	0.999556

30	0.000099	0.999655
31	0.000077	0.999732
32	0.000060	0.999791
33	0.000046	0.999838
34	0.000036	0.999874
35	0.000028	0.999902

k=1.0
Mean=3·55
Variance=16·12

n	P(n)	F(n)
0	0.220000	0.220000
1	0.171600	0.391600
2	0.133848	0.525448
3	0.104401	0.629849
4	0.081433	0.711283
5	0.063518	0.774800
6	0.049544	0.824344
7	0.038644	0.862989
8	0.030143	0.893131
9	0.023511	0.916642
10	0.018339	0.934981
11	0.014304	0.949285
12	0.011157	0.960442
13	0.008703	0.969145
14	0.006788	0.975933
15	0.005295	0.981228
16	0.004130	0.985358
17	0.003221	0.988579
18	0.002513	0.991092
19	0.001960	0.993051
20	0.001529	0.994580
21	0.001192	0.995773
22	0.000930	0.996703
23	0.000725	0.997428
24	0.000566	0.997994
25	0.000441	0.998435
26	0.000344	0.998779
27	0.000269	0.999048
28	0.000209	0.999257
29	0.000163	0.999421
30	0.000127	0.999548
31	0.000099	0.999648
32	0.000078	0.999725
33	0.000060	0.999786
34	0.000047	0.999833
35	0.000037	0.999870
36	0.000029	0.999898
37	0.000022	0.999921

k=1.1
Mean=3·90
Variance=17·73

n	P(n)	F(n)
0	0.189088	0.189088
1	0.162238	0.351326
2	0.132873	0.484199
3	0.107095	0.591295
4	0.085623	0.676917
5	0.068122	0.745039
6	0.054020	0.799059
7	0.042738	0.841797
8	0.033752	0.875549
9	0.026619	0.902169
10	0.020971	0.923139
11	0.016506	0.939645
12	0.012982	0.952627
13	0.010204	0.962831
14	0.008016	0.970846
15	0.006294	0.977140
16	0.004940	0.982080
17	0.003876	0.985956
18	0.003040	0.988996
19	0.002384	0.991380
20	0.001869	0.993248
21	0.001464	0.994713
22	0.001147	0.995860
23	0.000899	0.996759
24	0.000704	0.997463
25	0.000551	0.998014
26	0.000432	0.998446
27	0.000338	0.998784
28	0.000265	0.999049
29	0.000207	0.999256
30	0.000162	0.999418
31	0.000127	0.999545
32	0.000099	0.999644
33	0.000078	0.999721
34	0.000061	0.999782
35	0.000048	0.999830
36	0.000037	0.999867
37	0.000029	0.999896
38	0.000023	0.999919

k=1.2
Mean=4·25
Variance=19·34

n	P(n)	F(n)
0	0.162520	0.162520
1	0.152119	0.314639
2	0.130518	0.445157
3	0.108591	0.553748
4	0.088936	0.642684
5	0.072145	0.714829
6	0.058149	0.772978
7	0.046652	0.819630
8	0.037298	0.856928
9	0.029739	0.886667

n	P(n)	F(n)
10	0.023660	0.910327
11	0.018791	0.929118
12	0.014901	0.944019
13	0.011802	0.955821
14	0.009337	0.965157
15	0.007380	0.972537
16	0.005828	0.978365
17	0.004599	0.982965
18	0.003627	0.986592
19	0.002859	0.989451
20	0.002252	0.991704
21	0.001774	0.993478
22	0.001396	0.994874
23	0.001098	0.995972
24	0.000864	0.996836
25	0.000679	0.997515
26	0.000534	0.998049
27	0.000419	0.998468
28	0.000330	0.998798
29	0.000259	0.999057
30	0.000203	0.999260
31	0.000160	0.999419
32	0.000125	0.999545
33	0.000098	0.999643
34	0.000077	0.999720
35	0.000060	0.999781
36	0.000047	0.999828
37	0.000037	0.999865
38	0.000029	0.999894
39	0.000023	0.999917

n	P(n)	F(n)
25	0.000826	0.996928
26	0.000652	0.997580
27	0.000514	0.998094
28	0.000405	0.998500
29	0.000320	0.998819
30	0.000252	0.999071
31	0.000198	0.999269
32	0.000156	0.999425
33	0.000123	0.999548
34	0.000097	0.999645
35	0.000076	0.999721
36	0.000060	0.999781
37	0.000047	0.999828
38	0.000037	0.999865
39	0.000029	0.999894
40	0.000023	0.999916

n	P(n)	F(n)
35	0.000095	0.999649
36	0.000075	0.999723
37	0.000059	0.999782
38	0.000046	0.999828
39	0.000037	0.999865
40	0.000029	0.999894
41	0.000023	0.999916

$k = 1.5$
Mean = 5.32
Variance = 24.17

n	P(n)	F(n)
0	0.103189	0.103189
1	0.120731	0.223920
2	0.117713	0.341633
3	0.107119	0.448752
4	0.093997	0.542749
5	0.080649	0.623398
6	0.068149	0.691547
7	0.056953	0.748500
8	0.047200	0.795699
9	0.038861	0.834560
10	0.031827	0.866388
11	0.025954	0.892341
12	0.021087	0.913428
13	0.017081	0.930509
14	0.013799	0.944308
15	0.011122	0.955430
16	0.008946	0.964376
17	0.007183	0.971559
18	0.005759	0.977318
19	0.004610	0.981927
20	0.003686	0.985613
21	0.002943	0.988556
22	0.002348	0.990904
23	0.001871	0.992775
24	0.001490	0.994265
25	0.001185	0.995451
26	0.000942	0.996393
27	0.000749	0.997142
28	0.000594	0.997736
29	0.000472	0.998208
30	0.000374	0.998582
31	0.000296	0.998878
32	0.000235	0.999113
33	0.000186	0.999299
34	0.000147	0.999446
35	0.000116	0.999562
36	0.000092	0.999654
37	0.000073	0.999727
38	0.000058	0.999785
39	0.000045	0.999830
40	0.000036	0.999866
41	0.000028	0.999894
42	0.000022	0.999917

$k = 1.3$
Mean = 4.61
Variance = 20.95

n	P(n)	F(n)
0	0.139685	0.139685
1	0.141640	0.281325
2	0.127052	0.408377
3	0.109010	0.517387
4	0.091405	0.608792
5	0.075574	0.684366
6	0.061895	0.746261
7	0.050347	0.796608
8	0.040743	0.837351
9	0.032839	0.870190
10	0.026383	0.896573
11	0.021140	0.917713
12	0.016901	0.934615
13	0.013487	0.948102
14	0.010746	0.958847
15	0.008549	0.967397
16	0.006793	0.974190
17	0.005392	0.979582
18	0.004276	0.983858
19	0.003388	0.987246
20	0.002682	0.989929
21	0.002122	0.992051
22	0.001678	0.993729
23	0.001326	0.995054
24	0.001047	0.996101

$k = 1.4$
Mean = 4.96
Variance = 22.56

n	P(n)	F(n)
0	0.120058	0.120058
1	0.131104	0.251162
2	0.122713	0.373875
3	0.108478	0.482353
4	0.093074	0.575427
5	0.078406	0.653833
6	0.065234	0.719067
7	0.053790	0.772856
8	0.044054	0.816910
9	0.035889	0.852799
10	0.029113	0.881913
11	0.023534	0.905447
12	0.018969	0.924415
13	0.015251	0.939666
14	0.012235	0.951901
15	0.009798	0.961700
16	0.007834	0.969533
17	0.006254	0.975787
18	0.004987	0.980774
19	0.003971	0.984745
20	0.003160	0.987905
21	0.002511	0.990416
22	0.001995	0.992411
23	0.001583	0.993993
24	0.001255	0.995248
25	0.000995	0.996243
26	0.000788	0.997031
27	0.000624	0.997655
28	0.000493	0.998148
29	0.000390	0.998538
30	0.000308	0.998846
31	0.000244	0.999090
32	0.000192	0.999282
33	0.000152	0.999434
34	0.000120	0.999554

k=1·6
Mean=5·67
Variance=25·79

n	P(n)	F(n)
0	0.088690	0.088690
1	0.110686	0.199376
2	0.112235	0.311611
3	0.105052	0.416663
4	0.094232	0.510895
5	0.082321	0.593216
6	0.070631	0.663847
7	0.059815	0.723662
8	0.050155	0.773816
9	0.041729	0.815545
10	0.034501	0.850046
11	0.028379	0.878425
12	0.023242	0.901667
13	0.018966	0.920633
14	0.015427	0.936060
15	0.012515	0.948574
16	0.010127	0.958702
17	0.008178	0.966880
18	0.006592	0.973471
19	0.005304	0.978775
20	0.004261	0.983036
21	0.003419	0.986455
22	0.002739	0.989194
23	0.002192	0.991387
24	0.001753	0.993139
25	0.001400	0.994539
26	0.001117	0.995657
27	0.000891	0.996547
28	0.000710	0.997257
29	0.000565	0.997822
30	0.000450	0.998271
31	0.000357	0.998629
32	0.000284	0.998913
33	0.000226	0.999138
34	0.000179	0.999318
35	0.000142	0.999460
36	0.000113	0.999572
37	0.000089	0.999661
38	0.000071	0.999732
39	0.000056	0.999788
40	0.000044	0.999833
41	0.000035	0.999868
42	0.000028	0.999895
43	0.000022	0.999917

k=1·7
Mean=6·03
Variance=27·40

n	P(n)	F(n)
0	0.076229	0.076229
1	0.101079	0.177308
2	0.106436	0.283744
3	0.102392	0.386136
4	0.093842	0.479978
5	0.083444	0.563423
6	0.072680	0.636103
7	0.062360	0.698463
8	0.052896	0.751359
9	0.044468	0.795827
10	0.037113	0.832941
11	0.030791	0.863731
12	0.025418	0.889149
13	0.020893	0.910042
14	0.017112	0.927153
15	0.013970	0.941123
16	0.011373	0.952497
17	0.009236	0.961733
18	0.007485	0.969218
19	0.006053	0.975271
20	0.004887	0.980157
21	0.003939	0.984096
22	0.003170	0.987266
23	0.002548	0.989813
24	0.002045	0.991859
25	0.001640	0.993499
26	0.001314	0.994812
27	0.001051	0.995863
28	0.000840	0.996704
29	0.000671	0.997375
30	0.000536	0.997911
31	0.000427	0.998338
32	0.000341	0.998679
33	0.000271	0.998950
34	0.000216	0.999166
35	0.000172	0.999338
36	0.000137	0.999475
37	0.000109	0.999583
38	0.000086	0.999670
39	0.000069	0.999738
40	0.000054	0.999793
41	0.000043	0.999836
42	0.000034	0.999870
43	0.000027	0.999897
44	0.000021	0.999919

k=1·8
Mean=6·38
Variance=29·01

n	P(n)	F(n)
0	0.065518	0.065518
1	0.091987	0.157505
2	0.100450	0.257955
3	0.099245	0.357200
4	0.092893	0.450093
5	0.084050	0.534143
6	0.074300	0.608443
7	0.064577	0.673020
8	0.055407	0.728427
9	0.047059	0.775487
10	0.039643	0.815129
11	0.033170	0.848299
12	0.027598	0.875897
13	0.022851	0.898748
14	0.018842	0.917590

15	0.015481	0.933070
16	0.012679	0.945749
17	0.010355	0.956104
18	0.008436	0.964540
19	0.006857	0.971396
20	0.005562	0.976959
21	0.004504	0.981463
22	0.003641	0.985103
23	0.002939	0.988042
24	0.002368	0.990410
25	0.001907	0.992317
26	0.001533	0.993850
27	0.001231	0.995081
28	0.000988	0.996068
29	0.000792	0.996860
30	0.000634	0.997494
31	0.000507	0.998001
32	0.000406	0.998407
33	0.000324	0.998731
34	0.000259	0.998989
35	0.000206	0.999196
36	0.000165	0.999360
37	0.000131	0.999491
38	0.000104	0.999596
39	0.000083	0.999679
40	0.000066	0.999745
41	0.000053	0.999798
42	0.000042	0.999839
43	0.000033	0.999873
44	0.000026	0.999899
45	0.000021	0.999920

k=1·9
Mean=6·74
Variance=30·62

n	P(n)	F(n)
0	0.056312	0.056312
1	0.083455	0.139767
2	0.094387	0.234154
3	0.095709	0.329863
4	0.091450	0.421313
5	0.084170	0.505483
6	0.075501	0.580984
7	0.066462	0.647446
8	0.057673	0.705119
9	0.049483	0.754602
10	0.042071	0.796673
11	0.035500	0.832173
12	0.029767	0.861939
13	0.024825	0.886765
14	0.020609	0.907373
15	0.017039	0.924413
16	0.014038	0.938451
17	0.011529	0.949980
18	0.009443	0.959423
19	0.007714	0.967137

75

20	0.006288	0.973425
21	0.005115	0.978540
22	0.004153	0.982692
23	0.003366	0.986058
24	0.002724	0.988782
25	0.002201	0.990983
26	0.001776	0.992759
27	0.001432	0.994191
28	0.001153	0.995343
29	0.000927	0.996270
30	0.000745	0.997015
31	0.000598	0.997613
32	0.000479	0.998092
33	0.000384	0.998476
34	0.000308	0.998783
35	0.000246	0.999029
36	0.000197	0.999226
37	0.000157	0.999383
38	0.000125	0.999509
39	0.000100	0.999609
40	0.000080	0.999689
41	0.000064	0.999752
42	0.000051	0.999803
43	0.000040	0.999844
44	0.000032	0.999876
45	0.000026	0.999901

k=2·0
Mean=7·09
Variance=32·23

n	P(n)	F(n)
0	0.048400	0.048400
1	0.075504	0.123904
2	0.088340	0.212244
3	0.091873	0.304117
4	0.089576	0.393693
5	0.083844	0.477537
6	0.076298	0.553835
7	0.068014	0.621848
8	0.059682	0.681531
9	0.051725	0.733255
10	0.044380	0.777635
11	0.037763	0.815398
12	0.031910	0.847308
13	0.026804	0.874112
14	0.022401	0.896513
15	0.018637	0.915150
16	0.015446	0.930596
17	0.012756	0.943352
18	0.010503	0.953855
19	0.008623	0.962478
20	0.007062	0.969540
21	0.005771	0.975312
22	0.004706	0.980018
23	0.003830	0.983848
24	0.003112	0.986960
25	0.002525	0.989485
26	0.002045	0.991529
27	0.001654	0.993183
28	0.001336	0.994520
29	0.001078	0.995598
30	0.000869	0.996467
31	0.000700	0.997167
32	0.000563	0.997730
33	0.000452	0.998182
34	0.000363	0.998545
35	0.000291	0.998836
36	0.000234	0.999070
37	0.000187	0.999257
38	0.000150	0.999407
39	0.000120	0.999527
40	0.000096	0.999623
41	0.000077	0.999699
42	0.000061	0.999760
43	0.000049	0.999809
44	0.000039	0.999848
45	0.000031	0.999879
46	0.000025	0.999904

k=2·1
Mean=7·45
Variance=33·84

n	P(n)	F(n)
0	0.041599	0.041599
1	0.068140	0.109739
2	0.082381	0.192121
3	0.087818	0.279939
4	0.087335	0.367274
5	0.083108	0.450382
6	0.076709	0.527091
7	0.069235	0.596327
8	0.061429	0.657756
9	0.053771	0.711526
10	0.046555	0.758081
11	0.039944	0.798025
12	0.034012	0.832038
13	0.028774	0.860812
14	0.024208	0.885020
15	0.020267	0.905286
16	0.016895	0.922181
17	0.014031	0.936211
18	0.011613	0.947824
19	0.009582	0.957406
20	0.007885	0.965292
21	0.006473	0.971764
22	0.005301	0.977065
23	0.004333	0.981398
24	0.003534	0.984932
25	0.002878	0.987810
26	0.002340	0.990150
27	0.001899	0.992050
28	0.001540	0.993589
29	0.001247	0.994836

k=2·2
Mean=7·80
Variance=35·45

n	P(n)	F(n)
0	0.035754	0.035754
1	0.061355	0.097109
2	0.076571	0.173680
3	0.083615	0.257295
4	0.084786	0.342080
5	0.082005	0.424085
6	0.076756	0.500841
7	0.070133	0.570975
8	0.062910	0.633884
9	0.055612	0.689497
10	0.048583	0.738079
11	0.042029	0.780108
12	0.036060	0.816168
13	0.030724	0.846892
14	0.026018	0.872910
15	0.021918	0.894828
16	0.018378	0.913206
17	0.015347	0.928553
18	0.012769	0.941322
19	0.010589	0.951910
20	0.008755	0.960665
21	0.007219	0.967884
22	0.005938	0.973821
23	0.004873	0.978695
24	0.003991	0.982686
25	0.003262	0.985948
26	0.002662	0.988610
27	0.002169	0.990779
28	0.001764	0.992543
29	0.001433	0.993976
30	0.001162	0.995139
31	0.000942	0.996080
32	0.000762	0.996843
33	0.000616	0.997459
34	0.000498	0.997956

k=2·0 (continued)

| 25 | 0.002525 | 0.989485 |

k=2·1 (continued)

30	0.001008	0.995844
31	0.000814	0.996658
32	0.000657	0.997315
33	0.000529	0.997844
34	0.000426	0.998271
35	0.000343	0.998614
36	0.000276	0.998889
37	0.000221	0.999111
38	0.000178	0.999288
39	0.000143	0.999431
40	0.000114	0.999545
41	0.000091	0.999637
42	0.000073	0.999710
43	0.000059	0.999769
44	0.000047	0.999815
45	0.000037	0.999853
46	0.000030	0.999883
47	0.000024	0.999907

n	P(n)	F(n)
35	0.000401	0.998358
36	0.000323	0.998681
37	0.000261	0.998942
38	0.000210	0.999151
39	0.000169	0.999320
40	0.000135	0.999455
41	0.000109	0.999564
42	0.000087	0.999651
43	0.000070	0.999721
44	0.000056	0.999777
45	0.000045	0.999822
46	0.000036	0.999858
47	0.000029	0.999886
48	0.000023	0.999909

k = 2·3
Mean = 8·15
Variance = 37·07

n	P(n)	F(n)
0	0.030731	0.030731
1	0.055131	0.085862
2	0.070953	0.156815
3	0.079326	0.236141
4	0.081983	0.318124
5	0.080573	0.398697
6	0.076464	0.475161
7	0.070718	0.545880
8	0.064124	0.610003
9	0.057241	0.667244
10	0.050452	0.717697
11	0.044004	0.761700
12	0.038041	0.799742
13	0.032639	0.832381
14	0.027823	0.860203
15	0.023582	0.883786
16	0.019889	0.903675
17	0.016700	0.920374
18	0.013966	0.934341
19	0.011639	0.945980
20	0.009669	0.955649
21	0.008008	0.963657
22	0.006616	0.970273
23	0.005452	0.975725
24	0.004483	0.980208
25	0.003678	0.983886
26	0.003013	0.986899
27	0.002463	0.989362
28	0.002010	0.991372
29	0.001638	0.993011
30	0.001333	0.994344
31	0.001084	0.995427
32	0.000880	0.996307
33	0.000713	0.997020
34	0.000577	0.997597
35	0.000467	0.998065
36	0.000378	0.998442
37	0.000305	0.998747
38	0.000246	0.998993
39	0.000198	0.999191

n	P(n)	F(n)
40	0.000160	0.999351
41	0.000128	0.999479
42	0.000103	0.999582
43	0.000083	0.999665
44	0.000067	0.999732
45	0.000053	0.999785
46	0.000043	0.999828
47	0.000034	0.999863
48	0.000028	0.999890
49	0.000022	0.999912

k = 2·4
Mean = 8·51
Variance = 38·68

n	P(n)	F(n)
0	0.026413	0.026413
1	0.049445	0.075858
2	0.065564	0.141421
3	0.075005	0.216426
4	0.078980	0.295406
5	0.078854	0.374260
6	0.075857	0.450118
7	0.071003	0.521120
8	0.065074	0.586194
9	0.058653	0.644847
10	0.052154	0.697002
11	0.045858	0.742860
12	0.039942	0.782802
13	0.034510	0.817312
14	0.029610	0.846922
15	0.025251	0.872173
16	0.021419	0.893592
17	0.018083	0.911675
18	0.015202	0.926877
19	0.012731	0.939608
20	0.010625	0.950233
21	0.008840	0.959073
22	0.007334	0.966407
23	0.006069	0.972476
24	0.005010	0.977486
25	0.004127	0.981613
26	0.003392	0.985005
27	0.002783	0.987788
28	0.002279	0.990067
29	0.001864	0.991931
30	0.001521	0.993452
31	0.001240	0.994692
32	0.001010	0.995702
33	0.000821	0.996523
34	0.000667	0.997190
35	0.000541	0.997731
36	0.000438	0.998169
37	0.000355	0.998524
38	0.000287	0.998811
39	0.000232	0.999043
40	0.000187	0.999230
41	0.000151	0.999381
42	0.000122	0.999503
43	0.000098	0.999601
44	0.000079	0.999680

n	P(n)	F(n)
45	0.000063	0.999743
46	0.000051	0.999794
47	0.000041	0.999835
48	0.000033	0.999868
49	0.000026	0.999894
50	0.000021	0.999915

k = 2·5
Mean = 8·86
Variance = 40·29

n	P(n)	F(n)
0	0.022702	0.022702
1	0.044268	0.066970
2	0.060426	0.127396
3	0.070698	0.198094
4	0.075824	0.273918
5	0.076886	0.350804
6	0.074963	0.425767
7	0.071001	0.496769
8	0.065765	0.562533
9	0.059846	0.622379
10	0.053682	0.676061
11	0.047582	0.723643
12	0.041753	0.765396
13	0.036325	0.801721
14	0.031369	0.833090
15	0.026915	0.860005
16	0.022962	0.882966
17	0.019490	0.902457
18	0.016469	0.918926
19	0.013860	0.932786
20	0.011622	0.944408
21	0.009713	0.954121
22	0.008092	0.962213
23	0.006724	0.968937
24	0.005572	0.974509
25	0.004607	0.979116
26	0.003801	0.982917
27	0.003129	0.986046
28	0.002572	0.988618
29	0.002110	0.990728
30	0.001728	0.992456
31	0.001413	0.993869
32	0.001154	0.995022
33	0.000941	0.995963
34	0.000766	0.996729
35	0.000623	0.997353
36	0.000506	0.997859
37	0.000411	0.998270
38	0.000333	0.998603
39	0.000270	0.998873
40	0.000218	0.999092
41	0.000177	0.999268
42	0.000143	0.999411
43	0.000115	0.999526
44	0.000093	0.999619

n	P(n)	F(n)
45	0.000075	0.999694
46	0.000060	0.999754
47	0.000049	0.999803
48	0.000039	0.999842
49	0.000031	0.999873
50	0.000025	0.999898
51	0.000020	0.999919

k=3·0
Mean=10·64
Variance=48·35

n	P(n)	F(n)
0	0.010648	0.010648
1	0.024916	0.035564
2	0.038869	0.074434
3	0.050530	0.124964
4	0.059120	0.184085
5	0.064560	0.248644
6	0.067142	0.315786
7	0.067334	0.383120
8	0.065650	0.448770
9	0.062587	0.511357
10	0.058581	0.569938
11	0.054001	0.623939
12	0.049141	0.673080
13	0.044227	0.717307
14	0.039425	0.756732
15	0.034852	0.791584
16	0.030583	0.822167
17	0.026661	0.848828
18	0.023106	0.871934
19	0.019920	0.891853
20	0.017091	0.908944
21	0.014601	0.923545
22	0.012424	0.935969
23	0.010533	0.946502
24	0.008901	0.955403
25	0.007498	0.962901
26	0.006298	0.969199
27	0.005277	0.974476
28	0.004410	0.978885
29	0.003677	0.982562
30	0.003059	0.985621
31	0.002540	0.988161
32	0.002105	0.990266
33	0.001741	0.992008
34	0.001438	0.993446
35	0.001186	0.994632
36	0.000976	0.995608
37	0.000803	0.996411
38	0.000659	0.997070
39	0.000540	0.997611
40	0.000443	0.998053
41	0.000362	0.998415
42	0.000296	0.998711
43	0.000242	0.998953
44	0.000197	0.999150

n	P(n)	F(n)
45	0.000160	0.999310
46	0.000131	0.999441
47	0.000106	0.999547
48	0.000086	0.999633
49	0.000070	0.999703
50	0.000057	0.999760
51	0.000046	0.999806
52	0.000037	0.999844
53	0.000030	0.999874
54	0.000024	0.999898
55	0.000020	0.999918

k=3·5
Mean=12·41
Variance=56·40

n	P(n)	F(n)
0	0.004994	0.004994
1	0.013635	0.018629
2	0.023929	0.042558
3	0.034218	0.076776
4	0.043371	0.120147
5	0.050745	0.170892
6	0.056073	0.226964
7	0.059357	0.286321
8	0.060767	0.347088
9	0.060564	0.407652
10	0.059050	0.466702
11	0.056527	0.523229
12	0.053277	0.576506
13	0.049547	0.626053
14	0.045548	0.671601
15	0.041449	0.713050
16	0.037382	0.750431
17	0.033446	0.783877
18	0.029711	0.813588
19	0.026224	0.839811
20	0.023011	0.862823
21	0.020086	0.882908
22	0.017447	0.900355
23	0.015088	0.915443
24	0.012994	0.928438
25	0.011149	0.939587
26	0.009533	0.949120
27	0.008124	0.957244
28	0.006902	0.964146
29	0.005848	0.969994
30	0.004942	0.974936
31	0.004165	0.979101
32	0.003503	0.982604
33	0.002939	0.985543
34	0.002461	0.988004
35	0.002057	0.990060
36	0.001716	0.991776
37	0.001429	0.993205
38	0.001188	0.994392
39	0.000986	0.995378

n	P(n)	F(n)
40	0.000817	0.996195
41	0.000676	0.996871
42	0.000559	0.997430
43	0.000461	0.997891
44	0.000380	0.998271
45	0.000313	0.998584
46	0.000257	0.998842
47	0.000211	0.999053
48	0.000174	0.999226
49	0.000142	0.999369
50	0.000116	0.999485
51	0.000095	0.999581
52	0.000078	0.999658
53	0.000064	0.999722
54	0.000052	0.999774
55	0.000042	0.999816
56	0.000035	0.999851
57	0.000028	0.999879
58	0.000023	0.999902

k=4·0
Mean=14·18
Variance=64·46

n	P(n)	F(n)
0	0.002343	0.002343
1	0.007309	0.009651
2	0.014252	0.023903
3	0.022233	0.046137
4	0.030348	0.076485
5	0.037875	0.114360
6	0.044314	0.158674
7	0.049378	0.208052
8	0.052958	0.261010
9	0.055076	0.316086
10	0.055847	0.371934
11	0.055441	0.427375
12	0.054055	0.481430
13	0.051893	0.533323
14	0.049150	0.582473
15	0.046004	0.628478
16	0.042612	0.671089
17	0.039102	0.710192
18	0.035583	0.745775
19	0.032137	0.777912
20	0.028827	0.806739
21	0.025697	0.832437
22	0.022777	0.855214
23	0.020084	0.875297
24	0.017623	0.892921
25	0.015396	0.908316
26	0.013394	0.921711
27	0.011608	0.933319
28	0.010025	0.943344
29	0.008628	0.951972
30	0.007403	0.959375
31	0.006333	0.965708
32	0.005403	0.971111
33	0.004597	0.975708
34	0.003902	0.979610

n	P(n)	F(n)
35	0.003305	0.982915
36	0.002793	0.985708
37	0.002355	0.988062
38	0.001982	0.990044
39	0.001665	0.991709
40	0.001396	0.993105
41	0.001168	0.994273
42	0.000976	0.995249
43	0.000815	0.996064
44	0.000679	0.996743
45	0.000565	0.997308
46	0.000469	0.997777
47	0.000389	0.998166
48	0.000323	0.998489
49	0.000267	0.998756
50	0.000221	0.998977
51	0.000182	0.999160
52	0.000150	0.999310
53	0.000124	0.999434
54	0.000102	0.999536
55	0.000084	0.999620
56	0.000069	0.999689
57	0.000057	0.999746
58	0.000046	0.999792
59	0.000038	0.999830
60	0.000031	0.999862
61	0.000026	0.999887
62	0.000021	0.999908

k=4.5
Mean=15.95
Variance=72.52

n	P(n)	F(n)
0	0.001099	0.001099
1	0.003857	0.004955
2	0.008272	0.013228
3	0.013981	0.027208
4	0.020447	0.047655
5	0.027112	0.074767
6	0.033483	0.108250
7	0.039176	0.147426
8	0.043926	0.191352
9	0.047586	0.238938
10	0.050108	0.289046
11	0.051520	0.340566
12	0.051907	0.392473
13	0.051388	0.443860
14	0.050103	0.493963
15	0.048199	0.542162
16	0.045819	0.587982
17	0.043097	0.631079
18	0.040152	0.671231
19	0.037088	0.708318
20	0.033991	0.742309
21	0.030932	0.773241
22	0.027965	0.801206
23	0.025132	0.826338
24	0.022462	0.848800

n	P(n)	F(n)
25	0.019973	0.868773
26	0.017676	0.886450
27	0.015575	0.902024
28	0.013667	0.915691
29	0.011947	0.927638
30	0.010406	0.938043
31	0.009033	0.947076
32	0.007816	0.954892
33	0.006743	0.961635
34	0.005801	0.967436
35	0.004977	0.972413
36	0.004260	0.976673
37	0.003637	0.980310
38	0.003098	0.983408
39	0.002633	0.986042
40	0.002234	0.988275
41	0.001891	0.990166
42	0.001598	0.991764
43	0.001348	0.993112
44	0.001135	0.994247
45	0.000954	0.995201
46	0.000801	0.996002
47	0.000671	0.996673
48	0.000562	0.997235
49	0.000469	0.997704
50	0.000392	0.998096
51	0.000327	0.998423
52	0.000272	0.998695
53	0.000226	0.998921
54	0.000188	0.999108
55	0.000156	0.999264
56	0.000129	0.999393
57	0.000107	0.999500
58	0.000088	0.999589
59	0.000073	0.999662
60	0.000060	0.999722
61	0.000050	0.999772
62	0.000041	0.999813
63	0.000034	0.999846
64	0.000028	0.999874
65	0.000023	0.999897
66	0.000019	0.999916

k=5.0
Mean=17.73
Variance=80.58

n	P(n)	F(n)
0	0.000515	0.000515
1	0.002010	0.002525
2	0.004703	0.007228
3	0.008560	0.015788
4	0.013353	0.029142
5	0.018748	0.047890
6	0.024373	0.072262
7	0.029874	0.102136
8	0.034952	0.137088
9	0.039380	0.176468
10	0.043002	0.219470
11	0.045739	0.265209
12	0.047569	0.312778
13	0.048520	0.361298
14	0.048659	0.409956
15	0.048075	0.458031
16	0.046873	0.504904
17	0.045163	0.550067
18	0.043056	0.593123
19	0.040654	0.633776
20	0.038052	0.671828
21	0.035334	0.707162
22	0.032571	0.739733
23	0.029824	0.769557
24	0.027140	0.796697
25	0.024556	0.821254
26	0.022101	0.843354
27	0.019792	0.863146
28	0.017643	0.880790
29	0.015660	0.896450
30	0.013843	0.910293
31	0.012191	0.922484
32	0.010698	0.933182
33	0.009356	0.942538
34	0.008156	0.950694
35	0.007089	0.957782
36	0.006144	0.963926
37	0.005310	0.969236
38	0.004578	0.973814
39	0.003937	0.977751
40	0.003378	0.981128
41	0.002892	0.984020
42	0.002470	0.986491
43	0.002106	0.988597
44	0.001792	0.990389
45	0.001522	0.991911
46	0.001291	0.993202
47	0.001092	0.994294
48	0.000923	0.995217
49	0.000779	0.995996
50	0.000656	0.996651
51	0.000552	0.997203
52	0.000463	0.997667
53	0.000389	0.998056
54	0.000326	0.998381
55	0.000273	0.998654
56	0.000228	0.998882
57	0.000190	0.999072
58	0.000159	0.999230
59	0.000132	0.999362
60	0.000110	0.999472
61	0.000091	0.999563
62	0.000076	0.999639
63	0.000063	0.999702
64	0.000052	0.999754
65	0.000043	0.999797
66	0.000036	0.999833
67	0.000030	0.999863
68	0.000024	0.999887
69	0.000020	0.999907

k = 0·1
Mean = 0·32
Variance = 1·32

n	P(n)	F(n)
0	0.867004	0.867004
1	0.065892	0.932896
2	0.027543	0.960439
3	0.014653	0.975092
4	0.008631	0.983723
5	0.005379	0.989101
6	0.003475	0.992576
7	0.002301	0.994877
8	0.001552	0.996429
9	0.001062	0.997491
10	0.000734	0.998225
11	0.000512	0.998737
12	0.000360	0.999098
13	0.000255	0.999352
14	0.000181	0.999534
15	0.000129	0.999663
16	0.000093	0.999756
17	0.000067	0.999823
18	0.000048	0.999871
19	0.000035	0.999906

k = 0·2
Mean = 0·63
Variance = 2·64

n	P(n)	F(n)
0	0.751696	0.751696
1	0.114258	0.865954
2	0.052102	0.918055
3	0.029038	0.947093
4	0.017655	0.964748
5	0.011271	0.976019
6	0.007424	0.983443
7	0.004997	0.988440
8	0.003418	0.991859
9	0.002367	0.994226
10	0.001655	0.995880
11	0.001166	0.997047
12	0.000827	0.997874
13	0.000590	0.998464
14	0.000423	0.998887
15	0.000304	0.999191
16	0.000220	0.999411
17	0.000159	0.999570
18	0.000116	0.999685
19	0.000084	0.999769
20	0.000061	0.999831
21	0.000045	0.999876
22	0.000033	0.999908

k = 0·3
Mean = 09·5
Variance = 3·96

n	P(n)	F(n)
0	0.651723	0.651723
1	0.148593	0.800316
2	0.073405	0.873721
3	0.042771	0.916492
4	0.026817	0.943309
5	0.017528	0.960837
6	0.011767	0.972604
7	0.008049	0.980652
8	0.005582	0.986234
9	0.003912	0.990146
10	0.002765	0.992911
11	0.001968	0.994879
12	0.001408	0.996287
13	0.001013	0.997300
14	0.000731	0.998031
15	0.000530	0.998561
16	0.000385	0.998946
17	0.000281	0.999226
18	0.000205	0.999431
19	0.000150	0.999581
20	0.000110	0.999691
21	0.000081	0.999772
22	0.000059	0.999831
23	0.000044	0.999875
24	0.000032	0.999908

k = 0·4
Mean = 1·27
Variance = 5·28

n	P(n)	F(n)
0	0.565047	0.565047
1	0.171774	0.736821
2	0.091384	0.828205
3	0.055561	0.883766
4	0.035893	0.919659
5	0.024005	0.943664
6	0.016419	0.960084
7	0.011409	0.971493
8	0.008021	0.979513
9	0.005689	0.985203
10	0.004064	0.989267
11	0.002920	0.992188
12	0.002109	0.994296
13	0.001529	0.995825
14	0.001112	0.996937
15	0.000811	0.997748
16	0.000593	0.998341
17	0.000435	0.998777
18	0.000320	0.999096
19	0.000235	0.999331
20	0.000173	0.999505
21	0.000128	0.999633
22	0.000095	0.999728
23	0.000070	0.999798
24	0.000052	0.999850

| 25 | 0.000039 | 0.999888 |
| 26 | 0.000029 | 0.999917 |

k = 0·5
Mean = 1·58
Variance = 6·60

n	P(n)	F(n)
0	0.489898	0.489898
1	0.186161	0.676059
2	0.106112	0.782171
3	0.067204	0.849375
4	0.044691	0.894066
5	0.030569	0.924635
6	0.021296	0.945931
7	0.015029	0.960960
8	0.010708	0.971668
9	0.007686	0.979354
10	0.005549	0.984903
11	0.004026	0.988929
12	0.002932	0.991861
13	0.002143	0.994004
14	0.001570	0.995574
15	0.001154	0.996728
16	0.000849	0.997577
17	0.000627	0.998203
18	0.000463	0.998666
19	0.000343	0.999009
20	0.000254	0.999263
21	0.000188	0.999451
22	0.000140	0.999591
23	0.000104	0.999695
24	0.000077	0.999772
25	0.000058	0.999830
26	0.000043	0.999873
27	0.000032	0.999905

k = 0·6
Mean = 1·90
Variance = 7·92

n	P(n)	F(n)
0	0.424744	0.424744
1	0.193683	0.618427
2	0.117759	0.736186
3	0.077564	0.813750
4	0.053054	0.866804
5	0.037095	0.903899
6	0.026313	0.930212
7	0.018855	0.949067
8	0.013613	0.962680
9	0.009886	0.972567
10	0.007213	0.979780
11	0.005283	0.985062
12	0.003881	0.988943
13	0.002859	0.991802
14	0.002111	0.993913

n	P(n)	F(n)
15	0.001561	0.995474
16	0.001157	0.996631
17	0.000859	0.997489
18	0.000638	0.998127
19	0.000475	0.998602
20	0.000354	0.998956
21	0.000264	0.999219
22	0.000197	0.999416
23	0.000147	0.999563
24	0.000110	0.999672
25	0.000082	0.999755
26	0.000061	0.999816
27	0.000046	0.999862
28	0.000034	0.999896
29	0.000026	0.999922

k = 0·7
Mean = 2·22
Variance = 9·24

n	P(n)	F(n)
0	0.368254	0.368254
1	0.195911	0.564166
2	0.126559	0.690724
3	0.086566	0.777290
4	0.060856	0.838147
5	0.043476	0.881622
6	0.031389	0.913011
7	0.022833	0.935845
8	0.016703	0.952548
9	0.012271	0.964818
10	0.009046	0.973865
11	0.006688	0.980552
12	0.004955	0.985508
13	0.003679	0.989187
14	0.002736	0.991923
15	0.002038	0.993961
16	0.001520	0.995481
17	0.001135	0.996616
18	0.000848	0.997464
19	0.000634	0.998098
20	0.000475	0.998573
21	0.000356	0.998929
22	0.000267	0.999195
23	0.000200	0.999395
24	0.000150	0.999545
25	0.000113	0.999658
26	0.000085	0.999743
27	0.000064	0.999806
28	0.000048	0.999854
29	0.000036	0.999890
30	0.000027	0.999917

k = 0·8
Mean = 2·53
Variance = 10·56

n	P(n)	F(n)
0	0.319278	0.319278
1	0.194121	0.513399
2	0.132779	0.646178
3	0.094184	0.740362
4	0.068001	0.808363
5	0.049614	0.857977
6	0.036449	0.894426
7	0.026910	0.921337
8	0.019940	0.941277
9	0.014818	0.956095
10	0.011036	0.967131
11	0.008235	0.975367
12	0.006154	0.981521
13	0.004605	0.986126
14	0.003450	0.989576
15	0.002587	0.992164
16	0.001942	0.994105
17	0.001458	0.995563
18	0.001096	0.996659
19	0.000824	0.997484
20	0.000620	0.998104
21	0.000467	0.998571
22	0.000352	0.998922
23	0.000265	0.999187
24	0.000200	0.999386
25	0.000150	0.999537
26	0.000113	0.999650
27	0.000086	0.999736
28	0.000065	0.999801
29	0.000049	0.999849
30	0.000037	0.999886
31	0.000028	0.999914

k = 0·9
Mean = 2·85
Variance = 11·88

n	P(n)	F(n)
0	0.276815	0.276815
1	0.189342	0.466157
2	0.136705	0.602862
3	0.100432	0.703294
4	0.074420	0.777714
5	0.055428	0.833143
6	0.041423	0.874566
7	0.031032	0.905598
8	0.023290	0.928888
9	0.017503	0.946391
10	0.013170	0.959561
11	0.009918	0.969479
12	0.007475	0.976953
13	0.005637	0.982591
14	0.004254	0.986844

n	P(n)	F(n)
15	0.003211	0.990055
16	0.002425	0.992481
17	0.001832	0.994313
18	0.001385	0.995698
19	0.001047	0.996745
20	0.000792	0.997536
21	0.000599	0.998135
22	0.000453	0.998588
23	0.000343	0.998931
24	0.000259	0.999191
25	0.000196	0.999387
26	0.000149	0.999536
27	0.000113	0.999648
28	0.000085	0.999734
29	0.000065	0.999798
30	0.000049	0.999847
31	0.000037	0.999884
32	0.000028	0.999912

k = 1·0
Mean = 3·17
Variance = 13·19

n	P(n)	F(n)
0	0.240000	0.240000
1	0.182400	0.422400
2	0.138624	0.561024
3	0.105354	0.666378
4	0.080069	0.746447
5	0.060853	0.807300
6	0.046248	0.853548
7	0.035148	0.888697
8	0.026713	0.915409
9	0.020302	0.935711
10	0.015429	0.951140
11	0.011726	0.962867
12	0.008912	0.971779
13	0.006773	0.978552
14	0.005148	0.983699
15	0.003912	0.987612
16	0.002973	0.990585
17	0.002260	0.992844
18	0.001717	0.994562
19	0.001305	0.995867
20	0.000992	0.996859
21	0.000754	0.997613
22	0.000573	0.998186
23	0.000435	0.998621
24	0.000331	0.998952
25	0.000252	0.999204
26	0.000191	0.999395
27	0.000145	0.999540
28	0.000110	0.999650
29	0.000084	0.999734
30	0.000064	0.999798
31	0.000048	0.999847
32	0.000037	0.999883
33	0.000028	0.999911

k = 1·1
Mean = 3·48
Variance = 14·51

n	P(n)	F(n)
0	0.208081	0.208081
1	0.173956	0.382037
2	0.138817	0.520853
3	0.109017	0.629871
4	0.084925	0.714795
5	0.065833	0.780629
6	0.050867	0.831496
7	0.039211	0.870707
8	0.030173	0.900881
9	0.023186	0.924067
10	0.017798	0.941865
11	0.013649	0.955514
12	0.010460	0.965974
13	0.008011	0.973985
14	0.006132	0.980117
15	0.004691	0.984808
16	0.003588	0.988395
17	0.002743	0.991138
18	0.002096	0.993234
19	0.001601	0.994835
20	0.001223	0.996058
21	0.000934	0.996992
22	0.000713	0.997705
23	0.000544	0.998249
24	0.000415	0.998665
25	0.000317	0.998982
26	0.000242	0.999223
27	0.000184	0.999408
28	0.000141	0.999549
29	0.000107	0.999656
30	0.000082	0.999738
31	0.000062	0.999800
32	0.000048	0.999848
33	0.000036	0.999884
34	0.000028	0.999912

k = 1·2
Mean = 3·80
Variance = 15·83

n	P(n)	F(n)
0	0.180407	0.180407
1	0.164531	0.344938
2	0.137548	0.482486
3	0.111506	0.593992
4	0.088982	0.682974
5	0.070331	0.753305
6	0.055233	0.808538
7	0.043177	0.851714
8	0.033635	0.885349
9	0.026130	0.911479
10	0.020256	0.931736
11	0.015675	0.947410
12	0.012111	0.959522
13	0.009346	0.968868
14	0.007205	0.976072

n	P(n)	F(n)
15	0.005548	0.981621
16	0.004270	0.985890
17	0.003283	0.989173
18	0.002523	0.991696
19	0.001938	0.993634
20	0.001487	0.995121
21	0.001141	0.996262
22	0.000875	0.997137
23	0.000671	0.997808
24	0.000514	0.998322
25	0.000394	0.998716
26	0.000302	0.999018
27	0.000231	0.999249
28	0.000177	0.999425
29	0.000135	0.999561
30	0.000103	0.999664
31	0.000079	0.999743
32	0.000061	0.999804
33	0.000046	0.999850
34	0.000035	0.999885
35	0.000027	0.999912

k = 1·3
Mean = 4·12
Variance = 17·15

n	P(n)	F(n)
0	0.156414	0.156414
1	0.154537	0.310950
2	0.135065	0.446015
3	0.112914	0.558930
4	0.092251	0.651181
5	0.074317	0.725498
6	0.059305	0.784804
7	0.047004	0.831807
8	0.037062	0.868870
9	0.029106	0.897976
10	0.022784	0.920760
11	0.017788	0.938549
12	0.013857	0.952406
13	0.010775	0.963181
14	0.008364	0.971545
15	0.006484	0.978029
16	0.005020	0.983049
17	0.003883	0.986931
18	0.003000	0.989931
19	0.002316	0.992247
20	0.001787	0.994034
21	0.001377	0.995411
22	0.001061	0.996472
23	0.000817	0.997289
24	0.000629	0.997917
25	0.000483	0.998401
26	0.000372	0.998772
27	0.000286	0.999058
28	0.000219	0.999277
29	0.000168	0.999446

n	P(n)	F(n)
30	0.000129	0.999575
31	0.000099	0.999674
32	0.000076	0.999750
33	0.000058	0.999809
34	0.000045	0.999853
35	0.000034	0.999888
36	0.000026	0.999914

k = 1·4
Mean = 4·43
Variance = 18·47

n	P(n)	F(n)
0	0.135611	0.135611
1	0.144290	0.279902
2	0.131593	0.411494
3	0.113345	0.524840
4	0.094757	0.619596
5	0.077776	0.697373
6	0.063051	0.760423
7	0.050657	0.811080
8	0.040424	0.851504
9	0.032088	0.883592
10	0.025362	0.908954
11	0.019976	0.928930
12	0.015688	0.944618
13	0.012290	0.956907
14	0.009607	0.966515
15	0.007496	0.974011
16	0.005839	0.979850
17	0.004542	0.984392
18	0.003529	0.987921
19	0.002738	0.990660
20	0.002123	0.992783
21	0.001644	0.994427
22	0.001272	0.995699
23	0.000984	0.996683
24	0.000760	0.997443
25	0.000587	0.998030
26	0.000453	0.998482
27	0.000349	0.998832
28	0.000269	0.999101
29	0.000207	0.999308
30	0.000160	0.999468
31	0.000123	0.999591
32	0.000095	0.999686
33	0.000073	0.999759
34	0.000056	0.999815
35	0.000043	0.999858
36	0.000033	0.999891
37	0.000025	0.999916

k=1·5
Mean = 4·75
Variance = 19·79

n	P(n)	F(n)
0	0.117576	0.117576
1	0.134036	0.251612
2	0.127334	0.378946
3	0.112903	0.491849
4	0.096532	0.588381
5	0.080701	0.669082
6	0.066444	0.735526
7	0.054104	0.789630
8	0.043689	0.833319
9	0.035048	0.868367
10	0.027969	0.896336
11	0.022222	0.918558
12	0.017593	0.936151
13	0.013885	0.950035
14	0.010929	0.960965
15	0.008583	0.969548
16	0.006727	0.976275
17	0.005263	0.981538
18	0.004111	0.985649
19	0.003206	0.988855
20	0.002498	0.991353
21	0.001944	0.993296
22	0.001511	0.994807
23	0.001173	0.995980
24	0.000910	0.996890
25	0.000706	0.997596
26	0.000547	0.998142
27	0.000423	0.998565
28	0.000327	0.998893
29	0.000253	0.999146
30	0.000195	0.999341
31	0.000151	0.999492
32	0.000117	0.999609
33	0.000090	0.999699
34	0.000069	0.999768
35	0.000053	0.999821
36	0.000041	0.999863
37	0.000032	0.999894
38	0.000024	0.999919

k=1·6
Mean = 5·07
Variance = 21·11

n	P(n)	F(n)
0	0.101938	0.101938
1	0.123957	0.225896
2	0.122470	0.348365
3	0.111692	0.460058
4	0.097619	0.557677
5	0.083093	0.640770
6	0.069466	0.710236
7	0.057319	0.767556
8	0.046830	0.814385
9	0.037963	0.852349
10	0.030583	0.882932
11	0.024511	0.907444
12	0.019560	0.927004
13	0.015552	0.942555
14	0.012326	0.954881
15	0.009742	0.964623
16	0.007682	0.972305
17	0.006044	0.978349
18	0.004747	0.983096
19	0.003721	0.986817
20	0.002913	0.989731
21	0.002277	0.992008
22	0.001778	0.993786
23	0.001386	0.995172
24	0.001080	0.996252
25	0.000841	0.997093
26	0.000654	0.997746
27	0.000508	0.998254
28	0.000394	0.998648
29	0.000306	0.998954
30	0.000237	0.999191
31	0.000184	0.999375
32	0.000142	0.999517
33	0.000110	0.999627
34	0.000085	0.999712
35	0.000066	0.999778
36	0.000051	0.999829
37	0.000039	0.999868
38	0.000030	0.999898
39	0.000023	0.999921

k=1·7
Mean = 5·38
Variance = 22·43

n	P(n)	F(n)
0	0.088381	0.088381
1	0.114188	0.202569
2	0.117157	0.319727
3	0.109815	0.429542
4	0.098065	0.527607
5	0.084964	0.612571
6	0.072106	0.684676
7	0.060280	0.744957
8	0.049822	0.794779
9	0.040810	0.835588
10	0.033186	0.868775
11	0.026827	0.895601
12	0.021578	0.917179
13	0.017282	0.934461
14	0.013791	0.948252
15	0.010970	0.959222
16	0.008702	0.967924
17	0.006886	0.974810
18	0.005437	0.980247
19	0.004284	0.984531
20	0.003370	0.987901
21	0.002647	0.990548
22	0.002075	0.992623
23	0.001625	0.994248
24	0.001271	0.995520
25	0.000993	0.996513
26	0.000775	0.997288
27	0.000604	0.997893
28	0.000471	0.998363
29	0.000366	0.998730
30	0.000285	0.999015
31	0.000221	0.999236
32	0.000172	0.999408
33	0.000134	0.999542
34	0.000104	0.999645
35	0.000080	0.999726
36	0.000062	0.999788
37	0.000048	0.999836
38	0.000037	0.999873
39	0.000029	0.999902

k=1·8
Mean = 5·70
Variance = 23·75

n	P(n)	F(n)
0	0.076627	0.076627
1	0.104825	0.181452
2	0.111534	0.292986
3	0.107370	0.400356
4	0.097922	0.498278
5	0.086328	0.584606
6	0.074357	0.658963
7	0.062970	0.721933
8	0.052643	0.774575
9	0.043565	0.818140
10	0.035758	0.853898
11	0.029152	0.883050
12	0.023633	0.906683
13	0.019066	0.925750
14	0.015318	0.941068
15	0.012263	0.953331
16	0.009786	0.963117
17	0.007787	0.970904
18	0.006181	0.977085
19	0.004896	0.981981
20	0.003869	0.985850
21	0.003053	0.988903
22	0.002405	0.991308
23	0.001891	0.993199
24	0.001485	0.994684
25	0.001165	0.995849
26	0.000912	0.996761
27	0.000714	0.997475
28	0.000558	0.998033
29	0.000436	0.998469
30	0.000340	0.998809
31	0.000265	0.999074
32	0.000207	0.999281
33	0.000161	0.999442
34	0.000125	0.999567
35	0.000097	0.999664
36	0.000076	0.999740
37	0.000059	0.999798
38	0.000046	0.999844
39	0.000035	0.999879

| 40 | 0.000027 | 0.999906 |

k = 1·9
Mean = 6·02
Variance = 25·07

n	P(n)	F(n)
0	0.066436	0.066436
1	0.095933	0.162369
2	0.105718	0.268087
3	0.104450	0.372537
4	0.097243	0.469779
5	0.087207	0.556987
6	0.076219	0.633206
7	0.065374	0.698580
8	0.055274	0.753854
9	0.046209	0.800063
10	0.038280	0.838342
11	0.031473	0.869815
12	0.025713	0.895528
13	0.020895	0.916423
14	0.016901	0.933324
15	0.013615	0.946940
16	0.010930	0.957870
17	0.008746	0.966616
18	0.006980	0.973596
19	0.005556	0.979151
20	0.004412	0.983564
21	0.003497	0.987061
22	0.002767	0.989828
23	0.002185	0.992012
24	0.001723	0.993735
25	0.001356	0.995092
26	0.001067	0.996158
27	0.000838	0.996996
28	0.000657	0.997653
29	0.000515	0.998168
30	0.000403	0.998571
31	0.000315	0.998886
32	0.000246	0.999132
33	0.000192	0.999325
34	0.000150	0.999475
35	0.000117	0.999591
36	0.000091	0.999683
37	0.000071	0.999753
38	0.000055	0.999809
39	0.000043	0.999852
40	0.000033	0.999885
41	0.000026	0.999911

k = 2·0
Mean = 6·33
Variance = 26·39

n	P(n)	F(n)
0	0.057600	0.057600
1	0.087552	0.145152
2	0.099809	0.244961
3	0.101140	0.346101
4	0.096083	0.442184
5	0.087628	0.529812
6	0.077697	0.607509
7	0.067485	0.674994
8	0.057700	0.732694
9	0.048724	0.781418
10	0.040733	0.822151
11	0.033772	0.855923
12	0.027805	0.883728
13	0.022758	0.906486
14	0.018531	0.925017
15	0.015023	0.940040
16	0.012131	0.952171
17	0.009762	0.961932
18	0.007831	0.969763
19	0.006265	0.976028
20	0.004999	0.981028
21	0.003980	0.985008
22	0.003163	0.988171
23	0.002508	0.990679
24	0.001986	0.992664
25	0.001569	0.994234
26	0.001239	0.995472
27	0.000976	0.996449
28	0.000768	0.997217
29	0.000604	0.997821
30	0.000474	0.998296
31	0.000372	0.998668
32	0.000292	0.998960
33	0.000228	0.999188
34	0.000179	0.999367
35	0.000140	0.999506
36	0.000109	0.999616
37	0.000085	0.999701
38	0.000066	0.999767
39	0.000052	0.999819
40	0.000040	0.999859
41	0.000031	0.999891
42	0.000024	0.999915

k = 2·1
Mean = 6·65
Variance = 27·71

n	P(n)	F(n)
0	0.049939	0.049939
1	0.079703	0.129643
2	0.093891	0.223533
3	0.097521	0.321054
4	0.094498	0.415552
5	0.087618	0.503170
6	0.078798	0.581969
7	0.069297	0.651266
8	0.059908	0.711173
9	0.051094	0.762268
10	0.043103	0.805371
11	0.036034	0.841406
12	0.029897	0.871302
13	0.024644	0.895946
14	0.020201	0.916147
15	0.016479	0.932626
16	0.013385	0.946010
17	0.010831	0.956841
18	0.008734	0.965575
19	0.007022	0.972598
20	0.005631	0.978228
21	0.004503	0.982731
22	0.003594	0.986325
23	0.002862	0.989187
24	0.002275	0.991462
25	0.001805	0.993266
26	0.001430	0.994696
27	0.001131	0.995827
28	0.000893	0.996720
29	0.000705	0.997425
30	0.000555	0.997980
31	0.000437	0.998417
32	0.000343	0.998760
33	0.000270	0.999030
34	0.000212	0.999241
35	0.000166	0.999407
36	0.000130	0.999537
37	0.000102	0.999639
38	0.000080	0.999718
39	0.000062	0.999781
40	0.000049	0.999829
41	0.000038	0.999867
42	0.000030	0.999898
43	0.000023	0.999915

k = 2·2
Mean = 6·97
Variance = 29·03

n	P(n)	F(n)
0	0.043298	0.04329
1	0.072394	0.11569
2	0.088031	0.20372
3	0.093665	0.29738
4	0.092541	0.38992
5	0.087210	0.47713
6	0.079536	0.55667
7	0.070810	0.62748
8	0.061888	0.68937
9	0.053306	0.74267
10	0.045374	0.78805
11	0.038246	0.82629
12	0.031974	0.85827
13	0.026543	0.88481
14	0.021902	0.90671

15	0.017977	0.924693
16	0.014687	0.939381
17	0.011950	0.951331
18	0.009688	0.961019
19	0.007828	0.968846
20	0.006306	0.975152
21	0.005066	0.980219
22	0.004060	0.984279
23	0.003247	0.987526
24	0.002591	0.990117
25	0.002064	0.992181
26	0.001641	0.993822
27	0.001302	0.995124
28	0.001032	0.996156
29	0.000817	0.996973
30	0.000646	0.997619
31	0.000510	0.998129
32	0.000402	0.998531
33	0.000317	0.998847
34	0.000249	0.999097
35	0.000196	0.999292
36	0.000154	0.999446
37	0.000121	0.999567
38	0.000095	0.999661
39	0.000074	0.999736
40	0.000058	0.999794
41	0.000045	0.999839
42	0.000035	0.999874
43	0.000028	0.999902

k = 2.3
Mean = 7.28
Variance = 30.35

n	P(n)	F(n)
0	0.037539	0.037539
1	0.065619	0.103158
2	0.082286	0.185444
3	0.089637	0.275080
4	0.090264	0.365344
5	0.086437	0.451781
6	0.079925	0.531707
7	0.072024	0.603731
8	0.063633	0.667364
9	0.055347	0.722711
10	0.047532	0.770243
11	0.040393	0.810636
12	0.034025	0.844661
13	0.028445	0.873106
14	0.023625	0.896731
15	0.019511	0.916243
16	0.016033	0.932276
17	0.013117	0.945393
18	0.010689	0.956082
19	0.008680	0.964762
20	0.007025	0.971787
21	0.005670	0.977457
22	0.004564	0.982021
23	0.003664	0.985685
24	0.002936	0.988621

25	0.002347	0.990968
26	0.001873	0.992841
27	0.001492	0.994333
28	0.001187	0.995520
29	0.000942	0.996462
30	0.000747	0.997209
31	0.000592	0.997801
32	0.000468	0.998269
33	0.000370	0.998638
34	0.000292	0.998930
35	0.000230	0.999160
36	0.000181	0.999341
37	0.000142	0.999483
38	0.000112	0.999595
39	0.000088	0.999683
40	0.000069	0.999752
41	0.000054	0.999806
42	0.000042	0.999849
43	0.000033	0.999882
44	0.000026	0.999908

k = 2.4
Mean = 7.60
Variance = 31.67

n	P(n)	F(n)
0	0.032547	0.032547
1	0.059365	0.091912
2	0.076700	0.168612
3	0.085495	0.254106
4	0.087718	0.341824
5	0.085332	0.427156
6	0.079984	0.507140
7	0.072946	0.580086
8	0.065140	0.645226
9	0.057208	0.702434
10	0.049565	0.751999
11	0.042464	0.794462
12	0.036037	0.830499
13	0.030338	0.860837
14	0.025363	0.886200
15	0.021075	0.907274
16	0.017418	0.924693
17	0.014328	0.939021
18	0.011736	0.950757
19	0.009577	0.960333
20	0.007788	0.968121
21	0.006313	0.974434
22	0.005103	0.979538
23	0.004115	0.983653
24	0.003310	0.986962
25	0.002656	0.989618
26	0.002127	0.991746
27	0.001701	0.993446
28	0.001357	0.994804
29	0.001081	0.995885
30	0.000860	0.996745
31	0.000683	0.997428
32	0.000542	0.997970
33	0.000429	0.998399
34	0.000340	0.998739

35	0.000269	0.999007
36	0.000212	0.999219
37	0.000167	0.999387
38	0.000132	0.999518
39	0.000104	0.999622
40	0.000082	0.999704
41	0.000064	0.999768
42	0.000050	0.999818
43	0.000040	0.999858
44	0.000031	0.999889
45	0.000024	0.999913

k = 2.5
Mean = 7.92
Variance = 32.99

n	P(n)	F(n)
0	0.028218	0.028218
1	0.053614	0.081833
2	0.071307	0.153140
3	0.081290	0.234430
4	0.084948	0.319378
5	0.083929	0.403307
6	0.079732	0.483040
7	0.073582	0.556621
8	0.066407	0.623029
9	0.058881	0.681910
10	0.051462	0.733372
11	0.044445	0.777817
12	0.038000	0.815817
13	0.032212	0.848029
14	0.027104	0.875134
15	0.022659	0.897793
16	0.018836	0.916629
17	0.015578	0.932207
18	0.012826	0.945033
19	0.010517	0.955550
20	0.008593	0.964143
21	0.006997	0.971140
22	0.005680	0.976820
23	0.004598	0.981418
24	0.003713	0.985132
25	0.002991	0.988123
26	0.002405	0.990528
27	0.001929	0.992457
28	0.001545	0.994001
29	0.001235	0.995236
30	0.000985	0.996221
31	0.000785	0.997006
32	0.000625	0.997631
33	0.000496	0.998127
34	0.000394	0.998521
35	0.000312	0.998833
36	0.000247	0.999080
37	0.000195	0.999275
38	0.000154	0.999430
39	0.000122	0.999552

40	0.000096	0.999648
41	0.000076	0.999723
42	0.000060	0.999783
43	0.000047	0.999830
44	0.000037	0.999867

| 45 | 0.000029 | 0.999896 |
| 46 | 0.000023 | 0.999918 |

45	0.000065	0.999755
46	0.000051	0.999807
47	0.000041	0.999847
48	0.000032	0.999880
49	0.000025	0.999905

50	0.000043	0.999833
51	0.000034	0.999867
52	0.000027	0.999895
53	0.000022	0.999917

k = 3·5
Mean = 11·08
Variance = 46·18

k = 4·0
Mean = 12·67
Variance = 52·78

k = 3·0
Mean = 9·50
Variance = 39·58

n	P(n)	F(n)		n	P(n)	F(n)		n	P(n)	F(n)
0	0.013824	0.013824		0	0.006772	0.006772		0	0.003318	0.003318
1	0.031519	0.045343		1	0.018014	0.024787		1	0.010086	0.013404
2	0.047908	0.093251		2	0.030805	0.055592		2	0.019163	0.032567
3	0.060684	0.153935		3	0.042921	0.098513		3	0.029128	0.061695
4	0.069180	0.223115		4	0.053008	0.151520		4	0.038741	0.100436
5	0.073607	0.296722		5	0.060429	0.211949		5	0.047109	0.147545
6	0.074589	0.371311		6	0.065062	0.277011		6	0.053704	0.201249
7	0.072884	0.444195		7	0.067106	0.344117		7	0.058307	0.259556
8	0.069240	0.513435		8	0.066939	0.411056		8	0.060931	0.320487
9	0.064316	0.577751		9	0.065005	0.476061		9	0.061743	0.382230
10	0.058656	0.636407		10	0.061755	0.537816		10	0.061002	0.443206
11	0.052684	0.689091		11	0.057600	0.595416		11	0.059006	0.502238
12	0.046713	0.735804		12	0.052896	0.648312		12	0.056056	0.558294
13	0.040964	0.776767		13	0.047932	0.696244		13	0.052434	0.610728
14	0.035580	0.812347		14	0.042933	0.739178		14	0.048389	0.659116
15	0.030646	0.842994		15	0.038068	0.777245		15	0.044131	0.703247
16	0.026202	0.869196		16	0.033452	0.810697		16	0.039828	0.743075
17	0.022257	0.891453		17	0.029162	0.839860		17	0.035611	0.778685
18	0.018795	0.910247		18	0.025242	0.865101		18	0.031575	0.810260
19	0.015787	0.926035		19	0.021708	0.886809		19	0.027786	0.838046
20	0.013198	0.939233		20	0.018560	0.905369		20	0.024285	0.862331
21	0.010986	0.950219		21	0.015785	0.921154		21	0.021093	0.883424
22	0.009108	0.959327		22	0.013360	0.934514		22	0.018217	0.901641
23	0.007524	0.966852		23	0.011257	0.945771		23	0.015651	0.917292
24	0.006195	0.973047		24	0.009447	0.955218		24	0.013381	0.930673
25	0.005085	0.978132		25	0.007897	0.963115		25	0.011390	0.942063
26	0.004162	0.982293		26	0.006579	0.969694		26	0.009655	0.951718
27	0.003397	0.985691		27	0.005463	0.975157		27	0.008153	0.959872
28	0.002766	0.988457		28	0.004523	0.979680		28	0.006860	0.966732
29	0.002247	0.990704		29	0.003734	0.983413		29	0.005753	0.972485
30	0.001822	0.992526		30	0.003074	0.986487		30	0.004810	0.977295
31	0.001474	0.994000		31	0.002525	0.989012		31	0.004009	0.981304
32	0.001190	0.995191		32	0.002069	0.991080		32	0.003333	0.984637
33	0.000959	0.996150		33	0.001691	0.992772		33	0.002763	0.987400
34	0.000772	0.996922		34	0.001380	0.994151		34	0.002285	0.989685
35	0.000620	0.997542		35	0.001124	0.995275		35	0.001886	0.991571
36	0.000498	0.998040		36	0.000913	0.996188		36	0.001553	0.993124
37	0.000399	0.998438		37	0.000741	0.996929		37	0.001276	0.994399
38	0.000319	0.998757		38	0.000600	0.997529		38	0.001046	0.995444
39	0.000255	0.999012		39	0.000485	0.998015		39	0.000856	0.996301
40	0.000203	0.999215		40	0.000392	0.998407		40	0.000699	0.997001
41	0.000162	0.999377		41	0.000316	0.998723		41	0.000570	0.997571
42	0.000129	0.999507		42	0.000254	0.998977		42	0.000465	0.998036
43	0.000103	0.999609		43	0.000205	0.999182		43	0.000378	0.998414
44	0.000082	0.999691		44	0.000164	0.999346		44	0.000307	0.998720
				45	0.000132	0.999478		45	0.000249	0.998968
				46	0.000106	0.999584		46	0.000201	0.999170
				47	0.000085	0.999668		47	0.000163	0.999333
				48	0.000068	0.999736		48	0.000131	0.999464
				49	0.000054	0.999790		49	0.000106	0.999570

n		
50	0.000085	0.999655
51	0.000069	0.999724
52	0.000055	0.999779
53	0.000044	0.999823
54	0.000036	0.999859
55	0.000029	0.999887
56	0.000023	0.999910

k=4·5
Mean = 14·25
Variance = 59·38

n	P(n)	F(n)
0	0.001625	0.001625
1	0.005559	0.007184
2	0.011618	0.018802
3	0.019131	0.037932
4	0.027261	0.065194
5	0.035221	0.100415
6	0.042383	0.142798
7	0.048317	0.191115
8	0.052786	0.243901
9	0.055718	0.299619
10	0.057167	0.356786
11	0.057271	0.414057
12	0.056221	0.470279
13	0.054232	0.524510
14	0.051520	0.576030
15	0.048292	0.624322
16	0.044730	0.669052
17	0.040994	0.710046
18	0.037213	0.747259
19	0.033492	0.780751
20	0.029908	0.810660
21	0.026519	0.837178
22	0.023361	0.860539
23	0.020456	0.880995
24	0.017814	0.898808
25	0.015434	0.914242
26	0.013309	0.927550
27	0.011426	0.938976
28	0.009769	0.948745
29	0.008320	0.957065
30	0.007061	0.964126
31	0.005972	0.970099
32	0.005036	0.975134
33	0.004233	0.979367
34	0.003548	0.982916
35	0.002966	0.985882
36	0.002474	0.988355
37	0.002058	0.990413
38	0.001708	0.992121
39	0.001414	0.993535
40	0.001169	0.994705
41	0.000964	0.995669
42	0.000794	0.996463
43	0.000653	0.997115
44	0.000535	0.997651
45	0.000439	0.998089
46	0.000359	0.998448
47	0.000293	0.998741
48	0.000239	0.998980
49	0.000194	0.999174
50	0.000158	0.999332
51	0.000128	0.999461
52	0.000104	0.999565
53	0.000084	0.999649
54	0.000068	0.999718
55	0.000055	0.999773
56	0.000045	0.999817
57	0.000036	0.999853
58	0.000029	0.999882
59	0.000023	0.999906

k=5·0
Mean = 15·83
Variance = 65·97

n	P(n)	F(n)
0	0.000796	0.000796
1	0.003026	0.003822
2	0.006899	0.010721
3	0.012234	0.022955
4	0.018596	0.041550
5	0.025439	0.066989
6	0.032222	0.099211
7	0.038483	0.137694
8	0.043870	0.181564
9	0.048160	0.229724
10	0.051242	0.280966
11	0.053105	0.334071
12	0.053813	0.387885
13	0.053482	0.441367
14	0.052260	0.493627
15	0.050309	0.543936
16	0.047793	0.591729
17	0.044870	0.636599
18	0.041679	0.678277
19	0.038344	0.716622
20	0.034970	0.751592
21	0.031640	0.783232
22	0.028418	0.811650
23	0.025354	0.837004
24	0.022481	0.859484
25	0.019819	0.879303
26	0.017380	0.896683
27	0.015165	0.911848
28	0.013172	0.925020
29	0.011392	0.936412
30	0.009812	0.946224
31	0.008419	0.954643
32	0.007199	0.961842
33	0.006134	0.967976
34	0.005210	0.973186
35	0.004412	0.977598
36	0.003726	0.981324
37	0.003138	0.984462
38	0.002636	0.987098
39	0.002209	0.989307
40	0.001846	0.991153
41	0.001540	0.992694
42	0.001282	0.993976
43	0.001065	0.995041
44	0.000883	0.995924
45	0.000731	0.996654
46	0.000604	0.997258
47	0.000498	0.997756
48	0.000410	0.998166
49	0.000337	0.998503
50	0.000277	0.998779
51	0.000227	0.999006
52	0.000186	0.999191
53	0.000152	0.999343
54	0.000124	0.999467
55	0.000101	0.999568
56	0.000082	0.999650
57	0.000067	0.999717
58	0.000054	0.999771
59	0.000044	0.999815
60	0.000036	0.999851
61	0.000029	0.999880
62	0.000023	0.999903

P = 0·26

k = 0·1
Mean = 0·28
Variance = 1·09

n	P(n)	F(n)
0	0.873972	0.873972
1	0.064674	0.938646
2	0.026322	0.964968
3	0.013635	0.978603
4	0.007820	0.986422
5	0.004745	0.991167
6	0.002985	0.994152
7	0.001925	0.996077
8	0.001264	0.997341
9	0.000842	0.998182
10	0.000567	0.998749
11	0.000385	0.999134
12	0.000264	0.999398
13	0.000182	0.999580
14	0.000126	0.999705
15	0.000087	0.999793
16	0.000061	0.999854
17	0.000043	0.999897
18	0.000030	0.999927

k = 0·2
Mean = 0·57
Variance = 2·19

n	P(n)	F(n)
0	0.763826	0.763826
1	0.113046	0.876873
2	0.050193	0.927065
3	0.027238	0.954303
4	0.016125	0.970428
5	0.010023	0.980451
6	0.006428	0.986879
7	0.004213	0.991092
8	0.002806	0.993898
9	0.001892	0.995790
10	0.001288	0.997078
11	0.000884	0.997962
12	0.000610	0.998573
13	0.000424	0.998996
14	0.000296	0.999292
15	0.000207	0.999499
16	0.000146	0.999645
17	0.000103	0.999748
18	0.000073	0.999820
19	0.000051	0.999872
20	0.000037	0.999908

k = 0·3
Mean = 0·85
Variance = 3·28

n	P(n)	F(n)
0	0.667563	0.667563
1	0.148199	0.815762
2	0.071284	0.887045
3	0.040442	0.927487
4	0.024690	0.952176
5	0.015712	0.967889
6	0.010271	0.978160
7	0.006840	0.985000
8	0.004619	0.989619
9	0.003152	0.992771
10	0.002169	0.994940
11	0.001503	0.996443
12	0.001047	0.997491
13	0.000733	0.998224
14	0.000516	0.998740
15	0.000364	0.999103
16	0.000257	0.999361
17	0.000183	0.999543
18	0.000130	0.999673
19	0.000093	0.999766
20	0.000066	0.999832
21	0.000047	0.999879
22	0.000034	0.999913

k = 0·4
Mean = 1·14
Variance = 4·38

n	P(n)	F(n)
0	0.583431	0.583431
1	0.172696	0.756126
2	0.089456	0.845583
3	0.052958	0.898541
4	0.033311	0.931851
5	0.021692	0.953543
6	0.014447	0.967990
7	0.009774	0.977764
8	0.006691	0.984455
9	0.004621	0.989076
10	0.003214	0.992290
11	0.002249	0.994539
12	0.001581	0.996120
13	0.001116	0.997236
14	0.000790	0.998026
15	0.000561	0.998588
16	0.000400	0.998988
17	0.000285	0.999273
18	0.000204	0.999477
19	0.000146	0.999624
20	0.000105	0.999729
21	0.000076	0.999804
22	0.000054	0.999859
23	0.000039	0.999898
24	0.000028	0.999926

k = 0·5
Mean = 1·42
Variance = 5·47

n	P(n)	F(n)
0	0.509902	0.509902
1	0.188664	0.698566
2	0.104708	0.803274
3	0.064570	0.867844
4	0.041809	0.909653
5	0.027845	0.937498
6	0.018888	0.956386
7	0.012979	0.969365
8	0.009004	0.978369
9	0.006293	0.984662
10	0.004424	0.989086
11	0.003125	0.992211
12	0.002216	0.994427
13	0.001577	0.996004
14	0.001125	0.997129
15	0.000805	0.997934
16	0.000577	0.998511
17	0.000414	0.998925
18	0.000298	0.999223
19	0.000215	0.999438
20	0.000155	0.999593
21	0.000112	0.999705
22	0.000081	0.999786
23	0.000059	0.999845
24	0.000042	0.999887
25	0.000031	0.999918

k = 0·6
Mean = 1·71
Variance = 6·57

n	P(n)	F(n)
0	0.445640	0.445640
1	0.197864	0.643504
2	0.117136	0.760639
3	0.075123	0.835762
4	0.050032	0.885794
5	0.034062	0.919856
6	0.023525	0.943381
7	0.016414	0.959795
8	0.011539	0.971334
9	0.008159	0.979493
10	0.005796	0.985290
11	0.004133	0.989423
12	0.002957	0.992380
13	0.002121	0.994501
14	0.001524	0.996025
15	0.001098	0.997123
16	0.000792	0.997917
17	0.000572	0.998488
18	0.000414	0.998902
19	0.000300	0.999202

n	P(n)	F(n)
0	0.000218	0.999420
1	0.000158	0.999578
2	0.000115	0.999692
3	0.000083	0.999776
4	0.000061	0.999836
5	0.000044	0.999881
6	0.000032	0.999913

k=0.7
Mean=1·99
Variance=7·66

n	P(n)	F(n)
0	0.389477	0.389477
1	0.201749	0.591225
2	0.126900	0.718125
3	0.084515	0.802641
4	0.057851	0.860492
5	0.040241	0.900733
6	0.028289	0.929022
7	0.020037	0.949059
8	0.014271	0.963331
9	0.010209	0.973539
10	0.007328	0.980867
11	0.005275	0.986142
12	0.003806	0.989948
13	0.002751	0.992699
14	0.001992	0.994691
15	0.001445	0.996136
16	0.001049	0.997185
17	0.000763	0.997948
18	0.000555	0.998503
19	0.000404	0.998907
20	0.000295	0.999201
21	0.000215	0.999416
22	0.000157	0.999573
23	0.000115	0.999688
24	0.000084	0.999771
25	0.000061	0.999833
26	0.000045	0.999877
27	0.000033	0.999910

k=0.8
Mean=2·28
Variance=8·76

n	P(n)	F(n)
0	0.340391	0.340391
1	0.201512	0.541903
2	0.134207	0.676110
3	0.092692	0.768802
4	0.065163	0.833965
5	0.046292	0.880256
6	0.033114	0.913370
7	0.023804	0.937174
8	0.017175	0.954349
9	0.012427	0.966776
10	0.009012	0.975788
11	0.006548	0.982335
12	0.004764	0.987100
13	0.003471	0.990571
14	0.002532	0.993104
15	0.001849	0.994952
16	0.001351	0.996303
17	0.000988	0.997291
18	0.000723	0.998014
19	0.000529	0.998544
20	0.000388	0.998932
21	0.000284	0.999216
22	0.000208	0.999424
23	0.000153	0.999577
24	0.000112	0.999689
25	0.000082	0.999772
26	0.000060	0.999832
27	0.000044	0.999877
28	0.000033	0.999909

k=0.9
Mean=2·56
Variance=9·85

n	P(n)	F(n)
0	0.297492	0.297492
1	0.198130	0.495622
2	0.139285	0.634908
3	0.099635	0.734543
4	0.071887	0.806430
5	0.052132	0.858563
6	0.037935	0.896498
7	0.027671	0.924169
8	0.020221	0.944389
9	0.014797	0.959186
10	0.010840	0.970026
11	0.007949	0.977975
12	0.005833	0.983808
13	0.004283	0.988092
14	0.003147	0.991239
15	0.002313	0.993552
16	0.001701	0.995253
17	0.001251	0.996505
18	0.000921	0.997425
19	0.000678	0.998103
20	0.000499	0.998602
21	0.000368	0.998970
22	0.000271	0.999241
23	0.000200	0.999440
24	0.000147	0.999587
25	0.000108	0.999696
26	0.000080	0.999776
27	0.000059	0.999834
28	0.000043	0.999878
29	0.000032	0.999910

k=1.0
Mean=2·85
Variance=10·95

n	P(n)	F(n)
0	0.260000	0.260000
1	0.192400	0.452400
2	0.142376	0.594776
3	0.105358	0.700134
4	0.077965	0.778099
5	0.057694	0.835794
6	0.042694	0.878487
7	0.031593	0.910081
8	0.023379	0.933460
9	0.017301	0.950760
10	0.012802	0.963562
11	0.009474	0.973036
12	0.007011	0.980047
13	0.005188	0.985235
14	0.003839	0.989074
15	0.002841	0.991914
16	0.002102	0.994017
17	0.001556	0.995572
18	0.001151	0.996724
19	0.000852	0.997575
20	0.000630	0.998206
21	0.000466	0.998672
22	0.000345	0.999018
23	0.000255	0.999273
24	0.000189	0.999462
25	0.000140	0.999602
26	0.000104	0.999705
27	0.000077	0.999782
28	0.000057	0.999839
29	0.000042	0.999881
30	0.000031	0.999912

k=1.1
Mean=3·13
Variance=12·04

n	P(n)	F(n)
0	0.227233	0.227233
1	0.184967	0.412200
2	0.143720	0.555920
3	0.109898	0.665817
4	0.083357	0.749175
5	0.062918	0.812093
6	0.047335	0.859428
7	0.035529	0.894957
8	0.026620	0.921576
9	0.019918	0.941494
10	0.014886	0.956380
11	0.011116	0.967496
12	0.008294	0.975791
13	0.006185	0.981976
14	0.004610	0.986586

n	P(n)	F(n)
15	0.003434	0.990019
16	0.002557	0.992576
17	0.001903	0.994480
18	0.001416	0.995896
19	0.001054	0.996950
20	0.000784	0.997733
21	0.000583	0.998316
22	0.000433	0.998749
23	0.000322	0.999071
24	0.000239	0.999310
25	0.000178	0.999487
26	0.000132	0.999619
27	0.000098	0.999717
28	0.000073	0.999790
29	0.000054	0.999844
30	0.000040	0.999884
31	0.000030	0.999914

k=1·2
Mean=3·42
Variance=13·14

n	P(n)	F(n)
0	0.198595	0.198595
1	0.176352	0.374947
2	0.143551	0.518498
3	0.113309	0.631807
4	0.088041	0.719849
5	0.067757	0.787605
6	0.051811	0.839416
7	0.039436	0.878852
8	0.029912	0.908764
9	0.022627	0.931391
10	0.017079	0.948470
11	0.012868	0.961338
12	0.009681	0.971019
13	0.007274	0.978293
14	0.005460	0.983753
15	0.004094	0.987847
16	0.003068	0.990914
17	0.002297	0.993211
18	0.001718	0.994930
19	0.001285	0.996215
20	0.000960	0.997175
21	0.000717	0.997892
22	0.000536	0.998428
23	0.000400	0.998828
24	0.000298	0.999127
25	0.000223	0.999349
26	0.000166	0.999515
27	0.000124	0.999639
28	0.000092	0.999731
29	0.000069	0.999800
30	0.000051	0.999851
31	0.000038	0.999889
32	0.000028	0.999917

k=1·3
Mean=3·70
Variance=14·23

n	P(n)	F(n)
0	0.173566	0.173566
1	0.166971	0.340537
2	0.142092	0.482629
3	0.115663	0.598292
4	0.092010	0.690302
5	0.072173	0.762475
6	0.056078	0.818553
7	0.043276	0.861829
8	0.033225	0.895054
9	0.025406	0.920461
10	0.019365	0.939825
11	0.014721	0.954546
12	0.011166	0.965712
13	0.008453	0.974165
14	0.006389	0.980554
15	0.004823	0.985377
16	0.003636	0.989013
17	0.002738	0.991751
18	0.002060	0.993811
19	0.001548	0.995359
20	0.001163	0.996522
21	0.000873	0.997395
22	0.000655	0.998050
23	0.000491	0.998540
24	0.000368	0.998908
25	0.000275	0.999184
26	0.000206	0.999390
27	0.000154	0.999544
28	0.000115	0.999659
29	0.000086	0.999746
30	0.000064	0.999810
31	0.000048	0.999858
32	0.000036	0.999894
33	0.000027	0.999921

k=1·4
Mean=3·98
Variance=15·33

n	P(n)	F(n)
0	0.151692	0.151692
1	0.157153	0.308845
2	0.139552	0.448397
3	0.117037	0.565434
4	0.095268	0.660703
5	0.076139	0.736841
6	0.060099	0.796940
7	0.047014	0.843954
8	0.036530	0.880484
9	0.028234	0.908718
10	0.021729	0.930447
11	0.016664	0.947111
12	0.012742	0.959853
13	0.009719	0.969573
14	0.007398	0.976971

n	P(n)	F(n)
15	0.005620	0.982591
16	0.004263	0.986854
17	0.003229	0.990083
18	0.002443	0.992525
19	0.001846	0.994371
20	0.001393	0.995764
21	0.001050	0.996814
22	0.000791	0.997606
23	0.000596	0.998202
24	0.000448	0.998650
25	0.000337	0.998987
26	0.000253	0.999240
27	0.000190	0.999431
28	0.000143	0.999573
29	0.000107	0.999680
30	0.000080	0.999761
31	0.000060	0.999821
32	0.000045	0.999866
33	0.000034	0.999900
34	0.000025	0.999925

k=1·5
Mean=4·27
Variance=16·42

n	P(n)	F(n)
0	0.132575	0.132575
1	0.147158	0.279732
2	0.136121	0.415853
3	0.117518	0.533371
4	0.097833	0.631204
5	0.079636	0.710841
6	0.063842	0.774683
7	0.050617	0.825300
8	0.039798	0.865098
9	0.031087	0.896185
10	0.024154	0.920339
11	0.018687	0.939026
12	0.014404	0.953430
13	0.011069	0.964499
14	0.008484	0.972983
15	0.006487	0.979470
16	0.004951	0.984421
17	0.003771	0.988192
18	0.002868	0.991060
19	0.002178	0.993238
20	0.001652	0.994891
21	0.001252	0.996142
22	0.000947	0.997090
23	0.000716	0.997806
24	0.000541	0.998347
25	0.000408	0.998756
26	0.000308	0.999064
27	0.000232	0.999296
28	0.000175	0.999471
29	0.000132	0.999602
30	0.000099	0.999701
31	0.000074	0.999776
32	0.000056	0.999832
33	0.000042	0.999874
34	0.000032	0.999905

k=1·6
Mean=4·55
Variance=17·51

n	P(n)	F(n)
0	0.115866	0.115866
1	0.137186	0.253052
2	0.131973	0.385025
3	0.117192	0.502217
4	0.099730	0.601947
5	0.082656	0.684603
6	0.067282	0.751885
7	0.054057	0.805942
8	0.043002	0.848944
9	0.033943	0.882887
10	0.026625	0.909512
11	0.020777	0.930289
12	0.016144	0.946432
13	0.012498	0.958930
14	0.009645	0.968575
15	0.007423	0.975997
16	0.005699	0.981696
17	0.004366	0.986062
18	0.003338	0.989400
19	0.002548	0.991949
20	0.001942	0.993891
21	0.001478	0.995370
22	0.001124	0.996494
23	0.000853	0.997347
24	0.000647	0.997994
25	0.000490	0.998485
26	0.000371	0.998856
27	0.000281	0.999137
28	0.000212	0.999349
29	0.000160	0.999510
30	0.000121	0.999631
31	0.000091	0.999722
32	0.000069	0.999791
33	0.000052	0.999843
34	0.000039	0.999882
35	0.000029	0.999911

k=1·7
Mean=4·84
Variance=18·61

n	P(n)	F(n)
0	0.101264	0.101264
1	0.127390	0.228654
2	0.127263	0.355917
3	0.116148	0.472065
4	0.100991	0.573056
5	0.085196	0.658252
6	0.070400	0.728652
7	0.057306	0.785958
8	0.046117	0.832075
9	0.036781	0.868856

10	0.029123	0.897979
11	0.022922	0.920901
12	0.017952	0.938853
13	0.014000	0.952853
14	0.010878	0.963731
15	0.008425	0.972156
16	0.006507	0.978664
17	0.005014	0.983678
18	0.003855	0.987532
19	0.002957	0.990490
20	0.002265	0.992755
21	0.001732	0.994487
22	0.001322	0.995809
23	0.001008	0.996818
24	0.000768	0.997586
25	0.000584	0.998170
26	0.000444	0.998614
27	0.000337	0.998951
28	0.000256	0.999207
29	0.000194	0.999400
30	0.000147	0.999547
31	0.000111	0.999658
32	0.000084	0.999742
33	0.000063	0.999805
34	0.000048	0.999853
35	0.000036	0.999890
36	0.000027	0.999917

k=1·8
Mean=5·12
Variance=19·70

n	P(n)	F(n)
0	0.088502	0.088502
1	0.117884	0.206386
2	0.122128	0.328514
3	0.114475	0.442989
4	0.101654	0.544643
5	0.087260	0.631902
6	0.073182	0.705084
7	0.060343	0.765428
8	0.049120	0.814547
9	0.039579	0.854127
10	0.031632	0.885759
11	0.025110	0.910869
12	0.019820	0.930689
13	0.015569	0.946258
14	0.012180	0.958438
15	0.009494	0.967932
16	0.007377	0.975308
17	0.005716	0.981024
18	0.004418	0.985441
19	0.003407	0.988848
20	0.002622	0.991470
21	0.002014	0.993484
22	0.001545	0.995028
23	0.001183	0.996211
24	0.000904	0.997115

25	0.000691	0.997806
26	0.000527	0.998333
27	0.000401	0.998734
28	0.000306	0.999040
29	0.000232	0.999272
30	0.000177	0.999449
31	0.000134	0.999583
32	0.000102	0.999684
33	0.000077	0.999761
34	0.000058	0.999820
35	0.000044	0.999864
36	0.000033	0.999897
37	0.000025	0.999922

k=1·9
Mean=5·41
Variance=20·80

n	P(n)	F(n)
0	0.077348	0.077348
1	0.108751	0.186099
2	0.116690	0.302790
3	0.112256	0.415046
4	0.101760	0.516806
5	0.088857	0.605662
6	0.075617	0.681280
7	0.063151	0.744431
8	0.051989	0.796420
9	0.042319	0.838739
10	0.034135	0.872874
11	0.027326	0.900200
12	0.021738	0.921938
13	0.017200	0.939138
14	0.013546	0.952684
15	0.010626	0.963310
16	0.008305	0.971615
17	0.006471	0.978086
18	0.005028	0.983115
19	0.003897	0.987012
20	0.003014	0.990025
21	0.002326	0.992351
22	0.001791	0.994142
23	0.001377	0.995520
24	0.001058	0.996577
25	0.000811	0.997388
26	0.000621	0.998009
27	0.000475	0.998484
28	0.000363	0.998846
29	0.000277	0.999123
30	0.000211	0.999333
31	0.000161	0.999494
32	0.000122	0.999616
33	0.000093	0.999709
34	0.000071	0.999780
35	0.000054	0.999833
36	0.000041	0.999874
37	0.000031	0.999904

k=2·0
Mean = 5·69
Variance = 21·89

n	P(n)	F(n)
0	0.067600	0.067600
1	0.100048	0.167648
2	0.111053	0.278701
3	0.109573	0.388274
4	0.101355	0.489628
5	0.090003	0.579631
6	0.077703	0.657334
7	0.065714	0.723048
8	0.054707	0.777755
9	0.044981	0.822736
10	0.036615	0.859351
11	0.029558	0.888909
12	0.023696	0.912605
13	0.018884	0.931489
14	0.014972	0.946461
15	0.011818	0.958279
16	0.009292	0.967571
17	0.007280	0.974851
18	0.005687	0.980538
19	0.004430	0.984968
20	0.003442	0.988410
21	0.002668	0.991078
22	0.002064	0.993142
23	0.001594	0.994736
24	0.001229	0.995965
25	0.000946	0.996911
26	0.000727	0.997637
27	0.000558	0.998195
28	0.000427	0.998622
29	0.000327	0.998949
30	0.000250	0.999200
31	0.000191	0.999391
32	0.000146	0.999537
33	0.000111	0.999648
34	0.000085	0.999732
35	0.000064	0.999797
36	0.000049	0.999846
37	0.000037	0.999883
38	0.000028	0.999912

k=2·1
Mean = 5·98
Variance = 22·99

n	P(n)	F(n)
0	0.059080	0.059080
1	0.091811	0.150892
2	0.105307	0.256199
3	0.106501	0.362700
4	0.100483	0.463183
5	0.090716	0.553900
6	0.079437	0.633337
7	0.068021	0.701358
8	0.057257	0.758615
9	0.047549	0.806163
10	0.039056	0.845220
11	0.031792	0.877012
12	0.025683	0.902694
13	0.020613	0.923308
14	0.016452	0.939760
15	0.013068	0.952827
16	0.010335	0.963162
17	0.008143	0.971305
18	0.006394	0.977698
19	0.005005	0.982704
20	0.003908	0.986611
21	0.003043	0.989654
22	0.002364	0.992019
23	0.001833	0.993852
24	0.001419	0.995271
25	0.001096	0.996367
26	0.000846	0.997213
27	0.000651	0.997864
28	0.000501	0.998365
29	0.000385	0.998750
30	0.000295	0.999045
31	0.000226	0.999271
32	0.000173	0.999444
33	0.000132	0.999576
34	0.000101	0.999677
35	0.000077	0.999754
36	0.000059	0.999813
37	0.000045	0.999858
38	0.000034	0.999892
39	0.000026	0.999918

k=2·2
Mean = 6·26
Variance = 24·08

n	P(n)	F(n)
0	0.051635	0.051635
1	0.084061	0.135696
2	0.099529	0.235224
3	0.103112	0.338336
4	0.099193	0.437529
5	0.091020	0.528549
6	0.080826	0.609375
7	0.070064	0.679439
8	0.059625	0.739063
9	0.050005	0.789069
10	0.041444	0.830513
11	0.034014	0.864527
12	0.027688	0.892215
13	0.022380	0.914595
14	0.017981	0.932576
15	0.014370	0.946947
16	0.011432	0.958378
17	0.009057	0.967435
18	0.007149	0.974583
19	0.005624	0.980208
20	0.004412	0.984619
21	0.003451	0.988070
22	0.002693	0.990763
23	0.002097	0.992860
24	0.001629	0.994489

k=2·3
Mean = 6·55
Variance = 25·18

n	P(n)	F(n)
0	0.045127	0.045127
1	0.076807	0.121934
2	0.093781	0.215715
3	0.099470	0.315185
4	0.097530	0.412715
5	0.090937	0.503653
6	0.081874	0.585527
7	0.071839	0.657365
8	0.061799	0.719164
9	0.052337	0.771501
10	0.043764	0.815266
11	0.036213	0.851479
12	0.029701	0.881179
13	0.024176	0.905355
14	0.019552	0.924907
15	0.015722	0.940629
16	0.012580	0.953209
17	0.010021	0.963230
18	0.007951	0.971181
19	0.006286	0.977467
20	0.004954	0.982421
21	0.003893	0.986315
22	0.003051	0.989366
23	0.002385	0.991751
24	0.001861	0.993612
25	0.001449	0.995061
26	0.001126	0.996186
27	0.000873	0.997059
28	0.000676	0.997735
29	0.000523	0.998258
30	0.000404	0.998661
31	0.000311	0.998973
32	0.000240	0.999212
33	0.000184	0.999397
34	0.000142	0.999538
35	0.000109	0.999647
36	0.000083	0.999730
37	0.000064	0.999794
38	0.000049	0.999843
39	0.000037	0.999880

The following rows belong to the k=2·0 section (second column):

n	P(n)	F(n)
25	0.001264	0.995753
26	0.000978	0.996731
27	0.000756	0.997487
28	0.000583	0.998071
29	0.000450	0.998520
30	0.000346	0.998866
31	0.000266	0.999132
32	0.000204	0.999336
33	0.000157	0.999493
34	0.000120	0.999613
35	0.000092	0.999705
36	0.000070	0.999775
37	0.000054	0.999829
38	0.000041	0.999869
39	0.000031	0.999901

				k=2·5				5	0.081903	0.346524
40	0.000029	0.999909		Mean = 7·12				6	0.080811	0.427334
				Variance = 27·37				7	0.076886	0.504220
								8	0.071119	0.575339
				n	P(n)	F(n)		9	0.064323	0.639662

k=2·4
Mean = 6·83
Variance = 26·27

n	P(n)	F(n)		0	0.034469	0.034469		10	0.057119	0.696781
				1	0.063768	0.098238		11	0.049953	0.746735
0	0.039440	0.039440		2	0.082580	0.180818		12	0.043126	0.789861
1	0.070045	0.109485		3	0.091664	0.272482		13	0.036823	0.826684
2	0.088117	0.197602		4	0.093268	0.365749		14	0.031142	0.857826
3	0.095636	0.293239								
4	0.095541	0.388779		5	0.089724	0.455473		15	0.026118	0.883944
				6	0.082994	0.538468		16	0.021743	0.905687
5	0.090496	0.479275		7	0.074576	0.613044		17	0.017983	0.923669
6	0.082593	0.561868		8	0.065534	0.678578		18	0.014786	0.938455
7	0.073342	0.635210		9	0.056578	0.735156		19	0.012093	0.950548
8	0.063771	0.698982								
9	0.054531	0.753513		10	0.048148	0.783303		20	0.009844	0.960392
				11	0.040488	0.823791		21	0.007978	0.968371
10	0.046003	0.799516		12	0.033706	0.857497		22	0.006441	0.974811
11	0.038375	0.837891		13	0.027820	0.885318		23	0.005180	0.979992
12	0.031710	0.869601		14	0.022793	0.908111		24	0.004153	0.984145
13	0.025993	0.895594								
14	0.021158	0.916752		15	0.018553	0.926664		25	0.003319	0.987464
				16	0.015017	0.941681		26	0.002645	0.990109
15	0.017118	0.933870		17	0.012093	0.953774		27	0.002102	0.992211
16	0.013776	0.947646		18	0.009694	0.963468		28	0.001667	0.993878
17	0.011034	0.958679		19	0.007740	0.971208		29	0.001319	0.995197
18	0.008800	0.967479								
19	0.006992	0.974471		20	0.006157	0.977366		30	0.001041	0.996237
				21	0.004882	0.982248		31	0.000820	0.997057
20	0.005536	0.980007		22	0.003859	0.986107		32	0.000645	0.997702
21	0.004370	0.984377		23	0.003042	0.989148		33	0.000506	0.998208
22	0.003439	0.987817		24	0.002392	0.991540		34	0.000396	0.998604
23	0.002700	0.990517								
24	0.002115	0.992631		25	0.001876	0.993416		35	0.000310	0.998914
				26	0.001468	0.994884		36	0.000242	0.999157
25	0.001652	0.994284		27	0.001147	0.996031		37	0.000189	0.999345
26	0.001289	0.995573		28	0.000894	0.996926		38	0.000147	0.999493
27	0.001003	0.996576		29	0.000696	0.997622		39	0.000114	0.999607
28	0.000779	0.997355								
29	0.000605	0.997960		30	0.000541	0.998162		40	0.000089	0.999696
				31	0.000420	0.998582		41	0.000069	0.999765
30	0.000468	0.998428		32	0.000325	0.998907		42	0.000054	0.999819
31	0.000362	0.998790		33	0.000251	0.999158		43	0.000041	0.999860
32	0.000280	0.999070		34	0.000194	0.999352		44	0.000032	0.999892
33	0.000216	0.999286								
34	0.000166	0.999452		35	0.000150	0.999502		45	0.000025	0.999917
				36	0.000116	0.999618				
35	0.000128	0.999580		37	0.000089	0.999707				
36	0.000098	0.999678		38	0.000068	0.999775				
37	0.000076	0.999754		39	0.000053	0.999828				
38	0.000058	0.999812								
39	0.000044	0.999856		40	0.000040	0.999868				
				41	0.000031	0.999899				
40	0.000034	0.999890		42	0.000024	0.999923				
41	0.000026	0.999916								

k=3·5
Mean = 9·96
Variance = 38·31

				k=3·0				n	P(n)	F(n)
				Mean = 8·54						
				Variance = 32·84				0	0.008962	0.008962
								1	0.023212	0.032174
				n	P(n)	F(n)		2	0.038647	0.070821
								3	0.052432	0.123253
				0	0.017576	0.017576		4	0.063049	0.186302
				1	0.039019	0.056595				
				2	0.057748	0.114342		5	0.069985	0.256286
				3	0.071222	0.185565		6	0.073367	0.329654
				4	0.079057	0.264621		7	0.073682	0.403335
								8	0.071563	0.474898
								9	0.067667	0.542565

P = 0·26

n	P(n)	F(n)		n	P(n)	F(n)		n	P(n)	F(n)
10	0.062592	0.605157		15	0.040744	0.767981		15	0.046406	0.698479
11	0.056845	0.662002		16	0.035803	0.803785		16	0.041852	0.740331
12	0.050829	0.712831		17	0.031170	0.834955		17	0.037347	0.777678
13	0.044847	0.757677		18	0.026910	0.861865		18	0.033011	0.810689
14	0.039113	0.796790		19	0.023058	0.884923		19	0.028928	0.839617
15	0.033767	0.830557		20	0.019622	0.904545		20	0.025153	0.864769
16	0.028892	0.859450		21	0.016595	0.921139		21	0.021715	0.886485
17	0.024524	0.883974		22	0.013955	0.935094		22	0.018626	0.905110
18	0.020669	0.904642		23	0.011673	0.946768		23	0.015880	0.920991
19	0.017307	0.921950		24	0.009718	0.956486		24	0.013465	0.934456
20	0.014408	0.936358		25	0.008054	0.964540		25	0.011359	0.945815
21	0.011931	0.948289		26	0.006648	0.971188		26	0.009537	0.955353
22	0.009833	0.958122		27	0.005466	0.976654		27	0.007973	0.963325
23	0.008067	0.966189		28	0.004478	0.981132		28	0.006637	0.969962
24	0.006591	0.972780		29	0.003657	0.984789		29	0.005504	0.975467
25	0.005365	0.978145		30	0.002977	0.987766		30	0.004548	0.980015
26	0.004352	0.982498		31	0.002416	0.990181		31	0.003746	0.983761
27	0.003519	0.986016		32	0.001955	0.992137		32	0.003075	0.986836
28	0.002836	0.988853		33	0.001578	0.993715		33	0.002517	0.989353
29	0.002280	0.991133		34	0.001271	0.994986		34	0.002054	0.991407
30	0.001828	0.992960		35	0.001021	0.996008		35	0.001672	0.993079
31	0.001462	0.994422		36	0.000819	0.996826		36	0.001358	0.994437
32	0.001166	0.995588		37	0.000655	0.997481		37	0.001100	0.995537
33	0.000928	0.996516		38	0.000523	0.998004		38	0.000889	0.996425
34	0.000737	0.997254		39	0.000417	0.998421		39	0.000717	0.997142
35	0.000585	0.997838		40	0.000332	0.998753		40	0.000577	0.997719
36	0.000463	0.998301		41	0.000263	0.999016		41	0.000463	0.998182
37	0.000366	0.998667		42	0.000209	0.999225		42	0.000371	0.998553
38	0.000288	0.998955		43	0.000165	0.999390		43	0.000297	0.998851
39	0.000227	0.999182		44	0.000131	0.999520		44	0.000237	0.999088
40	0.000178	0.999360		45	0.000103	0.999623		45	0.000189	0.999277
41	0.000140	0.999501		46	0.000081	0.999705		46	0.000151	0.999428
42	0.000110	0.999610		47	0.000064	0.999769		47	0.000120	0.999548
43	0.000086	0.999696		48	0.000050	0.999819		48	0.000095	0.999643
44	0.000067	0.999764		49	0.000040	0.999859		49	0.000075	0.999719
45	0.000053	0.999816		50	0.000031	0.999890		50	0.000060	0.999778
46	0.000041	0.999857		51	0.000024	0.999914		51	0.000047	0.999826
47	0.000032	0.999889						52	0.000037	0.999863
48	0.000025	0.999914						53	0.000029	0.999892
								54	0.000023	0.999916

k = 4·0
Mean = 11·38
Variance = 43·79

k = 4·5
Mean = 12·81
Variance = 49·26

k = 5·0
Mean = 14·23
Variance = 54·73

n	P(n)	F(n)		n	P(n)	F(n)		n	P(n)	F(n)
0	0.004570	0.004570		0	0.002330	0.002330		0	0.001188	0.001188
1	0.013526	0.018096		1	0.007759	0.010089		1	0.004396	0.005584
2	0.025024	0.043120		2	0.015790	0.025880		2	0.009759	0.015344
3	0.037036	0.080156		3	0.025317	0.051197		3	0.016851	0.032195
4	0.047961	0.128117		4	0.035127	0.086324		4	0.024940	0.057134
5	0.056786	0.184903		5	0.044190	0.130514		5	0.033220	0.090354
6	0.063032	0.247935		6	0.051776	0.182291		6	0.040971	0.131325
7	0.066634	0.314569		7	0.057472	0.239762		7	0.047643	0.178969
8	0.067800	0.382369		8	0.061135	0.300897		8	0.052884	0.231853
9	0.066896	0.449265		9	0.062834	0.363731		9	0.056527	0.288380
10	0.064354	0.513620		10	0.062771	0.426502		10	0.058562	0.346942
11	0.060610	0.574230		11	0.061230	0.487732		11	0.059095	0.406037
12	0.056064	0.630294		12	0.058526	0.546258		12	0.058307	0.464344
13	0.051062	0.681355		13	0.054969	0.601227		13	0.056423	0.520767
14	0.045882	0.727238		14	0.050846	0.652073		14	0.053682	0.574449

15	0.050318	0.624768	30	0.006578	0.969043	45	0.000328	0.998689
16	0.046544	0.671312	31	0.005496	0.974539	46	0.000264	0.998953
17	0.042547	0.713859	32	0.004575	0.979114	47	0.000212	0.999165
18	0.038482	0.752341	33	0.003796	0.982911	48	0.000170	0.999335
19	0.034471	0.786812	34	0.003140	0.986050	49	0.000136	0.999471
20	0.030611	0.817422	35	0.002589	0.988639	50	0.000109	0.999580
21	0.026966	0.844389	36	0.002129	0.990768	51	0.000087	0.999667
22	0.023583	0.867972	37	0.001746	0.992513	52	0.000069	0.999736
23	0.020487	0.888459	38	0.001428	0.993941	53	0.000055	0.999791
24	0.017687	0.906146	39	0.001165	0.995106	54	0.000044	0.999835
25	0.015182	0.921328	40	0.000948	0.996054	55	0.000035	0.999869
26	0.012963	0.934292	41	0.000770	0.996824	56	0.000028	0.999897
27	0.011014	0.945306	42	0.000624	0.997448	57	0.000022	0.999919
28	0.009315	0.954621	43	0.000505	0.997953			
29	0.007844	0.962465	44	0.000408	0.998360			

k=0·1 Mean=0·26 Variance=0·92			k=0·2 Mean=0·51 Variance=1·84			k=0·3 Mean=0·77 Variance=2·76		
n	P(n)	F(n)	n	P(n)	F(n)	n	P(n)	F(n)
0	0.880473	0.880473	0	0.775232	0.775232	0	0.682570	0.682570
1	0.063394	0.943867	1	0.111633	0.886865	1	0.147435	0.830006
2	0.025104	0.968971	2	0.048226	0.935091	2	0.069000	0.899005
3	0.012652	0.981623	3	0.025463	0.960554	3	0.038088	0.937093
4	0.007060	0.988683	4	0.014667	0.975221	4	0.022624	0.959717
5	0.004168	0.992851	5	0.008870	0.984091	5	0.014009	0.973726
6	0.002551	0.995402	6	0.005535	0.989626	6	0.008910	0.982636
7	0.001601	0.997003	7	0.003530	0.993156	7	0.005773	0.988409
8	0.001023	0.998026	8	0.002287	0.995444	8	0.003793	0.992202
9	0.000663	0.998688	9	0.001500	0.996944	9	0.002519	0.994721
10	0.000434	0.999123	10	0.000994	0.997938	10	0.001686	0.996407
11	0.000287	0.999410	11	0.000664	0.998602	11	0.001137	0.997544
12	0.000191	0.999601	12	0.000446	0.999048	12	0.000771	0.998315
13	0.000128	0.999729	13	0.000301	0.999349	13	0.000525	0.998841
14	0.000086	0.999815	14	0.000205	0.999553	14	0.000359	0.999200
15	0.000058	0.999874	15	0.000139	0.999693	15	0.000247	0.999446
16	0.000040	0.999913	16	0.000095	0.999788	16	0.000170	0.999616
			17	0.000065	0.999854	17	0.000117	0.999733
			18	0.000045	0.999899	18	0.000081	0.999814
			19	0.000031	0.999930	19	0.000056	0.999871
						20	0.000039	0.999910

95

k=0·4
Mean=1·03
Variance=3·67

n	P(n)	F(n)
0	0.600984	0.600984
1	0.173084	0.774068
2	0.087234	0.861302
3	0.050247	0.911549
4	0.030751	0.942300
5	0.019484	0.961784
6	0.012626	0.974409
7	0.008311	0.982721
8	0.005535	0.988256
9	0.003720	0.991976
10	0.002517	0.994493
11	0.001714	0.996207
12	0.001172	0.997379
13	0.000805	0.998184
14	0.000555	0.998739
15	0.000383	0.999122
16	0.000266	0.999388
17	0.000185	0.999573
18	0.000128	0.999701
19	0.000090	0.999791
20	0.000063	0.999853
21	0.000044	0.999897
22	0.000031	0.999928

k=0·5
Mean=1·29
Variance=4·59

n	P(n)	F(n)
0	0.529150	0.529150
1	0.190494	0.719644
2	0.102867	0.822511
3	0.061720	0.884231
4	0.038884	0.923115
5	0.025197	0.948312
6	0.016630	0.964941
7	0.011118	0.976059
8	0.007505	0.983564
9	0.005103	0.988667
10	0.003491	0.992158
11	0.002399	0.994557
12	0.001655	0.996212
13	0.001146	0.997358
14	0.000796	0.998154
15	0.000554	0.998708
16	0.000386	0.999094
17	0.000270	0.999364
18	0.000189	0.999553
19	0.000132	0.999685
20	0.000093	0.999778
21	0.000065	0.999844
22	0.000046	0.999890
23	0.000032	0.999922

k=0·6
Mean=1·54
Variance=5·51

n	P(n)	F(n)
0	0.465902	0.465902
1	0.201270	0.667172
2	0.115931	0.783103
3	0.072341	0.855445
4	0.046877	0.902322
5	0.031051	0.933373
6	0.020867	0.954240
7	0.014165	0.968405
8	0.009689	0.978094
9	0.006666	0.984760
10	0.004608	0.989368
11	0.003197	0.992565
12	0.002225	0.994790
13	0.001553	0.996342
14	0.001086	0.997428
15	0.000761	0.998190
16	0.000534	0.998724
17	0.000376	0.999099
18	0.000264	0.999364
19	0.000186	0.999550
20	0.000132	0.999682
21	0.000093	0.999775
22	0.000066	0.999840
23	0.000046	0.999887
24	0.000033	0.999920

k=0·7
Mean=1·80
Variance=6·43

n	P(n)	F(n)
0	0.410214	0.410214
1	0.206748	0.616962
2	0.126530	0.743492
3	0.081991	0.825483
4	0.054606	0.880089
5	0.036957	0.917047
6	0.025279	0.942326
7	0.017421	0.959746
8	0.012073	0.971819
9	0.008403	0.980222
10	0.005868	0.986090
11	0.004110	0.990200
12	0.002885	0.993085
13	0.002029	0.995114
14	0.001430	0.996544
15	0.001009	0.997553
16	0.000713	0.998266
17	0.000504	0.998770
18	0.000357	0.999127
19	0.000253	0.999380
20	0.000179	0.999559
21	0.000127	0.999687
22	0.000090	0.999777
23	0.000064	0.999841
24	0.000046	0.999887

25	0.000032	0.999920

k=0·8
Mean=2·06
Variance=7·35

n	P(n)	F(n)
0	0.361182	0.361182
1	0.208041	0.569223
2	0.134811	0.704034
3	0.090593	0.794627
4	0.061965	0.856592
5	0.042830	0.899422
6	0.029810	0.929232
7	0.020850	0.950082
8	0.014637	0.964719
9	0.010304	0.975023
10	0.007271	0.982294
11	0.005140	0.987434
12	0.003639	0.991073
13	0.002580	0.993652
14	0.001831	0.995483
15	0.001301	0.996784
16	0.000925	0.997709
17	0.000658	0.998367
18	0.000468	0.998835
19	0.000334	0.999169
20	0.000238	0.999407
21	0.000170	0.999576
22	0.000121	0.999697
23	0.000086	0.999784
24	0.000062	0.999845
25	0.000044	0.999890
26	0.000031	0.999921

k=0·9
Mean=2·31
Variance=8·27

n	P(n)	F(n)
0	0.318011	0.318011
1	0.206071	0.524082
2	0.140953	0.665035
3	0.098103	0.763138
4	0.068868	0.832006
5	0.048594	0.880600
6	0.034404	0.915004
7	0.024417	0.939421
8	0.017361	0.956782
9	0.012361	0.969143
10	0.008811	0.977953
11	0.006286	0.984239
12	0.004488	0.988728
13	0.003207	0.991934
14	0.002292	0.994227

n	P(n)	F(n)
5	0.001639	0.995866
6	0.001173	0.997039
7	0.000840	0.997879
8	0.000601	0.998480
9	0.000431	0.998910
0	0.000308	0.999219
1	0.000221	0.999440
2	0.000158	0.999598
3	0.000114	0.999712
4	0.000081	0.999793
5	0.000058	0.999852
6	0.000042	0.999894
7	0.000030	0.999924

=1.0
Mean=2.57
Variance=9.18

n	P(n)	F(n)
0	0.280000	0.280000
1	0.201600	0.481600
2	0.145152	0.626752
3	0.104509	0.731261
4	0.075247	0.806508
5	0.054178	0.860686
6	0.039008	0.899694
7	0.028086	0.927780
8	0.020222	0.948001
9	0.014560	0.962561
0	0.010483	0.973044
1	0.007548	0.980592
2	0.005434	0.986026
3	0.003913	0.989939
4	0.002817	0.992756
5	0.002028	0.994784
6	0.001460	0.996245
7	0.001052	0.997296
8	0.000757	0.998053
9	0.000545	0.998598
0	0.000392	0.998991
1	0.000283	0.999273
2	0.000203	0.999477
3	0.000146	0.999623
4	0.000105	0.999729
5	0.000076	0.999805
6	0.000055	0.999859
7	0.000039	0.999899
8	0.000028	0.999927

=1.1
Mean=2.83
Variance=10.10

n	P(n)	F(n)
0	0.246532	0.246532
1	0.195254	0.441786
2	0.147612	0.589398
3	0.109823	0.699221
4	0.081049	0.780270

n	P(n)	F(n)
5	0.059523	0.839793
6	0.043571	0.883364
7	0.031819	0.915183
8	0.023196	0.938379
9	0.016887	0.955265
10	0.012280	0.967545
11	0.008922	0.976467
12	0.006477	0.982945
13	0.004700	0.987644
14	0.003408	0.991052
15	0.002470	0.993522
16	0.001790	0.995312
17	0.001296	0.996608
18	0.000938	0.997546
19	0.000679	0.998225
20	0.000491	0.998717
21	0.000356	0.999072
22	0.000257	0.999329
23	0.000186	0.999515
24	0.000134	0.999650
25	0.000097	0.999747
26	0.000070	0.999817
27	0.000051	0.999868
28	0.000037	0.999905

k=1.2
Mean=3.09
Variance=11.02

n	P(n)	F(n)
0	0.217065	0.217065
1	0.187544	0.404609
2	0.148535	0.553144
3	0.114075	0.667219
4	0.086241	0.753459
5	0.064577	0.818036
6	0.048045	0.866081
7	0.035581	0.901662
8	0.026259	0.927921
9	0.019326	0.947248
10	0.014193	0.961441
11	0.010405	0.971846
12	0.007616	0.979462
13	0.005568	0.985031
14	0.004066	0.989097
15	0.002967	0.992064
16	0.002163	0.994227
17	0.001576	0.995802
18	0.001147	0.996949
19	0.000835	0.997784
20	0.000607	0.998391
21	0.000441	0.998832
22	0.000320	0.999152
23	0.000233	0.999385
24	0.000169	0.999554
25	0.000123	0.999677
26	0.000089	0.999766
27	0.000065	0.999830
28	0.000047	0.999877
29	0.000034	0.999911

k=1.3
Mean=3.34
Variance=11.94

n	P(n)	F(n)
0	0.191120	0.191120
1	0.178888	0.370008
2	0.148119	0.518127
3	0.117310	0.635437
4	0.090798	0.726236
5	0.069297	0.795533
6	0.052389	0.847922
7	0.039336	0.887258
8	0.029384	0.916643
9	0.021862	0.938505
10	0.016213	0.954717
11	0.011992	0.966709
12	0.008850	0.975559
13	0.006519	0.982078
14	0.004794	0.986872
15	0.003521	0.990393
16	0.002583	0.992975
17	0.001892	0.994867
18	0.001385	0.996253
19	0.001013	0.997266
20	0.000740	0.998006
21	0.000541	0.998547
22	0.000395	0.998941
23	0.000288	0.999229
24	0.000210	0.999439
25	0.000153	0.999592
26	0.000111	0.999703
27	0.000081	0.999784
28	0.000059	0.999843
29	0.000043	0.999886
30	0.000031	0.999917

k=1.4
Mean=3.60
Variance=12.86

n	P(n)	F(n)
0	0.168276	0.168276
1	0.169622	0.337897
2	0.146553	0.484451
3	0.119587	0.604038
4	0.094713	0.698751
5	0.073649	0.772401
6	0.056562	0.828963
7	0.043052	0.872015
8	0.032547	0.904563
9	0.024476	0.929038
10	0.018327	0.947366
11	0.013676	0.961041
12	0.010175	0.971216
13	0.007551	0.978767
14	0.005592	0.984359

n	P(n)	F(n)
15	0.004134	0.988493
16	0.003051	0.991543
17	0.002248	0.993792
18	0.001655	0.995446
19	0.001216	0.996663
20	0.000893	0.997556
21	0.000655	0.998211
22	0.000481	0.998692
23	0.000352	0.999044
24	0.000258	0.999302
25	0.000188	0.999490
26	0.000138	0.999628
27	0.000101	0.999729
28	0.000074	0.999802
29	0.000054	0.999856
30	0.000039	0.999895
31	0.000029	0.999923

k=1·5
Mean=3·86
Variance=13·78

n	P(n)	F(n)
0	0.148162	0.148162
1	0.160015	0.308177
2	0.144014	0.452191
3	0.120971	0.573162
4	0.097987	0.671149
5	0.077606	0.748754
6	0.060532	0.809287
7	0.046696	0.855983
8	0.035723	0.891706
9	0.027149	0.918855
10	0.020525	0.939380
11	0.015450	0.954830
12	0.011587	0.966417
13	0.008664	0.975080
14	0.006461	0.981541
15	0.004807	0.986348
16	0.003569	0.989917
17	0.002645	0.992562
18	0.001957	0.994519
19	0.001446	0.995966
20	0.001067	0.997033
21	0.000787	0.997820
22	0.000579	0.998400
23	0.000426	0.998826
24	0.000313	0.999139
25	0.000230	0.999369
26	0.000169	0.999538
27	0.000124	0.999662
28	0.000091	0.999753
29	0.000066	0.999819
30	0.000049	0.999868
31	0.000036	0.999904

k=1·6
Mean=4·11
Variance=14·69

n	P(n)	F(n)
0	0.130453	0.130453
1	0.150281	0.280734
2	0.140663	0.421397
3	0.121533	0.542931
4	0.100629	0.643560
5	0.081148	0.724708
6	0.064269	0.788977
7	0.050240	0.839217
8	0.038886	0.878102
9	0.029864	0.907967
10	0.022792	0.930759
11	0.017306	0.948065
12	0.013083	0.961148
13	0.009855	0.971002
14	0.007399	0.978402
15	0.005541	0.983942
16	0.004139	0.988081
17	0.003085	0.991166
18	0.002295	0.993462
19	0.001705	0.995166
20	0.001264	0.996431
21	0.000936	0.997367
22	0.000693	0.998060
23	0.000512	0.998571
24	0.000378	0.998949
25	0.000278	0.999227
26	0.000205	0.999432
27	0.000151	0.999583
28	0.000111	0.999694
29	0.000082	0.999776
30	0.000060	0.999836
31	0.000044	0.999880
32	0.000032	0.999912

k=1·7
Mean=4·37
Variance=15·61

n	P(n)	F(n)
0	0.114860	0.114860
1	0.140589	0.255449
2	0.136652	0.392101
3	0.121347	0.513448
4	0.102660	0.616107
5	0.084263	0.700370
6	0.067747	0.768118
7	0.053656	0.821774
8	0.042013	0.863786
9	0.032602	0.896388
10	0.025116	0.921505
11	0.019235	0.940739
12	0.014557	0.955396
13	0.011121	0.966517
14	0.008408	0.974925

n	P(n)	F(n)
15	0.006336	0.981261
16	0.004761	0.986022
17	0.003569	0.989592
18	0.002670	0.992262
19	0.001993	0.994255
20	0.001485	0.995740
21	0.001105	0.996845
22	0.000821	0.997666
23	0.000609	0.998275
24	0.000451	0.998726
25	0.000334	0.999061
26	0.000247	0.999308
27	0.000182	0.999490
28	0.000135	0.999625
29	0.000099	0.999724
30	0.000073	0.999797
31	0.000054	0.999851
32	0.000040	0.999891
33	0.000029	0.999920

k=1·8
Mean=4·63
Variance=16·53

n	P(n)	F(n)
0	0.101131	0.10113
1	0.131066	0.23219
2	0.132114	0.36431
3	0.120488	0.48479
4	0.104102	0.58890
5	0.086946	0.67584
6	0.070948	0.74679
7	0.056920	0.80371
8	0.045081	0.84879
9	0.035343	0.88414
10	0.027483	0.91162
11	0.021227	0.93285
12	0.016302	0.94915
13	0.012460	0.96161
14	0.009484	0.97109
15	0.007193	0.97828
16	0.005438	0.98372
17	0.004099	0.98782
18	0.003083	0.99090
19	0.002313	0.99322
20	0.001732	0.99495
21	0.001295	0.99624
22	0.000966	0.99721
23	0.000720	0.99793
24	0.000535	0.99846
25	0.000398	0.99886
26	0.000295	0.99916
27	0.000219	0.99938
28	0.000162	0.99954
29	0.000120	0.99966
30	0.000089	0.99975
31	0.000065	0.99981
32	0.000048	0.99986
33	0.000036	0.99990

k=1·9
Mean = 4·89
Variance = 17·45

n	P(n)	F(n)
0	0.089043	0.089043
1	0.121811	0.210854
2	0.127171	0.338025
3	0.119032	0.457056
4	0.104986	0.562042
5	0.089196	0.651238
6	0.073854	0.725093
7	0.060012	0.785105
8	0.048070	0.833174
9	0.038071	0.871245
10	0.029878	0.901124
11	0.023272	0.924396
12	0.018013	0.942409
13	0.013867	0.956276
14	0.010626	0.966902
15	0.008110	0.975012
16	0.006168	0.981180
17	0.004676	0.985855
18	0.003535	0.989390
19	0.002666	0.992056
20	0.002006	0.994062
21	0.001506	0.995567
22	0.001129	0.996696
23	0.000844	0.997541
24	0.000631	0.998171
25	0.000471	0.998642
26	0.000350	0.998992
27	0.000261	0.999253
28	0.000194	0.999447
29	0.000144	0.999591
30	0.000107	0.999697
31	0.000079	0.999776
32	0.000059	0.999835
33	0.000043	0.999878
34	0.000032	0.999910

k=2·0
Mean = 5·14
Variance = 18·37

n	P(n)	F(n)
0	0.078400	0.078400
1	0.112896	0.191296
2	0.121928	0.313224
3	0.117051	0.430274
4	0.105346	0.535620
5	0.091019	0.626638
6	0.076456	0.703094
7	0.062912	0.766006
8	0.050959	0.816965
9	0.040767	0.857732
10	0.032287	0.890019
11	0.025360	0.915379
12	0.019781	0.935160
13	0.015338	0.950498
14	0.011832	0.962330

n	P(n)	F(n)
15	0.009087	0.971417
16	0.006952	0.978369
17	0.005300	0.983669
18	0.004028	0.987696
19	0.003053	0.990749
20	0.002308	0.993057
21	0.001741	0.994797
22	0.001310	0.996108
23	0.000984	0.997092
24	0.000738	0.997830
25	0.000553	0.998383
26	0.000413	0.998796
27	0.000309	0.999105
28	0.000230	0.999335
29	0.000171	0.999507
30	0.000128	0.999634
31	0.000095	0.999729
32	0.000070	0.999799
33	0.000052	0.999852
34	0.000039	0.999890
35	0.000029	0.999919

k=2·1
Mean = 5·40
Variance = 19·29

n	P(n)	F(n)
0	0.069029	0.069029
1	0.104372	0.173401
2	0.116479	0.289880
3	0.114615	0.404495
4	0.105217	0.509712
5	0.092423	0.602135
6	0.078744	0.680879
7	0.065605	0.746484
8	0.053731	0.800214
9	0.043414	0.843629
10	0.034697	0.878325
11	0.027480	0.905805
12	0.021599	0.927404
13	0.016867	0.944271
14	0.013099	0.957370
15	0.010123	0.967493
16	0.007789	0.975282
17	0.005971	0.981253
18	0.004562	0.985815
19	0.003475	0.989290
20	0.002639	0.991929
21	0.002000	0.993929
22	0.001512	0.995441
23	0.001141	0.996582
24	0.000859	0.997441
25	0.000646	0.998087
26	0.000485	0.998571
27	0.000363	0.998934
28	0.000272	0.999206
29	0.000203	0.999409

n	P(n)	F(n)
30	0.000152	0.999561
31	0.000113	0.999674
32	0.000084	0.999758
33	0.000063	0.999820
34	0.000047	0.999867
35	0.000035	0.999901

k=2·2
Mean = 5·66
Variance = 20·20

n	P(n)	F(n)
0	0.060778	0.060778
1	0.096273	0.157051
2	0.110906	0.267957
3	0.111793	0.379750
4	0.104639	0.484389
5	0.093421	0.577810
6	0.080716	0.658526
7	0.068078	0.726604
8	0.056369	0.782973
9	0.045997	0.828970
10	0.037092	0.866062
11	0.029620	0.895681
12	0.023459	0.919140
13	0.018449	0.937589
14	0.014422	0.952011
15	0.011215	0.963226
16	0.008680	0.971906
17	0.006691	0.978597
18	0.005139	0.983736
19	0.003933	0.987669
20	0.003002	0.990671
21	0.002285	0.992956
22	0.001735	0.994691
23	0.001314	0.996005
24	0.000994	0.996999
25	0.000750	0.997749
26	0.000565	0.998313
27	0.000425	0.998738
28	0.000319	0.999057
29	0.000239	0.999296
30	0.000179	0.999475
31	0.000134	0.999609
32	0.000100	0.999709
33	0.000075	0.999784
34	0.000056	0.999839
35	0.000041	0.999881
36	0.000031	0.999911

k = 2·3
Mean = 5·91
Variance = 21·12

n	P(n)	F(n)
0	0.053514	0.053514
1	0.088618	0.142132
2	0.105279	0.247411
3	0.108648	0.356058
4	0.103650	0.459708
5	0.094031	0.553739
6	0.082371	0.636110
7	0.070321	0.706432
8	0.058859	0.765291
9	0.048500	0.813791
10	0.039460	0.853250
11	0.031768	0.885019
12	0.025351	0.910370
13	0.020078	0.930448
14	0.015799	0.946247
15	0.012361	0.958608
16	0.009623	0.968230
17	0.007458	0.975689
18	0.005758	0.981447
19	0.004429	0.985876
20	0.003396	0.989272
21	0.002597	0.991869
22	0.001980	0.993849
23	0.001506	0.995356
24	0.001143	0.996499
25	0.000866	0.997365
26	0.000655	0.998020
27	0.000494	0.998514
28	0.000372	0.998886
29	0.000280	0.999166
30	0.000210	0.999376
31	0.000158	0.999534
32	0.000118	0.999652
33	0.000088	0.999741
34	0.000066	0.999807
35	0.000049	0.999856
36	0.000037	0.999893
37	0.000027	0.999921

k = 2·4
Mean = 6·17
Variance = 22·04

n	P(n)	F(n)
0	0.047117	0.047117
1	0.081418	0.128536
2	0.099656	0.228192
3	0.105237	0.333429
4	0.102290	0.435719
5	0.094271	0.529990
6	0.083712	0.613702
7	0.072328	0.686030
8	0.061189	0.747219
9	0.050909	0.798128
10	0.041786	0.839915
11	0.033915	0.873830
12	0.027268	0.901098
13	0.021747	0.922845
14	0.017224	0.940069
15	0.013559	0.953628
16	0.010616	0.964244
17	0.008273	0.972517
18	0.006420	0.978937
19	0.004963	0.983900
20	0.003824	0.987724
21	0.002936	0.990660
22	0.002249	0.992909
23	0.001718	0.994627
24	0.001309	0.995936
25	0.000995	0.996931
26	0.000755	0.997686
27	0.000572	0.998258
28	0.000432	0.998690
29	0.000326	0.999017
30	0.000246	0.999263
31	0.000185	0.999448
32	0.000139	0.999587
33	0.000104	0.999691
34	0.000078	0.999769
35	0.000059	0.999828
36	0.000044	0.999872
37	0.000033	0.999904

k = 2·5
Mean = 6·43
Variance = 22·96

n	P(n)	F(n)
0	0.041485	0.041485
1	0.074674	0.116159
2	0.094089	0.210248
3	0.101616	0.311864
4	0.100600	0.412464
5	0.094161	0.506625
6	0.084745	0.591370
7	0.074092	0.665462
8	0.063348	0.728810
9	0.053213	0.782023
10	0.044060	0.826083
11	0.036049	0.862132
12	0.029200	0.891332
13	0.023450	0.914781
14	0.018693	0.933474
15	0.014805	0.948279
16	0.011659	0.959937
17	0.009135	0.969072
18	0.007125	0.976197
19	0.005535	0.981733
20	0.004284	0.986017
21	0.003305	0.989322
22	0.002542	0.991864
23	0.001949	0.993813
24	0.001491	0.995304
25	0.001138	0.996443
26	0.000867	0.997309
27	0.000659	0.997968
28	0.000500	0.998468
29	0.000378	0.998846
30	0.000286	0.999132
31	0.000216	0.999348
32	0.000163	0.999511
33	0.000123	0.999634
34	0.000092	0.999726
35	0.000069	0.999795
36	0.000052	0.999847
37	0.000039	0.999886
38	0.000029	0.999915

k = 3·0
Mean = 7·71
Variance = 27·55

n	P(n)	F(n)
0	0.021952	0.021952
1	0.047416	0.069368
2	0.068280	0.137648
3	0.081935	0.219583
4	0.088490	0.308073
5	0.089198	0.397272
6	0.085630	0.482902
7	0.079269	0.562171
8	0.071342	0.633513
9	0.062781	0.696294
10	0.054243	0.750537
11	0.046156	0.796693
12	0.038771	0.835464
13	0.032210	0.867674
14	0.026504	0.894177
15	0.021627	0.915805
16	0.017518	0.933323
17	0.014097	0.947420
18	0.011277	0.958697
19	0.008975	0.967672
20	0.007108	0.974779
21	0.005605	0.980384
22	0.004402	0.984787
23	0.003445	0.988232
24	0.002687	0.990920
25	0.002090	0.993010
26	0.001620	0.994630
27	0.001253	0.995883
28	0.000967	0.996850
29	0.000744	0.997594
30	0.000571	0.998165
31	0.000438	0.998603
32	0.000335	0.998938
33	0.000256	0.999194
34	0.000195	0.999389
35	0.000148	0.999537
36	0.000113	0.999650
37	0.000086	0.999736
38	0.000065	0.999801
39	0.000049	0.999850

40	0.000037	0.999887
41	0.000028	0.999915

k=4.0
Mean = 10·29
Variance = 36·73

n	P(n)	F(n)
0	0.006147	0.006147
1	0.017702	0.023849
2	0.031864	0.055712
3	0.045884	0.101596
4	0.057814	0.159410

k=4.5
Mean = 11·57
Variance = 41·33

n	P(n)	F(n)
0	0.003252	0.003252
1	0.010538	0.013790
2	0.020865	0.034656
3	0.032550	0.067205
4	0.043942	0.111147

k=3·5
Mean = 9·00
Variance = 32·14

n	P(n)	F(n)
0	0.011616	0.011616
1	0.029272	0.040888
2	0.047421	0.088309
3	0.062595	0.150904
4	0.073237	0.224141
5	0.079096	0.303236
6	0.080677	0.383914
7	0.078833	0.462747
8	0.074498	0.537245
9	0.068538	0.605783
10	0.061684	0.667467
11	0.054506	0.721973
12	0.047420	0.769393
13	0.040709	0.810102
14	0.034544	0.844646
15	0.029017	0.873663
16	0.024157	0.897820
17	0.019951	0.917771
18	0.016360	0.934130
19	0.013329	0.947459
20	0.010796	0.958255
21	0.008699	0.966954
22	0.006975	0.973929
23	0.005568	0.979496
24	0.004426	0.983922
25	0.003506	0.987428
26	0.002767	0.990195
27	0.002177	0.992371
28	0.001707	0.994078
29	0.001335	0.995413
30	0.001041	0.996455
31	0.000810	0.997265
32	0.000629	0.997894
33	0.000487	0.998381
34	0.000377	0.998757
35	0.000290	0.999048
36	0.000224	0.999272
37	0.000172	0.999443
38	0.000132	0.999575
39	0.000101	0.999676
40	0.000077	0.999754
41	0.000059	0.999813
42	0.000045	0.999858
43	0.000034	0.999892
44	0.000026	0.999918

5	0.066601	0.226011
6	0.071929	0.297941
7	0.073985	0.371925
8	0.073245	0.445170
9	0.070315	0.515485
10	0.065815	0.581299
11	0.060310	0.641610
12	0.054279	0.695889
13	0.048100	0.743989
14	0.042053	0.786041
15	0.036334	0.822375
16	0.031065	0.853440
17	0.026314	0.879755
18	0.022104	0.901858
19	0.018428	0.920286
20	0.015258	0.935544
21	0.012555	0.948100
22	0.010272	0.958372
23	0.008361	0.966733
24	0.006772	0.973505
25	0.005461	0.978966
26	0.004386	0.983352
27	0.003509	0.986861
28	0.002797	0.989658
29	0.002222	0.991880
30	0.001760	0.993640
31	0.001390	0.995029
32	0.001094	0.996124
33	0.000860	0.996983
34	0.000674	0.997657
35	0.000527	0.998183
36	0.000411	0.998594
37	0.000320	0.998914
38	0.000248	0.999162
39	0.000193	0.999355
40	0.000149	0.999504
41	0.000115	0.999619
42	0.000089	0.999708
43	0.000068	0.999776
44	0.000053	0.999829
45	0.000040	0.999869
46	0.000031	0.999900

5	0.053785	0.164932
6	0.061315	0.226247
7	0.066220	0.292467
8	0.068538	0.361005
9	0.068538	0.429543
10	0.066619	0.496161
11	0.063227	0.559389
12	0.058801	0.618190
13	0.053735	0.671925
14	0.048362	0.720287
15	0.042945	0.763232
16	0.037685	0.800917
17	0.032719	0.833636
18	0.028138	0.861774
19	0.023992	0.885766
20	0.020297	0.906063
21	0.017049	0.923112
22	0.014229	0.937341
23	0.011803	0.949144
24	0.009738	0.958882
25	0.007993	0.966875
26	0.006530	0.973405
27	0.005311	0.978715
28	0.004302	0.983017
29	0.003471	0.986488
30	0.002791	0.989279
31	0.002236	0.991515
32	0.001786	0.993301
33	0.001422	0.994723
34	0.001130	0.995853
35	0.000895	0.996748
36	0.000707	0.997454
37	0.000557	0.998011
38	0.000438	0.998449
39	0.000344	0.998793
40	0.000269	0.999062
41	0.000210	0.999272
42	0.000164	0.999436
43	0.000128	0.999564
44	0.000099	0.999663
45	0.000077	0.999740
46	0.000060	0.999800
47	0.000046	0.999846
48	0.000036	0.999882
49	0.000028	0.999909

k=5·0
Mean=12·86
Variance=45·92

n	P(n)	F(n)	n	P(n)	F(n)	n	P(n)	F(n)
0	0.001721	0.001721	20	0.025634	0.869629	45	0.000139	0.999513
1	0.006196	0.007917	21	0.021972	0.891601	46	0.000108	0.999621
2	0.013383	0.021300	22	0.018696	0.910297	47	0.000085	0.999706
3	0.022483	0.043783	23	0.015802	0.926099	48	0.000066	0.999772
4	0.032376	0.076158	24	0.013274	0.939373	49	0.000051	0.999823
5	0.041959	0.118117	25	0.011086	0.950459	50	0.000040	0.999864
6	0.050351	0.168468	26	0.009210	0.959669	51	0.000031	0.999895
7	0.056968	0.225436	27	0.007614	0.967283	52	0.000024	0.999919
8	0.061526	0.286961	28	0.006265	0.973548			
9	0.063987	0.350948	29	0.005133	0.978681			
10	0.064498	0.415446	30	0.004188	0.982869			
11	0.063326	0.478772	31	0.003405	0.986274			
12	0.060793	0.539565	32	0.002758	0.989032			
13	0.057239	0.596803	33	0.002226	0.991258			
14	0.052987	0.649790	34	0.001792	0.993050			
15	0.048324	0.698114	35	0.001437	0.994487			
16	0.043491	0.741605	36	0.001150	0.995637			
17	0.038682	0.780287	37	0.000917	0.996555			
18	0.034040	0.814327	38	0.000730	0.997285			
19	0.029669	0.843996	39	0.000580	0.997864			
			40	0.000459	0.998323			
			41	0.000363	0.998686			
			42	0.000286	0.998972			
			43	0.000225	0.999197			
			44	0.000177	0.999374			

k=0·1 Mean=0·23 Variance=0·78			k=0·2 Mean=0·47 Variance=1·56			k=0·3 Mean=0·70 Variance=2·33		
n	P(n)	F(n)	n	P(n)	F(n)	n	P(n)	F(n)
0	0.886568	0.886568	0	0.786003	0.786003	0	0.696845	0.696845
1	0.062060	0.948628	1	0.110040	0.896044	1	0.146338	0.843183
2	0.023893	0.972521	2	0.046217	0.942261	2	0.066584	0.909766
3	0.011708	0.984229	3	0.023725	0.965985	3	0.035733	0.945500
4	0.006351	0.990580	4	0.013286	0.979271	4	0.020636	0.966135
5	0.003646	0.994226	5	0.007812	0.987083	5	0.012423	0.978558
6	0.002169	0.996395	6	0.004739	0.991822	6	0.007681	0.986240
7	0.001323	0.997718	7	0.002938	0.994761	7	0.004839	0.991079
8	0.000822	0.998540	8	0.001851	0.996612	8	0.003091	0.994170
9	0.000518	0.999058	9	0.001181	0.997793	9	0.001995	0.996166
10	0.000330	0.999388	10	0.000760	0.998553	10	0.001299	0.997465
11	0.000212	0.999600	11	0.000494	0.999047	11	0.000851	0.998316
12	0.000137	0.999737	12	0.000322	0.999369	12	0.000561	0.998877
13	0.000089	0.999827	13	0.000212	0.999581	13	0.000372	0.999249
14	0.000059	0.999885	14	0.000140	0.999721	14	0.000247	0.999496
15	0.000039	0.999924	15	0.000093	0.999813	15	0.000165	0.999661
			16	0.000062	0.999875	16	0.000110	0.999772
			17	0.000041	0.999916	17	0.000074	0.999846
						18	0.000050	0.999896
						19	0.000034	0.999929

k=0·4
Mean=0·93
Variance=3·11

n	P(n)	F(n)
0	0.617801	0.617801
1	0.172984	0.790785
2	0.084762	0.875547
3	0.047467	0.923014
4	0.028243	0.951257
5	0.017398	0.968655
6	0.010960	0.979615
7	0.007015	0.986630
8	0.004542	0.991172
9	0.002967	0.994139
10	0.001953	0.996092
11	0.001292	0.997384
12	0.000859	0.998243
13	0.000574	0.998817
14	0.000384	0.999202
15	0.000258	0.999460
16	0.000174	0.999634
17	0.000118	0.999752
18	0.000080	0.999831
19	0.000054	0.999885
20	0.000037	0.999922

k=0·6
Mean=1·40
Variance=4·67

n	P(n)	F(n)
0	0.485593	0.485593
1	0.203949	0.689543
2	0.114212	0.803754
3	0.069288	0.873043
4	0.043652	0.916694
5	0.028112	0.944806
6	0.018366	0.963172
7	0.012122	0.975294
8	0.008061	0.983355
9	0.005392	0.988747
10	0.003623	0.992370
11	0.002444	0.994814
12	0.001654	0.996468
13	0.001122	0.997590
14	0.000763	0.998353
15	0.000520	0.998873
16	0.000355	0.999228
17	0.000243	0.999470
18	0.000166	0.999636
19	0.000114	0.999750
20	0.000078	0.999828
21	0.000054	0.999882
22	0.000037	0.999918

k=0·8
Mean=1·87
Variance=6·22

n	P(n)	F(n)
0	0.381678	0.381678
1	0.213740	0.595418
2	0.134656	0.730073
3	0.087975	0.818049
4	0.058504	0.876552
5	0.039314	0.915867
6	0.026603	0.942469
7	0.018090	0.960559
8	0.012346	0.972905
9	0.008450	0.981356
10	0.005797	0.987153
11	0.003984	0.991137
12	0.002742	0.993879
13	0.001890	0.995769
14	0.001304	0.997074
15	0.000901	0.997974
16	0.000623	0.998597
17	0.000431	0.999028
18	0.000298	0.999326
19	0.000207	0.999532
20	0.000143	0.999676
21	0.000099	0.999775
22	0.000069	0.999844
23	0.000048	0.999891
24	0.000033	0.999925

k=0·5
Mean=1·17
Variance=3·89

n	P(n)	F(n)
0	0.547723	0.547723
1	0.191703	0.739425
2	0.100644	0.840069
3	0.058709	0.898778
4	0.035959	0.934738
5	0.022654	0.957392
6	0.014537	0.971929
7	0.009449	0.981377
8	0.006201	0.987578
9	0.004099	0.991677
10	0.002726	0.994404
11	0.001822	0.996225
12	0.001222	0.997447
13	0.000822	0.998270
14	0.000555	0.998825
15	0.000376	0.999200
16	0.000255	0.999455
17	0.000173	0.999628
18	0.000118	0.999746
19	0.000080	0.999826
20	0.000055	0.999881
21	0.000037	0.999918

k=0·7
Mean=1·63
Variance=5·44

n	P(n)	F(n)
0	0.430512	0.430512
1	0.210951	0.641462
2	0.125516	0.766978
3	0.079075	0.846053
4	0.051201	0.897254
5	0.033690	0.930944
6	0.022404	0.953348
7	0.015011	0.968359
8	0.010113	0.978472
9	0.006843	0.985316
10	0.004647	0.989962
11	0.003164	0.993126
12	0.002159	0.995286
13	0.001477	0.996762
14	0.001012	0.997774
15	0.000694	0.998468
16	0.000477	0.998945
17	0.000328	0.999272
18	0.000226	0.999498
19	0.000155	0.999653
20	0.000107	0.999760
21	0.000074	0.999834
22	0.000051	0.999885
23	0.000035	0.999921

k=0·9
Mean=2·10
Variance=7·00

n	P(n)	F(n)
0	0.338383	0.338383
1	0.213182	0.551565
2	0.141766	0.693331
3	0.095928	0.789259
4	0.065471	0.854730
5	0.044913	0.899643
6	0.030915	0.930558
7	0.021331	0.951890
8	0.014745	0.966635
9	0.010207	0.976842
10	0.007074	0.983916
11	0.004906	0.988822
12	0.003406	0.992228
13	0.002366	0.994594
14	0.001644	0.996238
15	0.001143	0.997381
16	0.000795	0.998177
17	0.000553	0.998730
18	0.000385	0.999115
19	0.000268	0.999383
20	0.000187	0.999570
21	0.000130	0.999700
22	0.000091	0.999791
23	0.000063	0.999854
24	0.000044	0.999898

25	0.000031	0.999929

k=1·0
Mean=2·33
Variance=7·78

n	P(n)	F(n)
0	0.300000	0.300000
1	0.210000	0.510000
2	0.147000	0.657000
3	0.102900	0.759900
4	0.072030	0.831930
5	0.050421	0.882351
6	0.035295	0.917646
7	0.024706	0.942352
8	0.017294	0.959646
9	0.012106	0.971752
10	0.008474	0.980227
11	0.005932	0.986159
12	0.004152	0.990311
13	0.002907	0.993218
14	0.002035	0.995252
15	0.001424	0.996677
16	0.000997	0.997674
17	0.000698	0.998372
18	0.000489	0.998860
19	0.000342	0.999202
20	0.000239	0.999441
21	0.000168	0.999609
22	0.000117	0.999726
23	0.000082	0.999808
24	0.000057	0.999866
25	0.000040	0.999906

k=1·1
Mean=2·57
Variance=8·56

n	P(n)	F(n)
0	0.265970	0.265970
1	0.204797	0.470768
2	0.150526	0.621294
3	0.108880	0.730174
4	0.078122	0.808296
5	0.055779	0.864075
6	0.039696	0.903771
7	0.028184	0.931955
8	0.019976	0.951930
9	0.014138	0.966069
10	0.009996	0.976064
11	0.007061	0.983125
12	0.004984	0.988109
13	0.003515	0.991624
14	0.002478	0.994102
15	0.001746	0.995849
16	0.001230	0.997079
17	0.000866	0.997945
18	0.000610	0.998555
19	0.000429	0.998984
20	0.000302	0.999285
21	0.000212	0.999498
22	0.000149	0.999647
23	0.000105	0.999752
24	0.000074	0.999826
25	0.000052	0.999878
26	0.000036	0.999914

k=1·2
Mean=2·80
Variance=9·33

n	P(n)	F(n)
0	0.235801	0.235801
1	0.198073	0.433874
2	0.152516	0.586390
3	0.113879	0.700268
4	0.083701	0.783969
5	0.060934	0.844903
6	0.044076	0.888979
7	0.031735	0.920714
8	0.022770	0.943483
9	0.016293	0.959776
10	0.011633	0.971409
11	0.008291	0.979700
12	0.005901	0.985601
13	0.004194	0.989795
14	0.002978	0.992773
15	0.002112	0.994885
16	0.001497	0.996382
17	0.001060	0.997442
18	0.000750	0.998192
19	0.000531	0.998723
20	0.000375	0.999099
21	0.000265	0.999364
22	0.000187	0.999551
23	0.000132	0.999683
24	0.000093	0.999777
25	0.000066	0.999843
26	0.000046	0.999889
27	0.000033	0.999922

k=1·3
Mean=3·03
Variance=10·11

n	P(n)	F(n)
0	0.209054	0.209054
1	0.190239	0.399292
2	0.153142	0.552435
3	0.117920	0.670354
4	0.088734	0.759088
5	0.065841	0.824929
6	0.048393	0.873323
7	0.035327	0.908649
8	0.025656	0.934306
9	0.018558	0.95286.
10	0.013380	0.96624.
11	0.009622	0.975866
12	0.006904	0.982769
13	0.004944	0.987713
14	0.003535	0.991248
15	0.002524	0.993772
16	0.001800	0.995572
17	0.001282	0.996852
18	0.000912	0.997762
19	0.000649	0.998412
20	0.000461	0.998872
21	0.000327	0.999202
22	0.000232	0.999432
23	0.000165	0.999602
24	0.000117	0.999712
25	0.000083	0.999802
26	0.000059	0.999852
27	0.000041	0.999902

k=1·4
Mean=3·27
Variance=10·89

n	P(n)	F(n)
0	0.185340	0.185342
1	0.181633	0.366972
2	0.152572	0.519542
3	0.121041	0.640582
4	0.093201	0.733782
5	0.070460	0.804242
6	0.052610	0.856852
7	0.038932	0.895782
8	0.028615	0.924402
9	0.020921	0.945322
10	0.015230	0.960552
11	0.011049	0.971602
12	0.007992	0.979592
13	0.005766	0.985362
14	0.004152	0.989512
15	0.002984	0.992492
16	0.002141	0.994632
17	0.001534	0.996172
18	0.001098	0.997272
19	0.000784	0.998052
20	0.000560	0.998612
21	0.000400	0.999012
22	0.000285	0.999292
23	0.000203	0.999502
24	0.000144	0.999642
25	0.000103	0.999742
26	0.000073	0.999822
27	0.000052	0.999872
28	0.000037	0.999912

k = 1·5
Mean = 3·50
Variance = 11·67

n	P(n)	F(n)
0	0.164317	0.164317
1	0.172533	0.336849
2	0.150966	0.487815
3	0.123289	0.611104
4	0.097090	0.708194
5	0.074759	0.782954
6	0.056692	0.839646
7	0.042519	0.882166
8	0.031624	0.913789
9	0.023366	0.937156
10	0.017174	0.954330
11	0.012568	0.966899
12	0.009165	0.976063
13	0.006662	0.982725
14	0.004830	0.987555
15	0.003494	0.991049
16	0.002522	0.993570
17	0.001817	0.995388
18	0.001307	0.996695
19	0.000939	0.997635
20	0.000674	0.998308
21	0.000483	0.998791
22	0.000346	0.999137
23	0.000247	0.999385
24	0.000177	0.999561
25	0.000126	0.999687
26	0.000090	0.999777
27	0.000064	0.999842
28	0.000046	0.999887
29	0.000033	0.999920

k = 1·6
Mean = 3·73
Variance = 12·44

n	P(n)	F(n)
0	0.145678	0.145678
1	0.163159	0.308837
2	0.148475	0.457312
3	0.124719	0.582031
4	0.100399	0.682430
5	0.078713	0.761143
6	0.060609	0.821752
7	0.046063	0.867814
8	0.034662	0.902476
9	0.025881	0.928358
10	0.019204	0.947561
11	0.014176	0.961737
12	0.010419	0.972156
13	0.007630	0.979787
14	0.005570	0.985357
15	0.004055	0.989411
16	0.002945	0.992356
17	0.002134	0.994491
18	0.001544	0.996034
19	0.001115	0.997149

n	P(n)	F(n)
20	0.000804	0.997953
21	0.000579	0.998531
22	0.000416	0.998948
23	0.000299	0.999246
24	0.000214	0.999461
25	0.000154	0.999615
26	0.000110	0.999725
27	0.000079	0.999803
28	0.000056	0.999860
29	0.000040	0.999900

k = 1·7
Mean = 3·97
Variance = 13·22

n	P(n)	F(n)
0	0.129153	0.129153
1	0.153693	0.282846
2	0.145240	0.428086
3	0.125390	0.553476
4	0.103133	0.656609
5	0.082300	0.738910
6	0.064332	0.803241
7	0.049535	0.852776
8	0.037709	0.890485
9	0.028449	0.918934
10	0.021308	0.940243
11	0.015865	0.956108
12	0.011753	0.967861
13	0.008670	0.976532
14	0.006373	0.982904
15	0.004669	0.987573
16	0.003411	0.990985
17	0.002486	0.993471
18	0.001808	0.995279
19	0.001312	0.996591
20	0.000951	0.997542
21	0.000688	0.998230
22	0.000497	0.998727
23	0.000358	0.999085
24	0.000258	0.999343
25	0.000186	0.999529
26	0.000134	0.999662
27	0.000096	0.999758
28	0.000069	0.999827
29	0.000049	0.999876
30	0.000035	0.999911

k = 1·8
Mean = 4·20
Variance = 14·00

n	P(n)	F(n)
0	0.114503	0.114503
1	0.144274	0.258778
2	0.141389	0.400166
3	0.125365	0.525531
4	0.105306	0.630837

n	P(n)	F(n)
5	0.085509	0.716346
6	0.067837	0.784183
7	0.052913	0.837096
8	0.040743	0.877839
9	0.031055	0.908894
10	0.023478	0.932372
11	0.017630	0.950001
12	0.013163	0.963165
13	0.009781	0.972946
14	0.007238	0.980184
15	0.005337	0.985521
16	0.003923	0.989444
17	0.002875	0.992319
18	0.002102	0.994421
19	0.001533	0.995955
20	0.001116	0.997071
21	0.000811	0.997882
22	0.000588	0.998471
23	0.000426	0.998897
24	0.000308	0.999205
25	0.000223	0.999428
26	0.000161	0.999589
27	0.000116	0.999704
28	0.000083	0.999788
29	0.000060	0.999848
30	0.000043	0.999891
31	0.000031	0.999922

k = 1·9
Mean = 4·43
Variance = 14·78

n	P(n)	F(n)
0	0.101515	0.101515
1	0.135015	0.236530
2	0.137040	0.373570
3	0.124707	0.498277
4	0.106936	0.605213
5	0.088329	0.693542
6	0.071105	0.764647
7	0.056173	0.820820
8	0.043745	0.864564
9	0.033683	0.898248
10	0.025700	0.923948
11	0.019462	0.943410
12	0.014645	0.958056
13	0.010961	0.969017
14	0.008166	0.977183
15	0.006059	0.983243
16	0.004480	0.987723
17	0.003302	0.991025
18	0.002427	0.993452
19	0.001779	0.995231
20	0.001302	0.996533
21	0.000950	0.997483
22	0.000692	0.998176
23	0.000504	0.998679
24	0.000366	0.999045

n	P(n)	F(n)
25	0.000265	0.999310
26	0.000192	0.999502
27	0.000139	0.999641
28	0.000100	0.999742
29	0.000072	0.999814
30	0.000052	0.999866
31	0.000038	0.999904

k=2·0
Mean=4·67
Variance=15·56

n	P(n)	F(n)
0	0.090000	0.090000
1	0.126000	0.216000
2	0.132300	0.348300
3	0.123480	0.471780
4	0.108045	0.579825
5	0.090758	0.670583
6	0.074119	0.744702
7	0.059295	0.803997
8	0.046695	0.850692
9	0.036318	0.887010
10	0.027965	0.914975
11	0.021355	0.936330
12	0.016194	0.952524
13	0.012208	0.964732
14	0.009156	0.973888
15	0.006836	0.980725
16	0.005085	0.985810
17	0.003769	0.989578
18	0.002785	0.992363
19	0.002052	0.994415
20	0.001508	0.995923
21	0.001106	0.997029
22	0.000809	0.997838
23	0.000591	0.998429
24	0.000431	0.998860
25	0.000314	0.999174
26	0.000228	0.999402
27	0.000166	0.999568
28	0.000120	0.999688
29	0.000087	0.999775
30	0.000063	0.999837
31	0.000045	0.999883
32	0.000033	0.999916

k=2·1
Mean=4·90
Variance=16·33

n	P(n)	F(n)
0	0.079791	0.079791
1	0.117293	0.197084
2	0.127263	0.324347
3	0.121748	0.446095
4	0.108660	0.554755

n	P(n)	F(n)
5	0.092796	0.647551
6	0.076866	0.724417
7	0.062261	0.786678
8	0.049576	0.836254
9	0.038944	0.875198
10	0.030260	0.905458
11	0.023300	0.928758
12	0.017805	0.946563
13	0.013518	0.960082
14	0.010206	0.970288
15	0.007668	0.977956
16	0.005737	0.983693
17	0.004276	0.987969
18	0.003176	0.991144
19	0.002352	0.993496
20	0.001737	0.995233
21	0.001279	0.996512
22	0.000940	0.997453
23	0.000690	0.998143
24	0.000505	0.998648
25	0.000369	0.999017
26	0.000269	0.999286
27	0.000196	0.999482
28	0.000143	0.999625
29	0.000104	0.999728
30	0.000075	0.999804
31	0.000055	0.999858
32	0.000039	0.999898
33	0.000029	0.999926

k=2·2
Mean=5·13
Variance=17·11

n	P(n)	F(n)
0	0.070740	0.070740
1	0.108940	0.179680
2	0.122013	0.301693
3	0.119573	0.421266
4	0.108811	0.530077
5	0.094448	0.624525
6	0.079336	0.703861
7	0.065056	0.768917
8	0.052370	0.821287
9	0.041547	0.862833
10	0.032573	0.895406
11	0.025288	0.920694
12	0.019472	0.940166
13	0.014889	0.955055
14	0.011315	0.966370
15	0.008554	0.974925
16	0.006437	0.981362
17	0.004824	0.986186
18	0.003602	0.989788
19	0.002681	0.992468
20	0.001989	0.994457
21	0.001472	0.995929
22	0.001087	0.997016
23	0.000800	0.997816
24	0.000588	0.998404

n	P(n)	F(n)
25	0.000431	0.998836
26	0.000316	0.999152
27	0.000231	0.999383
28	0.000169	0.999551
29	0.000123	0.999674
30	0.000089	0.999764
31	0.000065	0.999829
32	0.000047	0.999876
33	0.000034	0.999910

k=2·3
Mean=5·37
Variance=17·89

n	P(n)	F(n)
0	0.062716	0.062716
1	0.100973	0.163689
2	0.116624	0.280313
3	0.117012	0.397325
4	0.108529	0.505854
5	0.095723	0.601577
6	0.081524	0.683100
7	0.067665	0.750765
8	0.055062	0.805827
9	0.044111	0.849938
10	0.034892	0.884830
11	0.027311	0.912141
12	0.021189	0.933329
13	0.016315	0.949644
14	0.012481	0.962126
15	0.009494	0.971619
16	0.007186	0.978805
17	0.005415	0.984220
18	0.004064	0.988284
19	0.003039	0.991323
20	0.002266	0.993589
21	0.001684	0.995274
22	0.001249	0.996522
23	0.000923	0.997446
24	0.000681	0.998127
25	0.000502	0.998629
26	0.000369	0.998998
27	0.000271	0.999269
28	0.000198	0.999467
29	0.000145	0.999612
30	0.000106	0.999718
31	0.000077	0.999795
32	0.000056	0.999851
33	0.000041	0.999892
34	0.000030	0.999922

k=2·4
Mean=5·60
Variance=18·67

n	P(n)	F(n)
0	0.055602	0.055602
1	0.093411	0.149014
2	0.111160	0.260173
3	0.114124	0.374297
4	0.107847	0.482144

P(n)	F(n)
0.096631	0.578775
0.083425	0.662200
0.070077	0.732277
0.057638	0.789915
0.046623	0.836538
0.037205	0.873743
0.029358	0.903101
0.022948	0.926049
0.017794	0.943843
0.013701	0.957544
0.010486	0.968030
0.007982	0.976013
0.006048	0.982061
0.004563	0.986624
0.003429	0.990053
0.002569	0.992621
0.001918	0.994539
0.001428	0.995967
0.001060	0.997028
0.000786	0.997813
0.000581	0.998394
0.000428	0.998822
0.000315	0.999138
0.000232	0.999369
0.000170	0.999540
0.000125	0.999664
0.000091	0.999755
0.000067	0.999822
0.000049	0.999871
0.000035	0.999906

=2.5
Mean=5.83
Variance=19.44

n	P(n)	F(n)
0	0.049295	0.049295
1	0.086266	0.135561
2	0.105676	0.241238
3	0.110960	0.352198
4	0.106799	0.458997
5	0.097187	0.556184
6	0.085039	0.641222
7	0.072283	0.713505
8	0.060085	0.773591
9	0.049070	0.822660
10	0.039501	0.862161
11	0.031421	0.893582
12	0.024744	0.918327
13	0.019320	0.937646
14	0.014973	0.952619
15	0.011529	0.964148
16	0.008827	0.972975
17	0.006724	0.979699
18	0.005099	0.984798
19	0.003851	0.988649
20	0.002898	0.991547
21	0.002173	0.993720
22	0.001625	0.995345
23	0.001212	0.996557
24	0.000901	0.997458

n	P(n)	F(n)
25	0.000669	0.998127
26	0.000495	0.998622
27	0.000366	0.998988
28	0.000270	0.999258
29	0.000199	0.999456
30	0.000146	0.999602
31	0.000107	0.999710
32	0.000079	0.999788
33	0.000057	0.999846
34	0.000042	0.999888
35	0.000031	0.999918

k=3.0
Mean=7.00
Variance=23.33

n	P(n)	F(n)
0	0.027000	0.027000
1	0.056700	0.083700
2	0.079380	0.163080
3	0.092610	0.255690
4	0.097241	0.352931
5	0.095296	0.448226
6	0.088943	0.537169
7	0.080048	0.617217
8	0.070042	0.687260
9	0.059925	0.747185
10	0.050337	0.797522
11	0.041643	0.839164
12	0.034008	0.873172
13	0.027468	0.900640
14	0.021974	0.922615
15	0.017433	0.940048
16	0.013729	0.953776
17	0.010741	0.964517
18	0.008354	0.972871
19	0.006463	0.979334
20	0.004977	0.984310
21	0.003815	0.988126
22	0.002914	0.991039
23	0.002217	0.993256
24	0.001681	0.994937
25	0.001271	0.996208
26	0.000958	0.997166
27	0.000720	0.997887
28	0.000540	0.998427
29	0.000404	0.998831
30	0.000302	0.999133
31	0.000225	0.999358
32	0.000167	0.999525
33	0.000124	0.999650
34	0.000092	0.999742
35	0.000068	0.999810
36	0.000050	0.999860
37	0.000037	0.999897
38	0.000027	0.999925

k=3.5
Mean=8.17
Variance=27.22

n	P(n)	F(n)
0	0.014789	0.014789
1	0.036232	0.051020
2	0.057065	0.108086
3	0.073234	0.181319
4	0.083303	0.264622
5	0.087468	0.352091
6	0.086740	0.438830
7	0.082403	0.521233
8	0.075707	0.596940
9	0.067716	0.664656
10	0.059251	0.723908
11	0.050902	0.774810
12	0.043055	0.817865
13	0.035934	0.853799
14	0.029646	0.883445
15	0.024211	0.907656
16	0.019596	0.927252
17	0.015734	0.942986
18	0.012544	0.955529
19	0.009936	0.965465
20	0.007824	0.973289
21	0.006129	0.979419
22	0.004778	0.984197
23	0.003708	0.987905
24	0.002866	0.990771
25	0.002207	0.992978
26	0.001693	0.994671
27	0.001295	0.995966
28	0.000988	0.996954
29	0.000751	0.997704
30	0.000569	0.998274
31	0.000431	0.998705
32	0.000325	0.999030
33	0.000245	0.999274
34	0.000184	0.999458
35	0.000138	0.999596
36	0.000103	0.999700
37	0.000077	0.999777
38	0.000058	0.999834
39	0.000043	0.999877
40	0.000032	0.999909

k=4.0
Mean=9.33
Variance=31.11

n	P(n)	F(n)
0	0.008100	0.008100
1	0.022680	0.030780
2	0.039690	0.070470
3	0.055566	0.126036
4	0.068068	0.194104

n	P(n)	F(n)
5	0.076237	0.270341
6	0.080048	0.350389
7	0.080048	0.430438
8	0.077047	0.507484
9	0.071910	0.579394
10	0.065438	0.644833
11	0.058300	0.703132
12	0.051012	0.754144
13	0.043949	0.798093
14	0.037357	0.835450
15	0.031379	0.866829
16	0.026084	0.892913
17	0.021481	0.914394
18	0.017543	0.931937
19	0.014219	0.946156
20	0.011446	0.957602
21	0.009157	0.966759
22	0.007284	0.974043
23	0.005764	0.979807
24	0.004539	0.984346
25	0.003559	0.987905
26	0.002778	0.990683
27	0.002161	0.992844
28	0.001675	0.994519
29	0.001294	0.995813
30	0.000996	0.996809
31	0.000765	0.997574
32	0.000586	0.998159
33	0.000447	0.998606
34	0.000341	0.998947
35	0.000259	0.999206
36	0.000196	0.999402
37	0.000149	0.999551
38	0.000112	0.999663
39	0.000085	0.999747
40	0.000064	0.999811
41	0.000048	0.999859
42	0.000036	0.999895
43	0.000027	0.999922

n	P(n)	F(n)
15	0.038391	0.818076
16	0.032753	0.850829
17	0.027647	0.878476
18	0.023116	0.901592
19	0.019162	0.920754
20	0.015761	0.936514
21	0.012871	0.949386
22	0.010443	0.959829
23	0.008423	0.968252
24	0.006756	0.975007
25	0.005391	0.980399
26	0.004282	0.984680
27	0.003386	0.988066
28	0.002666	0.990732
29	0.002092	0.992824
30	0.001635	0.994459
31	0.001274	0.995733
32	0.000989	0.996722
33	0.000766	0.997488
34	0.000591	0.998079
35	0.000455	0.998534
36	0.000350	0.998884
37	0.000268	0.999152
38	0.000205	0.999356
39	0.000156	0.999513
40	0.000119	0.999632
41	0.000090	0.999722
42	0.000069	0.999791
43	0.000052	0.999842
44	0.000039	0.999882
45	0.000030	0.999911

n	P(n)	F(n)
20	0.020603	0.909528
21	0.017169	0.926698
22	0.014204	0.940901
23	0.011672	0.952573
24	0.009532	0.962105
25	0.007740	0.969845
26	0.006252	0.976097
27	0.005024	0.981121
28	0.004019	0.985140
29	0.003202	0.988342
30	0.002540	0.990883
31	0.002007	0.992890
32	0.001581	0.994471
33	0.001241	0.995712
34	0.000971	0.996683
35	0.000757	0.997439
36	0.000589	0.998028
37	0.000457	0.998485
38	0.000353	0.998838
39	0.000273	0.999111
40	0.000210	0.999321
41	0.000161	0.999482
42	0.000124	0.999606
43	0.000095	0.999701
44	0.000072	0.999773
45	0.000055	0.999828
46	0.000042	0.999870
47	0.000032	0.999902

k = 4·5
Mean = 10·50
Variance = 35·00

n	P(n)	F(n)
0	0.004437	0.004437
1	0.013975	0.018412
2	0.026902	0.045314
3	0.040802	0.086115
4	0.053552	0.139668
5	0.063727	0.203394
6	0.070631	0.274025
7	0.074162	0.348188
8	0.074626	0.422813
9	0.072553	0.495366
10	0.068562	0.563929
11	0.063264	0.627193
12	0.057202	0.684395
13	0.050821	0.735216
14	0.044469	0.779685

k = 5·0
Mean = 11·67
Variance = 38·89

n	P(n)	F(n)
0	0.002430	0.002430
1	0.008505	0.010935
2	0.017861	0.028796
3	0.029172	0.057968
4	0.040841	0.098809
5	0.051460	0.150268
6	0.060036	0.210305
7	0.066040	0.276345
8	0.069342	0.345686
9	0.070112	0.415799
10	0.068710	0.484509
11	0.065587	0.550096
12	0.061214	0.611310
13	0.056035	0.667345
14	0.050431	0.717776
15	0.044716	0.762492
16	0.039126	0.801619
17	0.033833	0.835451
18	0.028946	0.864397
19	0.024528	0.888925

k=0·1
Mean=0·21
Variance=0·66

n	P(n)	F(n)
0	0.892308	0.892308
1	0.060677	0.952985
2	0.022693	0.975679
3	0.010802	0.986481
4	0.005693	0.992173
5	0.003174	0.995347
6	0.001835	0.997182
7	0.001087	0.998269
8	0.000656	0.998925
9	0.000402	0.999327
10	0.000248	0.999575
11	0.000155	0.999731
12	0.000098	0.999828
13	0.000062	0.999890
14	0.000039	0.999929

k=0·2
Mean=0·42
Variance=1·33

n	P(n)	F(n)
0	0.796214	0.796214
1	0.108285	0.904499
2	0.044180	0.948680
3	0.022031	0.970711
4	0.011985	0.982696
5	0.006846	0.989542
6	0.004034	0.993576
7	0.002430	0.996006
8	0.001487	0.997493
9	0.000921	0.998415
10	0.000576	0.998991
11	0.000363	0.999355
12	0.000231	0.999585
13	0.000147	0.999732
14	0.000094	0.999827
15	0.000061	0.999888
16	0.000039	0.999927

k=0·3
Mean=0·64
Variance=1·99

n	P(n)	F(n)
0	0.710469	0.710469
1	0.144936	0.855404
2	0.064062	0.919466
3	0.033397	0.952863
4	0.018736	0.971599
5	0.010957	0.982556
6	0.006581	0.989137
7	0.004028	0.993165
8	0.002499	0.995665
9	0.001567	0.997232

10	0.000991	0.998223
11	0.000631	0.998854
12	0.000404	0.999258
13	0.000260	0.999518
14	0.000168	0.999686
15	0.000109	0.999795
16	0.000071	0.999866
17	0.000046	0.999912

k=0·4
Mean=0·85
Variance=2·66

n	P(n)	F(n)
0	0.633957	0.633957
1	0.172436	0.806394
2	0.082080	0.888473
3	0.044651	0.933125
4	0.025808	0.958933
5	0.015444	0.974377
6	0.009452	0.983829
7	0.005876	0.989705
8	0.003696	0.993401
9	0.002346	0.995747
10	0.001499	0.997246
11	0.000964	0.998210
12	0.000623	0.998833
13	0.000404	0.999237
14	0.000263	0.999500
15	0.000172	0.999671
16	0.000112	0.999784
17	0.000074	0.999857
18	0.000048	0.999906

k=0·5
Mean=1·06
Variance=3·32

n	P(n)	F(n)
0	0.565685	0.565685
1	0.192333	0.758018
2	0.098090	0.856108
3	0.055584	0.911693
4	0.033073	0.944765
5	0.020240	0.965006
6	0.012617	0.977622
7	0.007966	0.985589
8	0.005079	0.990667
9	0.003262	0.993929
10	0.002107	0.996036
11	0.001368	0.997403
12	0.000891	0.998295
13	0.000583	0.998877
14	0.000382	0.999260
15	0.000251	0.999511
16	0.000165	0.999676
17	0.000109	0.999785
18	0.000072	0.999858
19	0.000048	0.999905

k=0·6
Mean=1·28
Variance=3·98

n	P(n)	F(n)
0	0.504766	0.504766
1	0.205944	0.710710
2	0.112034	0.822744
3	0.066025	0.888769
4	0.040407	0.929177
5	0.025279	0.954456
6	0.016044	0.970499
7	0.010286	0.980786
8	0.006645	0.987431
9	0.004318	0.991748
10	0.002819	0.994567
11	0.001847	0.996414
12	0.001214	0.997628
13	0.000800	0.998428
14	0.000529	0.998957
15	0.000350	0.999307
16	0.000232	0.999539
17	0.000154	0.999693
18	0.000102	0.999795
19	0.000068	0.999863
20	0.000045	0.999909

k=0·7
Mean=1·49
Variance=4·65

n	P(n)	F(n)
0	0.450407	0.450407
1	0.214394	0.664801
2	0.123920	0.788720
3	0.075839	0.864559
4	0.047703	0.912261
5	0.030491	0.942753
6	0.019698	0.962450
7	0.012820	0.975271
8	0.008391	0.983661
9	0.005516	0.989177
10	0.003638	0.992815
11	0.002406	0.995222
12	0.001595	0.996817
13	0.001060	0.997877
14	0.000705	0.998582
15	0.000470	0.999052
16	0.000314	0.999366
17	0.000209	0.999575
18	0.000140	0.999715
19	0.000094	0.999809
20	0.000063	0.999872
21	0.000042	0.999914

k = 0·8
Mean = 1·70
Variance = 5·31

n	P(n)	F(n)
0	0.401902	0.401902
1	0.218635	0.620536
2	0.133804	0.754341
3	0.084921	0.839262
4	0.054859	0.894121
5	0.035812	0.929933
6	0.023540	0.953473
7	0.015550	0.969024
8	0.010310	0.979333
9	0.006855	0.986188
10	0.004568	0.990756
11	0.003050	0.993806
12	0.002039	0.995845
13	0.001365	0.997211
14	0.000915	0.998126
15	0.000614	0.998740
16	0.000412	0.999152
17	0.000277	0.999429
18	0.000186	0.999616
19	0.000125	0.999741
20	0.000084	0.999825
21	0.000057	0.999882
22	0.000038	0.999921

k = 0·9
Mean = 1·91
Variance = 5·98

n	P(n)	F(n)
0	0.358620	0.358620
1	0.219476	0.578096
2	0.141781	0.719877
3	0.093198	0.813075
4	0.061790	0.874865
5	0.041177	0.916042
6	0.027534	0.943575
7	0.018455	0.962031
8	0.012393	0.974423
9	0.008333	0.982757
10	0.005610	0.988367
11	0.003780	0.992147
12	0.002549	0.994696
13	0.001720	0.996416
14	0.001161	0.997578
15	0.000784	0.998362
16	0.000530	0.998892
17	0.000358	0.999250
18	0.000242	0.999493
19	0.000164	0.999657
20	0.000111	0.999768
21	0.000075	0.999843
22	0.000051	0.999893
23	0.000034	0.999928

k = 1·0
Mean = 2·13
Variance = 6·64

n	P(n)	F(n)
0	0.320000	0.320000
1	0.217600	0.537600
2	0.147968	0.685568
3	0.100618	0.786186
4	0.068420	0.854607
5	0.046526	0.901133
6	0.031638	0.932770
7	0.021514	0.954284
8	0.014629	0.968913
9	0.009948	0.978861
10	0.006765	0.985625
11	0.004600	0.990225
12	0.003128	0.993353
13	0.002127	0.995480
14	0.001446	0.996926
15	0.000984	0.997910
16	0.000669	0.998579
17	0.000455	0.999034
18	0.000309	0.999343
19	0.000210	0.999553
20	0.000143	0.999696
21	0.000097	0.999793
22	0.000066	0.999859
23	0.000045	0.999904

k = 1·1
Mean = 2·34
Variance = 7·30

n	P(n)	F(n)
0	0.285539	0.285539
1	0.213583	0.499122
2	0.152498	0.651620
3	0.107155	0.758775
4	0.074687	0.833463
5	0.051803	0.885266
6	0.035813	0.921079
7	0.024701	0.945780
8	0.017007	0.962786
9	0.011693	0.974479
10	0.008031	0.982510
11	0.005511	0.988021
12	0.003778	0.991799
13	0.002589	0.994388
14	0.001773	0.996161
15	0.001214	0.997375
16	0.000831	0.998206
17	0.000568	0.998774
18	0.000388	0.999162
19	0.000266	0.999428
20	0.000181	0.999609
21	0.000124	0.999733
22	0.000085	0.999818
23	0.000058	0.999876
24	0.000039	0.999915

k = 1·2
Mean = 2·55
Variance = 7·97

n	P(n)	F(n)
0	0.254789	0.254789
1	0.207907	0.462696
2	0.155515	0.618211
3	0.112800	0.731011
4	0.080539	0.811550
5	0.056957	0.868508
6	0.040022	0.908530
7	0.027993	0.936522
8	0.019511	0.956033
9	0.013562	0.969595
10	0.009407	0.979002
11	0.006513	0.985515
12	0.004503	0.990017
13	0.003109	0.993126
14	0.002144	0.995270
15	0.001478	0.996748
16	0.001017	0.997765
17	0.000700	0.998465
18	0.000481	0.998946
19	0.000331	0.999277
20	0.000227	0.999504
21	0.000156	0.999660
22	0.000107	0.999767
23	0.000073	0.999840
24	0.000050	0.999890
25	0.000034	0.999925

k = 1·3
Mean = 2·76
Variance = 8·63

n	P(n)	F(n)
0	0.227350	0.227350
1	0.200977	0.428327
2	0.157164	0.585491
3	0.117559	0.703054
4	0.085936	0.788980
5	0.061942	0.850922
6	0.044227	0.895151
7	0.031363	0.926514
8	0.022127	0.948641
9	0.015548	0.964190
10	0.010890	0.975080
11	0.007607	0.982687
12	0.005302	0.987990
13	0.003689	0.991680
14	0.002562	0.994242
15	0.001777	0.996019
16	0.001231	0.997250
17	0.000852	0.998102
18	0.000589	0.998691
19	0.000407	0.999098

n	P(n)	F(n)
20	0.000281	0.999378
21	0.000194	0.999572
22	0.000133	0.999705
23	0.000092	0.999797
24	0.000063	0.999861
25	0.000044	0.999904

k=1·4
Mean = 2·98
Variance = 9·30

n	P(n)	F(n)
0	0.202866	0.202866
1	0.193129	0.395995
2	0.157593	0.553588
3	0.121452	0.675040
4	0.090846	0.765886
5	0.066717	0.832603
6	0.048392	0.880995
7	0.034787	0.915782
8	0.024838	0.940620
9	0.017640	0.958261
10	0.012475	0.970736
11	0.008792	0.979528
12	0.006178	0.985705
13	0.004330	0.990036
14	0.003029	0.993064
15	0.002114	0.995178
16	0.001474	0.996652
17	0.001026	0.997678
18	0.000713	0.998391
19	0.000495	0.998886
20	0.000343	0.999229
21	0.000238	0.999467
22	0.000165	0.999632
23	0.000114	0.999746
24	0.000079	0.999825
25	0.000054	0.999879
26	0.000038	0.999917

k=1·5
Mean = 3·19
Variance = 9·96

n	P(n)	F(n)
0	0.181019	0.181019
1	0.184640	0.365659
2	0.156944	0.522603
3	0.124509	0.647112
4	0.095249	0.742361
5	0.071246	0.813607
6	0.052485	0.866092
7	0.038239	0.904331
8	0.027628	0.931959
9	0.019831	0.951789

n	P(n)	F(n)
10	0.014159	0.965948
11	0.010066	0.976014
12	0.007130	0.983144
13	0.005035	0.988178
14	0.003546	0.991724
15	0.002492	0.994216
16	0.001747	0.995963
17	0.001223	0.997186
18	0.000855	0.998041
19	0.000597	0.998638
20	0.000416	0.999053
21	0.000289	0.999343
22	0.000201	0.999544
23	0.000140	0.999684
24	0.000097	0.999781
25	0.000067	0.999849
26	0.000047	0.999895
27	0.000032	0.999928

k=1·6
Mean = 3·40
Variance = 10·63

n	P(n)	F(n)
0	0.161525	0.161525
1	0.175739	0.337264
2	0.155354	0.492618
3	0.126768	0.619386
4	0.099133	0.718519
5	0.075500	0.794019
6	0.056474	0.850493
7	0.041694	0.892186
8	0.030478	0.922665
9	0.022107	0.944771
10	0.015935	0.960706
11	0.011427	0.972133
12	0.008159	0.980291
13	0.005804	0.986095
14	0.004116	0.990211
15	0.002911	0.993121
16	0.002053	0.995175
17	0.001446	0.996621
18	0.001016	0.997636
19	0.000713	0.998349
20	0.000499	0.998848
21	0.000349	0.999197
22	0.000244	0.999441
23	0.000170	0.999611
24	0.000119	0.999730
25	0.000083	0.999812
26	0.000057	0.999870
27	0.000040	0.999910

k=1·7
Mean = 3·61
Variance = 11·29

n	P(n)	F(n)
0	0.144130	0.144130
1	0.166614	0.310745
2	0.152952	0.463697
3	0.128276	0.591973
4	0.102492	0.694465
5	0.079452	0.773917
6	0.060331	0.834248
7	0.045127	0.879375
8	0.033372	0.912747
9	0.024458	0.937204
10	0.017795	0.955000
11	0.012871	0.967871
12	0.009263	0.977134
13	0.006638	0.983771
14	0.004739	0.988511
15	0.003373	0.991884
16	0.002394	0.994278
17	0.001695	0.995973
18	0.001197	0.997171
19	0.000844	0.998015
20	0.000594	0.998609
21	0.000418	0.999027
22	0.000293	0.999320
23	0.000205	0.999525
24	0.000144	0.999669
25	0.000100	0.999769
26	0.000070	0.999839
27	0.000049	0.999888
28	0.000034	0.999922

k=1·8
Mean = 3·83
Variance = 11·95

n	P(n)	F(n)
0	0.128609	0.128609
1	0.157417	0.286025
2	0.149861	0.435886
3	0.129080	0.564967
4	0.105329	0.670296
5	0.083084	0.753380
6	0.064030	0.817410
7	0.048516	0.865926
8	0.036290	0.902217
9	0.026871	0.929087
10	0.019734	0.948821
11	0.014395	0.963217
12	0.010441	0.973658
13	0.007537	0.981195
14	0.005418	0.986613
15	0.003881	0.990493
16	0.002771	0.993264
17	0.001973	0.995237
18	0.001401	0.996638
19	0.000993	0.997631

20	0.000702	0.998333
21	0.000496	0.998829
22	0.000349	0.999178
23	0.000246	0.999424
24	0.000173	0.999597
25	0.000121	0.999718
26	0.000085	0.999803
27	0.000059	0.999862
28	0.000042	0.999904

k = 1·9
Mean = 4·04
Variance = 12·62

n	P(n)	F(n)
0	0.114759	0.114759
1	0.148268	0.263027
2	0.146192	0.409219
3	0.129234	0.538453
4	0.107652	0.646105
5	0.086380	0.732485
6	0.067549	0.800034
7	0.051839	0.851873
8	0.039216	0.891089
9	0.029334	0.920423
10	0.021742	0.942165
11	0.015994	0.958159
12	0.011692	0.969851
13	0.008501	0.978352
14	0.006152	0.984504
15	0.004435	0.988939
16	0.003185	0.992124
17	0.002281	0.994404
18	0.001628	0.996033
19	0.001160	0.997192
20	0.000824	0.998016
21	0.000584	0.998601
22	0.000414	0.999014
23	0.000292	0.999307
24	0.000206	0.999513
25	0.000145	0.999658
26	0.000102	0.999760
27	0.000072	0.999832
28	0.000050	0.999883
29	0.000035	0.999918

k = 2·0
Mean = 4·25
Variance = 13·28

n	P(n)	F(n)
0	0.102400	0.102400
1	0.139264	0.241664
2	0.142049	0.383713
3	0.128791	0.512505
4	0.109473	0.621977
5	0.089330	0.711307
6	0.070868	0.782175
7	0.055075	0.837250
8	0.042132	0.879382
9	0.031833	0.911215

10	0.023811	0.935026
11	0.017664	0.952690
12	0.013012	0.965702
13	0.009529	0.975231
14	0.006943	0.982174
15	0.005036	0.987209
16	0.003638	0.990848
17	0.002620	0.993467
18	0.001880	0.995347
19	0.001346	0.996693
20	0.000961	0.997654
21	0.000685	0.998339
22	0.000487	0.998825
23	0.000345	0.999171
24	0.000245	0.999415
25	0.000173	0.999588
26	0.000122	0.999710
27	0.000086	0.999797
28	0.000061	0.999857
29	0.000043	0.999900
30	0.000030	0.999930

k = 2·1
Mean = 4·46
Variance = 13·95

n	P(n)	F(n)
0	0.091372	0.091372
1	0.130480	0.221852
2	0.137526	0.359378
3	0.127807	0.487185
4	0.110809	0.597994
5	0.091927	0.689921
6	0.073971	0.763891
7	0.058204	0.822096
8	0.045021	0.867117
9	0.034356	0.901473
10	0.025932	0.927405
11	0.019397	0.946802
12	0.014399	0.961201
13	0.010620	0.971821
14	0.007789	0.979610
15	0.005685	0.985295
16	0.004131	0.989426
17	0.002991	0.992417
18	0.002158	0.994576
19	0.001553	0.996128
20	0.001114	0.997242
21	0.000797	0.998039
22	0.000569	0.998608
23	0.000406	0.999014
24	0.000288	0.999302
25	0.000205	0.999507
26	0.000145	0.999652
27	0.000103	0.999755
28	0.000073	0.999827
29	0.000051	0.999879

30	0.000036	0.999915

k = 2·2
Mean = 4·67
Variance = 14·61

n	P(n)	F(n)
0	0.081532	0.081532
1	0.121972	0.203505
2	0.132706	0.336211
3	0.126336	0.462547
4	0.111681	0.574228
5	0.094169	0.668397
6	0.076842	0.745240
7	0.061210	0.806450
8	0.047867	0.854317
9	0.036889	0.891206
10	0.028095	0.919300
11	0.021189	0.940489
12	0.015849	0.956338
13	0.011772	0.968110
14	0.008691	0.976802
15	0.006383	0.983184
16	0.004666	0.987850
17	0.003397	0.991247
18	0.002464	0.993711
19	0.001781	0.995492
20	0.001284	0.996776
21	0.000923	0.997699
22	0.000662	0.998361
23	0.000474	0.998834
24	0.000338	0.999172
25	0.000241	0.999413
26	0.000171	0.999584
27	0.000122	0.999706
28	0.000086	0.999793
29	0.000061	0.999854
30	0.000043	0.999897
31	0.000031	0.999927

k = 2·3
Mean = 4·89
Variance = 15·27

n	P(n)	F(n)
0	0.072752	0.072752
1	0.113784	0.186536
2	0.127666	0.314202
3	0.124432	0.438634
4	0.112113	0.550746
5	0.096058	0.646805
6	0.079472	0.726277
7	0.064077	0.790354
8	0.050653	0.841007
9	0.039419	0.880427

n	P(n)	F(n)
10	0.030290	0.910717
11	0.023031	0.933748
12	0.017358	0.951106
13	0.012984	0.964090
14	0.009649	0.973738
15	0.007130	0.980868
16	0.005242	0.986110
17	0.003837	0.989948
18	0.002798	0.992745
19	0.002033	0.994778
20	0.001472	0.996250
21	0.001063	0.997313
22	0.000766	0.998079
23	0.000550	0.998629
24	0.000394	0.999023
25	0.000282	0.999305
26	0.000201	0.999506
27	0.000144	0.999650
28	0.000102	0.999752
29	0.000073	0.999825
30	0.000051	0.999876
31	0.000036	0.999912

k=2·4
Mean=5·10
Variance=15·94

n	P(n)	F(n)
0	0.064917	0.064917
1	0.105945	0.170862
2	0.122472	0.293334
3	0.122146	0.415480
4	0.112130	0.527610
5	0.097598	0.625208
6	0.081852	0.707060
7	0.066791	0.773851
8	0.053366	0.827217
9	0.041934	0.869151
10	0.032507	0.901658
11	0.024918	0.926577
12	0.018921	0.945498
13	0.014252	0.959750
14	0.010661	0.970410
15	0.007926	0.978336
16	0.005861	0.984197
17	0.004314	0.988511
18	0.003162	0.991673
19	0.002308	0.993981
20	0.001679	0.995660
21	0.001218	0.996878
22	0.000881	0.997760
23	0.000636	0.998395
24	0.000457	0.998853
25	0.000328	0.999181
26	0.000235	0.999416
27	0.000168	0.999585
28	0.000120	0.999705
29	0.000086	0.999791

n	P(n)	F(n)
30	0.000061	0.999852
31	0.000043	0.999895
32	0.000031	0.999926

k=2·5
Mean=5·31
Variance=16·60

n	P(n)	F(n)
0	0.057926	0.057926
1	0.098475	0.156401
2	0.117185	0.273585
3	0.119528	0.393114
4	0.111759	0.504873
5	0.098795	0.603668
6	0.083976	0.687643
7	0.069340	0.756983
8	0.055992	0.812975
9	0.044420	0.857396
10	0.034737	0.892133
11	0.026842	0.918975
12	0.020534	0.939509
13	0.015574	0.955083
14	0.011725	0.966808
15	0.008770	0.975579
16	0.006523	0.982102
17	0.004827	0.986929
18	0.003556	0.990485
19	0.002609	0.993094
20	0.001907	0.995001
21	0.001389	0.996390
22	0.001009	0.997400
23	0.000731	0.998131
24	0.000528	0.998659
25	0.000381	0.999040
26	0.000274	0.999313
27	0.000197	0.999510
28	0.000141	0.999651
29	0.000101	0.999751
30	0.000072	0.999823
31	0.000051	0.999875
32	0.000036	0.999911

k=3·0
Mean=6·38
Variance=19·92

n	P(n)	F(n)
0	0.032768	0.032768
1	0.066847	0.099615
2	0.090912	0.190526
3	0.103033	0.293559
4	0.105094	0.398653
5	0.100049	0.498702
6	0.090711	0.589414
7	0.079308	0.668721
8	0.067411	0.736133
9	0.056026	0.792159

n	P(n)	F(n)
10	0.045718	0.837877
11	0.036740	0.874617
12	0.029147	0.903764
13	0.022869	0.926634
14	0.017773	0.944406
15	0.013697	0.958103
16	0.010478	0.968582
17	0.007963	0.976545
18	0.006017	0.982562
19	0.004522	0.987084
20	0.003383	0.990466
21	0.002519	0.992985
22	0.001869	0.994854
23	0.001381	0.996235
24	0.001018	0.997253
25	0.000747	0.998000
26	0.000547	0.998548
27	0.000400	0.998947
28	0.000291	0.999238
29	0.000212	0.999450
30	0.000154	0.999604
31	0.000111	0.999715
32	0.000080	0.999795
33	0.000058	0.999853
34	0.000042	0.999895
35	0.000030	0.999925

k=3·5
Mean=7·44
Variance=23·24

n	P(n)	F(n)
0	0.018536	0.018536
1	0.044117	0.062653
2	0.067498	0.130151
3	0.084148	0.214299
4	0.092984	0.307283
5	0.094843	0.402126
6	0.091366	0.493492
7	0.084317	0.577809
8	0.075253	0.653062
9	0.065387	0.718449
10	0.055579	0.774028
11	0.046383	0.820417
12	0.038111	0.858522
13	0.030900	0.889422
14	0.024764	0.914185
15	0.019646	0.933831
16	0.015447	0.949278
17	0.012048	0.961326
18	0.009331	0.970657
19	0.007180	0.977837
20	0.005493	0.983329
21	0.004180	0.987509
22	0.003165	0.990674
23	0.002386	0.993060
24	0.001792	0.994852

n	P(n)	F(n)
25	0.001340	0.996192
26	0.000999	0.997191
27	0.000742	0.997933
28	0.000550	0.998483
29	0.000406	0.998889
30	0.000299	0.999188
31	0.000220	0.999408
32	0.000161	0.999569
33	0.000118	0.999687
34	0.000086	0.999773
35	0.000063	0.999835
36	0.000046	0.999881
37	0.000033	0.999914

k = 4·0
Mean = 8·50
Variance = 26·56

n	P(n)	F(n)
0	0.010486	0.010486
1	0.028521	0.039007
2	0.048486	0.087493
3	0.065941	0.153434
4	0.078470	0.231904
5	0.085375	0.317280
6	0.087083	0.404363
7	0.084595	0.488957
8	0.079096	0.568053
9	0.071714	0.639767
10	0.063395	0.703162
11	0.054865	0.758028
12	0.046636	0.804663
13	0.039030	0.843694
14	0.032228	0.875922
15	0.026298	0.902220
16	0.021236	0.923456
17	0.016989	0.940444
18	0.013478	0.953922
19	0.010612	0.964534
20	0.008298	0.972832
21	0.006449	0.979281
22	0.004983	0.984265
23	0.003831	0.988095
24	0.002930	0.991026
25	0.002232	0.993258
26	0.001693	0.994950
27	0.001279	0.996229
28	0.000963	0.997192
29	0.000723	0.997915
30	0.000540	0.998455
31	0.000403	0.998858
32	0.000300	0.999158
33	0.000222	0.999380
34	0.000165	0.999545
35	0.000121	0.999666
36	0.000089	0.999756
37	0.000066	0.999822
38	0.000048	0.999870
39	0.000035	0.999905

k = 4·5
Mean = 9·56
Variance = 29·88

n	P(n)	F(n)
0	0.005932	0.005932
1	0.018151	0.024082
2	0.033942	0.058025
3	0.050008	0.108032
4	0.063760	0.171793
5	0.073707	0.245499
6	0.079358	0.324857
7	0.080945	0.405802
8	0.079123	0.484925
9	0.074728	0.559653
10	0.068600	0.628253
11	0.061491	0.689743
12	0.054009	0.743752
13	0.046614	0.790367
14	0.039622	0.829989
15	0.033230	0.863218
16	0.027539	0.890757
17	0.022582	0.913339
18	0.018342	0.931681
19	0.014770	0.946451
20	0.011801	0.958252
21	0.009362	0.967614
22	0.007379	0.974993
23	0.005781	0.980775
24	0.004505	0.985279
25	0.003492	0.988771
26	0.002694	0.991465
27	0.002070	0.993535
28	0.001583	0.995118
29	0.001207	0.996325
30	0.000916	0.997241
31	0.000693	0.997934
32	0.000523	0.998457
33	0.000393	0.998851
34	0.000295	0.999146
35	0.000221	0.999366
36	0.000165	0.999531
37	0.000123	0.999654
38	0.000091	0.999745
39	0.000067	0.999812
40	0.000050	0.999862
41	0.000037	0.999899
42	0.000027	0.999926

k = 5·0
Mean = 10·62
Variance = 33·20

n	P(n)	F(n)
0	0.003355	0.003355
1	0.011409	0.014764
2	0.023273	0.038037
3	0.036927	0.074964
4	0.050221	0.125185
5	0.061470	0.186655
6	0.069666	0.256322
7	0.074443	0.330765
8	0.075932	0.406697
9	0.074582	0.481280
10	0.071002	0.552282
11	0.065839	0.618121
12	0.059694	0.677814
13	0.053081	0.730896
14	0.046408	0.777304
15	0.039973	0.817277
16	0.033977	0.851254
17	0.028541	0.879795
18	0.023721	0.903516
19	0.019526	0.923041
20	0.015933	0.938974
21	0.012898	0.951873
22	0.010365	0.962238
23	0.008274	0.970512
24	0.006564	0.977077
25	0.005178	0.982255
26	0.004063	0.986317
27	0.003172	0.989489
28	0.002465	0.991954
29	0.001907	0.993861
30	0.001470	0.995331
31	0.001129	0.996460
32	0.000863	0.997323
33	0.000658	0.997982
34	0.000500	0.998482
35	0.000379	0.998861
36	0.000286	0.999147
37	0.000216	0.999363
38	0.000162	0.999525
39	0.000122	0.999647
40	0.000091	0.999738
41	0.000068	0.999806
42	0.000051	0.999856
43	0.000038	0.999894
44	0.000028	0.999922

k = 0·1
Mean = 0·19
Variance = 0·57

n	P(n)	F(n)
0	0.897734	0.897734
1	0.059250	0.956985
2	0.021508	0.978493
3	0.009937	0.988430
4	0.005083	0.993512
5	0.002751	0.996263
6	0.001543	0.997806
7	0.000888	0.998693
8	0.000520	0.999213
9	0.000309	0.999522
10	0.000185	0.999708
11	0.000112	0.999820
12	0.000069	0.999889
13	0.000042	0.999931

k = 0·2
Mean = 0·39
Variance = 1·14

n	P(n)	F(n)
0	0.805927	0.805927
1	0.106382	0.912310
2	0.042127	0.954437
3	0.020390	0.974827
4	0.010766	0.985592
5	0.005969	0.991561
6	0.003414	0.994975
7	0.001996	0.996971
8	0.001185	0.998156
9	0.000713	0.998869
10	0.000433	0.999302
11	0.000265	0.999567
12	0.000163	0.999730
13	0.000101	0.999831
14	0.000063	0.999894
15	0.000039	0.999933

k = 0·3
Mean = 0·58
Variance = 1·71

n	P(n)	F(n)
0	0.723509	0.723509
1	0.143255	0.866763
2	0.061456	0.928220
3	0.031097	0.959316
4	0.016932	0.976249
5	0.009611	0.985859
6	0.005603	0.991462
7	0.003328	0.994791
8	0.002004	0.996795
9	0.001220	0.998015

10	0.000749	0.998764
11	0.000463	0.999227
12	0.000288	0.999514
13	0.000180	0.999694
14	0.000113	0.999807
15	0.000071	0.999877
16	0.000045	0.999922

k = 0·4
Mean = 0·78
Variance = 2·28

n	P(n)	F(n)
0	0.649519	0.649519
1	0.171473	0.820991
2	0.079220	0.900212
3	0.041828	0.942040
4	0.023466	0.965506
5	0.013629	0.979135
6	0.008096	0.987231
7	0.004885	0.992116
8	0.002982	0.995098
9	0.001837	0.996935
10	0.001140	0.998075
11	0.000711	0.998786
12	0.000446	0.999232
13	0.000281	0.999513
14	0.000177	0.999690
15	0.000112	0.999802
16	0.000071	0.999874
17	0.000045	0.999919

k = 0·5
Mean = 0·97
Variance = 2·85

n	P(n)	F(n)
0	0.583095	0.583095
1	0.192421	0.775517
2	0.095249	0.870765
3	0.052387	0.923152
4	0.030253	0.953405
5	0.017970	0.971376
6	0.010872	0.982248
7	0.006663	0.988911
8	0.004123	0.993034
9	0.002570	0.995604
10	0.001611	0.997215
11	0.001015	0.998230
12	0.000642	0.998872
13	0.000407	0.999280
14	0.000259	0.999539
15	0.000165	0.999704
16	0.000106	0.999810
17	0.000068	0.999878
18	0.000043	0.999921

k = 0·6
Mean = 1·16
Variance = 3·43

n	P(n)	F(n)
0	0.523465	0.523465
1	0.207292	0.730757
2	0.109450	0.840207
3	0.062606	0.902812
4	0.037188	0.940000
5	0.022580	0.962580
6	0.013909	0.976490
7	0.008656	0.985146
8	0.005427	0.990573
9	0.003423	0.993995
10	0.002169	0.996164
11	0.001379	0.997543
12	0.000880	0.998423
13	0.000563	0.998986
14	0.000361	0.999347
15	0.000232	0.999579
16	0.000149	0.999728
17	0.000096	0.999824
18	0.000062	0.999886
19	0.000040	0.999926

k = 0·7
Mean = 1·36
Variance = 4·00

n	P(n)	F(n)
0	0.469932	0.469932
1	0.217109	0.687041
2	0.121798	0.808839
3	0.072348	0.881187
4	0.044168	0.925355
5	0.027402	0.952757
6	0.017181	0.969939
7	0.010854	0.980792
8	0.006895	0.987687
9	0.004399	0.992086
10	0.002816	0.994902
11	0.001808	0.996710
12	0.001163	0.997873
13	0.000750	0.998623
14	0.000484	0.999108
15	0.000313	0.999421
16	0.000203	0.999624
17	0.000132	0.999756
18	0.000085	0.999841
19	0.000055	0.999897
20	0.000036	0.999933

k = 0·8
Mean = 1·55
Variance = 4·57

n	P(n)	F(n)
0	0.421874	0.421874
1	0.222750	0.644624
2	0.132313	0.776937
3	0.081505	0.858442
4	0.051104	0.909546
5	0.032379	0.941925
6	0.020658	0.962583
7	0.013245	0.975828
8	0.008523	0.984351
9	0.005500	0.989851
10	0.003558	0.993409
11	0.002305	0.995714
12	0.001496	0.997210
13	0.000972	0.998182
14	0.000633	0.998815
15	0.000412	0.999227
16	0.000268	0.999495
17	0.000175	0.999670
18	0.000114	0.999784
19	0.000075	0.999859
20	0.000049	0.999908

k = 1·0
Mean = 1·94
Variance = 5·71

n	P(n)	F(n)
0	0.340000	0.340000
1	0.224400	0.564400
2	0.148104	0.712504
3	0.097749	0.810253
4	0.064514	0.874767
5	0.042579	0.917346
6	0.028102	0.945448
7	0.018548	0.963996
8	0.012241	0.976237
9	0.008079	0.984317
10	0.005332	0.989649
11	0.003519	0.993168
12	0.002323	0.995491
13	0.001533	0.997024
14	0.001012	0.998036
15	0.000668	0.998704
16	0.000441	0.999144
17	0.000291	0.999435
18	0.000192	0.999627
19	0.000127	0.999754
20	0.000084	0.999838
21	0.000055	0.999893
22	0.000036	0.999929

k = 1·2
Mean = 2·33
Variance = 6·85

n	P(n)	F(n)
0	0.274015	0.274015
1	0.217020	0.491035
2	0.157557	0.648592
3	0.110920	0.759512
4	0.076867	0.836379
5	0.052762	0.889141
6	0.035984	0.925124
7	0.024428	0.949552
8	0.016525	0.966077
9	0.011149	0.977227
10	0.007506	0.984732
11	0.005044	0.989776
12	0.003384	0.993160
13	0.002268	0.995428
14	0.001518	0.996947
15	0.001015	0.997962
16	0.000679	0.998641
17	0.000453	0.999094
18	0.000302	0.999396
19	0.000202	0.999598
20	0.000134	0.999732
21	0.000090	0.999822
22	0.000060	0.999881
23	0.000040	0.999921

k = 0·9
Mean = 1·75
Variance = 5·14

ñ	P(n)	F(n)
0	0.378731	0.378731
1	0.224966	0.603697
2	0.141054	0.744751
3	0.089992	0.834744
4	0.057910	0.892654
5	0.037456	0.930110
6	0.024309	0.954419
7	0.015815	0.970234
8	0.010307	0.980541
9	0.006727	0.987268
10	0.004396	0.991664
11	0.002875	0.994539
12	0.001881	0.996420
13	0.001232	0.997652
14	0.000807	0.998460
15	0.000529	0.998989
16	0.000347	0.999337
17	0.000228	0.999564
18	0.000150	0.999714
19	0.000098	0.999812
20	0.000064	0.999876
21	0.000042	0.999919

k = 1·1
Mean = 2·14
Variance = 6·28

n	P(n)	F(n)
0	0.305230	0.305230
1	0.221597	0.526826
2	0.153567	0.680393
3	0.104732	0.785125
4	0.070851	0.855977
5	0.047697	0.903674
6	0.032005	0.935679
7	0.021425	0.957104
8	0.014317	0.971421
9	0.009554	0.980975
10	0.006369	0.987344
11	0.004242	0.991586
12	0.002823	0.994409
13	0.001877	0.996286
14	0.001248	0.997534
15	0.000829	0.998363
16	0.000551	0.998914
17	0.000366	0.999280
18	0.000243	0.999522
19	0.000161	0.999683
20	0.000107	0.999790
21	0.000071	0.999861
22	0.000047	0.999908

k = 1·3
Mean = 2·52
Variance = 7·42

n	P(n)	F(n)
0	0.245993	0.245993
1	0.211062	0.457055
2	0.160196	0.617251
3	0.116302	0.733553
4	0.082516	0.816070
5	0.057729	0.873798
6	0.040006	0.913804
7	0.027535	0.941339
8	0.018855	0.960194
9	0.012859	0.973053
10	0.008742	0.981795
11	0.005927	0.987722
12	0.004009	0.991731
13	0.002707	0.994439
14	0.001825	0.996264
15	0.001229	0.997492
16	0.000826	0.998317
17	0.000555	0.998872
18	0.000372	0.999246
19	0.000250	0.999495
20	0.000167	0.999662
21	0.000112	0.999773
22	0.000075	0.999848
23	0.000050	0.999899
24	0.000033	0.999933

k=1·4
Mean = 2·72
Variance = 7·99

n	P(n)	F(n)
0	0.220836	0.220836
1	0.204053	0.424889
2	0.161610	0.586499
3	0.120884	0.707383
4	0.087762	0.795145
5	0.062557	0.857701
6	0.044040	0.901741
7	0.030727	0.932469
8	0.021294	0.953763
9	0.014679	0.968441
10	0.010075	0.978517
11	0.006892	0.985408
12	0.004700	0.990108
13	0.003197	0.993306
14	0.002171	0.995476
15	0.001471	0.996947
16	0.000995	0.997942
17	0.000672	0.998614
18	0.000453	0.999068
19	0.000306	0.999374
20	0.000206	0.999579
21	0.000138	0.999718
22	0.000093	0.999811
23	0.000062	0.999873
24	0.000042	0.999915

k=1·5
Mean = 2·91
Variance = 8·56

n	P(n)	F(n)
0	0.198252	0.198252
1	0.196270	0.394522
2	0.161923	0.556445
3	0.124680	0.681125
4	0.092575	0.773700
5	0.067210	0.840910
6	0.048055	0.888965
7	0.033982	0.922947
8	0.023830	0.946776
9	0.016601	0.963378
10	0.011505	0.974882
11	0.007938	0.982820
12	0.005458	0.988278
13	0.003741	0.992019
14	0.002557	0.994575
15	0.001744	0.996319
16	0.001187	0.997506
17	0.000806	0.998313
18	0.000547	0.998860
19	0.000371	0.999230
20	0.000251	0.999481
21	0.000169	0.999650
22	0.000114	0.999764
23	0.000077	0.999841
24	0.000052	0.999893

| 25 | 0.000035 | 0.999928 |

k=1·6
Mean = 3·11
Variance = 9·13

n	P(n)	F(n)
0	0.177978	0.177978
1	0.187945	0.365923
2	0.161257	0.527179
3	0.127715	0.654895
4	0.096936	0.751830
5	0.071655	0.823485
6	0.052022	0.875507
7	0.037277	0.912784
8	0.026448	0.939232
9	0.018619	0.957852
10	0.013026	0.970878
11	0.009066	0.979944
12	0.006283	0.986227
13	0.004338	0.990565
14	0.002986	0.993551
15	0.002049	0.995600
16	0.001403	0.997004
17	0.000959	0.997963
18	0.000654	0.998617
19	0.000445	0.999062
20	0.000303	0.999365
21	0.000205	0.999570
22	0.000139	0.999709
23	0.000094	0.999804
24	0.000064	0.999868
25	0.000043	0.999911

k=1·7
Mean = 3·30
Variance = 9·71

n	P(n)	F(n)
0	0.159777	0.159777
1	0.179270	0.339047
2	0.159729	0.498776
3	0.130020	0.628796
4	0.100830	0.729626
5	0.075865	0.805491
6	0.055912	0.861403
7	0.040592	0.901995
8	0.029135	0.931130
9	0.020725	0.951855
10	0.014636	0.966491
11	0.010274	0.976765
12	0.007177	0.983942
13	0.004992	0.988934
14	0.003459	0.992393
15	0.002390	0.994783
16	0.001646	0.996429
17	0.001131	0.997560
18	0.000776	0.998336
19	0.000531	0.998866
20	0.000363	0.999229
21	0.000247	0.999476
22	0.000168	0.999645
23	0.000115	0.999759
24	0.000078	0.999837
25	0.000053	0.999890
26	0.000036	0.999925

k=1·8
Mean = 3·49
Variance = 10·28

n	P(n)	F(n)
0	0.143437	0.143437
1	0.170403	0.313841
2	0.157453	0.471294
3	0.131631	0.602924
4	0.104251	0.707176
5	0.079815	0.786990
6	0.059702	0.846692
7	0.043906	0.890598
8	0.031876	0.922474
9	0.022908	0.945382
10	0.016329	0.961711
11	0.011561	0.973272
12	0.008139	0.981411
13	0.005702	0.987113
14	0.003979	0.991092
15	0.002766	0.993858
16	0.001917	0.995774
17	0.001325	0.997099
18	0.000913	0.998012
19	0.000628	0.998640
20	0.000431	0.999071
21	0.000295	0.999366
22	0.000202	0.999568
23	0.000138	0.999706
24	0.000094	0.999800
25	0.000064	0.999864
26	0.000044	0.999908

k=1·9
Mean = 3·69
Variance = 10·85

n	P(n)	F(n)
0	0.128769	0.128769
1	0.161476	0.290244
2	0.154532	0.444777
3	0.132589	0.577366
4	0.107198	0.684564

117

n	P(n)	F(n)
5	0.083486	0.768049
6	0.063366	0.831415
7	0.047198	0.878613
8	0.034655	0.913269
9	0.025160	0.938429
10	0.018100	0.956529
11	0.012923	0.969452
12	0.009169	0.978621
13	0.006471	0.985092
14	0.004545	0.989637
15	0.003180	0.992817
16	0.002217	0.995034
17	0.001540	0.996574
18	0.001068	0.997642
19	0.000738	0.998380
20	0.000509	0.998888
21	0.000350	0.999239
22	0.000241	0.999479
23	0.000165	0.999645
24	0.000113	0.999758
25	0.000077	0.999835
26	0.000053	0.999888
27	0.000036	0.999924

k = 2·0
Mean = 3·88
Variance = 11·42

n	P(n)	F(n)
0	0.115600	0.115600
1	0.152592	0.268192
2	0.151066	0.419258
3	0.132938	0.552196
4	0.109674	0.661870
5	0.086862	0.748732
6	0.066884	0.815616
7	0.050449	0.866065
8	0.037459	0.903524
9	0.027470	0.930993
10	0.019943	0.950936
11	0.014359	0.965295
12	0.010267	0.975562
13	0.007297	0.982859
14	0.005160	0.988019
15	0.003633	0.991652
16	0.002547	0.994199
17	0.001780	0.995980
18	0.001240	0.997220
19	0.000862	0.998081
20	0.000597	0.998679
21	0.000413	0.999091
22	0.000285	0.999376
23	0.000196	0.999572
24	0.000135	0.999707
25	0.000093	0.999800
26	0.000063	0.999863
27	0.000043	0.999907

k = 2·1
Mean = 4·08
Variance = 11·99

n	P(n)	F(n)
0	0.103778	0.103778
1	0.143836	0.247615
2	0.147145	0.394759
3	0.132725	0.527484
4	0.111688	0.639171
5	0.089931	0.729102
6	0.070236	0.799338
7	0.053640	0.852979
8	0.040270	0.893249
9	0.029827	0.923076
10	0.021851	0.944927
11	0.015864	0.960791
12	0.011430	0.972221
13	0.008182	0.980403
14	0.005825	0.986228
15	0.004126	0.990354
16	0.002910	0.993264
17	0.002045	0.995310
18	0.001432	0.996742
19	0.001000	0.997742
20	0.000696	0.998438
21	0.000484	0.998922
22	0.000335	0.999257
23	0.000232	0.999489
24	0.000160	0.999649
25	0.000110	0.999759
26	0.000076	0.999835
27	0.000052	0.999887
28	0.000036	0.999923

k = 2·2
Mean = 4·27
Variance = 12·56

n	P(n)	F(n)
0	0.093165	0.093165
1	0.135276	0.228441
2	0.142851	0.371292
3	0.131995	0.503287
4	0.113251	0.616538
5	0.092685	0.709223
6	0.073406	0.782630
7	0.056754	0.839383
8	0.043076	0.882459
9	0.032221	0.914680
10	0.023818	0.938498
11	0.017435	0.955932
12	0.012657	0.968590
13	0.009125	0.977715
14	0.006539	0.984254
15	0.004661	0.988915
16	0.003307	0.992221
17	0.002337	0.994558
18	0.001645	0.996203
19	0.001154	0.997357

n	P(n)	F(n)
20	0.000808	0.998165
21	0.000563	0.998728
22	0.000392	0.999120
23	0.000272	0.999393
24	0.000189	0.999581
25	0.000131	0.999712
26	0.000090	0.999802
27	0.000062	0.999864
28	0.000043	0.999907

k = 2·3
Mean = 4·46
Variance = 13·13

n	P(n)	F(n)
0	0.083638	0.083638
1	0.126962	0.210599
2	0.138261	0.348861
3	0.130795	0.479656
4	0.114381	0.594037
5	0.095119	0.689156
6	0.076380	0.765536
7	0.059773	0.825309
8	0.045861	0.871170
9	0.034640	0.905810
10	0.025835	0.931645
11	0.019066	0.950711
12	0.013947	0.964658
13	0.010125	0.974783
14	0.007303	0.982087
15	0.005238	0.987325
16	0.003738	0.991063
17	0.002656	0.993718
18	0.001879	0.995598
19	0.001325	0.996923
20	0.000932	0.997854
21	0.000653	0.998507
22	0.000456	0.998963
23	0.000318	0.999282
24	0.000221	0.999503
25	0.000154	0.999657
26	0.000107	0.999763
27	0.000074	0.999837
28	0.000051	0.999888
29	0.000035	0.999923

k = 2·4
Mean = 4·66
Variance = 13·70

n	P(n)	F(n)
0	0.075084	0.075084
1	0.118934	0.194018
2	0.133444	0.327461
3	0.129173	0.456635
4	0.115093	0.571728
5	0.097231	0.668959
6	0.079146	0.748105
7	0.062684	0.810789
8	0.048611	0.859400
9	0.037074	0.896474

n	P(n)	F(n)
0	0.027895	0.924368
1	0.020754	0.945122
2	0.015295	0.960417
3	0.011182	0.971599
4	0.008118	0.979718
5	0.005858	0.985576
6	0.004205	0.989780
7	0.003004	0.992784
8	0.002137	0.994921
9	0.001514	0.996435
0	0.001069	0.997504
1	0.000753	0.998257
2	0.000528	0.998785
3	0.000370	0.999155
4	0.000258	0.999413
5	0.000180	0.999593
6	0.000125	0.999719
7	0.000087	0.999806
8	0.000060	0.999866
9	0.000042	0.999908

=2.5
Mean = 4.85
Variance = 14.27

n	P(n)	F(n)
0	0.067406	0.067406
1	0.111220	0.178625
2	0.128459	0.307084
3	0.127174	0.434258
4	0.115410	0.549668
5	0.099022	0.648691
6	0.081693	0.730384
7	0.065471	0.795855
8	0.051313	0.847168
9	0.039511	0.886679
10	0.029989	0.916668
11	0.022492	0.939160
12	0.016700	0.955860
13	0.012294	0.968154
14	0.008983	0.977137
15	0.006522	0.983659
16	0.004708	0.988367
17	0.003381	0.991749
18	0.002418	0.994166
19	0.001722	0.995888
20	0.001222	0.997110
21	0.000864	0.997973
22	0.000609	0.998582
23	0.000428	0.999010
24	0.000300	0.999311
25	0.000210	0.999521
26	0.000147	0.999667
27	0.000102	0.999769
28	0.000071	0.999840
29	0.000049	0.999890
30	0.000034	0.999924

k = 3.0
Mean = 5.82
Variance = 17.13

n	P(n)	F(n)
0	0.039304	0.039304
1	0.077822	0.117126
2	0.102725	0.219851
3	0.112997	0.332848
4	0.111867	0.444716
5	0.103366	0.548081
6	0.090962	0.639043
7	0.077187	0.716230
8	0.063680	0.779910
9	0.051368	0.831278
10	0.040684	0.871962
11	0.031733	0.903695
12	0.024435	0.928130
13	0.018608	0.946738
14	0.014036	0.960773
15	0.010499	0.971272
16	0.007795	0.979067
17	0.005750	0.984818
18	0.004217	0.989034
19	0.003076	0.992110
20	0.002233	0.994344
21	0.001614	0.995958
22	0.001162	0.997120
23	0.000834	0.997954
24	0.000596	0.998550
25	0.000425	0.998975
26	0.000302	0.999277
27	0.000214	0.999491
28	0.000151	0.999643
29	0.000107	0.999749
30	0.000075	0.999825
31	0.000053	0.999877
32	0.000037	0.999915

k = 3.5
Mean = 6.79
Variance = 19.98

n	P(n)	F(n)
0	0.022918	0.022918
1	0.052941	0.075858
2	0.078617	0.154475
3	0.095126	0.249601
4	0.102023	0.351624
5	0.101003	0.452627
6	0.094437	0.547064
7	0.084589	0.631653
8	0.073275	0.704928
9	0.061795	0.766724
10	0.050981	0.817705
11	0.041295	0.859000
12	0.032933	0.891932
13	0.025915	0.917848
14	0.020158	0.938006
15	0.015522	0.953528
16	0.011845	0.965373
17	0.008968	0.974341
18	0.006741	0.981082
19	0.005034	0.986115
20	0.003738	0.989854
21	0.002761	0.992614
22	0.002029	0.994643
23	0.001485	0.996128
24	0.001082	0.997210
25	0.000786	0.997996
26	0.000568	0.998564
27	0.000410	0.998974
28	0.000295	0.999269
29	0.000211	0.999480
30	0.000151	0.999631
31	0.000108	0.999739
32	0.000077	0.999815
33	0.000054	0.999870
34	0.000039	0.999908

k = 4.0
Mean = 7.76
Variance = 22.84

n	P(n)	F(n)
0	0.013363	0.013363
1	0.035279	0.048643
2	0.058211	0.106853
3	0.076838	0.183692
4	0.088748	0.272440
5	0.093718	0.366158
6	0.092781	0.458939
7	0.087479	0.546418
8	0.079387	0.625805
9	0.069861	0.695666
10	0.059941	0.755607
11	0.050350	0.805957
12	0.041539	0.847496
13	0.033742	0.881238
14	0.027042	0.908280
15	0.021417	0.929697
16	0.016786	0.946483
17	0.013034	0.959517
18	0.010036	0.969553
19	0.007670	0.977222
20	0.005821	0.983044
21	0.004391	0.987434
22	0.003293	0.990728
23	0.002457	0.993184
24	0.001824	0.995009
25	0.001349	0.996357
26	0.000993	0.997350
27	0.000728	0.998078
28	0.000532	0.998610
29	0.000387	0.998997
30	0.000281	0.999279
31	0.000204	0.999482
32	0.000147	0.999629
33	0.000106	0.999735
34	0.000076	0.999811

35	0.000054	0.999866
36	0.000039	0.999904

k = 4·5
Mean = 8·74
Variance = 25·69

n	P(n)	F(n)
0	0.007792	0.007792
1	0.023143	0.030935
2	0.042004	0.072938
3	0.060065	0.133004
4	0.074331	0.207335
5	0.083399	0.290734
6	0.087152	0.377886
7	0.086281	0.464167
8	0.081859	0.546026
9	0.075037	0.621063
10	0.066858	0.687921
11	0.058167	0.746088
12	0.049587	0.795675
13	0.041539	0.837214
14	0.034269	0.871483
15	0.027895	0.899378
16	0.022438	0.921817
17	0.017858	0.939675
18	0.014078	0.953753
19	0.011003	0.964756
20	0.008533	0.973290
21	0.006570	0.979860
22	0.005026	0.984886
23	0.003822	0.988709
24	0.002891	0.991599
25	0.002175	0.993774
26	0.001629	0.995403
27	0.001214	0.996617
28	0.000902	0.997518
29	0.000667	0.998185
30	0.000491	0.998677
31	0.000361	0.999038
32	0.000264	0.999302
33	0.000193	0.999495
34	0.000140	0.999635
35	0.000102	0.999737
36	0.000074	0.999811
37	0.000053	0.999865
38	0.000038	0.999903

5	0.071694	0.226987
6	0.078864	0.305850
7	0.081793	0.387643
8	0.080975	0.468618
9	0.077196	0.545815
10	0.071329	0.617144
11	0.064196	0.681340
12	0.056493	0.737833
13	0.048758	0.786591
14	0.041374	0.827965
15	0.034589	0.862554
16	0.028536	0.891090
17	0.023265	0.914355
18	0.018767	0.933122
19	0.014994	0.948116
20	0.011875	0.959992
21	0.009331	0.969322
22	0.007278	0.976600
23	0.005639	0.982239
24	0.004342	0.986581
25	0.003324	0.989905
26	0.002531	0.992436
27	0.001918	0.994354
28	0.001447	0.995801
29	0.001087	0.996888
30	0.000813	0.997701
31	0.000606	0.998306
32	0.000450	0.998756
33	0.000333	0.999089
34	0.000245	0.999335
35	0.000181	0.999515
36	0.000132	0.999647
37	0.000097	0.999744
38	0.000071	0.999815
39	0.000051	0.999866
40	0.000037	0.999904

k = 5·0
Mean = 9·71
Variance = 28·55

n	P(n)	F(n)
0	0.004544	0.004544
1	0.014994	0.019537
2	0.029688	0.049225
3	0.045719	0.094943
4	0.060349	0.155292

k=0·1
Mean=0·18
Variance=0·49

n	P(n)	F(n)
0	0.902880	0.902880
1	0.057784	0.960665
2	0.020340	0.981005
3	0.009112	0.990117
4	0.004520	0.994637
5	0.002372	0.997009
6	0.001290	0.998299
7	0.000720	0.999019
8	0.000409	0.999428
9	0.000235	0.999663
10	0.000137	0.999800
11	0.000081	0.999881
12	0.000048	0.999929

k=0·2
Mean=0·36
Variance=0·99

n	P(n)	F(n)
0	0.815193	0.815193
1	0.104345	0.919538
2	0.040068	0.959606
3	0.018805	0.978412
4	0.009628	0.988040
5	0.005176	0.993216
6	0.002871	0.996087
7	0.001627	0.997715
8	0.000937	0.998652
9	0.000547	0.999199
10	0.000322	0.999521
11	0.000191	0.999712
12	0.000114	0.999826
13	0.000069	0.999894
14	0.000041	0.999936

k=0·3
Mean=0·53
Variance=1·48

n	P(n)	F(n)
0	0.736022	0.736022
1	0.141316	0.877338
2	0.058788	0.936126
3	0.028845	0.964971
4	0.015230	0.980201
5	0.008383	0.988584
6	0.004739	0.993323
7	0.002730	0.996052
8	0.001594	0.997647
9	0.000941	0.998587
10	0.000560	0.999147
11	0.000336	0.999483
12	0.000202	0.999685
13	0.000122	0.999808
14	0.000074	0.999882

| 15 | 0.000045 | 0.999928 |

k=0·4
Mean=0·71
Variance=1·98

n	P(n)	F(n)
0	0.664540	0.664540
1	0.170122	0.834662
2	0.076215	0.910877
3	0.039022	0.949899
4	0.021228	0.971127
5	0.011956	0.983082
6	0.006886	0.989969
7	0.004030	0.993998
8	0.002385	0.996384
9	0.001425	0.997809
10	0.000857	0.998666
11	0.000519	0.999185
12	0.000315	0.999500
13	0.000193	0.999692
14	0.000118	0.999810
15	0.000072	0.999883
16	0.000045	0.999927

k=0·5
Mean=0·89
Variance=2·47

n	P(n)	F(n)
0	0.600000	0.600000
1	0.192000	0.792000
2	0.092160	0.884160
3	0.049152	0.933312
4	0.027525	0.960837
5	0.015854	0.976692
6	0.009301	0.985993
7	0.005528	0.991521
8	0.003317	0.994837
9	0.002005	0.996842
10	0.001219	0.998061
11	0.000745	0.998805
12	0.000457	0.999262
13	0.000281	0.999543
14	0.000173	0.999716
15	0.000107	0.999824
16	0.000067	0.999890
17	0.000041	0.999932

k=0·6
Mean=1·07
Variance=2·96

n	P(n)	F(n)
0	0.541728	0.541728
1	0.208024	0.749752
2	0.106508	0.856260
3	0.059076	0.915337
4	0.034028	0.949365
5	0.020036	0.969400
6	0.011968	0.981368
7	0.007222	0.988590
8	0.004391	0.992981
9	0.002685	0.995666
10	0.001650	0.997316
11	0.001017	0.998334
12	0.000629	0.998963
13	0.000390	0.999354
14	0.000243	0.999596
15	0.000151	0.999748
16	0.000094	0.999842
17	0.000059	0.999901

k=0·7
Mean=1·24
Variance=3·46

n	P(n)	F(n)
0	0.489116	0.489116
1	0.219124	0.708240
2	0.119203	0.827443
3	0.068661	0.896104
4	0.040647	0.936752
5	0.024453	0.961205
6	0.014868	0.976073
7	0.009108	0.985180
8	0.005610	0.990791
9	0.003471	0.994262
10	0.002155	0.996416
11	0.001341	0.997758
12	0.000837	0.998595
13	0.000523	0.999118
14	0.000328	0.999446
15	0.000206	0.999651
16	0.000129	0.999781
17	0.000081	0.999862
18	0.000051	0.999913

k=0·8
Mean=1·42
Variance=3·95

n	P(n)	F(n)
0	0.441613	0.441613
1	0.226106	0.667719
2	0.130237	0.797956
3	0.077795	0.875751
4	0.047299	0.923050

5	0.029061	0.952111	10	0.004151	0.992621	10	0.005909	0.989015
6	0.017979	0.970090	11	0.002656	0.995278	11	0.003851	0.992866
7	0.011178	0.981268	12	0.001700	0.996978	12	0.002506	0.995372
8	0.006975	0.988243	13	0.001088	0.998066	13	0.001628	0.997000
9	0.004365	0.992607	14	0.000696	0.998762	14	0.001057	0.998057
10	0.002738	0.995345	15	0.000446	0.999208	15	0.000685	0.998742
11	0.001720	0.997065	16	0.000285	0.999493	16	0.000444	0.999186
12	0.001083	0.998148	17	0.000183	0.999675	17	0.000288	0.999474
13	0.000682	0.998830	18	0.000117	0.999792	18	0.000186	0.999660
14	0.000430	0.999260	19	0.000075	0.999867	19	0.000120	0.999780
15	0.000272	0.999532	20	0.000048	0.999915	20	0.000078	0.999858
16	0.000172	0.999704				21	0.000050	0.999909
17	0.000109	0.999812						
18	0.000069	0.999881						
19	0.000044	0.999925						

k=0·9
Mean=1·60
Variance=4·44

n	P(n)	F(n)
0	0.398724	0.398724
1	0.229665	0.628389
2	0.139636	0.768025
3	0.086388	0.854413
4	0.053906	0.908320
5	0.033810	0.942130
6	0.021278	0.963408
7	0.013423	0.976831
8	0.008483	0.985314
9	0.005369	0.990683
10	0.003402	0.994085
11	0.002157	0.996243
12	0.001369	0.997612
13	0.000870	0.998481
14	0.000553	0.999034
15	0.000351	0.999385
16	0.000223	0.999609
17	0.000142	0.999751
18	0.000090	0.999841
19	0.000058	0.999899
20	0.000037	0.999936

k=1·1
Mean=1·96
Variance=5·43

n	P(n)	F(n)
0	0.325037	0.325037
1	0.228826	0.553863
2	0.153771	0.707634
3	0.101694	0.809328
4	0.066711	0.876039
5	0.043549	0.919588
6	0.028336	0.947924
7	0.018394	0.966318
8	0.011919	0.978238
9	0.007713	0.985951
10	0.004986	0.990937
11	0.003220	0.994157
12	0.002078	0.996234
13	0.001340	0.997575
14	0.000864	0.998438
15	0.000557	0.998995
16	0.000358	0.999353
17	0.000231	0.999584
18	0.000148	0.999732
19	0.000096	0.999828
20	0.000061	0.999889
21	0.000040	0.999929

k=1·3
Mean=2·31
Variance=6·42

n	P(n)	F(n)
0	0.264968	0.264968
1	0.220453	0.485421
2	0.162254	0.647675
3	0.114227	0.761901
4	0.078588	0.840489
5	0.053314	0.893803
6	0.035827	0.929630
7	0.023912	0.953542
8	0.015878	0.969420
9	0.010500	0.979920
10	0.006922	0.986842
11	0.004551	0.991393
12	0.002985	0.994378
13	0.001955	0.996333
14	0.001278	0.997611
15	0.000834	0.998445
16	0.000544	0.998989
17	0.000354	0.999343
18	0.000230	0.999573
19	0.000150	0.999723
20	0.000097	0.999820
21	0.000063	0.999884
22	0.000041	0.999925

k=1·0
Mean=1·78
Variance=4·94

n	P(n)	F(n)
0	0.360000	0.360000
1	0.230400	0.590400
2	0.147456	0.737856
3	0.094372	0.832228
4	0.060398	0.892626
5	0.038655	0.931281
6	0.024739	0.956020
7	0.015833	0.971853
8	0.010133	0.981986
9	0.006485	0.988471

k=1·2
Mean=2·13
Variance=5·93

n	P(n)	F(n)
0	0.293470	0.293470
1	0.225385	0.518854
2	0.158671	0.677525
3	0.108319	0.785844
4	0.072791	0.858635
5	0.048449	0.907084
6	0.032041	0.939125
7	0.021092	0.960217
8	0.013837	0.974054
9	0.009052	0.983106

k=1·4
Mean=2·49
Variance=6·91

n	P(n)	F(n)
0	0.239234	0.239234
1	0.214354	0.453588
2	0.164624	0.618212
3	0.119407	0.737619
4	0.084063	0.821682
5	0.058104	0.879786
6	0.039666	0.919452
7	0.026837	0.946288
8	0.018034	0.964323
9	0.012055	0.976378

n	P(n)	F(n)
10	0.008024	0.984401
11	0.005322	0.989723
12	0.003520	0.993243
13	0.002322	0.995565
14	0.001528	0.997093
15	0.001004	0.998097
16	0.000659	0.998756
17	0.000432	0.999188
18	0.000282	0.999470
19	0.000184	0.999655
20	0.000120	0.999775
21	0.000079	0.999854
22	0.000051	0.999905

n	P(n)	F(n)
10	0.010493	0.978662
11	0.007082	0.985744
12	0.004759	0.990503
13	0.003186	0.993689
14	0.002127	0.995816
15	0.001415	0.997231
16	0.000940	0.998171
17	0.000623	0.998794
18	0.000412	0.999206
19	0.000272	0.999478
20	0.000179	0.999657
21	0.000118	0.999775
22	0.000078	0.999852
23	0.000051	0.999903

n	P(n)	F(n)
10	0.013305	0.971692
11	0.009134	0.980826
12	0.006236	0.987062
13	0.004236	0.991298
14	0.002866	0.994165
15	0.001932	0.996097
16	0.001298	0.997395
17	0.000870	0.998265
18	0.000582	0.998847
19	0.000388	0.999235
20	0.000258	0.999493
21	0.000172	0.999665
22	0.000114	0.999778
23	0.000075	0.999854
24	0.000050	0.999904

k = 1·5
Mean = 2·67
Variance = 7·41

n	P(n)	F(n)
0	0.216000	0.216000
1	0.207360	0.423360
2	0.165888	0.589248
3	0.123863	0.713111
4	0.089181	0.802292
5	0.062784	0.865076
6	0.043530	0.908606
7	0.029849	0.938455
8	0.020297	0.958753
9	0.013712	0.972465
10	0.009214	0.981679
11	0.006165	0.987845
12	0.004110	0.991955
13	0.002732	0.994687
14	0.001811	0.996497
15	0.001198	0.997695
16	0.000790	0.998485
17	0.000521	0.999006
18	0.000343	0.999348
19	0.000225	0.999573
20	0.000148	0.999721
21	0.000097	0.999818
22	0.000063	0.999881
23	0.000041	0.999922

k = 1·7
Mean = 3·02
Variance = 8·40

n	P(n)	F(n)
0	0.176082	0.176082
1	0.191577	0.367659
2	0.165522	0.533181
3	0.130652	0.663833
4	0.098251	0.762084
5	0.071684	0.833768
6	0.051230	0.884998
7	0.036066	0.921063
8	0.025102	0.946165
9	0.017315	0.963480
10	0.011857	0.975337
11	0.008071	0.983408
12	0.005467	0.988876
13	0.003687	0.992563
14	0.002478	0.995041
15	0.001660	0.996701
16	0.001109	0.997809
17	0.000739	0.998548
18	0.000491	0.999039
19	0.000326	0.999365
20	0.000216	0.999581
21	0.000143	0.999724
22	0.000094	0.999818
23	0.000062	0.999881
24	0.000041	0.999922

k = 1·9
Mean = 3·38
Variance = 9·38

n	P(n)	F(n)
0	0.143541	0.143541
1	0.174545	0.318086
2	0.161978	0.480064
3	0.134766	0.614830
4	0.105656	0.720486
5	0.079792	0.800278
6	0.058727	0.859005
7	0.042417	0.901422
8	0.030201	0.931623
9	0.021262	0.952885
10	0.014832	0.967717
11	0.010269	0.977986
12	0.007065	0.985052
13	0.004835	0.989886
14	0.003293	0.993179
15	0.002234	0.995414
16	0.001510	0.996924
17	0.001018	0.997942
18	0.000684	0.998625
19	0.000458	0.999084
20	0.000307	0.999391
21	0.000205	0.999595
22	0.000136	0.999731
23	0.000091	0.999822
24	0.000060	0.999882
25	0.000040	0.999922

k = 1·6
Mean = 2·84
Variance = 7·90

n	P(n)	F(n)
0	0.195022	0.195022
1	0.199703	0.394725
2	0.166153	0.560878
3	0.127605	0.688483
4	0.093917	0.782400
5	0.067320	0.849720
6	0.047393	0.897114
7	0.032932	0.930045
8	0.022657	0.952702
9	0.015467	0.968169

k = 1·8
Mean = 3·20
Variance = 8·89

n	P(n)	F(n)
0	0.158981	0.158981
1	0.183146	0.342127
2	0.164099	0.506225
3	0.133029	0.639254
4	0.102167	0.741421
5	0.075848	0.817269
6	0.055015	0.872285
7	0.039234	0.911519
8	0.027621	0.939139
9	0.019248	0.958388

k = 2·0
Mean = 3·56
Variance = 9·88

n	P(n)	F(n)
0	0.129600	0.129600
1	0.165888	0.295488
2	0.159252	0.454740
3	0.135895	0.590636
4	0.108716	0.699352

n	P(n)	F(n)
5	0.083494	0.782846
6	0.062342	0.845189
7	0.045599	0.890788
8	0.032831	0.923619
9	0.023347	0.946966
10	0.016436	0.963402
11	0.011475	0.974877
12	0.007956	0.982833
13	0.005484	0.988317
14	0.003760	0.992077
15	0.002567	0.994644
16	0.001746	0.996390
17	0.001183	0.997573
18	0.000799	0.998372
19	0.000538	0.998910
20	0.000362	0.999272
21	0.000243	0.999514
22	0.000162	0.999677
23	0.000108	0.999785
24	0.000072	0.999857
25	0.000048	0.999905

k = 2·1
Mean = 3·73
Variance = 10·37

n	P(n)	F(n)
0	0.117013	0.117013
1	0.157266	0.274279
2	0.156008	0.430287
3	0.136455	0.566742
4	0.111347	0.678089
5	0.086940	0.765029
6	0.065842	0.830871
7	0.048761	0.879632
8	0.035498	0.915130
9	0.025495	0.940626
10	0.018112	0.958738
11	0.012751	0.971488
12	0.008909	0.980397
13	0.006184	0.986581
14	0.004269	0.990850
15	0.002932	0.993782
16	0.002006	0.995788
17	0.001367	0.997154
18	0.000928	0.998082
19	0.000628	0.998711
20	0.000424	0.999135
21	0.000286	0.999421
22	0.000192	0.999613
23	0.000129	0.999742
24	0.000086	0.999828
25	0.000058	0.999886
26	0.000038	0.999924

k = 2·2
Mean = 3·91
Variance = 10·86

n	P(n)	F(n)
0	0.105649	0.105649
1	0.148754	0.254403
2	0.152324	0.406727
3	0.136482	0.543209
4	0.113553	0.656762
5	0.090116	0.746878
6	0.069209	0.816087
7	0.051887	0.867974
8	0.038189	0.906163
9	0.027700	0.933862
10	0.019855	0.953717
11	0.014093	0.967811
12	0.009922	0.977733
13	0.006936	0.984669
14	0.004820	0.989488
15	0.003331	0.992820
16	0.002292	0.995112
17	0.001570	0.996682
18	0.001072	0.997754
19	0.000729	0.998484
20	0.000495	0.998978
21	0.000335	0.999313
22	0.000226	0.999539
23	0.000152	0.999691
24	0.000102	0.999794
25	0.000069	0.999862
26	0.000046	0.999908

k = 2·3
Mean = 4·09
Variance = 11·36

n	P(n)	F(n)
0	0.095388	0.095388
1	0.140412	0.235800
2	0.148275	0.384075
3	0.136017	0.520093
4	0.115343	0.635435
5	0.093012	0.728448
6	0.072426	0.800873
7	0.054961	0.855834
8	0.040891	0.896725
9	0.029950	0.926675
10	0.021660	0.948335
11	0.015501	0.963836
12	0.010995	0.974831
13	0.007741	0.982572
14	0.005414	0.987986
15	0.003765	0.991751
16	0.002606	0.994356
17	0.001795	0.996152
18	0.001232	0.997383
19	0.000842	0.998226

n	P(n)	F(n)
20	0.000574	0.998800
21	0.000390	0.999190
22	0.000264	0.999454
23	0.000179	0.999633
24	0.000121	0.999754
25	0.000081	0.999835
26	0.000055	0.999890
27	0.000037	0.999926

k = 2·4
Mean = 4·27
Variance = 11·85

n	P(n)	F(n)
0	0.086124	0.086124
1	0.132287	0.218411
2	0.143928	0.362340
3	0.135101	0.497440
4	0.116727	0.614167
5	0.095623	0.709790
6	0.075478	0.785268
7	0.057967	0.843236
8	0.043591	0.886827
9	0.032238	0.919065
10	0.023521	0.942586
11	0.016969	0.959556
12	0.012127	0.971683
13	0.008597	0.980280
14	0.006053	0.986333
15	0.004235	0.990568
16	0.002948	0.993516
17	0.002042	0.995558
18	0.001408	0.996966
19	0.000968	0.997934
20	0.000663	0.998597
21	0.000452	0.999049
22	0.000308	0.999357
23	0.000209	0.999566
24	0.000142	0.999708
25	0.000096	0.999804
26	0.000065	0.999868
27	0.000043	0.999912

k = 2·5
Mean = 4·44
Variance = 12·35

n	P(n)	F(n)
0	0.077760	0.077760
1	0.124416	0.202176
2	0.139346	0.341522
3	0.133772	0.475294
4	0.117719	0.593013
5	0.097943	0.690956
6	0.078354	0.769310
7	0.060892	0.830202
8	0.046278	0.876481
9	0.034554	0.911035

n	P(n)	F(n)
10	0.025432	0.936467
11	0.018496	0.954963
12	0.013317	0.968280
13	0.009506	0.977786
14	0.006736	0.984522
15	0.004742	0.989264
16	0.003319	0.992584
17	0.002312	0.994896
18	0.001603	0.996499
19	0.001107	0.997606
20	0.000762	0.998367
21	0.000522	0.998889
22	0.000357	0.999246
23	0.000243	0.999490
24	0.000165	0.999655
25	0.000112	0.999767
26	0.000076	0.999843
27	0.000051	0.999895
28	0.000035	0.999929

k = 3.0
Mean = 5.33
Variance = 14.81

n	P(n)	F(n)
0	0.046656	0.046656
1	0.089580	0.136236
2	0.114662	0.250897
3	0.122306	0.373203
4	0.117414	0.490617
5	0.105203	0.595820
6	0.089773	0.685592
7	0.073870	0.759463
8	0.059096	0.818559
9	0.046226	0.864785
10	0.035502	0.900287
11	0.026852	0.927140
12	0.020050	0.947189
13	0.014806	0.961995
14	0.010829	0.972825
15	0.007855	0.980680
16	0.005656	0.986335
17	0.004045	0.990381
18	0.002877	0.993258
19	0.002035	0.995292
20	0.001433	0.996725
21	0.001004	0.997729
22	0.000701	0.998430
23	0.000488	0.998918
24	0.000338	0.999256
25	0.000234	0.999490
26	0.000161	0.999651
27	0.000111	0.999762
28	0.000076	0.999838
29	0.000052	0.999890
30	0.000035	0.999925

k = 3.5
Mean = 6.22
Variance = 17.28

n	P(n)	F(n)
0	0.027994	0.027994
1	0.062706	0.090699
2	0.090296	0.180995
3	0.105947	0.286943
4	0.110185	0.397128
5	0.105778	0.502906
6	0.095905	0.598812
7	0.083301	0.682112
8	0.069973	0.752085
9	0.057222	0.809307
10	0.045778	0.855084
11	0.035956	0.891041
12	0.027806	0.918847
13	0.021218	0.940065
14	0.016005	0.956070
15	0.011950	0.968020
16	0.008843	0.976863
17	0.006492	0.983355
18	0.004732	0.988087
19	0.003427	0.991513
20	0.002467	0.993981
21	0.001767	0.995748
22	0.001259	0.997007
23	0.000894	0.997901
24	0.000632	0.998532
25	0.000445	0.998977
26	0.000312	0.999289
27	0.000218	0.999507
28	0.000152	0.999659
29	0.000106	0.999765
30	0.000073	0.999838
31	0.000051	0.999889
32	0.000035	0.999924

k = 4.0
Mean = 7.11
Variance = 19.75

n	P(n)	F(n)
0	0.016796	0.016796
1	0.042998	0.059794
2	0.068797	0.128591
3	0.088060	0.216652
4	0.098627	0.315279
5	0.100995	0.416274
6	0.096955	0.513228
7	0.088644	0.601873
8	0.078007	0.679880
9	0.066566	0.746446
10	0.055383	0.801829
11	0.045112	0.846941
12	0.036090	0.883030
13	0.028427	0.911458
14	0.022092	0.933550

n	P(n)	F(n)
15	0.016967	0.950517
16	0.012895	0.963411
17	0.009709	0.973120
18	0.007249	0.980370
19	0.005372	0.985742
20	0.003954	0.989696
21	0.002892	0.992588
22	0.002103	0.994691
23	0.001522	0.996213
24	0.001096	0.997308
25	0.000785	0.998094
26	0.000561	0.998654
27	0.000399	0.999053
28	0.000282	0.999335
29	0.000199	0.999535
30	0.000140	0.999675
31	0.000099	0.999774
32	0.000069	0.999843
33	0.000048	0.999891
34	0.000034	0.999925

k = 4.5
Mean = 8.00
Variance = 22.22

n	P(n)	F(n)
0	0.010078	0.010078
1	0.029024	0.039101
2	0.051082	0.090183
3	0.070833	0.161017
4	0.085000	0.246017
5	0.092480	0.338497
6	0.093713	0.432210
7	0.089965	0.522175
8	0.082768	0.604943
9	0.073571	0.678514
10	0.063565	0.742079
11	0.053626	0.795705
12	0.044331	0.840036
13	0.036010	0.876047
14	0.028808	0.904855
15	0.022739	0.927594
16	0.017737	0.945331
17	0.013689	0.959019
18	0.010464	0.969484
19	0.007931	0.977414
20	0.005964	0.983378
21	0.004453	0.987831
22	0.003303	0.991135
23	0.002436	0.993570
24	0.001786	0.995357
25	0.001303	0.996660
26	0.000946	0.997606
27	0.000684	0.998291
28	0.000493	0.998783
29	0.000353	0.999137
30	0.000253	0.999389
31	0.000180	0.999569
32	0.000128	0.999697
33	0.000090	0.999787
34	0.000064	0.999851

35	0.000045	0.999896
36	0.000032	0.999927

k=5·0
Mean=8·89
Variance=24·69

n	P(n)	F(n)
0	0.006047	0.006047
1	0.019349	0.025396
2	0.037150	0.062546
3	0.055478	0.118024
4	0.071012	0.189036
5	0.081806	0.270842
6	0.087259	0.358101
7	0.087758	0.445859
8	0.084248	0.530106
9	0.077882	0.607989
10	0.069782	0.677771
11	0.060901	0.738672
12	0.051969	0.790641
13	0.043494	0.834135
14	0.035789	0.869924

n	P(n)	F(n)
15	0.029013	0.898938
16	0.023211	0.922148
17	0.018350	0.940498
18	0.014354	0.954852
19	0.011120	0.965972
20	0.008540	0.974513
21	0.006507	0.981020
22	0.004922	0.985941
23	0.003698	0.989639
24	0.002761	0.992400
25	0.002050	0.994450
26	0.001514	0.995963
27	0.001112	0.997076
28	0.000814	0.997889
29	0.000592	0.998482
30	0.000430	0.998911
31	0.000311	0.999222
32	0.000224	0.999445
33	0.000160	0.999606
34	0.000115	0.999721
35	0.000082	0.999803
36	0.000058	0.999861
37	0.000041	0.999902

k=0·1
Mean=0·16
Variance=0·43

n	P(n)	F(n)
0	0.907775	0.907775
1	0.056282	0.964057
2	0.019192	0.983250
3	0.008329	0.991579
4	0.004002	0.995581
5	0.002035	0.997616
6	0.001072	0.998688
7	0.000579	0.999268
8	0.000319	0.999586
9	0.000178	0.999764
10	0.000100	0.999865
11	0.000057	0.999922

k=0·2
Mean=0·33
Variance=0·86

n	P(n)	F(n)
0	0.824056	0.824056
1	0.102183	0.926239
2	0.038012	0.964251
3	0.017283	0.981534
4	0.008572	0.990106
5	0.004464	0.994571
6	0.002399	0.996969
7	0.001317	0.998287
8	0.000735	0.999022
9	0.000415	0.999437
10	0.000237	0.999674
11	0.000136	0.999810
12	0.000079	0.999889
13	0.000046	0.999935

k=0·3
Mean=0·49
Variance=1·29

n	P(n)	F(n)
0	0.748058	0.748058
1	0.139139	0.887196
2	0.056073	0.943269
3	0.026653	0.969923
4	0.013633	0.983556
5	0.007269	0.990825
6	0.003981	0.994806
7	0.002221	0.997028
8	0.001257	0.998284
9	0.000719	0.999003
10	0.000414	0.999417
11	0.000241	0.999658
12	0.000140	0.999798
13	0.000082	0.999881
14	0.000049	0.999929

k=0·4
Mean=0·65
Variance=1·72

n	P(n)	F(n)
0	0.679068	0.679068
1	0.168409	0.847477
2	0.073089	0.920567
3	0.036252	0.956819
4	0.019105	0.975924
5	0.010424	0.986348
6	0.005816	0.992164
7	0.003297	0.995461
8	0.001891	0.997352
9	0.001094	0.998446
10	0.000638	0.999084
11	0.000374	0.999458
12	0.000220	0.999678
13	0.000130	0.999808
14	0.000077	0.999885
15	0.000046	0.999931

k=0·5
Mean=0·82
Variance=2·15

n	P(n)	F(n)
0	0.616441	0.616441
1	0.191097	0.807538
2	0.088860	0.896398
3	0.045911	0.942309
4	0.024907	0.967216
5	0.013898	0.981114
6	0.007899	0.989013
7	0.004547	0.993560
8	0.002643	0.996203
9	0.001548	0.997751
10	0.000912	0.998662
11	0.000540	0.999202
12	0.000321	0.999523
13	0.000191	0.999714
14	0.000114	0.999828
15	0.000068	0.999896
16	0.000041	0.999938

k=0·6
Mean=0·98
Variance=2·58

n	P(n)	F(n)
0	0.559590	0.559590
1	0.208168	0.767758
2	0.103251	0.871009
3	0.055480	0.926489
4	0.030958	0.957447
5	0.017658	0.975106
6	0.010218	0.985324
7	0.005973	0.991297
8	0.003518	0.994816
9	0.002084	0.996900
10	0.001241	0.998141
11	0.000741	0.998882
12	0.000444	0.999326
13	0.000267	0.999593
14	0.000161	0.999754
15	0.000097	0.999851
16	0.000059	0.999910

k=0·7
Mean=1·14
Variance=3·01

n	P(n)	F(n)
0	0.507982	0.507982
1	0.220464	0.728447
2	0.116185	0.844631
3	0.064831	0.909462
4	0.037181	0.946643
5	0.021669	0.968312
6	0.012763	0.981075
7	0.007574	0.988649
8	0.004520	0.993168
9	0.002709	0.995877
10	0.001629	0.997506
11	0.000982	0.998489
12	0.000594	0.999083
13	0.000360	0.999442
14	0.000218	0.999661
15	0.000133	0.999793
16	0.000081	0.999874
17	0.000049	0.999923

k=0·8
Mean=1·31
Variance=3·43

n	P(n)	F(n)
0	0.461134	0.461134
1	0.228722	0.689856
2	0.127627	0.817483
3	0.073854	0.891337
4	0.043500	0.934836
5	0.025891	0.960727
6	0.015517	0.976245
7	0.009346	0.985591
8	0.005650	0.991240
9	0.003425	0.994665
10	0.002081	0.996746
11	0.001267	0.998013
12	0.000772	0.998785
13	0.000471	0.999257
14	0.000288	0.999545
15	0.000176	0.999721
16	0.000108	0.999829
17	0.000066	0.999895
18	0.000041	0.999936

k=0·9
Mean=1·47
Variance=3·86

n	P(n)	F(n)
0	0.418606	0.418606
1	0.233582	0.652188
2	0.137580	0.789768
3	0.082456	0.872224
4	0.049845	0.922069
5	0.030286	0.952354
6	0.018464	0.970818
7	0.011284	0.982103
8	0.006909	0.989011
9	0.004236	0.993247
10	0.002600	0.995847
11	0.001597	0.997445
12	0.000982	0.998427
13	0.000604	0.999031
14	0.000372	0.999403
15	0.000229	0.999632
16	0.000141	0.999773
17	0.000087	0.999860
18	0.000054	0.999914

k=1·0
Mean=1·63
Variance=4·29

n	P(n)	F(n)
0	0.380000	0.380000
1	0.235600	0.615600
2	0.146072	0.761672
3	0.090565	0.852237
4	0.056150	0.908387
5	0.034813	0.943200
6	0.021584	0.964784
7	0.013382	0.978166
8	0.008297	0.986463
9	0.005144	0.991607
10	0.003189	0.994796
11	0.001977	0.996774
12	0.001226	0.998000
13	0.000760	0.998760
14	0.000471	0.999231
15	0.000292	0.999523
16	0.000181	0.999704
17	0.000112	0.999817
18	0.000070	0.999886
19	0.000043	0.999930

k=1·1
Mean=1·79
Variance=4·72

n	P(n)	F(n)
0	0.344955	0.344955
1	0.235259	0.580214
2	0.153154	0.733367
3	0.098120	0.831488
4	0.062356	0.893843
5	0.039434	0.933277
6	0.024856	0.958133
7	0.015631	0.973764
8	0.009812	0.983577
9	0.006151	0.989728
10	0.003852	0.993580
11	0.002410	0.995990
12	0.001507	0.997496
13	0.000941	0.998438
14	0.000588	0.999026
15	0.000367	0.999392
16	0.000229	0.999621
17	0.000143	0.999764
18	0.000089	0.999853
19	0.000055	0.999908

k=1·2
Mean=1·96
Variance=5·15

n	P(n)	F(n)
0	0.313141	0.313141
1	0.232977	0.546118
2	0.158890	0.705009
3	0.105080	0.810088
4	0.068407	0.878495
5	0.044109	0.922604
6	0.028259	0.950863
7	0.018021	0.968884
8	0.011452	0.980336
9	0.007258	0.987595
10	0.004590	0.992185
11	0.002898	0.995082
12	0.001826	0.996909
13	0.001150	0.998059
14	0.000723	0.998782
15	0.000454	0.999236
16	0.000285	0.999521
17	0.000179	0.999700
18	0.000112	0.999812
19	0.000070	0.999883
20	0.000044	0.999927

k=1·4
Mean=2·28
Variance=6·01

n	P(n)	F(n)
0	0.258046	0.258046
1	0.223984	0.482030
2	0.166644	0.648674
3	0.117095	0.765769
4	0.079859	0.845628
5	0.053474	0.899101
6	0.035364	0.934465
7	0.023178	0.957644
8	0.015089	0.972733
9	0.009771	0.982504
10	0.006300	0.988804
11	0.004048	0.992853
12	0.002594	0.995446
13	0.001658	0.997104
14	0.001057	0.998161
15	0.000673	0.998834
16	0.000428	0.999261
17	0.000271	0.999533
18	0.000172	0.999705
19	0.000109	0.999813
20	0.000069	0.999882
21	0.000043	0.999926

k=1·6
Mean=2·61
Variance=6·87

n	P(n)	F(n)
0	0.212644	0.21264
1	0.210943	0.42358
2	0.170020	0.59360
3	0.126495	0.72010
4	0.090191	0.81029
5	0.062629	0.87292
6	0.042713	0.91563
7	0.028752	0.94438
8	0.019163	0.96355
9	0.012673	0.97622
10	0.008329	0.98455
11	0.005446	0.98999
12	0.003545	0.99354
13	0.002299	0.99584
14	0.001487	0.99732
15	0.000959	0.99828
16	0.000617	0.99890
17	0.000396	0.99929
18	0.000254	0.99955
19	0.000162	0.99971
20	0.000104	0.99981
21	0.000066	0.99988
22	0.000042	0.99992

k=1·3
Mean=2·12
Variance=5·58

n	P(n)	F(n)
0	0.284262	0.284262
1	0.229115	0.513377
2	0.163359	0.676736
3	0.111411	0.788147
4	0.074255	0.862402
5	0.048801	0.911203
6	0.031769	0.942972
7	0.020541	0.963513
8	0.013213	0.976726
9	0.008465	0.985191
10	0.005406	0.990597
11	0.003443	0.994040
12	0.002188	0.996228
13	0.001388	0.997616
14	0.000879	0.998495
15	0.000556	0.999051
16	0.000351	0.999402
17	0.000222	0.999624
18	0.000140	0.999763
19	0.000088	0.999851
20	0.000055	0.999906

k=1·5
Mean=2·45
Variance=6·44

n	P(n)	F(n)
0	0.234248	0.234248
1	0.217850	0.452098
2	0.168834	0.620932
3	0.122123	0.743055
4	0.085181	0.828236
5	0.058093	0.886330
6	0.039019	0.925349
7	0.025920	0.951269
8	0.017075	0.968344
9	0.011175	0.979519
10	0.007275	0.986793
11	0.004715	0.991509
12	0.003045	0.994554
13	0.001961	0.996515
14	0.001259	0.997774
15	0.000807	0.998580
16	0.000516	0.999096
17	0.000329	0.999425
18	0.000210	0.999635
19	0.000133	0.999768
20	0.000085	0.999853
21	0.000054	0.999907

k=1·7
Mean=2·77
Variance=7·30

n	P(n)	F(n)
0	0.193033	0.19303
1	0.203457	0.39649
2	0.170294	0.56678
3	0.130218	0.69700
4	0.094864	0.79186
5	0.067050	0.85891
6	0.046421	0.90533
7	0.031659	0.93699
8	0.021346	0.95834
9	0.014264	0.97260
10	0.009463	0.98206
11	0.006240	0.98830
12	0.004095	0.99240
13	0.002675	0.99507
14	0.001742	0.99681
15	0.001130	0.99794
16	0.000731	0.99868
17	0.000472	0.99915
18	0.000304	0.99945
19	0.000195	0.99965
20	0.000125	0.99977
21	0.000080	0.99985
22	0.000051	0.99991

k=1·8
Mean=2·94
Variance=7·73

n	P(n)	F(n)
0	0.175231	0.175231
1	0.195558	0.370788
2	0.169744	0.540532
3	0.133306	0.673838
4	0.099179	0.773017
5	0.071330	0.844347
6	0.050121	0.894468
7	0.034627	0.929095
8	0.023615	0.952710
9	0.015943	0.968653
10	0.010675	0.979328
11	0.007100	0.986428
12	0.004696	0.991124
13	0.003090	0.994214
14	0.002026	0.996240
15	0.001323	0.997563
16	0.000861	0.998424
17	0.000559	0.998983
18	0.000362	0.999345
19	0.000234	0.999579
20	0.000151	0.999730
21	0.000097	0.999827
22	0.000062	0.999889
23	0.000040	0.999929

k=2·0
Mean=3·26
Variance=8·59

n	P(n)	F(n)
0	0.144400	0.144400
1	0.179056	0.323456
2	0.166522	0.489978
3	0.137658	0.627636
4	0.106685	0.734321
5	0.079374	0.813695
6	0.057414	0.871109
7	0.040682	0.911791
8	0.028375	0.940166
9	0.019548	0.959714
10	0.013331	0.973045
11	0.009017	0.982062
12	0.006056	0.988118
13	0.004044	0.992162
14	0.002686	0.994848
15	0.001776	0.996625
16	0.001170	0.997795
17	0.000768	0.998563
18	0.000503	0.999066
19	0.000328	0.999394
20	0.000214	0.999608
21	0.000139	0.999747
22	0.000090	0.999836
23	0.000058	0.999895
24	0.000038	0.999932

k=2·2
Mean=3·59
Variance=9·45

n	P(n)	F(n)
0	0.118994	0.118994
1	0.162307	0.281301
2	0.161009	0.442310
3	0.139756	0.582066
4	0.112643	0.694709
5	0.086600	0.781309
6	0.064430	0.845739
7	0.046795	0.892534
8	0.033365	0.925899
9	0.023444	0.949343
10	0.016280	0.965623
11	0.011195	0.976818
12	0.007635	0.984452
13	0.005170	0.989623
14	0.003480	0.993103
15	0.002331	0.995434
16	0.001553	0.996987
17	0.001031	0.998018
18	0.000682	0.998700
19	0.000449	0.999149
20	0.000295	0.999445
21	0.000194	0.999638
22	0.000127	0.999765
23	0.000083	0.999847
24	0.000054	0.999901

k=1·9
Mean=3·10
Variance=8·16

n	P(n)	F(n)
0	0.159070	0.159070
1	0.187385	0.346455
2	0.168459	0.514914
3	0.135778	0.650692
4	0.103123	0.753815
5	0.075445	0.829260
6	0.053792	0.883052
7	0.037639	0.920691
8	0.025962	0.946653
9	0.017706	0.964359
10	0.011966	0.976324
11	0.008026	0.984350
12	0.005349	0.989699
13	0.003546	0.993245
14	0.002340	0.995585
15	0.001538	0.997123
16	0.001007	0.998130
17	0.000657	0.998787
18	0.000428	0.999215
19	0.000278	0.999493
20	0.000180	0.999673
21	0.000116	0.999790
22	0.000075	0.999865
23	0.000048	0.999913

k=2·1
Mean=3·43
Variance=9·02

n	P(n)	F(n)
0	0.131083	0.131083
1	0.170670	0.301752
2	0.164014	0.465766
3	0.138974	0.604740
4	0.109859	0.714599
5	0.083097	0.797697
6	0.060966	0.858663
7	0.043739	0.902401
8	0.030847	0.933248
9	0.021462	0.954710
10	0.014770	0.969481
11	0.010073	0.979554
12	0.006818	0.986372
13	0.004585	0.990957
14	0.003066	0.994023
15	0.002040	0.996063
16	0.001352	0.997415
17	0.000892	0.998308
18	0.000587	0.998895
19	0.000385	0.999280
20	0.000252	0.999532
21	0.000164	0.999696
22	0.000107	0.999803
23	0.000070	0.999873
24	0.000045	0.999918

k=2·3
Mean=3·75
Variance=9·88

n	P(n)	F(n)
0	0.108020	0.108020
1	0.154036	0.262055
2	0.157579	0.419634
3	0.140035	0.559669
4	0.115039	0.674708
5	0.089868	0.764576
6	0.067791	0.832366
7	0.049836	0.882202
8	0.035919	0.918121
9	0.025487	0.943608
10	0.017856	0.961464
11	0.012379	0.973843
12	0.008506	0.982349
13	0.005801	0.988151
14	0.003931	0.992082
15	0.002648	0.994730
16	0.001775	0.996505
17	0.001185	0.997690
18	0.000788	0.998478
19	0.000522	0.999000
20	0.000345	0.999344
21	0.000227	0.999571
22	0.000149	0.999720
23	0.000098	0.999818
24	0.000064	0.999881

25	0.000042	0.999923

k=2·4
Mean=3·92
Variance=10·30

n	P(n)	F(n)
0	0.098057	0.098057
1	0.145909	0.243967
2	0.153789	0.397756
3	0.139845	0.537601
4	0.117050	0.654651
5	0.092891	0.747542
6	0.071031	0.818573
7	0.052847	0.871420
8	0.038499	0.909919
9	0.027582	0.937501
10	0.019495	0.956996
11	0.013625	0.970622
12	0.009433	0.980055
13	0.006479	0.986534
14	0.004418	0.990952
15	0.002995	0.993947
16	0.002019	0.995966
17	0.001355	0.997322
18	0.000906	0.998227
19	0.000603	0.998830
20	0.000400	0.999230
21	0.000264	0.999494
22	0.000174	0.999669
23	0.000115	0.999783
24	0.000075	0.999859
25	0.000049	0.999908

k=2·5
Mean=4·08
Variance=10·73

n	P(n)	F(n)
0	0.089014	0.089014
1	0.137972	0.226986
2	0.149700	0.376686
3	0.139221	0.515906
4	0.118686	0.634592
5	0.095661	0.730252
6	0.074137	0.804389
7	0.055815	0.860204
8	0.041093	0.901297
9	0.029724	0.931021
10	0.021193	0.952215
11	0.014932	0.967146
12	0.010415	0.977561
13	0.007202	0.984764
14	0.004944	0.989707

15	0.003372	0.993079
16	0.002286	0.995366
17	0.001543	0.996908
18	0.001036	0.997944
19	0.000693	0.998638
20	0.000462	0.999099
21	0.000307	0.999406
22	0.000203	0.999610
23	0.000134	0.999744
24	0.000088	0.999832
25	0.000058	0.999890
26	0.000038	0.999928

k=3·0
Mean=4·89
Variance=12·88

n	P(n)	F(n)
0	0.054872	0.054872
1	0.102062	0.156934
2	0.126557	0.283491
3	0.130775	0.414266
4	0.121621	0.535887
5	0.105567	0.641454
6	0.087269	0.728723
7	0.069566	0.798289
8	0.053913	0.852202
9	0.040854	0.893056
10	0.030396	0.923452
11	0.022272	0.945724
12	0.016110	0.961834
13	0.011525	0.973359
14	0.008166	0.981525
15	0.005738	0.987263
16	0.004002	0.991265
17	0.002773	0.994038
18	0.001911	0.995949
19	0.001309	0.997258
20	0.000893	0.998151
21	0.000606	0.998757
22	0.000410	0.999167
23	0.000276	0.999444
24	0.000186	0.999629
25	0.000124	0.999754
26	0.000083	0.999837
27	0.000055	0.999892
28	0.000037	0.999929

k=3·5
Mean=5·71
Variance=15·03

n	P(n)	F(n)
0	0.033825	0.033825
1	0.073401	0.107226
2	0.102394	0.209621
3	0.116388	0.326009
4	0.117261	0.443271

5	0.109053	0.552324
6	0.095785	0.648108
7	0.080596	0.728705
8	0.065585	0.794290
9	0.051958	0.846248
10	0.040267	0.886515
11	0.030640	0.917155
12	0.022954	0.940109
13	0.016969	0.957078
14	0.012399	0.969477
15	0.008969	0.978446
16	0.006429	0.984875
17	0.004572	0.989448
18	0.003229	0.992677
19	0.002265	0.994942
20	0.001580	0.996522
21	0.001096	0.997618
22	0.000757	0.998375
23	0.000520	0.998895
24	0.000356	0.999251
25	0.000243	0.999494
26	0.000165	0.999659
27	0.000112	0.999771
28	0.000076	0.999846
29	0.000051	0.999897
30	0.000034	0.999932

k=4·0
Mean=6·53
Variance=17·17

n	P(n)	F(n)
0	0.020851	0.020851
1	0.051711	0.072563
2	0.080153	0.152715
3	0.099389	0.252105
4	0.107837	0.359942
5	0.106975	0.466917
6	0.099486	0.566403
7	0.088117	0.654520
8	0.075119	0.729639
9	0.062099	0.791738
10	0.050052	0.841789
11	0.039495	0.881284
12	0.030609	0.911893
13	0.023357	0.935250
14	0.017584	0.952834
15	0.013083	0.965917
16	0.009632	0.975549
17	0.007026	0.982575
18	0.005082	0.987657
19	0.003648	0.991306
20	0.002601	0.993907
21	0.001843	0.995750
22	0.001299	0.997049
23	0.000910	0.997959
24	0.000635	0.998594

n	P(n)	F(n)
25	0.000441	0.999034
26	0.000305	0.999339
27	0.000210	0.999549
28	0.000144	0.999693
29	0.000099	0.999792
30	0.000067	0.999859
31	0.000046	0.999905

x = 4·5
Mean = 7·34
Variance = 19·32

n	P(n)	F(n)
0	0.012854	0.012854
1	0.035862	0.048715
2	0.061144	0.109859
3	0.082137	0.191996
4	0.095484	0.287481
5	0.100640	0.388121
6	0.098795	0.486916
7	0.091880	0.578796
8	0.081888	0.660684
9	0.070514	0.731198
10	0.059021	0.790218
11	0.048236	0.838454
12	0.038629	0.877083
13	0.030398	0.907481
14	0.023558	0.931040
15	0.018014	0.949054
16	0.013612	0.962666
17	0.010177	0.972843
18	0.007537	0.980380
19	0.005533	0.985913
20	0.004031	0.989944
21	0.002916	0.992860
22	0.002095	0.994956
23	0.001497	0.996453
24	0.001063	0.997516
25	0.000752	0.998268
26	0.000529	0.998796
27	0.000370	0.999167
28	0.000258	0.999425
29	0.000179	0.999605
30	0.000124	0.999729
31	0.000086	0.999815
32	0.000059	0.999873
33	0.000040	0.999914

= 5·0
Mean = 8·16
Variance = 21·47

n	P(n)	F(n)
0	0.007924	0.007924
1	0.024563	0.032486
2	0.045687	0.078173
3	0.066094	0.144267
4	0.081956	0.226224
5	0.091463	0.317687
6	0.094512	0.412199
7	0.092082	0.504281
8	0.085636	0.589917
9	0.076692	0.666609
10	0.066569	0.733177
11	0.056281	0.789458
12	0.046525	0.835983
13	0.037721	0.873705
14	0.030069	0.903774
15	0.023614	0.927388
16	0.018301	0.945689
17	0.014017	0.959706
18	0.010621	0.970327
19	0.007972	0.978299
20	0.005931	0.984230
21	0.004378	0.988608
22	0.003208	0.991815
23	0.002335	0.994150
24	0.001689	0.995838
25	0.001214	0.997053
26	0.000869	0.997922
27	0.000618	0.998540
28	0.000438	0.998978
29	0.000309	0.999288
30	0.000217	0.999505
31	0.000152	0.999657
32	0.000106	0.999763
33	0.000074	0.999837
34	0.000051	0.999888
35	0.000035	0.999923

<table>
<tr><td>

k = 0·1
Mean = 0·15
Variance = 0·37

n	P(n)	F(n)
0	0.912444	0.912444
1	0.054747	0.967190
2	0.018066	0.985257
3	0.007588	0.992844
4	0.003528	0.996373
5	0.001736	0.998109
6	0.000885	0.998994
7	0.000463	0.999457
8	0.000246	0.999703
9	0.000133	0.999837
10	0.000073	0.999909

k = 0·2
Mean = 0·30
Variance = 0·75

n	P(n)	F(n)
0	0.832553	0.832553
1	0.099906	0.932460
2	0.035966	0.968426
3	0.015825	0.984251
4	0.007596	0.991847
5	0.003828	0.995676
6	0.001991	0.997666
7	0.001058	0.998724
8	0.000571	0.999296
9	0.000312	0.999608
10	0.000172	0.999780
11	0.000096	0.999876
12	0.000054	0.999930

k = 0·3
Mean = 0·45
Variance = 1·12

n	P(n)	F(n)
0	0.759658	0.759658
1	0.136738	0.896396
2	0.053328	0.949724
3	0.024531	0.974255
4	0.012143	0.986398
5	0.006266	0.992663
6	0.003321	0.995984
7	0.001793	0.997778
8	0.000982	0.998759
9	0.000543	0.999303
10	0.000303	0.999606
11	0.000170	0.999776
12	0.000096	0.999872
13	0.000055	0.999927

</td><td>

k = 0·4
Mean = 0·60
Variance = 1·50

n	P(n)	F(n)
0	0.693145	0.693145
1	0.166355	0.859500
2	0.069869	0.929369
3	0.033537	0.962906
4	0.017104	0.980010
5	0.009031	0.989041
6	0.004877	0.993917
7	0.002675	0.996592
8	0.001485	0.998077
9	0.000831	0.998909
10	0.000469	0.999378
11	0.000266	0.999644
12	0.000152	0.999795
13	0.000087	0.999882
14	0.000050	0.999932

k = 0·5
Mean = 0·75
Variance = 1·87

n	P(n)	F(n)
0	0.632456	0.632456
1	0.189737	0.822192
2	0.085381	0.907574
3	0.042691	0.950264
4	0.022413	0.972677
5	0.012103	0.984780
6	0.006657	0.991436
7	0.003709	0.995145
8	0.002086	0.997231
9	0.001182	0.998413
10	0.000674	0.999087
11	0.000386	0.999473
12	0.000222	0.999695
13	0.000128	0.999823
14	0.000074	0.999897
15	0.000043	0.999940

k = 0·6
Mean = 0·90
Variance = 2·25

n	P(n)	F(n)
0	0.577080	0.577080
1	0.207749	0.784829
2	0.099719	0.884548
3	0.051854	0.936402
4	0.028001	0.964403
5	0.015457	0.979860
6	0.008656	0.988516
7	0.004897	0.993413
8	0.002791	0.996204
9	0.001600	0.997804

</td><td>

10	0.000922	0.998726
11	0.000533	0.999259
12	0.000309	0.999568
13	0.000180	0.999747
14	0.000105	0.999852
15	0.000061	0.999913

k = 0·7
Mean = 1·05
Variance = 2·63

n	P(n)	F(n)
0	0.526553	0.526553
1	0.221152	0.747705
2	0.112788	0.860493
3	0.060905	0.921398
4	0.033802	0.955200
5	0.019065	0.974265
6	0.010867	0.985132
7	0.006241	0.991373
8	0.003604	0.994977
9	0.002090	0.997067
10	0.001217	0.998283
11	0.000710	0.998993
12	0.000415	0.999409
13	0.000243	0.999652
14	0.000143	0.999795
15	0.000084	0.999879
16	0.000049	0.999929

k = 0·8
Mean = 1·20
Variance = 3·00

n	P(n)	F(n)
0	0.480450	0.480450
1	0.230616	0.711066
2	0.124533	0.835598
3	0.069738	0.905336
4	0.039751	0.945087
5	0.022896	0.967984
6	0.013280	0.981264
7	0.007740	0.989004
8	0.004528	0.993532
9	0.002656	0.996189
10	0.001562	0.997751
11	0.000920	0.998671
12	0.000543	0.999214
13	0.000321	0.999535
14	0.000190	0.999724
15	0.000112	0.999836
16	0.000067	0.999903

</td></tr>
</table>

k=0·9
Mean=1·35
Variance=3·38

n	P(n)	F(n)
0	0.438383	0.438383
1	0.236727	0.675110
2	0.134934	0.810045
3	0.078262	0.888307
4	0.045783	0.934090
5	0.026921	0.961010
6	0.015883	0.976893
7	0.009394	0.986287
8	0.005566	0.991853
9	0.003302	0.995155
10	0.001962	0.997117
11	0.001166	0.998283
12	0.000694	0.998977
13	0.000413	0.999390
14	0.000246	0.999636
15	0.000147	0.999783
16	0.000087	0.999871
17	0.000052	0.999923

k=1·0
Mean=1·50
Variance=3·75

n	P(n)	F(n)
0	0.400000	0.400000
1	0.240000	0.640000
2	0.144000	0.784000
3	0.086400	0.870400
4	0.051840	0.922240
5	0.031104	0.953344
6	0.018662	0.972006
7	0.011197	0.983204
8	0.006718	0.989922
9	0.004031	0.993953
10	0.002419	0.996372
11	0.001451	0.997823
12	0.000871	0.998694
13	0.000522	0.999216
14	0.000313	0.999530
15	0.000188	0.999718
16	0.000113	0.999831
17	0.000068	0.999898
18	0.000041	0.999939

k=1·1
Mean=1·65
Variance=4·13

n	P(n)	F(n)
0	0.364977	0.364977
1	0.240885	0.605863
2	0.151758	0.757620
3	0.094090	0.851710
4	0.057865	0.909575

5	0.035413	0.944988
6	0.021602	0.966591
7	0.013146	0.979737
8	0.007986	0.987724
9	0.004845	0.992569
10	0.002936	0.995505
11	0.001778	0.997283
12	0.001076	0.998358
13	0.000650	0.999009
14	0.000393	0.999401
15	0.000237	0.999639
16	0.000143	0.999782
17	0.000086	0.999869
18	0.000052	0.999921

k=1·2
Mean=1·80
Variance=4·50

n	P(n)	F(n)
0	0.333021	0.333021
1	0.239775	0.572797
2	0.158252	0.731048
3	0.101281	0.832329
4	0.063807	0.896137
5	0.039816	0.935952
6	0.024686	0.960638
7	0.015235	0.975872
8	0.009369	0.985242
9	0.005746	0.990988
10	0.003517	0.994505
11	0.002148	0.996654
12	0.001311	0.997964
13	0.000798	0.998763
14	0.000486	0.999248
15	0.000295	0.999544
16	0.000179	0.999723
17	0.000109	0.999832
18	0.000066	0.999898
19	0.000040	0.999938

k=1·3
Mean=1·95
Variance=4·87

n	P(n)	F(n)
0	0.303863	0.303863
1	0.237013	0.540876
2	0.163539	0.704415
3	0.107936	0.812351
4	0.069619	0.881970
5	0.044277	0.926247
6	0.027895	0.954142
7	0.017454	0.971596
8	0.010865	0.982462
9	0.006736	0.989198
10	0.004163	0.993361
11	0.002566	0.995927
12	0.001578	0.997505
13	0.000969	0.998474
14	0.000594	0.999068

15	0.000363	0.999431
16	0.000222	0.999653
17	0.000136	0.999789
18	0.000083	0.999871
19	0.000050	0.999922

k=1·4
Mean=2·10
Variance=5·25

n	P(n)	F(n)
0	0.277258	0.277258
1	0.232897	0.510155
2	0.167686	0.677840
3	0.114026	0.791866
4	0.075257	0.867124
5	0.048767	0.915890
6	0.031211	0.947101
7	0.019797	0.966898
8	0.012472	0.979369
9	0.007816	0.987185
10	0.004877	0.992062
11	0.003033	0.995095
12	0.001880	0.996975
13	0.001163	0.998138
14	0.000718	0.998855
15	0.000442	0.999297
16	0.000272	0.999569
17	0.000167	0.999736
18	0.000102	0.999839
19	0.000063	0.999901

k=1·5
Mean=2·25
Variance=5·63

n	P(n)	F(n)
0	0.252982	0.252982
1	0.227684	0.480666
2	0.170763	0.651429
3	0.119534	0.770963
4	0.080686	0.851649
5	0.053252	0.904901
6	0.034614	0.939515
7	0.022252	0.961767
8	0.014186	0.975953
9	0.008984	0.984937
10	0.005660	0.990597
11	0.003550	0.994147
12	0.002219	0.996366
13	0.001383	0.997749
14	0.000859	0.998608
15	0.000533	0.999141
16	0.000330	0.999471
17	0.000204	0.999674
18	0.000126	0.999800
19	0.000077	0.999877
20	0.000048	0.999925

P=0·40

k=1·6
Mean = 2·40
Variance = 6·00

n	P(n)	F(n)
0	0.230832	0.230832
1	0.221599	0.452431
2	0.172847	0.625278
3	0.124450	0.749728
4	0.085870	0.835598
5	0.057705	0.893303
6	0.038085	0.931388
7	0.024810	0.956198
8	0.016002	0.972200
9	0.010241	0.982442
10	0.006514	0.988955
11	0.004121	0.993077
12	0.002596	0.995673
13	0.001630	0.997303
14	0.001020	0.998323
15	0.000636	0.998959
16	0.000396	0.999355
17	0.000246	0.999601
18	0.000153	0.999754
19	0.000094	0.999848
20	0.000058	0.999906

k=1·8
Mean = 2·70
Variance = 6·75

n	P(n)	F(n)
0	0.192180	0.192180
1	0.207554	0.399734
2	0.174346	0.574080
3	0.132503	0.706582
4	0.095402	0.801984
5	0.066400	0.868384
6	0.045152	0.913536
7	0.030187	0.943723
8	0.019924	0.963647
9	0.013017	0.976663
10	0.008435	0.985098
11	0.005429	0.990527
12	0.003475	0.994002
13	0.002213	0.996215
14	0.001404	0.997619
15	0.000887	0.998506
16	0.000559	0.999065
17	0.000351	0.999416
18	0.000220	0.999636
19	0.000138	0.999773
20	0.000086	0.999859
21	0.000053	0.999913

k=2·0
Mean = 3·00
Variance = 7·50

n	P(n)	F(n)
0	0.160000	0.160000
1	0.192000	0.352000
2	0.172800	0.524800
3	0.138240	0.663040
4	0.103680	0.766720
5	0.074650	0.841370
6	0.052255	0.893624
7	0.035832	0.929456
8	0.024186	0.953643
9	0.016124	0.969767
10	0.010642	0.980409
11	0.006966	0.987375
12	0.004528	0.991902
13	0.002926	0.994828
14	0.001881	0.996709
15	0.001204	0.997912
16	0.000767	0.998680
17	0.000487	0.999167
18	0.000309	0.999476
19	0.000195	0.999671
20	0.000123	0.999794
21	0.000077	0.999871
22	0.000048	0.999919

k=1·7
Mean = 2·55
Variance = 6·38

n	P(n)	F(n)
0	0.210621	0.210621
1	0.214834	0.425455
2	0.174015	0.599470
3	0.128771	0.728241
4	0.090784	0.819025
5	0.062096	0.881121
6	0.041604	0.922725
7	0.027459	0.950184
8	0.017917	0.968101
9	0.011586	0.979687
10	0.007438	0.987126
11	0.004747	0.991873
12	0.003014	0.994887
13	0.001906	0.996793
14	0.001201	0.997994
15	0.000754	0.998748
16	0.000472	0.999220
17	0.000295	0.999515
18	0.000184	0.999699
19	0.000114	0.999814
20	0.000071	0.999885
21	0.000044	0.999929

k=1·9
Mean = 2·85
Variance = 7·13

n	P(n)	F(n)
0	0.175353	0.175353
1	0.199903	0.375256
2	0.173915	0.549172
3	0.135654	0.684826
4	0.099706	0.784531
5	0.070592	0.855123
6	0.048708	0.903831
7	0.032982	0.936814
8	0.022016	0.958829
9	0.014530	0.973360
10	0.009503	0.982863
11	0.006168	0.989031
12	0.003979	0.993009
13	0.002552	0.995562
14	0.001630	0.997192
15	0.001037	0.998228
16	0.000657	0.998885
17	0.000415	0.999300
18	0.000261	0.999562
19	0.000164	0.999726
20	0.000103	0.999829
21	0.000064	0.999893
22	0.000040	0.999934

k=2·1
Mean = 3·15
Variance = 7·88

n	P(n)	F(n)
0	0.145991	0.145991
1	0.183949	0.329940
2	0.171072	0.501012
3	0.140279	0.641291
4	0.107314	0.748605
5	0.078554	0.827158
6	0.055773	0.882931
7	0.038722	0.921654
8	0.026428	0.948082
9	0.017795	0.965877
10	0.011851	0.977728
11	0.007822	0.985550
12	0.005123	0.990673
13	0.003334	0.994007
14	0.002158	0.996165
15	0.001390	0.997555
16	0.000891	0.998446
17	0.000569	0.999015
18	0.000362	0.999377
19	0.000230	0.999607
20	0.000146	0.999753
21	0.000092	0.999845
22	0.000058	0.999903

k = 2·2
Mean = 3·30
Variance = 8·25

n	P(n)	F(n)
0	0.133209	0.133209
1	0.175835	0.309044
2	0.168802	0.477846
3	0.141794	0.619639
4	0.110599	0.730238
5	0.082286	0.812524
6	0.059246	0.871769
7	0.041641	0.913411
8	0.028732	0.942143
9	0.019538	0.961681
10	0.013130	0.974811
11	0.008737	0.983548
12	0.005767	0.989314
13	0.003779	0.993094
14	0.002462	0.995556
15	0.001595	0.997151
16	0.001029	0.998180
17	0.000661	0.998841
18	0.000423	0.999264
19	0.000270	0.999534
20	0.000172	0.999705
21	0.000109	0.999814
22	0.000069	0.999883
23	0.000043	0.999927

k = 2·3
Mean = 3·45
Variance = 8·63

n	P(n)	F(n)
0	0.121545	0.121545
1	0.167732	0.289278
2	0.166055	0.455333
3	0.142807	0.598140
4	0.113532	0.711672
5	0.085830	0.797502
6	0.062656	0.860158
7	0.044575	0.904733
8	0.031091	0.935825
9	0.021349	0.957174
10	0.014475	0.971649
11	0.009711	0.981360
12	0.006458	0.987818
13	0.004262	0.992080
14	0.002795	0.994875
15	0.001822	0.996697
16	0.001182	0.997880
17	0.000764	0.998643
18	0.000491	0.999134
19	0.000315	0.999449
20	0.000201	0.999651
21	0.000128	0.999779
22	0.000081	0.999860
23	0.000052	0.999912

k = 2·4
Mean = 3·60
Variance = 9·00

n	P(n)	F(n)
0	0.110903	0.110903
1	0.159701	0.270604
2	0.162895	0.433498
3	0.143347	0.576846
4	0.116111	0.692957
5	0.089173	0.782130
6	0.065988	0.848119
7	0.047512	0.895630
8	0.033496	0.929126
9	0.023224	0.952350
10	0.015885	0.968235
11	0.010744	0.978979
12	0.007199	0.986177
13	0.004784	0.990961
14	0.003158	0.994119
15	0.002071	0.996190
16	0.001352	0.997542
17	0.000878	0.998420
18	0.000568	0.998987
19	0.000366	0.999353
20	0.000235	0.999588
21	0.000150	0.999738
22	0.000096	0.999834
23	0.000061	0.999895
24	0.000039	0.999934

k = 2·5
Mean = 3·75
Variance = 9·37

n	P(n)	F(n)
0	0.101193	0.101193
1	0.151789	0.252982
2	0.159379	0.412361
3	0.143441	0.555802
4	0.118339	0.674141
5	0.092304	0.766445
6	0.069228	0.835673
7	0.050438	0.886111
8	0.035937	0.922048
9	0.025156	0.947203
10	0.017357	0.964561
11	0.011835	0.976396
12	0.007988	0.984384
13	0.005346	0.989730
14	0.003551	0.993281
15	0.002344	0.995625
16	0.001538	0.997163
17	0.001004	0.998168
18	0.000653	0.998820
19	0.000423	0.999243
20	0.000273	0.999516
21	0.000175	0.999691
22	0.000112	0.999803
23	0.000072	0.999875
24	0.000046	0.999921

k = 3·0
Mean = 4·50
Variance = 11·25

n	P(n)	F(n)
0	0.064000	0.064000
1	0.115200	0.179200
2	0.138240	0.317440
3	0.138240	0.455680
4	0.124416	0.580096
5	0.104509	0.684605
6	0.083608	0.768213
7	0.064497	0.832710
8	0.048373	0.881083
9	0.035473	0.916557
10	0.025541	0.942098
11	0.018111	0.960208
12	0.012678	0.972886
13	0.008777	0.981663
14	0.006018	0.987681
15	0.004092	0.991774
16	0.002762	0.994536
17	0.001852	0.996389
18	0.001235	0.997623
19	0.000819	0.998442
20	0.000541	0.998983
21	0.000355	0.999338
22	0.000232	0.999571
23	0.000152	0.999722
24	0.000099	0.999821
25	0.000064	0.999885
26	0.000041	0.999926

k = 3·5
Mean = 5·25
Variance = 13·13

n	P(n)	F(n)
0	0.040477	0.040477
1	0.085002	0.125479
2	0.114753	0.240232
3	0.126228	0.366460
4	0.123072	0.489532
5	0.110765	0.600297
6	0.094150	0.694448
7	0.076665	0.771113
8	0.060374	0.831487
9	0.046287	0.877773
10	0.034715	0.912488
11	0.025563	0.938051
12	0.018533	0.956584
13	0.013258	0.969843
14	0.009375	0.979218
15	0.006563	0.985781
16	0.004553	0.990334
17	0.003134	0.993467
18	0.002141	0.995609
19	0.001454	0.997062

n	P(n)	F(n)
20	0.000981	0.998044
21	0.000659	0.998703
22	0.000440	0.999143
23	0.000293	0.999436
24	0.000194	0.999630
25	0.000128	0.999758
26	0.000084	0.999842
27	0.000055	0.999897
28	0.000036	0.999933

k=4·0
Mean = 6·00
Variance = 15·00

n	P(n)	F(n)
0	0.025600	0.025600
1	0.061440	0.087040
2	0.092160	0.179200
3	0.110592	0.289792
4	0.116122	0.405914
5	0.111477	0.517390
6	0.100329	0.617719
7	0.085996	0.703716
8	0.070947	0.774663
9	0.056758	0.831420
10	0.044271	0.875691
11	0.033807	0.909498
12	0.025355	0.934853
13	0.018724	0.953577
14	0.013642	0.967219
15	0.009822	0.977041
16	0.006998	0.984039
17	0.004940	0.988979
18	0.003458	0.992437
19	0.002402	0.994839
20	0.001658	0.996497
21	0.001137	0.997633
22	0.000775	0.998408
23	0.000526	0.998934
24	0.000355	0.999289
25	0.000238	0.999527
26	0.000160	0.999687
27	0.000106	0.999793
28	0.000071	0.999864
29	0.000047	0.999911

k=4·5
Mean = 6·75
Variance = 16·87

n	P(n)	F(n)
0	0.016191	0.016191
1	0.043715	0.059906
2	0.072130	0.132036
3	0.093769	0.225806
4	0.105491	0.331296
5	0.107600	0.438897
6	0.102220	0.541117
7	0.091998	0.633115
8	0.079349	0.712464
9	0.066124	0.778588
10	0.053560	0.832148
11	0.042361	0.874509
12	0.032830	0.907339
13	0.025001	0.932341
14	0.018751	0.951092
15	0.013876	0.964967
16	0.010147	0.975114
17	0.007341	0.982455
18	0.005261	0.987717
19	0.003738	0.991455
20	0.002636	0.994090
21	0.001845	0.995935
22	0.001283	0.997218
23	0.000887	0.998105
24	0.000610	0.998715
25	0.000417	0.999132
26	0.000284	0.999416
27	0.000192	0.999609
28	0.000130	0.999738
29	0.000087	0.999826
30	0.000059	0.999884
31	0.000039	0.999923

k=5·0
Mean = 7·50
Variance = 18·75

n	P(n)	F(n)
0	0.010240	0.010240
1	0.030720	0.040960
2	0.055296	0.096256
3	0.077414	0.173670
4	0.092897	0.266568
5	0.100329	0.366897
6	0.100329	0.467226
7	0.094596	0.561822
8	0.085136	0.646958
9	0.073785	0.720743
10	0.061979	0.782722
11	0.050710	0.833433
12	0.040568	0.874001
13	0.031830	0.905831
14	0.024555	0.930386
15	0.018662	0.949048
16	0.013996	0.963044
17	0.010374	0.973418
18	0.007607	0.981026
19	0.005525	0.986551
20	0.003978	0.990529
21	0.002842	0.993371
22	0.002015	0.995386
23	0.001419	0.996805
24	0.000993	0.997798
25	0.000691	0.998490
26	0.000479	0.998969
27	0.000330	0.999298
28	0.000226	0.999525
29	0.000154	0.999679
30	0.000105	0.999784
31	0.000071	0.999855
32	0.000048	0.999903

k=0·1
Mean=0·14
Variance=0·33

n	P(n)	F(n)
0	0.916906	0.916906
1	0.053181	0.970087
2	0.016965	0.987051
3	0.006888	0.993939
4	0.003096	0.997035
5	0.001472	0.998507
6	0.000726	0.999233
7	0.000367	0.999600
8	0.000189	0.999789
9	0.000099	0.999888
10	0.000052	0.999940

k=0·2
Mean=0·28
Variance=0·66

n	P(n)	F(n)
0	0.840717	0.840717
1	0.097523	0.938240
2	0.033938	0.972178
3	0.014435	0.986613
4	0.006698	0.993311
5	0.003263	0.996574
6	0.001640	0.998215
7	0.000843	0.999057
8	0.000440	0.999497
9	0.000232	0.999730
10	0.000124	0.999854
11	0.000067	0.999920

k=0·3
Mean=0·41
Variance=0·99

n	P(n)	F(n)
0	0.770859	0.770859
1	0.134129	0.904988
2	0.050567	0.955555
3	0.022485	0.978040
4	0.010759	0.988800
5	0.005367	0.994166
6	0.002750	0.996916
7	0.001435	0.998351
8	0.000760	0.999111
9	0.000406	0.999517
10	0.000219	0.999736
11	0.000119	0.999855
12	0.000065	0.999920

k=0·4
Mean=0·55
Variance=1·32

n	P(n)	F(n)
0	0.706805	0.706805
1	0.163979	0.870784
2	0.066575	0.937359
3	0.030891	0.968250
4	0.015229	0.983480
5	0.007773	0.991253
6	0.004058	0.995310
7	0.002152	0.997462
8	0.001154	0.998616
9	0.000625	0.999241
10	0.000341	0.999582
11	0.000187	0.999769
12	0.000103	0.999871
13	0.000057	0.999928

k=0·5
Mean=0·69
Variance=1·64

n	P(n)	F(n)
0	0.648074	0.648074
1	0.187941	0.836016
2	0.081755	0.917770
3	0.039515	0.957285
4	0.020054	0.977339
5	0.010468	0.987807
6	0.005566	0.993372
7	0.002997	0.996369
8	0.001630	0.997999
9	0.000893	0.998892
10	0.000492	0.999384
11	0.000272	0.999656
12	0.000151	0.999808
13	0.000084	0.999892
14	0.000047	0.999939

k=0·6
Mean=0·83
Variance=1·97

n	P(n)	F(n)
0	0.594223	0.594223
1	0.206790	0.801013
2	0.095950	0.896963
3	0.048231	0.945194
4	0.025177	0.970371
5	0.013434	0.983805
6	0.007272	0.991078
7	0.003977	0.995055
8	0.002191	0.997246
9	0.001214	0.998460
10	0.000676	0.999137
11	0.000378	0.999514
12	0.000212	0.999726
13	0.000119	0.999845
14	0.000067	0.999913

k=0·7
Mean=0·97
Variance=2·30

n	P(n)	F(n)
0	0.544847	0.544847
1	0.221208	0.766055
2	0.109055	0.875110
3	0.056927	0.932037
4	0.030541	0.962579
5	0.016651	0.979230
6	0.009175	0.988404
7	0.005093	0.993498
8	0.002843	0.996341
9	0.001594	0.997935
10	0.000897	0.998832
11	0.000506	0.999338
12	0.000286	0.999624
13	0.000162	0.999786
14	0.000092	0.999878
15	0.000052	0.999931

k=0·8
Mean=1·10
Variance=2·63

n	P(n)	F(n)
0	0.499574	0.499574
1	0.231802	0.731376
2	0.121001	0.852376
3	0.065502	0.917878
4	0.036091	0.953970
5	0.020096	0.974065
6	0.011267	0.985332
7	0.006348	0.991680
8	0.003590	0.995270
9	0.002036	0.997306
10	0.001157	0.998463
11	0.000659	0.999122
12	0.000376	0.999498
13	0.000215	0.999713
14	0.000123	0.999835
15	0.000070	0.999906

k=0·9
Mean=1·24
Variance=2·96

n	P(n)	F(n)
0	0.458062	0.458062
1	0.239108	0.697171
2	0.131749	0.828919
3	0.073867	0.902786
4	0.041772	0.944558

n	P(n)	F(n)
5	0.023743	0.968301
6	0.013541	0.981843
7	0.007742	0.989585
8	0.004434	0.994019
9	0.002543	0.996562
10	0.001460	0.998022
11	0.000839	0.998862
12	0.000483	0.999344
13	0.000278	0.999622
14	0.000160	0.999782
15	0.000092	0.999874
16	0.000053	0.999928

k=1·0
Mean=1·38
Variance=3·29

n	P(n)	F(n)
0	0.420000	0.420000
1	0.243600	0.663600
2	0.141288	0.804888
3	0.081947	0.886835
4	0.047529	0.934364
5	0.027567	0.961931
6	0.015989	0.977920
7	0.009274	0.987194
8	0.005379	0.992572
9	0.003120	0.995692
10	0.001809	0.997501
11	0.001049	0.998551
12	0.000609	0.999159
13	0.000353	0.999512
14	0.000205	0.999717
15	0.000119	0.999836
16	0.000069	0.999905

k=1·1
Mean=1·52
Variance=3·62

n	P(n)	F(n)
0	0.385101	0.385101
1	0.245694	0.630795
2	0.149628	0.780423
3	0.089677	0.870099
4	0.053313	0.923412
5	0.031540	0.954952
6	0.018598	0.973550
7	0.010941	0.984491
8	0.006425	0.990916
9	0.003768	0.994684
10	0.002207	0.996892
11	0.001292	0.998183
12	0.000756	0.998939
13	0.000442	0.999381
14	0.000258	0.999639

n	P(n)	F(n)
15	0.000151	0.999789
16	0.000088	0.999877
17	0.000051	0.999928

k=1·2
Mean=1·66
Variance=3·95

n	P(n)	F(n)
0	0.353101	0.353101
1	0.245758	0.598860
2	0.156794	0.755653
3	0.097003	0.852657
4	0.059075	0.911731
5	0.035634	0.947365
6	0.021357	0.968722
7	0.012741	0.981463
8	0.007574	0.989037
9	0.004491	0.993528
10	0.002657	0.996185
11	0.001569	0.997754
12	0.000925	0.998679
13	0.000545	0.999224
14	0.000321	0.999544
15	0.000188	0.999733
16	0.000111	0.999843
17	0.000065	0.999908

k=1·3
Mean=1·80
Variance=4·27

n	P(n)	F(n)
0	0.323761	0.323761
1	0.244116	0.567876
2	0.162825	0.730701
3	0.103882	0.834584
4	0.064771	0.899354
5	0.039821	0.939175
6	0.024251	0.963426
7	0.014668	0.978095
8	0.008827	0.986921
9	0.005290	0.992212
10	0.003160	0.995372
11	0.001883	0.997255
12	0.001119	0.998374
13	0.000664	0.999039
14	0.000394	0.999432
15	0.000233	0.999665
16	0.000138	0.999802
17	0.000081	0.999884
18	0.000048	0.999932

k=1·4
Mean=1·93
Variance=4·60

n	P(n)	F(n)
0	0.296858	0.296858
1	0.241049	0.537907
2	0.167770	0.705677
3	0.110281	0.815958
4	0.070359	0.886317
5	0.044073	0.930390
6	0.027266	0.957656
7	0.016718	0.974375
8	0.010181	0.984556
9	0.006168	0.990724
10	0.003720	0.994444
11	0.002236	0.996680
12	0.001340	0.998020
13	0.000801	0.998821
14	0.000478	0.999300
15	0.000285	0.999585
16	0.000169	0.999754
17	0.000100	0.999854
18	0.000060	0.999914

k=1·5
Mean=2·07
Variance=4·93

n	P(n)	F(n)
0	0.272191	0.272191
1	0.236806	0.508997
2	0.171685	0.680682
3	0.116173	0.796855
4	0.075803	0.872658
5	0.048362	0.921020
6	0.030388	0.951408
7	0.018884	0.970292
8	0.011637	0.981929
9	0.007125	0.989054
10	0.004339	0.993393
11	0.002631	0.996024
12	0.001590	0.997614
13	0.000957	0.998571
14	0.000575	0.999146
15	0.000345	0.999491
16	0.000206	0.999697
17	0.000123	0.999820
18	0.000073	0.999893
19	0.000044	0.999937

k=1·6
Mean=2·21
Variance=5·26

n	P(n)	F(n)
0	0.249574	0.249574
1	0.231604	0.481178
2	0.174630	0.655808
3	0.121542	0.777350
4	0.081069	0.858419

n	P(n)	F(n)
5	0.052662	0.911081
6	0.033599	0.944680
7	0.021157	0.965837
8	0.013192	0.979029
9	0.008161	0.987190
10	0.005018	0.992208
11	0.003069	0.995276
12	0.001869	0.997145
13	0.001134	0.998279
14	0.000686	0.998965
15	0.000414	0.999379
16	0.000249	0.999628
17	0.000150	0.999778
18	0.000090	0.999867
19	0.000054	0.999921

k=1·7
Mean=2·35
Variance=5·59

n	P(n)	F(n)
0	0.228836	0.228836
1	0.225632	0.454468
2	0.176670	0.631138
3	0.126378	0.757515
4	0.086127	0.843642
5	0.056947	0.900589
6	0.036883	0.937471
7	0.023531	0.961002
8	0.014842	0.975845
9	0.009278	0.985123
10	0.005758	0.990881
11	0.003552	0.994433
12	0.002180	0.996613
13	0.001333	0.997946
14	0.000812	0.998758
15	0.000493	0.999250
16	0.000298	0.999549
17	0.000180	0.999729
18	0.000109	0.999837
19	0.000065	0.999902

k=1·8
Mean=2·49
Variance=5·92

n	P(n)	F(n)
0	0.209821	0.209821
1	0.219053	0.428874
2	0.177871	0.606745
3	0.130676	0.737421
4	0.090950	0.828371
5	0.061191	0.889563
6	0.040223	0.929786
7	0.025996	0.955782
8	0.016585	0.972367
9	0.010474	0.982841
10	0.006561	0.989403
11	0.004082	0.993485
12	0.002526	0.996010
13	0.001555	0.997565
14	0.000953	0.998519

n	P(n)	F(n)
15	0.000582	0.999101
16	0.000355	0.999456
17	0.000215	0.999671
18	0.000130	0.999802
19	0.000079	0.999881
20	0.000048	0.999928

k=1·9
Mean=2·62
Variance=6·25

n	P(n)	F(n)
0	0.192386	0.192386
1	0.212009	0.404396
2	0.178300	0.582696
3	0.134438	0.717134
4	0.095518	0.812652
5	0.065373	0.878025
6	0.043604	0.921628
7	0.028542	0.950170
8	0.018417	0.968587
9	0.011750	0.980336
10	0.007428	0.987764
11	0.004661	0.992425
12	0.002906	0.995331
13	0.001802	0.997134
14	0.001112	0.998246
15	0.000684	0.998930
16	0.000419	0.999349
17	0.000256	0.999605
18	0.000156	0.999761
19	0.000095	0.999855
20	0.000057	0.999913

k=2·0
Mean=2·76
Variance=6·58

n	P(n)	F(n)
0	0.176400	0.176400
1	0.204624	0.381024
2	0.178023	0.559047
3	0.137671	0.696718
4	0.099811	0.796529
5	0.069469	0.865998
6	0.047007	0.913005
7	0.031159	0.944164
8	0.020331	0.964496
9	0.013102	0.977598
10	0.008359	0.985958
11	0.005289	0.991247
12	0.003323	0.994570
13	0.002076	0.996646
14	0.001290	0.997936

n	P(n)	F(n)
15	0.000798	0.998734
16	0.000492	0.999226
17	0.000302	0.999528
18	0.000185	0.999713
19	0.000113	0.999826
20	0.000069	0.999894
21	0.000042	0.999936

k=2·1
Mean=2·90
Variance=6·90

n	P(n)	F(n)
0	0.161742	0.161742
1	0.197002	0.358744
2	0.177105	0.535849
3	0.140385	0.676234
4	0.103815	0.780049
5	0.073459	0.853508
6	0.050418	0.903926
7	0.033837	0.937763
8	0.022324	0.960088
9	0.014531	0.974618
10	0.009355	0.983973
11	0.005968	0.989941
12	0.003779	0.993720
13	0.002377	0.996098
14	0.001487	0.997585
15	0.000926	0.998511
16	0.000574	0.999085
17	0.000354	0.999439
18	0.000218	0.999657
19	0.000134	0.999791
20	0.000082	0.999873
21	0.000050	0.999923

k=2·2
Mean=3·04
Variance=7·23

n	P(n)	F(n)
0	0.148302	0.148302
1	0.189234	0.337536
2	0.175609	0.513146
3	0.142595	0.655740
4	0.107516	0.763257
5	0.077326	0.840582
6	0.053819	0.894401
7	0.036566	0.930967
8	0.024390	0.955357
9	0.016032	0.971389
10	0.010414	0.981803
11	0.006699	0.988502
12	0.004274	0.992776
13	0.002708	0.995484
14	0.001705	0.997189

n	P(n)	F(n)		n	P(n)	F(n)		n	P(n)	F(n)
15	0.001068	0.998258		15	0.001400	0.997651		15	0.002849	0.99479
16	0.000666	0.998924		16	0.000883	0.998534		16	0.001859	0.99665
17	0.000414	0.999337		17	0.000555	0.999088		17	0.001205	0.99786
18	0.000256	0.999593		18	0.000347	0.999435		18	0.000777	0.99864
19	0.000158	0.999751		19	0.000216	0.999651		19	0.000498	0.99913
20	0.000097	0.999848		20	0.000134	0.999785		20	0.000318	0.99945
21	0.000059	0.999907		21	0.000083	0.999868		21	0.000202	0.99965
				22	0.000051	0.999919		22	0.000128	0.99978
								23	0.000080	0.99986
								24	0.000051	0.99991

k = 2·3   Mean = 3·18   Variance = 7·56
k = 2·5   Mean = 3·45   Variance = 8·22
k = 3·5   Mean = 4·83   Variance = 11·51

n	P(n)	F(n)		n	P(n)	F(n)		n	P(n)	F(n)
0	0.135979	0.135979		0	0.114320	0.114320		0	0.048015	0.04801
1	0.181397	0.317376		1	0.165764	0.280085		1	0.097469	0.14548
2	0.173597	0.490973		2	0.168251	0.448336		2	0.127198	0.27268
3	0.144317	0.635289		3	0.146378	0.594714		3	0.135253	0.40793
4	0.110907	0.746197		4	0.116737	0.711450		4	0.127476	0.53541
5	0.081051	0.827248		5	0.088019	0.799470		5	0.110904	0.64631
6	0.057195	0.884443		6	0.063814	0.863284		6	0.091127	0.73744
7	0.039334	0.923777		7	0.044943	0.908227		7	0.071730	0.80917
8	0.026521	0.950297		8	0.030955	0.939182		8	0.054604	0.86377
9	0.017604	0.967901		9	0.020946	0.960128		9	0.040468	0.90424
10	0.011538	0.979439		10	0.013971	0.974099		10	0.029339	0.93358
11	0.007483	0.986922		11	0.009208	0.983307		11	0.020884	0.95446
12	0.004810	0.991732		12	0.006008	0.989316		12	0.014636	0.96910
13	0.003069	0.994801		13	0.003887	0.993202		13	0.010122	0.97922
14	0.001945	0.996746		14	0.002496	0.995698		14	0.006919	0.98614
15	0.001226	0.997972		15	0.001592	0.997291		15	0.004682	0.99082
16	0.000769	0.998741		16	0.001010	0.998301		16	0.003140	0.99396
17	0.000480	0.999221		17	0.000638	0.998939		17	0.002089	0.99605
18	0.000299	0.999519		18	0.000401	0.999339		18	0.001380	0.99743
19	0.000185	0.999704		19	0.000251	0.999590		19	0.000906	0.99833
20	0.000114	0.999819		20	0.000156	0.999746		20	0.000591	0.99893
21	0.000070	0.999889		21	0.000097	0.999843		21	0.000384	0.99931
22	0.000043	0.999932		22	0.000060	0.999904		22	0.000248	0.99956
								23	0.000159	0.99972
								24	0.000102	0.99982
								25	0.000065	0.99988
								26	0.000041	0.99992

k = 2·4   Mean = 3·31   Variance = 7·89
k = 3·0   Mean = 4·14   Variance = 9·86
k = 4·0   Mean = 5·52   Variance = 13·15

n	P(n)	F(n)		n	P(n)	F(n)		n	P(n)	F(n)
0	0.124680	0.124680		0	0.074088	0.074088		0	0.031117	0.03111
1	0.173555	0.298236		1	0.128913	0.203001		1	0.072191	0.10330
2	0.171125	0.469361		2	0.149539	0.352540		2	0.104677	0.20798
3	0.145571	0.614932		3	0.144555	0.497095		3	0.121426	0.32941
4	0.113982	0.728913		4	0.125762	0.622857		4	0.123247	0.45265
5	0.084620	0.813534		5	0.102119	0.724977		5	0.114373	0.56703
6	0.060532	0.874065		6	0.078972	0.803949		6	0.099505	0.66653
7	0.042130	0.916195		7	0.058891	0.862839		7	0.082447	0.74898
8	0.028712	0.944907		8	0.042696	0.905535		8	0.065751	0.81473
9	0.019243	0.964150		9	0.030267	0.935802		9	0.050848	0.86558
10	0.012724	0.976873		10	0.021065	0.956867				
11	0.008319	0.985192		11	0.014439	0.971307				
12	0.005388	0.990580		12	0.009771	0.981077				
13	0.003462	0.994042		13	0.006539	0.987616				
14	0.002208	0.996250		14	0.004334	0.991950				

n	P(n)	F(n)
10	0.038339	0.903922
11	0.028301	0.932224
12	0.020518	0.952742
13	0.014647	0.967389
14	0.010316	0.977705
15	0.007180	0.984885
16	0.004945	0.989830
17	0.003374	0.993204
18	0.002283	0.995487
19	0.001533	0.997021
20	0.001023	0.998043
21	0.000678	0.998721
22	0.000447	0.999168
23	0.000293	0.999461
24	0.000191	0.999652
25	0.000124	0.999776
26	0.000080	0.999857
27	0.000052	0.999908

k=4·5
Mean=6·21
Variance=14·80

n	P(n)	F(n)
0	0.020166	0.020166
1	0.052634	0.072800
2	0.083950	0.156750
3	0.105498	0.262248
4	0.114729	0.376977
5	0.113123	0.490099
6	0.103884	0.593983
7	0.090379	0.684363
8	0.075354	0.759716
9	0.060702	0.820418
10	0.047529	0.867947
11	0.036338	0.904286
12	0.027223	0.931509
13	0.020041	0.951550
14	0.014529	0.966079
15	0.010393	0.976473
16	0.007347	0.983820
17	0.005138	0.988958
18	0.003560	0.992518
19	0.002445	0.994963
20	0.001666	0.996629
21	0.001128	0.997757
22	0.000758	0.998515
23	0.000507	0.999021
24	0.000337	0.999358
25	0.000223	0.999581
26	0.000146	0.999727
27	0.000096	0.999823
28	0.000063	0.999886
29	0.000041	0.999926

k=5·0
Mean=6·90
Variance=16·44

n	P(n)	F(n)
0	0.013069	0.013069
1	0.037900	0.050970
2	0.065947	0.116916
3	0.089248	0.206164
4	0.103528	0.309692
5	0.108083	0.417775
6	0.104480	0.522255
7	0.095226	0.617481
8	0.082847	0.700328
9	0.069407	0.769735
10	0.056359	0.826094
11	0.044575	0.870668
12	0.034471	0.905139
13	0.026145	0.931284
14	0.019497	0.950781
15	0.014324	0.965104
16	0.010385	0.975489
17	0.007440	0.982929
18	0.005274	0.988204
19	0.003703	0.991907
20	0.002577	0.994484
21	0.001780	0.996264
22	0.001220	0.997484
23	0.000831	0.998314
24	0.000562	0.998876
25	0.000378	0.999254
26	0.000253	0.999507
27	0.000169	0.999676
28	0.000112	0.999787
29	0.000074	0.999861
30	0.000048	0.999910

k=5·5
Mean=7·60
Variance=18·08

n	P(n)	F(n)
0	0.008470	0.008470
1	0.027019	0.035488
2	0.050930	0.086418
3	0.073848	0.160267
4	0.091018	0.251285
5	0.100302	0.351587
6	0.101807	0.453393
7	0.097007	0.550400
8	0.087913	0.638313
9	0.076484	0.714797
10	0.064323	0.779120
11	0.052569	0.831690
12	0.041924	0.873614
13	0.032733	0.906347
14	0.025088	0.931435

n	P(n)	F(n)
15	0.018916	0.950351
16	0.014057	0.964408
17	0.010311	0.974719
18	0.007476	0.982194
19	0.005363	0.987557
20	0.003810	0.991367
21	0.002684	0.994051
22	0.001875	0.995926
23	0.001300	0.997226
24	0.000895	0.998121
25	0.000613	0.998734
26	0.000417	0.999151
27	0.000282	0.999433
28	0.000190	0.999623
29	0.000127	0.999751
30	0.000085	0.999835
31	0.000056	0.999892
32	0.000037	0.999929

k=6·0
Mean=8·29
Variance=19·73

n	P(n)	F(n)
0	0.005489	0.005489
1	0.019102	0.024591
2	0.038777	0.063368
3	0.059975	0.123342
4	0.078267	0.201609
5	0.090790	0.292399
6	0.096540	0.388938
7	0.095988	0.484926
8	0.090469	0.575395
9	0.081623	0.657018
10	0.071012	0.728030
11	0.059908	0.787938
12	0.049225	0.837163
13	0.039531	0.876694
14	0.031117	0.907810
15	0.024064	0.931874
16	0.018318	0.950192
17	0.013750	0.963942
18	0.010190	0.974132
19	0.007465	0.981597
20	0.005412	0.987010
21	0.003887	0.990896
22	0.002767	0.993663
23	0.001953	0.995616
24	0.001369	0.996985
25	0.000953	0.997938
26	0.000659	0.998597
27	0.000453	0.999050
28	0.000310	0.999360
29	0.000211	0.999570
30	0.000142	0.999713
31	0.000096	0.999809
32	0.000064	0.999873
33	0.000043	0.999916

P=0·42

k = 6·5
Mean = 8·98
Variance = 21·37

n	P(n)	F(n)
0	0.003557	0.003557
1	0.013411	0.016968
2	0.029169	0.046137
3	0.047934	0.094072
4	0.066030	0.160101
5	0.080424	0.240525
6	0.089405	0.329930
7	0.092598	0.422527
8	0.090630	0.513157
9	0.084689	0.597846
10	0.076135	0.673981
11	0.066238	0.740219
12	0.056026	0.796245
13	0.046243	0.842488
14	0.037358	0.879845
15	0.029612	0.909458
16	0.023079	0.932537
17	0.017717	0.950253
18	0.013415	0.963668
19	0.010033	0.973702
20	0.007420	0.981121
21	0.005430	0.986552
22	0.003937	0.990489
23	0.002830	0.993318
24	0.002017	0.995336
25	0.001427	0.996763
26	0.001003	0.997766
27	0.000700	0.998466
28	0.000486	0.998952
29	0.000335	0.999288
30	0.000230	0.999518
31	0.000157	0.999675
32	0.000107	0.999782
33	0.000072	0.999854
34	0.000049	0.999903

k = 7·0
Mean = 9·67
Variance = 23·02

n	P(n)	F(n)
0	0.002305	0.002305
1	0.009360	0.011665
2	0.021715	0.033380
3	0.037784	0.071164
4	0.054787	0.125951
5	0.069908	0.195859
6	0.081093	0.276952
7	0.087349	0.364302
8	0.088659	0.452961
9	0.085704	0.538665
10	0.079533	0.618198
11	0.071291	0.689489
12	0.062023	0.751512
13	0.052576	0.804088
14	0.043563	0.847652
15	0.035373	0.883025
16	0.028210	0.911235
17	0.022137	0.933372
18	0.017119	0.950491
19	0.013065	0.963556
20	0.009851	0.973406
21	0.007346	0.980752
22	0.005423	0.986175
23	0.003966	0.990140
24	0.002875	0.993015
25	0.002068	0.995083
26	0.001476	0.996559
27	0.001046	0.997605
28	0.000737	0.998342
29	0.000516	0.998858
30	0.000359	0.999217
31	0.000249	0.999466
32	0.000171	0.999637
33	0.000117	0.999754
34	0.000080	0.999834
35	0.000054	0.999889
36	0.000037	0.999925

k = 7·5
Mean = 10·36
Variance = 24·66

n	P(n)	F(n)
0	0.001494	0.001494
1	0.006499	0.007993
2	0.016020	0.024014
3	0.029424	0.053438
4	0.044799	0.098237
5	0.059761	0.157998
6	0.072211	0.230209
7	0.080774	0.310983
8	0.084913	0.395896
9	0.084819	0.480715
10	0.081172	0.561887
11	0.074899	0.636786
12	0.066973	0.703759
13	0.058266	0.762025
14	0.049485	0.811510
15	0.041138	0.852648
16	0.033553	0.886201
17	0.026902	0.913103
18	0.021238	0.934340
19	0.016532	0.950872
20	0.012705	0.963577
21	0.009649	0.973226
22	0.007250	0.980477
23	0.005394	0.985870
24	0.003976	0.989846
25	0.002905	0.992751
26	0.002106	0.994857
27	0.001516	0.996373
28	0.001083	0.997456
29	0.000769	0.998225
30	0.000543	0.998768
31	0.000381	0.999149
32	0.000266	0.999415
33	0.000184	0.999599
34	0.000127	0.999727
35	0.000088	0.999814
36	0.000060	0.999874
37	0.000041	0.999915

k = 8·0
Mean = 11·05
Variance = 26·30

n	P(n)	F(n)
0	0.000968	0.000968
1	0.004493	0.005461
2	0.011726	0.017187
3	0.022670	0.039858
4	0.036159	0.076017
5	0.050334	0.126351
6	0.063253	0.189603
7	0.073373	0.262977
8	0.079793	0.342770
9	0.082276	0.425046
10	0.081124	0.506170
11	0.076994	0.583164
12	0.070706	0.653870
13	0.063092	0.716962
14	0.054890	0.771851
15	0.046693	0.818544
16	0.038930	0.857474
17	0.031877	0.889351
18	0.025679	0.915030
19	0.020381	0.935411
20	0.015958	0.951369
21	0.012341	0.963710
22	0.009435	0.973145
23	0.007138	0.980283
24	0.005348	0.985631
25	0.003970	0.989601
26	0.002923	0.992523
27	0.002135	0.994658
28	0.001548	0.996205
29	0.001114	0.997319
30	0.000797	0.998116
31	0.000567	0.998683
32	0.000401	0.999084
33	0.000282	0.999365
34	0.000197	0.999562
35	0.000137	0.999699
36	0.000095	0.999794
37	0.000066	0.999860
38	0.000045	0.999905

k=8.5
Mean=11·74
Variance=27·95

n	P(n)	F(n)
0	0.000628	0.000628
1	0.003094	0.003721
2	0.008523	0.012244
3	0.017301	0.029546
4	0.028850	0.058396
5	0.041833	0.100229
6	0.054592	0.154820
7	0.065588	0.220409
8	0.073705	0.294113
9	0.078373	0.372486
10	0.079548	0.452034
11	0.077596	0.529630
12	0.073134	0.602764
13	0.066889	0.669654
14	0.059579	0.729233
15	0.051834	0.781067
16	0.044156	0.825223
17	0.036909	0.862133
18	0.030327	0.892460
19	0.024533	0.916993
20	0.019565	0.936558
21	0.015401	0.951959
22	0.011977	0.963936
23	0.009212	0.973149
24	0.007013	0.980161
25	0.005288	0.985449
26	0.003952	0.989401
27	0.002929	0.992329
28	0.002153	0.994482
29	0.001572	0.996055
30	0.001140	0.997194
31	0.000821	0.998015
32	0.000588	0.998603
33	0.000418	0.999021
34	0.000296	0.999318
35	0.000209	0.999526
36	0.000146	0.999672
37	0.000102	0.999774
38	0.000071	0.999845
39	0.000049	0.999894
40	0.000034	0.999928

k=9.0
Mean=12·43
Variance=29·59

n	P(n)	F(n)
0	0.000407	0.000407
1	0.002123	0.002529
2	0.006156	0.008686
3	0.013092	0.021778
4	0.022780	0.044558

n	P(n)	F(n)
5	0.034353	0.078911
6	0.046491	0.125402
7	0.057781	0.183183
8	0.067026	0.250210
9	0.073431	0.323641
10	0.076662	0.400303
11	0.076802	0.477105
12	0.074241	0.551346
13	0.069559	0.620905
14	0.063398	0.684302
15	0.056382	0.740684
16	0.049052	0.789736
17	0.041839	0.831574
18	0.035051	0.866626
19	0.028890	0.895516
20	0.023458	0.918974
21	0.018789	0.937763
22	0.014860	0.952624
23	0.011617	0.964241
24	0.008984	0.973224
25	0.006878	0.980102
26	0.005217	0.985319
27	0.003922	0.989241
28	0.002925	0.992166
29	0.002164	0.994330
30	0.001590	0.995921
31	0.001160	0.997081
32	0.000841	0.997922
33	0.000606	0.998528
34	0.000434	0.998962
35	0.000309	0.999272
36	0.000219	0.999491
37	0.000155	0.999646
38	0.000109	0.999755
39	0.000076	0.999831
40	0.000053	0.999884
41	0.000037	0.999920

k=9.5
Mean=13·12
Variance=31·24

n	P(n)	F(n)
0	0.000264	0.000264
1	0.001452	0.001716
2	0.004422	0.006138
3	0.009831	0.015969
4	0.017819	0.033788
5	0.027905	0.061693
6	0.039113	0.100807
7	0.050233	0.151039
8	0.060091	0.211131
9	0.067769	0.278900
10	0.072717	0.351616
11	0.074766	0.426382
12	0.074080	0.500463
13	0.071060	0.571523
14	0.066238	0.637761

n	P(n)	F(n)
15	0.060189	0.697950
16	0.053455	0.751405
17	0.046506	0.797911
18	0.039711	0.837621
19	0.033336	0.870957
20	0.027552	0.898510
21	0.022449	0.920958
22	0.018051	0.939009
23	0.014339	0.953348
24	0.011262	0.964609
25	0.008753	0.973362
26	0.006736	0.980098
27	0.005137	0.985235
28	0.003884	0.989119
29	0.002913	0.992032
30	0.002168	0.994200
31	0.001602	0.995802
32	0.001176	0.996979
33	0.000858	0.997837
34	0.000622	0.998459
35	0.000448	0.998907
36	0.000321	0.999228
37	0.000229	0.999458
38	0.000163	0.999620
39	0.000115	0.999735
40	0.000081	0.999816
41	0.000057	0.999873
42	0.000039	0.999912

k=10·0
Mean=13·81
Variance=32·88

n	P(n)	F(n)
0	0.000171	0.000171
1	0.000991	0.001161
2	0.003160	0.004322
3	0.007332	0.011653
4	0.013820	0.025473
5	0.022444	0.047917
6	0.032544	0.080461
7	0.043143	0.123604
8	0.053174	0.176778
9	0.061682	0.238461
10	0.067974	0.306434
11	0.071681	0.378116
12	0.072757	0.450873
13	0.071413	0.522286
14	0.068047	0.590333
15	0.063147	0.653480
16	0.057227	0.710708
17	0.050764	0.761472
18	0.044165	0.805636
19	0.037749	0.843386
20	0.031747	0.875133
21	0.026305	0.901437
22	0.021498	0.922936
23	0.017348	0.940284
24	0.013835	0.954119

25	0.010913	0.965032
26	0.008521	0.973552
27	0.006589	0.980142
28	0.005050	0.985192
29	0.003838	0.989030
30	0.002894	0.991924
31	0.002166	0.994090
32	0.001609	0.995699
33	0.001188	0.996887
34	0.000871	0.997759
35	0.000635	0.998394
36	0.000461	0.998855
37	0.000332	0.999187
38	0.000238	0.999426
39	0.000170	0.999596
40	0.000121	0.999717
41	0.000085	0.999802
42	0.000060	0.999862
43	0.000042	0.999905

k=0·1
Mean=0·13
Variance=0·29

n	P(n)	F(n)
0	0.921182	0.921182
1	0.051586	0.972768
2	0.015889	0.988656
3	0.006228	0.994885
4	0.002703	0.997588
5	0.001241	0.998829
6	0.000591	0.999420
7	0.000288	0.999708
8	0.000143	0.999851
9	0.000072	0.999924

k=0·2
Mean=0·25
Variance=0·58

n	P(n)	F(n)
0	0.848576	0.848576
1	0.095040	0.943616
2	0.031934	0.975550
3	0.013114	0.988664
4	0.005875	0.994539
5	0.002764	0.997302
6	0.001341	0.998644
7	0.000665	0.999309
8	0.000335	0.999644
9	0.000171	0.999815

10	0.000088	0.999904

k=0·3
Mean=0·38
Variance=0·87

n	P(n)	F(n)
0	0.781692	0.781692
1	0.131324	0.913017
2	0.047802	0.960819
3	0.020523	0.981342
4	0.009482	0.990823
5	0.004566	0.995390
6	0.002259	0.997648
7	0.001138	0.998787
8	0.000582	0.999369
9	0.000300	0.999669
10	0.000156	0.999826
11	0.000082	0.999908

k=0·4
Mean=0·51
Variance=1·16

n	P(n)	F(n)
0	0.720081	0.720081
1	0.161298	0.881379
2	0.063229	0.944607
3	0.028327	0.972934
4	0.013483	0.986417
5	0.006645	0.993062
6	0.003349	0.996411
7	0.001715	0.998125
8	0.000888	0.999013
9	0.000464	0.999478
10	0.000244	0.999722
11	0.000129	0.999853
12	0.000069	0.999920

k=0·5
Mean=0·64
Variance=1·45

n	P(n)	F(n)
0	0.663325	0.663325
1	0.185731	0.849056
2	0.078007	0.927063
3	0.036403	0.963466
4	0.017838	0.981304

n	P(n)	F(n)
5	0.008990	0.990294
6	0.004615	0.994909
7	0.002400	0.997309
8	0.001260	0.998569
9	0.000666	0.999235
10	0.000354	0.999589
11	0.000189	0.999779
12	0.000102	0.999881
13	0.000055	0.999935

k=0·6
Mean=0·76
Variance=1·74

n	P(n)	F(n)
0	0.611043	0.611043
1	0.205310	0.816353
2	0.091979	0.908332
3	0.044640	0.952973
4	0.022499	0.975471
5	0.011591	0.987063
6	0.006058	0.993121
7	0.003199	0.996320
8	0.001702	0.998022
9	0.000911	0.998933
10	0.000490	0.999422
11	0.000264	0.999686
12	0.000143	0.999829
13	0.000078	0.999907

k=0·7
Mean=0·89
Variance=2·02

n	P(n)	F(n)
0	0.562881	0.562881
1	0.220649	0.783531
2	0.105029	0.888560
3	0.052935	0.941495
4	0.027420	0.968915
5	0.014434	0.983349
6	0.007679	0.991028
7	0.004116	0.995144
8	0.002218	0.997362
9	0.001201	0.998563
10	0.000652	0.999215
11	0.000355	0.999571
12	0.000194	0.999765
13	0.000106	0.999871
14	0.000058	0.999929

k=0·8
Mean=1·02
Variance=2·31

n	P(n)	F(n)
0	0.518516	0.518516
1	0.232295	0.750811
2	0.117077	0.867888
3	0.061192	0.929080
4	0.032554	0.961634
5	0.017501	0.979135
6	0.009474	0.988609
7	0.005154	0.993763
8	0.002814	0.996577
9	0.001541	0.998118
10	0.000846	0.998964
11	0.000465	0.999428
12	0.000256	0.999684
13	0.000141	0.999826
14	0.000078	0.999904

k=0·9
Mean=1·15
Variance=2·60

n	P(n)	F(n)
0	0.477647	0.477647
1	0.240734	0.718382
2	0.128071	0.846452
3	0.069329	0.915781
4	0.037854	0.953635
5	0.020774	0.974409
6	0.011440	0.985848
7	0.006315	0.992163
8	0.003492	0.995655
9	0.001934	0.997589
10	0.001072	0.998661
11	0.000595	0.999256
12	0.000330	0.999586
13	0.000184	0.999770
14	0.000102	0.999872
15	0.000057	0.999929

k=1·0
Mean=1·27
Variance=2·89

n	P(n)	F(n)
0	0.440000	0.440000
1	0.246400	0.686400
2	0.137984	0.824384
3	0.077271	0.901655
4	0.043272	0.944927
5	0.024232	0.969159
6	0.013570	0.982729
7	0.007599	0.990328
8	0.004256	0.994584
9	0.002383	0.996967
10	0.001335	0.998301
11	0.000747	0.999049
12	0.000419	0.999467
13	0.000234	0.999702
14	0.000131	0.999833
15	0.000073	0.999906

k=1·1
Mean=1·40
Variance=3·18

n	P(n)	F(n)
0	0.405320	0.405320
1	0.249677	0.654997
2	0.146810	0.801807
3	0.084954	0.886761
4	0.048764	0.935525
5	0.027854	0.963379
6	0.015858	0.979237
7	0.009007	0.988244
8	0.005107	0.993351
9	0.002892	0.996243
10	0.001636	0.997879
11	0.000924	0.998803
12	0.000522	0.999325
13	0.000295	0.999619
14	0.000166	0.999786
15	0.000094	0.999879
16	0.000053	0.999932

k=1·2
Mean=1·53
Variance=3·47

n	P(n)	F(n)
0	0.373373	0.373373
1	0.250907	0.624280
2	0.154559	0.778839
3	0.092323	0.871162
4	0.054286	0.925448
5	0.031616	0.957064
6	0.018295	0.975359
7	0.010538	0.985897
8	0.006049	0.991946
9	0.003463	0.995408
10	0.001978	0.997386
11	0.001128	0.998514
12	0.000642	0.999156
13	0.000365	0.999521
14	0.000207	0.999729
15	0.000118	0.999846
16	0.000067	0.999913

k=1·3
Mean=1·65
Variance=3·76

n	P(n)	F(n)
0	0.343945	0.343945
1	0.250392	0.594336
2	0.161252	0.755588
3	0.099331	0.854920
4	0.059797	0.914717

5	0.035496	0.950213
6	0.020872	0.971085
7	0.012189	0.983274
8	0.007082	0.990355
9	0.004098	0.994453

10	0.002364	0.996817
11	0.001360	0.998177
12	0.000781	0.998957
13	0.000447	0.999405
14	0.000256	0.999660

15	0.000146	0.999807
16	0.000083	0.999890
17	0.000048	0.999937

k=1·4
Mean=1·78
Variance=4·05

n	P(n)	F(n)
0	0.316835	0.316835
1	0.248399	0.565234
2	0.166924	0.732159
3	0.105941	0.838100
4	0.065260	0.903359

5	0.039469	0.942829
6	0.023576	0.966405
7	0.013957	0.980362
8	0.008207	0.988569
9	0.004800	0.993369

10	0.002796	0.996164
11	0.001622	0.997787
12	0.000939	0.998726
13	0.000542	0.999268
14	0.000312	0.999580

15	0.000179	0.999759
16	0.000103	0.999862
17	0.000059	0.999921

k=1·5
Mean=1·91
Variance=4·34

n	P(n)	F(n)
0	0.291863	0.291863
1	0.245165	0.537028
2	0.171615	0.708643
3	0.112122	0.820765
4	0.070637	0.891402

5	0.043512	0.934915
6	0.026397	0.961312
7	0.015838	0.977151
8	0.009424	0.986575
9	0.005571	0.992145

10	0.003275	0.995421
11	0.001918	0.997338
12	0.001119	0.998457
13	0.000651	0.999107
14	0.000377	0.999485

15	0.000218	0.999703
16	0.000126	0.999829
17	0.000073	0.999902

k=1·6
Mean=2·04
Variance=4·68

n	P(n)	F(n)
0	0.268859	0.268859
1	0.240897	0.509756
2	0.175373	0.685130
3	0.117851	0.802981
4	0.075896	0.878877

5	0.047602	0.926479
6	0.029323	0.955801
7	0.017828	0.973630
8	0.010733	0.984362
9	0.006411	0.990773

10	0.003806	0.994579
11	0.002247	0.996826
12	0.001321	0.998148
13	0.000774	0.998922
14	0.000452	0.999374

15	0.000263	0.999637
16	0.000153	0.999790
17	0.000089	0.999879
18	0.000051	0.999930

k=1·7
Mean=2·16
Variance=4·92

n	P(n)	F(n)
0	0.247668	0.247668
1	0.235780	0.483448
2	0.178249	0.661697
3	0.123111	0.784808
4	0.081007	0.865815

5	0.051715	0.917530
6	0.032339	0.949869
7	0.019921	0.969790
8	0.012132	0.981922
9	0.007322	0.989244

10	0.004387	0.993631
11	0.002613	0.996245
12	0.001549	0.997793
13	0.000914	0.998708
14	0.000537	0.999245

15	0.000315	0.999560
16	0.000184	0.999744
17	0.000107	0.999852
18	0.000062	0.999914

k=1·8
Mean=2·29
Variance=5·21

n	P(n)	F(n)
0	0.228147	0.228147
1	0.229972	0.458119
2	0.180298	0.638417
3	0.127892	0.766309
4	0.085943	0.852252

5	0.055829	0.908081
6	0.035433	0.943513
7	0.022110	0.965623
8	0.013620	0.979243
9	0.008305	0.987548

10	0.005023	0.992571
11	0.003017	0.995588
12	0.001802	0.997391
13	0.001071	0.998462
14	0.000634	0.999096

15	0.000374	0.999470
16	0.000220	0.999690
17	0.000129	0.999819
18	0.000075	0.999895
19	0.000044	0.999939

k=1·9
Mean=2·42
Variance=5·50

n	P(n)	F(n)
0	0.210165	0.210165
1	0.223615	0.433780
2	0.181576	0.615356
3	0.132187	0.747543
4	0.090680	0.838223

5	0.059922	0.898145
6	0.038589	0.936735
7	0.024389	0.961123
8	0.015194	0.976317
9	0.009360	0.985677

10	0.005713	0.991390
11	0.003461	0.994851
12	0.002084	0.996934
13	0.001248	0.998182
14	0.000744	0.998926

15	0.000441	0.999367
16	0.000261	0.999628
17	0.000154	0.999782
18	0.000091	0.999872
19	0.000053	0.999926

k=2·0
Mean=2·55
Variance=5·79

n	P(n)	F(n)
0	0.193600	0.193600
1	0.216832	0.410432
2	0.182139	0.592571
3	0.135997	0.728568
4	0.095198	0.823766

5	0.063973	0.887739	10	0.008122	0.987049	10	0.010016	0.983417
6	0.041796	0.929535	11	0.005045	0.992093	11	0.006323	0.989739
7	0.026749	0.956284	12	0.003108	0.995201	12	0.003954	0.993693
8	0.016852	0.973136	13	0.001901	0.997102	13	0.002453	0.996146
9	0.010486	0.983622	14	0.001156	0.998258	14	0.001511	0.997657
10	0.006459	0.990081	15	0.000699	0.998957	15	0.000925	0.998582
11	0.003946	0.994027	16	0.000421	0.999377	16	0.000563	0.999145
12	0.002394	0.996421	17	0.000252	0.999630	17	0.000341	0.999487
13	0.001444	0.997864	18	0.000151	0.999780	18	0.000206	0.999693
14	0.000866	0.998730	19	0.000090	0.999870	19	0.000124	0.999817
15	0.000517	0.999248	20	0.000053	0.999923	20	0.000074	0.999891
16	0.000308	0.999556				21	0.000044	0.999935
17	0.000183	0.999738						
18	0.000108	0.999846						
19	0.000064	0.999910						

k = 2·1 Mean = 2·67 Variance = 6·07 **k = 2·3** Mean = 2·93 Variance = 6·65 **k = 2·5** Mean = 3·18 Variance = 7·23

n	P(n)	F(n)	n	P(n)	F(n)	n	P(n)	F(n)
0	0.178341	0.178341	0	0.151336	0.151336	0	0.128420	0.128420
1	0.209729	0.388069	1	0.194920	0.346256	1	0.179788	0.308207
2	0.182045	0.570114	2	0.180106	0.526362	2	0.176192	0.484399
3	0.139325	0.709439	3	0.144565	0.670928	3	0.148001	0.632400
4	0.099478	0.808917	4	0.107267	0.778195	4	0.113961	0.746361
5	0.067963	0.876880	5	0.075688	0.853883	5	0.082964	0.829325
6	0.045037	0.921917	6	0.051569	0.905452	6	0.058074	0.887399
7	0.029184	0.951101	7	0.034242	0.939693	7	0.039491	0.926890
8	0.018590	0.969691	8	0.022291	0.961985	8	0.026261	0.953151
9	0.011683	0.981374	9	0.014286	0.976271	9	0.017157	0.970308
10	0.007262	0.988636	10	0.009040	0.985311	10	0.011049	0.981358
11	0.004473	0.993110	11	0.005661	0.990972	11	0.007031	0.988389
12	0.002735	0.995844	12	0.003514	0.994486	12	0.004430	0.992819
13	0.001661	0.997505	13	0.002164	0.996650	13	0.002767	0.995586
14	0.001003	0.998509	14	0.001325	0.997975	14	0.001715	0.997301
15	0.000603	0.999112	15	0.000806	0.998781	15	0.001057	0.998358
16	0.000361	0.999473	16	0.000488	0.999269	16	0.000647	0.999005
17	0.000215	0.999688	17	0.000294	0.999563	17	0.000394	0.999400
18	0.000128	0.999816	18	0.000177	0.999740	18	0.000239	0.999639
19	0.000076	0.999891	19	0.000106	0.999845	19	0.000145	0.999784
20	0.000045	0.999936	20	0.000063	0.999908	20	0.000087	0.999871
						21	0.000052	0.999923

k = 2·2 Mean = 2·80 Variance = 6·36 **k = 2·4** Mean = 3·05 Variance = 6·94 **k = 3·0** Mean = 3·82 Variance = 8·68

n	P(n)	F(n)	n	P(n)	F(n)	n	P(n)	F(n)
0	0.164284	0.164284	0	0.139408	0.139408	0	0.085184	0.085184
1	0.202398	0.366682	1	0.187364	0.326771	1	0.143109	0.228293
2	0.181349	0.548031	2	0.178370	0.505142	2	0.160282	0.388575
3	0.142177	0.690209	3	0.146502	0.651643	3	0.149597	0.538172
4	0.103505	0.793714	4	0.110755	0.762398	4	0.125661	0.663833
5	0.071874	0.865588	5	0.079389	0.841788	5	0.098518	0.762352
6	0.048299	0.913887	6	0.054832	0.896619	6	0.073560	0.835912
7	0.031684	0.945571	7	0.036847	0.933466	7	0.052964	0.888876
8	0.020405	0.965976	8	0.024245	0.957711	8	0.037074	0.925950
9	0.012950	0.978926	9	0.015689	0.973401	9	0.025375	0.951326

n	P(n)	F(n)
10	0.017052	0.968378
11	0.011286	0.979663
12	0.007373	0.987037
13	0.004764	0.991801
14	0.003049	0.994850
15	0.001935	0.996785
16	0.001219	0.998004
17	0.000763	0.998767
18	0.000475	0.999242
19	0.000294	0.999536
20	0.000181	0.999717
21	0.000111	0.999828
22	0.000068	0.999896
23	0.000041	0.999937

k=3·5
Mean=4·45
Variance=10·12

n	P(n)	F(n)
0	0.056505	0.056505
1	0.110749	0.167254
2	0.139544	0.306798
3	0.143265	0.450063
4	0.130371	0.580434
5	0.109512	0.689946
6	0.086879	0.776825
7	0.066028	0.842854
8	0.048531	0.891385
9	0.034727	0.926111
10	0.024309	0.950420
11	0.016707	0.967126
12	0.011305	0.978431
13	0.007548	0.985979
14	0.004982	0.990961
15	0.003255	0.994216
16	0.002107	0.996323
17	0.001354	0.997677
18	0.000863	0.998540
19	0.000547	0.999087
20	0.000345	0.999432
21	0.000216	0.999648
22	0.000135	0.999783
23	0.000084	0.999866
24	0.000052	0.999918

k=4·0
Mean=5·09
Variance=11·57

n	P(n)	F(n)
0	0.037481	0.037481
1	0.083957	0.121438
2	0.117540	0.238979
3	0.131645	0.370624
4	0.129012	0.499636
5	0.115595	0.615231
6	0.097100	0.712331
7	0.077680	0.790010
8	0.059813	0.849824
9	0.044661	0.894485

n	P(n)	F(n)
10	0.032513	0.926998
11	0.023173	0.950171
12	0.016221	0.966392
13	0.011180	0.977572
14	0.007602	0.985174
15	0.005109	0.990283
16	0.003397	0.993680
17	0.002238	0.995918
18	0.001462	0.997381
19	0.000948	0.998329
20	0.000611	0.998940
21	0.000391	0.999330
22	0.000249	0.999579
23	0.000157	0.999737
24	0.000099	0.999836
25	0.000062	0.999898
26	0.000039	0.999937

k=4·5
Mean=5·73
Variance=13·02

n	P(n)	F(n)
0	0.024862	0.024862
1	0.062652	0.087514
2	0.096485	0.183999
3	0.117068	0.301067
4	0.122921	0.423989
5	0.117021	0.541010
6	0.103759	0.644769
7	0.087157	0.731926
8	0.070162	0.802088
9	0.054570	0.856658
10	0.041255	0.897913
11	0.030454	0.928367
12	0.022028	0.950395
13	0.015657	0.966052
14	0.010960	0.977012
15	0.007570	0.984582
16	0.005166	0.989748
17	0.003489	0.993237
18	0.002334	0.995570
19	0.001548	0.997118
20	0.001018	0.998136
21	0.000665	0.998801
22	0.000432	0.999233
23	0.000279	0.999512
24	0.000179	0.999691
25	0.000114	0.999805
26	0.000073	0.999877
27	0.000046	0.999923

k=5·0
Mean=6·36
Variance=14·46

n	P(n)	F(n)
0	0.016492	0.016492
1	0.046177	0.062668
2	0.077577	0.140245
3	0.101367	0.241612
4	0.113531	0.355142
5	0.114439	0.469581
6	0.106810	0.576391
7	0.093993	0.670384
8	0.078954	0.749337
9	0.063865	0.813202
10	0.050070	0.863272
11	0.038235	0.901507
12	0.028549	0.930056
13	0.020907	0.950963
14	0.015053	0.966016
15	0.010677	0.976693
16	0.007474	0.984168
17	0.005170	0.989338
18	0.003539	0.992877
19	0.002399	0.995276
20	0.001612	0.996888
21	0.001075	0.997963
22	0.000711	0.998674
23	0.000468	0.999141
24	0.000305	0.999447
25	0.000198	0.999645
26	0.000128	0.999774
27	0.000082	0.999856
28	0.000053	0.999909

k=5·5
Mean=7·00
Variance=15·91

n	P(n)	F(n)
0	0.010939	0.010939
1	0.033693	0.044632
2	0.061321	0.105954
3	0.085850	0.191804
4	0.102161	0.293965
5	0.108700	0.402665
6	0.106526	0.509190
7	0.098004	0.607194
8	0.085753	0.692947
9	0.072033	0.764980
10	0.058491	0.823471
11	0.046154	0.869625
12	0.035539	0.905164
13	0.026791	0.931955
14	0.019825	0.951780
15	0.014433	0.966213
16	0.010356	0.976568
17	0.007334	0.983902
18	0.005134	0.989036
19	0.003556	0.992592

20	0.002439	0.995031
21	0.001659	0.996690
22	0.001119	0.997809
23	0.000749	0.998558
24	0.000498	0.999056
25	0.000329	0.999386
26	0.000216	0.999602
27	0.000141	0.999743
28	0.000092	0.999835
29	0.000059	0.999895
30	0.000038	0.999933

k = 6·0
Mean = 7·64
Variance = 17·36

n	P(n)	F(n)
0	0.007256	0.007256
1	0.024381	0.031638
2	0.047787	0.079425
3	0.071362	0.150787
4	0.089916	0.240703
5	0.100706	0.341410
6	0.103392	0.444801
7	0.099256	0.544058
8	0.090323	0.634381
9	0.078681	0.713062
10	0.066092	0.779155
11	0.053835	0.832990
12	0.042709	0.875699
13	0.033116	0.908815
14	0.025168	0.933984
15	0.018792	0.952776
16	0.013812	0.966588
17	0.010010	0.976598
18	0.007163	0.983761
19	0.005067	0.988827
20	0.003547	0.992374
21	0.002459	0.994833
22	0.001690	0.996523
23	0.001152	0.997675
24	0.000780	0.998455
25	0.000524	0.998979
26	0.000350	0.999328
27	0.000232	0.999561
28	0.000153	0.999714
29	0.000101	0.999814
30	0.000066	0.999880
31	0.000043	0.999923

k = 6·5
Mean = 8·27
Variance = 18·80

n	P(n)	F(n)
0	0.004813	0.004813
1	0.017520	0.022334
2	0.036793	0.059127
3	0.058378	0.117504
4	0.077643	0.195147
5	0.091308	0.286455
6	0.098004	0.384459
7	0.098004	0.482462
8	0.092613	0.575076
9	0.083558	0.658634
10	0.072528	0.731162
11	0.060924	0.792086
12	0.049754	0.841840
13	0.039650	0.881491
14	0.030927	0.912418
15	0.023670	0.936088
16	0.017811	0.953899
17	0.013201	0.967100
18	0.009652	0.976752
19	0.006970	0.983722
20	0.004976	0.988698
21	0.003517	0.992215
22	0.002462	0.994676
23	0.001708	0.996384
24	0.001176	0.997560
25	0.000803	0.998363
26	0.000545	0.998908
27	0.000367	0.999276
28	0.000246	0.999522
29	0.000164	0.999686
30	0.000109	0.999794
31	0.000072	0.999866
32	0.000047	0.999913

k = 7·0
Mean = 8·91
Variance = 20·25

n	P(n)	F(n)
0	0.003193	0.003193
1	0.012516	0.015708
2	0.028035	0.043744
3	0.047099	0.090843
4	0.065939	0.156781
5	0.081236	0.238018
6	0.090985	0.329003
7	0.094624	0.423627
8	0.092732	0.516358
9	0.086550	0.602908
10	0.077548	0.680457
11	0.067115	0.747571
12	0.056376	0.803947
13	0.046142	0.850089
14	0.036913	0.887003

15	0.028940	0.915943
16	0.022284	0.938227
17	0.016883	0.955110
18	0.012606	0.967716
19	0.009289	0.977005
20	0.006762	0.983768
21	0.004869	0.988636
22	0.003470	0.992106
23	0.002450	0.994557
24	0.001715	0.996272
25	0.001191	0.997463
26	0.000821	0.998284
27	0.000562	0.998846
28	0.000382	0.999228
29	0.000258	0.999486
30	0.000174	0.999659
31	0.000116	0.999775
32	0.000077	0.999852
33	0.000051	0.999904

k = 7·5
Mean = 9·55
Variance = 21·69

n	P(n)	F(n)
0	0.002118	0.002118
1	0.008895	0.011013
2	0.021170	0.032183
3	0.037542	0.069724
4	0.055186	0.124910
5	0.071080	0.195990
6	0.082926	0.278916
7	0.089560	0.368476
8	0.090904	0.459380
9	0.087672	0.547052
10	0.081009	0.628060
11	0.072171	0.700231
12	0.062308	0.762539
13	0.052339	0.814878
14	0.042918	0.857795
15	0.034449	0.892244
16	0.027128	0.919372
17	0.021000	0.940373
18	0.016007	0.956380
19	0.012031	0.968410
20	0.008927	0.977337
21	0.006546	0.983883
22	0.004749	0.988632
23	0.003411	0.992043
24	0.002427	0.994471
25	0.001713	0.996183
26	0.001199	0.997382
27	0.000833	0.998215
28	0.000575	0.998790
29	0.000394	0.999184
30	0.000268	0.999453
31	0.000182	0.999635
32	0.000123	0.999757
33	0.000082	0.999839
34	0.000055	0.999894

n	P(n)	F(n)
35	0.000036	0.999930

k = 8·0
Mean = 10·18
Variance = 23·14

n	P(n)	F(n)
0	0.001405	0.001405
1	0.006294	0.007698
2	0.015860	0.023558
3	0.029605	0.053163
4	0.045592	0.098755
5	0.061275	0.160031
6	0.074348	0.234378
7	0.083269	0.317648
8	0.087433	0.405080
9	0.087044	0.492125
10	0.082866	0.574991
11	0.075935	0.650926
12	0.067329	0.718255
13	0.058007	0.776262
14	0.048726	0.824988
15	0.040020	0.865008
16	0.032216	0.897224
17	0.025470	0.922694
18	0.019810	0.942504
19	0.015181	0.957685
20	0.011477	0.969161
21	0.008569	0.977730
22	0.006326	0.984056
23	0.004620	0.988676
24	0.003342	0.992018
25	0.002396	0.994414
26	0.001703	0.996117
27	0.001201	0.997317
28	0.000841	0.998158
29	0.000584	0.998742
30	0.000404	0.999146
31	0.000277	0.999423
32	0.000189	0.999612
33	0.000128	0.999740
34	0.000087	0.999827
35	0.000058	0.999885
36	0.000039	0.999924

k = 8·5
Mean = 10·82
Variance = 24·59

n	P(n)	F(n)
0	0.000932	0.000932
1	0.004436	0.005367
2	0.011799	0.017166
3	0.023126	0.040292
4	0.037232	0.077524
5	0.052125	0.129649
6	0.065678	0.195327
7	0.076186	0.271512
8	0.082662	0.354174
9	0.084866	0.439040
10	0.083169	0.522209
11	0.078330	0.600539
12	0.071280	0.671819
13	0.062946	0.734765
14	0.054133	0.788898
15	0.045472	0.834370
16	0.037401	0.871771
17	0.030185	0.901956
18	0.023946	0.925902
19	0.018703	0.944606
20	0.014402	0.959007
21	0.010945	0.969953
22	0.008219	0.978172
23	0.006103	0.984275
24	0.004486	0.988761
25	0.003266	0.992027
26	0.002356	0.994383
27	0.001686	0.996069
28	0.001197	0.997267
29	0.000844	0.998110
30	0.000591	0.998701
31	0.000411	0.999112
32	0.000284	0.999396
33	0.000195	0.999591
34	0.000133	0.999724
35	0.000091	0.999815
36	0.000061	0.999876
37	0.000041	0.999918

k = 9·0
Mean = 11·45
Variance = 26·03

n	P(n)	F(n)
0	0.000618	0.000618
1	0.003115	0.003733
2	0.008723	0.012456
3	0.017911	0.030367
4	0.030091	0.060458
5	0.043812	0.104270
6	0.057248	0.161518
7	0.068697	0.230215
8	0.076941	0.307156
9	0.081386	0.388542
10	0.082037	0.470579
11	0.079353	0.549932
12	0.074062	0.623994
13	0.066998	0.690992
14	0.058958	0.749950
15	0.050625	0.800576
16	0.042525	0.843101
17	0.035021	0.878122
18	0.028328	0.906450
19	0.022543	0.928993
20	0.017674	0.946667
21	0.013668	0.960335
22	0.010437	0.970772
23	0.007878	0.978650
24	0.005882	0.984532
25	0.004348	0.988880
26	0.003184	0.992064
27	0.002311	0.994376
28	0.001664	0.996040
29	0.001189	0.997229
30	0.000843	0.998072
31	0.000594	0.998666
32	0.000416	0.999082
33	0.000289	0.999372
34	0.000200	0.999572
35	0.000138	0.999710
36	0.000094	0.999804
37	0.000064	0.999868
38	0.000044	0.999912

k = 9·5
Mean = 12·09
Variance = 27·48

n	P(n)	F(n)
0	0.000410	0.000410
1	0.002181	0.002591
2	0.006413	0.009004
3	0.013767	0.022771
4	0.024091	0.046862
5	0.036426	0.083288
6	0.049297	0.132585
7	0.061128	0.193713
8	0.070603	0.264316
9	0.076879	0.341195
10	0.079646	0.420841
11	0.079067	0.499908
12	0.075641	0.575549
13	0.070055	0.645604
14	0.063050	0.708653
15	0.055315	0.763969
16	0.047433	0.811402
17	0.039844	0.851246
18	0.032849	0.884095
19	0.026625	0.910719
20	0.021247	0.931966
21	0.016714	0.948680
22	0.012976	0.961656
23	0.009952	0.971609
24	0.007547	0.979156
25	0.005663	0.984819
26	0.004208	0.989027
27	0.003099	0.992126
28	0.002262	0.994388
29	0.001638	0.996026
30	0.001177	0.997203
31	0.000840	0.998043
32	0.000595	0.998638
33	0.000419	0.999057
34	0.000293	0.999351

n	P(n)	F(n)	n	P(n)	F(n)	n	P(n)	F(n)
35	0.000204	0.999555	15	0.059401	0.724975	40	0.000047	0.999901
36	0.000141	0.999696	16	0.051975	0.776951			
37	0.000097	0.999794	17	0.044515	0.821466			
38	0.000067	0.999861	18	0.037393	0.858859			
39	0.000046	0.999906	19	0.030859	0.889718			

k=10·0
Mean=12·73
Variance=28·93

n	P(n)	F(n)	n	P(n)	F(n)
0	0.000272	0.000272	20	0.025058	0.914776
1	0.001523	0.001795	21	0.020046	0.934822
2	0.004691	0.006486	22	0.015818	0.950640
3	0.010508	0.016994	23	0.012324	0.962964
4	0.019124	0.036118	24	0.009490	0.972454
5	0.029987	0.066105	25	0.007227	0.979681
6	0.041982	0.108087	26	0.005448	0.985130
7	0.053736	0.161823	27	0.004068	0.989198
8	0.063946	0.225769	28	0.003010	0.992208
9	0.071620	0.297389	29	0.002209	0.994417
10	0.076204	0.373593	30	0.001608	0.996025
11	0.077589	0.451182	31	0.001162	0.997188
12	0.076037	0.527219	32	0.000834	0.998021
13	0.072060	0.599279	33	0.000594	0.998615
14	0.066295	0.665575	34	0.000421	0.999036
			35	0.000296	0.999333
			36	0.000207	0.999540
			37	0.000144	0.999684
			38	0.000100	0.999784
			39	0.000069	0.999853

k=0·1
Mean=0·12
Variance=0·26

n	P(n)	F(n)
0	0.925286	0.925286
1	0.049965	0.975251
2	0.014840	0.990091
3	0.005609	0.995700
4	0.002348	0.998048
5	0.001039	0.999087
6	0.000477	0.999564
7	0.000225	0.999789
8	0.000108	0.999896
9	0.000052	0.999949

k=0·2
Mean=0·23
Variance=0·51

n	P(n)	F(n)
0	0.856153	0.856153
1	0.092465	0.948618
2	0.029959	0.978576
3	0.011864	0.990440
4	0.005125	0.995565
5	0.002325	0.997890
6	0.001088	0.998978
7	0.000520	0.999498
8	0.000253	0.999751
9	0.000124	0.999875

| 10 | 0.000062 | 0.999937 |

k=0·3
Mean=0·35
Variance=0·77

n	P(n)	F(n)
0	0.792186	0.792186
1	0.128334	0.920521
2	0.045045	0.965566
3	0.018649	0.984215
4	0.008308	0.992523
5	0.003858	0.996381
6	0.001840	0.998221
7	0.000894	0.999116
8	0.000441	0.999556
9	0.000219	0.999776
10	0.000110	0.999886
11	0.000056	0.999942

k=0·4
Mean=0·47
Variance=1·02

n	P(n)	F(n)
0	0.732999	0.732999
1	0.158328	0.891326
2	0.059848	0.951174
3	0.025854	0.977028
4	0.011867	0.988896
5	0.005639	0.994535
6	0.002741	0.997275
7	0.001353	0.998629
8	0.000676	0.999304
9	0.000341	0.999645
10	0.000173	0.999818
11	0.000088	0.999906

k=0·5
Mean=1·59
Variance=1·28

n	P(n)	F(n)
0	0.678233	0.678233
1	0.183123	0.861356
2	0.074165	0.935521
3	0.033374	0.968895
4	0.015769	0.984664

n	P(n)	F(n)
5	0.007664	0.992328
6	0.003794	0.996122
7	0.001902	0.998024
8	0.000963	0.998987
9	0.000491	0.999478
10	0.000252	0.999730
11	0.000130	0.999860
12	0.000067	0.999927

k=0·6
Mean=0·70
Variance=1·53

n	P(n)	F(n)
0	0.627559	0.627559
1	0.203329	0.830888
2	0.087838	0.918727
3	0.041108	0.959835
4	0.019979	0.979813
5	0.009925	0.989739
6	0.005002	0.994741
7	0.002547	0.997288
8	0.001307	0.998595
9	0.000674	0.999269
10	0.000350	0.999618
11	0.000182	0.999800
12	0.000095	0.999895
13	0.000050	0.999945

k=0·7
Mean=0·82
Variance=1·79

n	P(n)	F(n)
0	0.580671	0.580671
1	0.219494	0.800165
2	0.100748	0.900913
3	0.048963	0.949876
4	0.024457	0.974333
5	0.012414	0.986748
6	0.006369	0.993117
7	0.003292	0.996408
8	0.001711	0.998119
9	0.000893	0.999012
10	0.000468	0.999480
11	0.000246	0.999726
12	0.000129	0.999855
13	0.000068	0.999923

k=0·8
Mean=0·94
Variance=2·04

n	P(n)	F(n)
0	0.537287	0.537287
1	0.232108	0.769395
2	0.112804	0.882199
3	0.056853	0.939053
4	0.029166	0.968219

n	P(n)	F(n)
5	0.015120	0.983338
6	0.007892	0.991231
7	0.004140	0.995371
8	0.002180	0.997550
9	0.001151	0.998701
10	0.000609	0.999310
11	0.000323	0.999633
12	0.000171	0.999805
13	0.000091	0.999896
14	0.000049	0.999945

k=0·9
Mean=1·06
Variance=2·30

n	P(n)	F(n)
0	0.497144	0.497144
1	0.241612	0.738756
2	0.123947	0.862703
3	0.064700	0.927403
4	0.034065	0.961468
5	0.018027	0.979495
6	0.009572	0.989067
7	0.005095	0.994162
8	0.002717	0.996879
9	0.001451	0.998330
10	0.000776	0.999106
11	0.000415	0.999521
12	0.000222	0.999743
13	0.000119	0.999862
14	0.000064	0.999926

k=1·0
Mean=1·17
Variance=2·55

n	P(n)	F(n)
0	0.460000	0.460000
1	0.248400	0.708400
2	0.134136	0.842536
3	0.072433	0.914969
4	0.039114	0.954083
5	0.021122	0.975205
6	0.011406	0.986611
7	0.006159	0.992770
8	0.003326	0.996096
9	0.001796	0.997892
10	0.000970	0.998862
11	0.000524	0.999385
12	0.000283	0.999668
13	0.000153	0.999821
14	0.000082	0.999903

k=1·1
Mean=1·29
Variance=2·81

n	P(n)	F(n)
0	0.425631	0.425631
1	0.252825	0.678456
2	0.143352	0.821808
3	0.079990	0.901798
4	0.044275	0.946073

n	P(n)	F(n)
5	0.024386	0.970460
6	0.013388	0.983848
7	0.007333	0.991181
8	0.004009	0.995190
9	0.002189	0.997379
10	0.001194	0.998573
11	0.000651	0.999223
12	0.000354	0.999578
13	0.000193	0.999770
14	0.000105	0.999875
15	0.000057	0.999932

k=1·2
Mean=1·41
Variance=3·06

n	P(n)	F(n)
0	0.393831	0.393831
1	0.255202	0.649033
2	0.151590	0.800623
3	0.087316	0.887939
4	0.049508	0.937447
5	0.027804	0.965251
6	0.015514	0.980765
7	0.008617	0.989382
8	0.004770	0.994152
9	0.002633	0.996785
10	0.001450	0.998235
11	0.000797	0.999032
12	0.000438	0.999470
13	0.000240	0.999710
14	0.000131	0.999841
15	0.000072	0.999913

k=1·3
Mean=1·53
Variance=3·32

n	P(n)	F(n)
0	0.364406	0.364406
1	0.255813	0.620219
2	0.158860	0.779078
3	0.094363	0.873441
4	0.054778	0.928219
5	0.031355	0.959571
6	0.017778	0.977350
7	0.010012	0.987362
8	0.005609	0.992972
9	0.003130	0.996102
10	0.001741	0.997841
11	0.000966	0.998808
12	0.000535	0.999341
13	0.000295	0.999636
14	0.000163	0.999800

n	P(n)	F(n)
15	0.000090	0.999891
16	0.000049	0.999940

k=1·4
Mean=1·64
Variance=3·57

n	P(n)	F(n)
0	0.337179	0.337179
1	0.254908	0.592087
2	0.165180	0.757267
3	0.101090	0.858357
4	0.060048	0.918405
5	0.035020	0.953425
6	0.020171	0.973596
7	0.011515	0.985111
8	0.006529	0.991640
9	0.003682	0.995322
10	0.002068	0.997390
11	0.001157	0.998548
12	0.000646	0.999193
13	0.000359	0.999553
14	0.000200	0.999753
15	0.000111	0.999863
16	0.000061	0.999925

k=1·5
Mean=1·76
Variance=3·83

n	P(n)	F(n)
0	0.311987	0.311987
1	0.252710	0.564697
2	0.170579	0.735276
3	0.107465	0.842741
4	0.065285	0.908025
5	0.038779	0.946805
6	0.022686	0.969490
7	0.013125	0.982616
8	0.007531	0.990146
9	0.004292	0.994439
10	0.002434	0.996873
11	0.001374	0.998247
12	0.000773	0.999020
13	0.000433	0.999453
14	0.000242	0.999696
15	0.000135	0.999831
16	0.000075	0.999906

k=1·6
Mean=1·88
Variance=4·08

n	P(n)	F(n)
0	0.288677	0.288677
1	0.249417	0.538094
2	0.175091	0.713185
3	0.113459	0.826644
4	0.070458	0.897102
5	0.042613	0.939715
6	0.025312	0.965027
7	0.014840	0.979867
8	0.008615	0.988482
9	0.004962	0.993444
10	0.002840	0.996284
11	0.001617	0.997902
12	0.000917	0.998819
13	0.000518	0.999337
14	0.000292	0.999629
15	0.000164	0.999792
16	0.000092	0.999884
17	0.000051	0.999935

k=1·7
Mean=2·00
Variance=4·34

n	P(n)	F(n)
0	0.267109	0.267109
1	0.245206	0.512315
2	0.178755	0.691070
3	0.119051	0.810121
4	0.075538	0.885659
5	0.046501	0.932160
6	0.028040	0.960200
7	0.016656	0.976856
8	0.009781	0.986637
9	0.005693	0.992330
10	0.003289	0.995619
11	0.001889	0.997508
12	0.001080	0.998588
13	0.000614	0.999202
14	0.000348	0.999550
15	0.000197	0.999747
16	0.000111	0.999858
17	0.000062	0.999921

k=1·8
Mean=2·11
Variance=4·59

n	P(n)	F(n)
0	0.247152	0.247152
1	0.240232	0.487384
2	0.181615	0.668999
3	0.124225	0.793224
4	0.080498	0.873721
5	0.050424	0.924145
6	0.030859	0.955004
7	0.018568	0.973573
8	0.011030	0.984603
9	0.006485	0.991088
10	0.003782	0.994870
11	0.002191	0.997061
12	0.001262	0.998323
13	0.000723	0.999047
14	0.000413	0.999460
15	0.000235	0.999695
16	0.000133	0.999828
17	0.000075	0.999903

k=1·9
Mean=2·23
Variance=4·85

n	P(n)	F(n)
0	0.228686	0.228686
1	0.234632	0.463318
2	0.183717	0.647035
3	0.128969	0.776004
4	0.085313	0.861317
5	0.054362	0.915679
6	0.033759	0.949437
7	0.020573	0.970011
8	0.012359	0.982370
9	0.007342	0.989712
10	0.004321	0.994033
11	0.002524	0.996557
12	0.001465	0.998023
13	0.000846	0.998869
14	0.000486	0.999355
15	0.000278	0.999634
16	0.000159	0.999792
17	0.000090	0.999883
18	0.000051	0.999934

k=2·0
Mean=2·35
Variance=5·10

n	P(n)	F(n)
0	0.211600	0.211600
1	0.228528	0.440128
2	0.185108	0.625236
3	0.133278	0.758513
4	0.089962	0.848476
5	0.058296	0.906771
6	0.036726	0.943497
7	0.022665	0.966163
8	0.013769	0.979932
9	0.008262	0.988193
10	0.004907	0.993101
11	0.002891	0.995992
12	0.001691	0.997683
13	0.000983	0.998666
14	0.000569	0.999235

n	P(n)	F(n)
15	0.000328	0.999563
16	0.000188	0.999751
17	0.000108	0.999859
18	0.000061	0.999920

k=2·1
Mean=2·47
Variance=5·36

n	P(n)	F(n)
0	0.195790	0.195790
1	0.222026	0.417817
2	0.185836	0.603653
3	0.137147	0.740800
4	0.094426	0.835226
5	0.062208	0.897433
6	0.039751	0.937184
7	0.024839	0.962022
8	0.015257	0.977279
9	0.009246	0.986525
10	0.005542	0.992067
11	0.003292	0.995359
12	0.001941	0.997300
13	0.001137	0.998436
14	0.000662	0.999098
15	0.000384	0.999482
16	0.000221	0.999703
17	0.000127	0.999831
18	0.000073	0.999904

k=2·2
Mean=2·58
Variance=5·61

n	P(n)	F(n)
0	0.181162	0.181162
1	0.215221	0.396383
2	0.185951	0.582333
3	0.140579	0.722912
4	0.098686	0.821598
5	0.066080	0.887678
6	0.042820	0.930498
7	0.027087	0.957585
8	0.016821	0.974406
9	0.010294	0.984700
10	0.006226	0.990926
11	0.003729	0.994655
12	0.002215	0.996870
13	0.001306	0.998176
14	0.000766	0.998942
15	0.000447	0.999389
16	0.000259	0.999648
17	0.000150	0.999798
18	0.000086	0.999885
19	0.000050	0.999934

k=2·3
Mean=2·70
Variance=5·87

n	P(n)	F(n)
0	0.167627	0.167627
1	0.208192	0.375819
2	0.185499	0.561318
3	0.143576	0.704895
4	0.102729	0.807624
5	0.069897	0.877520
6	0.045922	0.923443
7	0.029403	0.952846
8	0.018458	0.971304
9	0.011407	0.982711
10	0.006961	0.989671
11	0.004203	0.993874
12	0.002515	0.996390
13	0.001494	0.997884
14	0.000882	0.998766
15	0.000517	0.999283
16	0.000302	0.999585
17	0.000176	0.999761
18	0.000102	0.999863
19	0.000059	0.999921

k=2·4
Mean=2·82
Variance=6·12

n	P(n)	F(n)
0	0.155103	0.155103
1	0.201013	0.356115
2	0.184530	0.540645
3	0.146148	0.686793
4	0.106542	0.793334
5	0.073642	0.866976
6	0.049045	0.916021
7	0.031781	0.947802
8	0.020165	0.967968
9	0.012583	0.980551
10	0.007746	0.988297
11	0.004715	0.993012
12	0.002843	0.995856
13	0.001701	0.997556
14	0.001010	0.998567
15	0.000596	0.999163
16	0.000350	0.999513
17	0.000205	0.999718
18	0.000119	0.999837
19	0.000069	0.999906

k=2·5
Mean=2·93
Variance=6·38

n	P(n)	F(n)
0	0.143514	0.143514
1	0.193744	0.337258
2	0.183088	0.520346
3	0.148301	0.668648
4	0.110114	0.778761
5	0.077300	0.856061
6	0.052177	0.908239
7	0.034213	0.942452
8	0.021939	0.964392
9	0.013822	0.978213
10	0.008583	0.986797
11	0.005267	0.992064
12	0.003200	0.995263
13	0.001927	0.997191
14	0.001152	0.998343
15	0.000684	0.999027
16	0.000404	0.999432
17	0.000238	0.999669
18	0.000139	0.999808
19	0.000081	0.999889
20	0.000047	0.999936

k=3·0
Mean=3·52
Variance=7·66

n	P(n)	F(n)
0	0.097336	0.097336
1	0.157684	0.255020
2	0.170299	0.425319
3	0.153269	0.578589
4	0.124148	0.702737
5	0.093856	0.796592
6	0.067576	0.864169
7	0.046917	0.911086
8	0.031669	0.942755
9	0.020902	0.963657
10	0.013544	0.977201
11	0.008644	0.985845
12	0.005446	0.991290
13	0.003393	0.994683
14	0.002094	0.996777
15	0.001282	0.998059
16	0.000779	0.998837
17	0.000470	0.999307
18	0.000282	0.999589
19	0.000168	0.999757
20	0.000100	0.999857
21	0.000059	0.999916

k=3·5
Mean=4·11
Variance=8·93

n	P(n)	F(n)
0	0.066016	0.066016
1	0.124771	0.190788
2	0.151597	0.342385
3	0.150081	0.492466
4	0.131696	0.624162

n	P(n)	F(n)
5	0.106674	0.730835
6	0.081605	0.812441
7	0.059805	0.872246
8	0.042387	0.914633
9	0.029247	0.943880
10	0.019742	0.963622
11	0.013083	0.976705
12	0.008537	0.985242
13	0.005496	0.990738
14	0.003498	0.994236
15	0.002204	0.996440
16	0.001376	0.997816
17	0.000852	0.998669
18	0.000524	0.999193
19	0.000320	0.999513
20	0.000195	0.999708
21	0.000118	0.999825
22	0.000071	0.999896
23	0.000042	0.999938

k=4.0
Mean=4·70
Variance=10·21

n	P(n)	F(n)
0	0.044775	0.044775
1	0.096713	0.141488
2	0.130563	0.272050
3	0.141008	0.413058
4	0.133252	0.546310
5	0.115130	0.661440
6	0.093255	0.754695
7	0.071940	0.826635
8	0.053415	0.880050
9	0.038459	0.918509
10	0.026998	0.945507
11	0.018555	0.964063
12	0.012525	0.976587
13	0.008324	0.984911
14	0.005458	0.990370
15	0.003537	0.993907
16	0.002268	0.996175
17	0.001441	0.997615
18	0.000908	0.998523
19	0.000568	0.999091
20	0.000352	0.999443
21	0.000218	0.999661
22	0.000133	0.999794
23	0.000081	0.999876
24	0.000050	0.999925

k=4.5
Mean=5·28
Variance=11·48

n	P(n)	F(n)
0	0.030368	0.030368
1	0.073793	0.104161
2	0.109583	0.213744
3	0.128212	0.341956
4	0.129815	0.471771
5	0.119170	0.590940
6	0.101890	0.692831
7	0.082531	0.775362
8	0.064065	0.839427
9	0.048049	0.887475
10	0.035027	0.922503
11	0.024933	0.947436
12	0.017391	0.964827
13	0.011919	0.976746
14	0.008046	0.984792
15	0.005358	0.990150
16	0.003526	0.993676
17	0.002296	0.995973
18	0.001481	0.997454
19	0.000947	0.998401
20	0.000601	0.999002
21	0.000379	0.999381
22	0.000237	0.999618
23	0.000147	0.999765
24	0.000091	0.999856
25	0.000056	0.999913

k=5.0
Mean=5·87
Variance=12·76

n	P(n)	F(n)
0	0.020596	0.020596
1	0.055610	0.076206
2	0.090088	0.166295
3	0.113511	0.279806
4	0.122592	0.402398
5	0.119159	0.521557
6	0.107244	0.628801
7	0.091004	0.719804
8	0.073713	0.793517
9	0.057496	0.851014
10	0.043467	0.894481
11	0.032008	0.926488
12	0.023045	0.949534
13	0.016274	0.965808
14	0.011299	0.977106
15	0.007728	0.984834
16	0.005217	0.990051
17	0.003480	0.993531
18	0.002297	0.995827
19	0.001501	0.997328
20	0.000973	0.998301
21	0.000625	0.998927
22	0.000399	0.999326
23	0.000253	0.999579
24	0.000159	0.999738
25	0.000100	0.999838
26	0.000062	0.999900

k=5·5
Mean=6·46
Variance=14·04

n	P(n)	F(n)
0	0.013969	0.013969
1	0.041488	0.055457
2	0.072812	0.128269
3	0.098296	0.226565
4	0.112795	0.339360
5	0.115727	0.455087
6	0.109362	0.564449
7	0.097020	0.661469
8	0.081861	0.743329
9	0.066307	0.809636
10	0.051918	0.861555
11	0.039505	0.901060
12	0.029333	0.930393
13	0.021323	0.951715
14	0.015215	0.966930
15	0.010681	0.977611
16	0.007390	0.985001
17	0.005047	0.990048
18	0.003407	0.993455
19	0.002275	0.995730
20	0.001505	0.997235
21	0.000987	0.998222
22	0.000642	0.998864
23	0.000414	0.999279
24	0.000266	0.999544
25	0.000169	0.999714
26	0.000107	0.999821
27	0.000068	0.999889
28	0.000042	0.999931

k=6·0
Mean=7·04
Variance=15·31

n	P(n)	F(n)
0	0.009474	0.009474
1	0.030697	0.040171
2	0.058017	0.098188
3	0.083544	0.181732
4	0.101506	0.283238
5	0.109627	0.392865
6	0.108530	0.501395
7	0.100468	0.601864
8	0.088161	0.690024
9	0.074055	0.764079
10	0.059985	0.824064
11	0.047115	0.871179
12	0.036043	0.907222
13	0.026949	0.934172
14	0.019750	0.953921
15	0.014220	0.968141
16	0.010078	0.978220
17	0.007043	0.985263
18	0.004860	0.990122
19	0.003315	0.993437

n	P(n)	F(n)
20	0.002237	0.995675
21	0.001496	0.997171
22	0.000991	0.998162
23	0.000652	0.998814
24	0.000425	0.999239
25	0.000276	0.999515
26	0.000177	0.999692
27	0.000114	0.999806
28	0.000072	0.999878
29	0.000046	0.999924

k=6·5
Mean=7·63
Variance=16·59

n	P(n)	F(n)
0	0.006426	0.006426
1	0.022554	0.028980
2	0.045673	0.074653
3	0.069879	0.144533
4	0.089620	0.234153
5	0.101630	0.335782
6	0.105187	0.440969
7	0.101430	0.542399
8	0.092428	0.634827
9	0.080412	0.715239
10	0.067305	0.782544
11	0.054517	0.837062
12	0.042932	0.879994
13	0.032992	0.912986
14	0.024815	0.937800
15	0.018313	0.956113
16	0.013288	0.969402
17	0.009497	0.978899
18	0.006696	0.985595
19	0.004662	0.990257
20	0.003210	0.993467
21	0.002187	0.995654
22	0.001476	0.997131
23	0.000988	0.998119
24	0.000656	0.998775
25	0.000432	0.999207
26	0.000283	0.999489
27	0.000184	0.999673
28	0.000119	0.999792
29	0.000076	0.999868
30	0.000049	0.999917

k=7·0
Mean=8·22
Variance=17·86

n	P(n)	F(n)
0	0.004358	0.004358
1	0.016474	0.020832
2	0.035584	0.056416
3	0.057645	0.114061
4	0.077821	0.191883
5	0.092452	0.284334
6	0.099848	0.384182
7	0.100133	0.484316
8	0.094626	0.578942
9	0.085163	0.664105
10	0.073581	0.737686
11	0.061407	0.799093
12	0.049740	0.848833
13	0.039256	0.888088
14	0.030283	0.918372
15	0.022894	0.941266
16	0.016999	0.958265
17	0.012419	0.970684
18	0.008942	0.979625
19	0.006353	0.985979
20	0.004460	0.990439
21	0.003097	0.993536
22	0.002128	0.995664
23	0.001449	0.997113
24	0.000978	0.998091
25	0.000655	0.998746
26	0.000435	0.999181
27	0.000287	0.999468
28	0.000188	0.999657
29	0.000123	0.999779
30	0.000080	0.999859
31	0.000051	0.999910

k=7·5
Mean=8·80
Variance=19·14

n	P(n)	F(n)
0	0.002956	0.002956
1	0.011971	0.014927
2	0.027474	0.042401
3	0.046980	0.089382
4	0.066595	0.155976
5	0.082711	0.238687
6	0.093050	0.331737
7	0.096905	0.428641
8	0.094845	0.523487
9	0.088206	0.611693
10	0.078592	0.690285
11	0.067517	0.757802
12	0.056208	0.814010
13	0.045529	0.859539
14	0.036000	0.895539
15	0.027864	0.923403
16	0.021159	0.944563
17	0.015795	0.960357
18	0.011609	0.971967
19	0.008414	0.980380
20	0.006020	0.986400
21	0.004257	0.990657
22	0.002978	0.993635
23	0.002063	0.995698
24	0.001415	0.997113

n	P(n)	F(n)
25	0.000963	0.99807
26	0.000650	0.99872
27	0.000436	0.99916
28	0.000290	0.99945
29	0.000192	0.99964
30	0.000126	0.999769
31	0.000082	0.99985
32	0.000053	0.99990

k=8·0
Mean=9·39
Variance=20·42

n	P(n)	F(n)
0	0.002005	0.00200
1	0.008661	0.01066
2	0.021045	0.03171
3	0.037881	0.06959
4	0.056254	0.12584
5	0.072905	0.19875
6	0.085299	0.28404
7	0.092123	0.37617
8	0.093274	0.46944
9	0.089543	0.55898
10	0.082201	0.64119
11	0.072635	0.71382
12	0.062103	0.77592
13	0.051594	0.82752
14	0.041791	0.86931
15	0.033098	0.90241
16	0.025693	0.92810
17	0.019587	0.94769
18	0.014690	0.96238
19	0.010855	0.97323
20	0.007913	0.98114
21	0.005698	0.98684
22	0.004056	0.99090
23	0.002857	0.99375
24	0.001993	0.99575
25	0.001377	0.99712
26	0.000944	0.99807
27	0.000642	0.99871
28	0.000433	0.99914
29	0.000290	0.99943
30	0.000193	0.99963
31	0.000128	0.99976
32	0.000084	0.99984
33	0.000055	0.99989
34	0.000036	0.99993

k=8·5
Mean=9·98
Variance=21·69

n	P(n)	F(n)
0	0.001360	0.00136
1	0.006241	0.00760
2	0.016008	0.02360
3	0.030255	0.05386
4	0.046972	0.10083

n	P(n)	F(n)
5	0.063412	0.164247
6	0.077045	0.241293
7	0.086180	0.327473
8	0.090166	0.417639
9	0.089265	0.506904
0	0.084355	0.591259
1	0.076610	0.667869
2	0.067225	0.735094
3	0.057245	0.792339
4	0.047472	0.839811
5	0.038453	0.878263
6	0.030498	0.908761
7	0.023734	0.932495
8	0.018157	0.950652
9	0.013675	0.964327
0	0.010154	0.974481
1	0.007441	0.981922
2	0.005388	0.987310
3	0.003858	0.991168
4	0.002735	0.993903
5	0.001920	0.995823
6	0.001336	0.997158
7	0.000922	0.998080
8	0.000631	0.998711
9	0.000429	0.999140
0	0.000289	0.999429
1	0.000194	0.999623
2	0.000129	0.999753
3	0.000086	0.999838
4	0.000057	0.999895
5	0.000037	0.999932

=9·0
ean=10·57
ariance=22·97

n	P(n)	F(n)
0	0.000922	0.000922
1	0.004482	0.005404
2	0.012101	0.017505
3	0.023960	0.041465
4	0.038815	0.080280
5	0.054496	0.134776
6	0.068665	0.203442
7	0.079456	0.282898
8	0.085812	0.368710
9	0.087528	0.456238
0	0.085078	0.541316
1	0.079354	0.620670
2	0.071419	0.692089
3	0.062299	0.754388
4	0.052865	0.807254
5	0.043772	0.851026
6	0.035456	0.886482
7	0.028156	0.914638
8	0.021962	0.936600
9	0.016853	0.953452

n	P(n)	F(n)
20	0.012741	0.966193
21	0.009501	0.975694
22	0.006996	0.982690
23	0.005092	0.987782
24	0.003666	0.991448
25	0.002613	0.994061
26	0.001845	0.995907
27	0.001292	0.997198
28	0.000897	0.998095
29	0.000618	0.998713
30	0.000423	0.999136
31	0.000287	0.999423
32	0.000194	0.999617
33	0.000130	0.999747
34	0.000087	0.999833
35	0.000058	0.999891
36	0.000038	0.999929

k=9·5
Mean=11·15
Variance=24·24

n	P(n)	F(n)
0	0.000625	0.000625
1	0.003209	0.003834
2	0.009096	0.012930
3	0.018830	0.031760
4	0.031775	0.063535
5	0.046328	0.109863
6	0.060458	0.170320
7	0.072290	0.242611
8	0.080513	0.323124
9	0.084539	0.407663
10	0.084454	0.492117
11	0.080846	0.572963
12	0.074580	0.647543
13	0.066606	0.714149
14	0.057804	0.771953
15	0.048903	0.820856
16	0.040436	0.861292
17	0.032753	0.894046
18	0.026039	0.920085
19	0.020351	0.940436
20	0.015660	0.956097
21	0.011880	0.967976
22	0.008893	0.976870
23	0.006577	0.983447
24	0.004810	0.988257
25	0.003480	0.991737
26	0.002494	0.994231
27	0.001771	0.996001
28	0.001246	0.997248
29	0.000870	0.998118
30	0.000603	0.998721
31	0.000415	0.999136
32	0.000284	0.999420
33	0.000193	0.999612
34	0.000130	0.999742

n	P(n)	F(n)
35	0.000087	0.999829
36	0.000058	0.999888
37	0.000039	0.999926

k=10·0
Mean=11·74
Variance=25·52

n	P(n)	F(n)
0	0.000424	0.000424
1	0.002291	0.002715
2	0.006803	0.009518
3	0.014695	0.024214
4	0.025790	0.050004
5	0.038995	0.088999
6	0.052644	0.141643
7	0.064977	0.206620
8	0.074561	0.281181
9	0.080526	0.361708
10	0.082620	0.444327
11	0.081118	0.525445
12	0.076656	0.602101
13	0.070052	0.672153
14	0.062146	0.734299
15	0.053694	0.787994
16	0.045305	0.833298
17	0.037416	0.870714
18	0.030307	0.901022
19	0.024118	0.925140
20	0.018884	0.944024
21	0.014568	0.958592
22	0.011085	0.969677
23	0.008328	0.978005
24	0.006184	0.984189
25	0.004541	0.988730
26	0.003301	0.992031
27	0.002377	0.994408
28	0.001696	0.996104
29	0.001200	0.997304
30	0.000842	0.998147
31	0.000587	0.998734
32	0.000406	0.999140
33	0.000279	0.999419
34	0.000191	0.999610
35	0.000129	0.999739
36	0.000087	0.999826
37	0.000059	0.999885
38	0.000039	0.999924

k = 0·1
Mean = 0·11
Variance = 0·23

n	P(n)	F(n)
0	0.929232	0.929232
1	0.048320	0.977552
2	0.013820	0.991372
3	0.005030	0.996402
4	0.002027	0.998429
5	0.000864	0.999293
6	0.000382	0.999676
7	0.000173	0.999849
8	0.000080	0.999929

k = 0·2
Mean = 0·22
Variance = 0·45

n	P(n)	F(n)
0	0.863472	0.863472
1	0.089801	0.953273
2	0.028018	0.981291
3	0.010684	0.991975
4	0.004445	0.996420
5	0.001941	0.998361
6	0.000875	0.999236
7	0.000403	0.999639
8	0.000189	0.999828
9	0.000089	0.999917

k = 0·3
Mean = 0·33
Variance = 0·68

n	P(n)	F(n)
0	0.802366	0.802366
1	0.125169	0.927535
2	0.042307	0.969842
3	0.016866	0.986708
4	0.007236	0.993944
5	0.003236	0.997180
6	0.001486	0.998666
7	0.000696	0.999362
8	0.000330	0.999692
9	0.000158	0.999850
10	0.000077	0.999927

k = 0·4
Mean = 0·43
Variance = 0·90

n	P(n)	F(n)
0	0.745584	0.745584
1	0.155081	0.900665
2	0.056450	0.957115
3	0.023483	0.980598
4	0.010380	0.990978
5	0.004750	0.995727
6	0.002223	0.997950
7	0.001057	0.999007
8	0.000508	0.999515
9	0.000247	0.999762
10	0.000121	0.999882
11	0.000059	0.999942

k = 0·5
Mean = 0·54
Variance = 1·13

n	P(n)	F(n)
0	0.692820	0.692820
1	0.180133	0.872954
2	0.070252	0.943206
3	0.030443	0.973648
4	0.013851	0.987499
5	0.006482	0.993982
6	0.003090	0.997072
7	0.001492	0.998564
8	0.000727	0.999291
9	0.000357	0.999648
10	0.000176	0.999825
11	0.000088	0.999912

k = 0·6
Mean = 0·65
Variance = 1·35

n	P(n)	F(n)
0	0.643791	0.643791
1	0.200863	0.844653
2	0.083559	0.928212
3	0.037657	0.965870
4	0.017624	0.983493
5	0.008431	0.991924
6	0.004092	0.996016
7	0.002006	0.998022
8	0.000991	0.999013
9	0.000492	0.999506
10	0.000246	0.999752
11	0.000123	0.999875
12	0.000062	0.999937

k = 0·7
Mean = 0·76
Variance = 1·58

n	P(n)	F(n)
0	0.598231	0.598231
1	0.217756	0.815987
2	0.096248	0.912235
3	0.045044	0.957279
4	0.021666	0.978946
5	0.010590	0.98953
6	0.005232	0.99476
7	0.002604	0.99737
8	0.001303	0.99867
9	0.000655	0.99933
10	0.000330	0.99966
11	0.000167	0.99982
12	0.000085	0.99991

k = 0·8
Mean = 0·87
Variance = 1·81

n	P(n)	F(n)
0	0.555895	0.55589
1	0.231252	0.78714
2	0.108226	0.89537
3	0.052526	0.94790
4	0.025948	0.97384
5	0.012953	0.98680
6	0.006511	0.99331
7	0.003289	0.99660
8	0.001668	0.99826
9	0.000848	0.99911
10	0.000432	0.99954
11	0.000221	0.99976
12	0.000113	0.99988
13	0.000058	0.99993

k = 0·9
Mean = 0·98
Variance = 2·03

n	P(n)	F(n)
0	0.516556	0.51655
1	0.241748	0.75830
2	0.119424	0.87772
3	0.060030	0.93775
4	0.030435	0.96819
5	0.015510	0.98370
6	0.007931	0.99163
7	0.004065	0.99569
8	0.002087	0.99778
9	0.001073	0.99885
10	0.000553	0.99941
11	0.000285	0.99969
12	0.000147	0.99984
13	0.000076	0.99991

k = 1·0
Mean = 1·08
Variance = 2·26

n	P(n)	F(n)
0	0.480000	0.48000
1	0.249600	0.72960
2	0.129792	0.85939
3	0.067492	0.92688
4	0.035096	0.96198

5	0.018250	0.980229	5	0.027440	0.967454	15	0.000082	0.999906
6	0.009490	0.989719	6	0.014982	0.982436			
7	0.004935	0.994654	7	0.008125	0.990560			
8	0.002566	0.997220	8	0.004383	0.994943			
9	0.001334	0.998554	9	0.002355	0.997299			

0	0.000694	0.999248	10	0.001261	0.998560
1	0.000361	0.999609	11	0.000674	0.999234
2	0.000188	0.999797	12	0.000359	0.999593
3	0.000098	0.999894	13	0.000191	0.999784
4	0.000051	0.999945	14	0.000101	0.999886

k=1·6
Mean=1·73
Variance=3·61

n	P(n)	F(n)
0	0.309020	0.309020
1	0.257104	0.566124
2	0.173802	0.739926
3	0.108453	0.848379
4	0.064855	0.913234

=1·1
Mean=1·19
Variance=2·48

	P(n)	F(n)
0	0.446031	0.446031
1	0.255130	0.701161
2	0.139301	0.840462
3	0.074851	0.915313
4	0.039896	0.955209

k=1·4
Mean=1·52
Variance=3·16

n	P(n)	F(n)
0	0.357880	0.357880
1	0.260537	0.618417
2	0.162575	0.780992
3	0.095811	0.876803
4	0.054804	0.931607

5	0.037771	0.951005
6	0.021605	0.972610
7	0.012198	0.984808
8	0.006819	0.991627
9	0.003782	0.995409

10	0.002085	0.997493
11	0.001143	0.998636
12	0.000624	0.999261
13	0.000340	0.999600
14	0.000184	0.999784

5	0.021161	0.976369
6	0.011187	0.987556
7	0.005900	0.993457
8	0.003107	0.996563
9	0.001633	0.998197

5	0.030778	0.962385
6	0.017071	0.979456
7	0.009384	0.988840
8	0.005124	0.993964
9	0.002783	0.996747

15	0.000100	0.999884
16	0.000054	0.999938

0	0.000858	0.999054
1	0.000450	0.999504
2	0.000236	0.999740
3	0.000124	0.999864
4	0.000065	0.999929

10	0.001505	0.998252
11	0.000811	0.999063
12	0.000436	0.999499
13	0.000234	0.999732
14	0.000125	0.999857

k=1·7
Mean=1·84
Variance=3·84

n	P(n)	F(n)
0	0.287151	0.287151
1	0.253841	0.540992
2	0.178197	0.719189
3	0.114283	0.833472
4	0.069827	0.903299

=1·2
Mean=1·30
Variance=2·71

	P(n)	F(n)
0	0.414467	0.414467
1	0.258627	0.673094
2	0.147935	0.821028
3	0.082054	0.903083
4	0.044802	0.947885

15	0.000067	0.999924

5	0.041394	0.944693
6	0.024036	0.968729
7	0.013749	0.982477
8	0.007775	0.990252
9	0.004357	0.994609

5	0.024229	0.972113
6	0.013019	0.985132
7	0.006963	0.992096
8	0.003711	0.995807
9	0.001973	0.997780

10	0.002424	0.997034
11	0.001341	0.998375
12	0.000738	0.999113
13	0.000404	0.999517
14	0.000221	0.999738

0	0.001046	0.998826
1	0.000554	0.999380
2	0.000293	0.999673
3	0.000155	0.999828
4	0.000082	0.999909

k=1·5
Mean=1·63
Variance=3·39

n	P(n)	F(n)
0	0.332554	0.332554
1	0.259392	0.591946
2	0.168605	0.760550
3	0.102287	0.862837
4	0.059838	0.922675

15	0.000120	0.999858
16	0.000065	0.999923

=1·3
Mean=1·41
Variance=2·93

	P(n)	F(n)
0	0.385136	0.385136
1	0.260352	0.645487
2	0.155690	0.801177
3	0.089055	0.890232
4	0.049782	0.940014

5	0.034227	0.956902
6	0.019281	0.976184
7	0.010742	0.986926
8	0.005935	0.992861
9	0.003258	0.996119

10	0.001779	0.997898
11	0.000967	0.998865
12	0.000524	0.999389
13	0.000283	0.999672
14	0.000152	0.999824

P=0·48

k=1·8
Mean=1·95
Variance=4·06

n	P(n)	F(n)
0	0.266830	0.266830
1	0.249753	0.515582
2	0.181820	0.698402
3	0.119759	0.818161
4	0.074729	0.892890
5	0.045077	0.937967
6	0.026565	0.964533
7	0.015393	0.979925
8	0.008805	0.988730
9	0.004985	0.993715
10	0.002800	0.996515
11	0.001562	0.998077
12	0.000866	0.998943
13	0.000478	0.999421
14	0.000263	0.999684
15	0.000144	0.999828
16	0.000079	0.999907

k=1·9
Mean=2·06
Variance=4·29

n	P(n)	F(n)
0	0.247947	0.247947
1	0.244971	0.492918
2	0.184708	0.677626
3	0.124863	0.802489
4	0.079538	0.882027
5	0.048804	0.930831
6	0.029185	0.960016
7	0.017127	0.977144
8	0.009908	0.987052
9	0.005667	0.992719
10	0.003212	0.995932
11	0.001807	0.997739
12	0.001010	0.998749
13	0.000562	0.999311
14	0.000311	0.999621
15	0.000171	0.999793
16	0.000094	0.999887
17	0.000052	0.999938

k=2·0
Mean=2·17
Variance=4·51

n	P(n)	F(n)
0	0.230400	0.230400
1	0.239616	0.470016
2	0.186900	0.656916
3	0.129584	0.786501
4	0.084230	0.870731
5	0.052559	0.923290
6	0.031886	0.955176
7	0.018949	0.974125
8	0.011085	0.985211
9	0.006405	0.991616
10	0.003664	0.995279
11	0.002078	0.997358
12	0.001171	0.998528
13	0.000656	0.999184
14	0.000365	0.999549
15	0.000203	0.999752
16	0.000112	0.999864
17	0.000062	0.999926

k=2·1
Mean=2·27
Variance=4·74

n	P(n)	F(n)
0	0.214095	0.214095
1	0.233792	0.447887
2	0.188436	0.636323
3	0.133915	0.770238
4	0.088786	0.859024
5	0.056326	0.915350
6	0.034659	0.950009
7	0.020855	0.970864
8	0.012336	0.983200
9	0.007199	0.990398
10	0.004155	0.994553
11	0.002377	0.996930
12	0.001349	0.998279
13	0.000761	0.999040
14	0.000427	0.999467
15	0.000238	0.999705
16	0.000132	0.999837
17	0.000073	0.999910

k=2·2
Mean=2·38
Variance=4·97

n	P(n)	F(n)
0	0.198944	0.198944
1	0.227592	0.426536
2	0.189356	0.615892
3	0.137851	0.753744
4	0.093188	0.846931
5	0.060087	0.907019
6	0.037495	0.944513
7	0.022840	0.967353
8	0.013658	0.981011
9	0.008049	0.989060
10	0.004688	0.993748
11	0.002704	0.996451
12	0.001546	0.997998
13	0.000878	0.998876
14	0.000496	0.999372

k=2·3
Mean=2·49
Variance=5·19

n	P(n)	F(n)
0	0.184865	0.184865
1	0.221099	0.405964
2	0.189703	0.595666
3	0.141392	0.737058
4	0.097419	0.834477
5	0.063829	0.898306
6	0.040382	0.938688
7	0.024899	0.963587
8	0.015051	0.978638
9	0.008957	0.987595
10	0.005263	0.992858
11	0.003060	0.995919
12	0.001764	0.997682
13	0.001009	0.998691
14	0.000573	0.999265
15	0.000324	0.999589
16	0.000182	0.999771
17	0.000102	0.999873
18	0.000057	0.999929

k=2·4
Mean=2·60
Variance=5·42

n	P(n)	F(n)
0	0.171783	0.171783
1	0.214385	0.386167
2	0.189516	0.575683
3	0.144538	0.720221
4	0.101465	0.821686
5	0.067535	0.889221
6	0.043313	0.932534
7	0.027027	0.959561
8	0.016514	0.976075
9	0.009923	0.985997
10	0.005882	0.991880
11	0.003448	0.995328
12	0.002002	0.997330
13	0.001153	0.998483
14	0.000660	0.999143
15	0.000375	0.999518
16	0.000212	0.999730
17	0.000119	0.999849
18	0.000067	0.999916

And k=2·2 continued:

n	P(n)	F(n)
15	0.000279	0.999651
16	0.000156	0.999806
17	0.000087	0.999893
18	0.000048	0.999941

k=2·5
Mean = 2·71
Variance = 5·64

n	P(n)	F(n)
0	0.159626	0.159626
1	0.207514	0.367139
2	0.188837	0.555977
3	0.147293	0.703270
4	0.105315	0.808584
5	0.071193	0.879777
6	0.046275	0.926052
7	0.029219	0.955272
8	0.018043	0.973315
9	0.010946	0.984261
10	0.006546	0.990807
11	0.003868	0.994675
12	0.002263	0.996937
13	0.001312	0.998250
14	0.000756	0.999005
15	0.000432	0.999438
16	0.000246	0.999683
17	0.000139	0.999822
18	0.000078	0.999901

k=3·0
Mean = 3·25
Variance = 6·77

n	P(n)	F(n)
0	0.110592	0.110592
1	0.172524	0.283116
2	0.179424	0.462540
3	0.155501	0.618041
4	0.121291	0.739332
5	0.088300	0.827632
6	0.061221	0.888853
7	0.040931	0.929784
8	0.026605	0.956389
9	0.016909	0.973298
10	0.010551	0.983849
11	0.006484	0.990333
12	0.003934	0.994267
13	0.002360	0.996627
14	0.001403	0.998030
15	0.000827	0.998856
16	0.000484	0.999340
17	0.000281	0.999621
18	0.000162	0.999783
19	0.000093	0.999877
20	0.000053	0.999930

k=3·5
Mean = 3·79
Variance = 7·90

n	P(n)	F(n)
0	0.076620	0.076620
1	0.139449	0.216069
2	0.163155	0.379225
3	0.155542	0.534766
4	0.131433	0.666199
5	0.102517	0.768716
6	0.075521	0.844238
7	0.053296	0.897534
8	0.036375	0.933909
9	0.024169	0.958078
10	0.015710	0.973788
11	0.010026	0.983813
12	0.006300	0.990113
13	0.003906	0.994019
14	0.002394	0.996412
15	0.001452	0.997864
16	0.000873	0.998737
17	0.000521	0.999258
18	0.000308	0.999567
19	0.000181	0.999748
20	0.000106	0.999854
21	0.000062	0.999916

k=4·0
Mean = 4·33
Variance = 9·03

n	P(n)	F(n)
0	0.053084	0.053084
1	0.110415	0.163499
2	0.143540	0.307039
3	0.149281	0.456320
4	0.135846	0.592166
5	0.113024	0.705190
6	0.088159	0.793348
7	0.065489	0.858837
8	0.046825	0.905662
9	0.032465	0.938127
10	0.021946	0.960074
11	0.014525	0.974598
12	0.009441	0.984039
13	0.006042	0.990081
14	0.003815	0.993897
15	0.002381	0.996277
16	0.001470	0.997747
17	0.000899	0.998647
18	0.000546	0.999192
19	0.000329	0.999521
20	0.000196	0.999717
21	0.000117	0.999834
22	0.000069	0.999903

k=4·5
Mean = 4·87
Variance = 10·16

n	P(n)	F(n)
0	0.036778	0.036778
1	0.086060	0.122838
2	0.123066	0.245904
3	0.138654	0.384558
4	0.135188	0.519746
5	0.119506	0.639252
6	0.098393	0.737645
7	0.076747	0.814392
8	0.057368	0.871760
9	0.041433	0.913192
10	0.029086	0.942278
11	0.019937	0.962215
12	0.013391	0.975606
13	0.008838	0.984444
14	0.005745	0.990189
15	0.003684	0.993873
16	0.002335	0.996208
17	0.001464	0.997672
18	0.000909	0.998581
19	0.000560	0.999141
20	0.000342	0.999484
21	0.000208	0.999691
22	0.000125	0.999816
23	0.000075	0.999891
24	0.000045	0.999936

k=5·0
Mean = 5·42
Variance = 11·28

n	P(n)	F(n)
0	0.025480	0.025480
1	0.066249	0.091729
2	0.103348	0.195078
3	0.125396	0.320474
4	0.130412	0.450886
5	0.122066	0.572952
6	0.105790	0.678742
7	0.086446	0.765188
8	0.067428	0.832615
9	0.050646	0.883261
10	0.036870	0.920131
11	0.026144	0.946275
12	0.018127	0.964402
13	0.012326	0.976728
14	0.008241	0.984969
15	0.005428	0.990397
16	0.003528	0.993925
17	0.002266	0.996192
18	0.001440	0.997632
19	0.000907	0.998539
20	0.000566	0.999104
21	0.000350	0.999455
22	0.000215	0.999670
23	0.000131	0.999801
24	0.000080	0.999881

n	P(n)	F(n)
25	0.000048	0.999929

k = 5.5
Mean = 5·96
Variance = 12·41

n	P(n)	F(n)
0	0.017653	0.017653
1	0.050489	0.068142
2	0.085326	0.153468
3	0.110923	0.264391
4	0.122570	0.386961
5	0.121099	0.508061
6	0.110200	0.618261
7	0.094143	0.712404
8	0.076491	0.788895
9	0.059663	0.848558
10	0.044986	0.893543
11	0.032962	0.926506
12	0.023568	0.950074
13	0.016498	0.966572
14	0.011336	0.977908
15	0.007663	0.985571
16	0.005106	0.990677
17	0.003358	0.994035
18	0.002183	0.996217
19	0.001404	0.997621
20	0.000894	0.998515
21	0.000565	0.999080
22	0.000354	0.999433
23	0.000220	0.999653
24	0.000136	0.999789
25	0.000083	0.999872
26	0.000051	0.999923

k = 6.0
Mean = 6·50
Variance = 13·54

n	P(n)	F(n)
0	0.012231	0.012231
1	0.038159	0.050390
2	0.069450	0.119840
3	0.096304	0.216144
4	0.112676	0.328820
5	0.117183	0.446003
6	0.111714	0.557718
7	0.099585	0.657303
8	0.084150	0.741453
9	0.068068	0.809521
10	0.053093	0.862614
11	0.040158	0.902771
12	0.029583	0.932354
13	0.021300	0.953654
14	0.015031	0.968685
15	0.010422	0.979107
16	0.007113	0.986220
17	0.004787	0.991006
18.	0.003180	0.994187
19	0.002089	0.996276
20	0.001358	0.997633
21	0.000874	0.998508
22	0.000558	0.999065
23	0.000353	0.999419
24	0.000222	0.999641
25	0.000138	0.999779
26	0.000086	0.999865
27	0.000053	0.999918

k = 6.5
Mean = 7·04
Variance = 14·67

n	P(n)	F(n)
0	0.008474	0.008474
1	0.028641	0.037114
2	0.055850	0.092964
3	0.082285	0.175249
4	0.101622	0.276871
5	0.110971	0.387842
6	0.110601	0.498443
7	0.102701	0.601144
8	0.090120	0.691264
9	0.075501	0.766765
10	0.060854	0.827619
11	0.047466	0.875085
12	0.035995	0.911079
13	0.026636	0.937716
14	0.019292	0.957008
15	0.013710	0.970718
16	0.009580	0.980298
17	0.006593	0.986892
18	0.004476	0.991368
19	0.003001	0.994369
20	0.001990	0.996359
21	0.001306	0.997665
22	0.000849	0.998514
23	0.000547	0.999061
24	0.000350	0.999410
25	0.000222	0.999632
26	0.000140	0.999772
27	0.000087	0.999859
28	0.000054	0.999913

k = 7.0
Mean ≐ 7·58
Variance = 15·80

n	P(n)	F(n)
0	0.005871	0.005871
1	0.021369	0.027240
2	0.044448	0.071688
3	0.069339	0.141027
4	0.090141	0.231168
5	0.103121	0.334289
6	0.107246	0.441535
7	0.103569	0.545104
8	0.094248	0.639351
9	0.081681	0.721033
10	0.067959	0.788992
11	0.054614	0.843606
12	0.042599	0.886205
13	0.032375	0.918580
14	0.024050	0.942631
15	0.017509	0.960139
16	0.012519	0.972658
17	0.008807	0.981465
18	0.006106	0.987571
19	0.004178	0.991749
20	0.002824	0.994574
21	0.001888	0.996462
22	0.001250	0.997712
23	0.000819	0.998531
24	0.000533	0.999064
25	0.000343	0.999407
26	0.000220	0.999627
27	0.000140	0.999766
28	0.000088	0.999855
29	0.000055	0.999910

k = 7.5
Mean = 8·12
Variance = 16·93

n	P(n)	F(n)
0	0.004067	0.004067
1	0.015863	0.019930
2	0.035056	0.054986
3	0.057726	0.112712
4	0.078796	0.191508
5	0.094240	0.285748
6	0.102093	0.387842
7	0.102385	0.490227
8	0.096498	0.586725
9	0.086419	0.673144
10	0.074148	0.747292
11	0.061340	0.808632
12	0.049175	0.857807
13	0.038356	0.896163
14	0.029205	0.925369
15	0.021768	0.947136
16	0.015918	0.963054
17	0.011442	0.974496
18	0.008098	0.982595
19	0.005652	0.988246
20	0.003894	0.992141
21	0.002652	0.994792
22	0.001786	0.996579
23	0.001191	0.997770
24	0.000787	0.998557
25	0.000516	0.999073
26	0.000335	0.999408
27	0.000216	0.999625
28	0.000139	0.999763
29	0.000088	0.999852

30	0.000056	0.999907

k = 8·0
Mean = 8·67
Variance = 18·06

n	P(n)	F(n)
0	0.002818	0.002818
1	0.011723	0.014541
2	0.027431	0.041971
3	0.047547	0.089518
4	0.067992	0.157510
5	0.084854	0.242364
6	0.095602	0.337966
7	0.099426	0.437392
8	0.096940	0.534333
9	0.089616	0.623949
10	0.079221	0.703169
11	0.067410	0.770579
12	0.055501	0.826079
13	0.044400	0.870480
14	0.034632	0.905112
15	0.026413	0.931525
16	0.019744	0.951269
17	0.014494	0.965763
18	0.010468	0.976231
19	0.007449	0.983680
20	0.005229	0.988909
21	0.003625	0.992534
22	0.002485	0.995019
23	0.001686	0.996705
24	0.001132	0.997837
25	0.000754	0.998591
26	0.000497	0.999088
27	0.000326	0.999414
28	0.000212	0.999625
29	0.000137	0.999762
30	0.000088	0.999850
31	0.000056	0.999905

k = 8·5
Mean = 9·21
Variance = 19·18

n	P(n)	F(n)
0	0.001952	0.001952
1	0.008629	0.010582
2	0.021314	0.031896
3	0.038792	0.070688
4	0.057994	0.128682
5	0.075392	0.204074
6	0.088209	0.292282
7	0.095013	0.387296
8	0.095726	0.483022
9	0.091259	0.574281
10	0.083045	0.657326
11	0.072627	0.729953
12	0.061370	0.791323
13	0.050323	0.841646
14	0.040187	0.881833
15	0.031346	0.913179
16	0.023940	0.937119
17	0.017941	0.955060
18	0.013217	0.968277
19	0.009586	0.977862
20	0.006854	0.984716
21	0.004837	0.989553
22	0.003373	0.992925
23	0.002326	0.995251
24	0.001587	0.996838
25	0.001073	0.997911
26	0.000719	0.998630
27	0.000478	0.999107
28	0.000315	0.999422
29	0.000206	0.999628
30	0.000134	0.999762
31	0.000087	0.999849
32	0.000056	0.999904

k = 9·0
Mean = 9·75
Variance = 20·31

n	P(n)	F(n)
0	0.001353	0.001353
1	0.006330	0.007683
2	0.016459	0.024141
3	0.031381	0.055522
4	0.048954	0.104476
5	0.066186	0.170662
6	0.080306	0.250968
7	0.089484	0.340452
8	0.093063	0.433515
9	0.091408	0.524923
10	0.085558	0.610481
11	0.076847	0.687328
12	0.066601	0.753929
13	0.055945	0.809873
14	0.045715	0.855588
15	0.036450	0.892038
16	0.028431	0.920469
17	0.021741	0.942210
18	0.016330	0.958540
19	0.012067	0.970607
20	0.008785	0.979392
21	0.006308	0.985700
22	0.004473	0.990173
23	0.003135	0.993309
24	0.002174	0.995482
25	0.001492	0.996974
26	0.001015	0.997989
27	0.000684	0.998673
28	0.000457	0.999130
29	0.000303	0.999433

30	0.000200	0.999633
31	0.000131	0.999764
32	0.000085	0.999849
33	0.000055	0.999904

k = 9·5
Mean = 10·29
Variance = 21·44

n	P(n)	F(n)
0	0.000937	0.000937
1	0.004629	0.005566
2	0.012638	0.018205
3	0.025192	0.043396
4	0.040937	0.084333
5	0.057475	0.141809
6	0.072227	0.214036
7	0.083165	0.297201
8	0.089194	0.386395
9	0.090185	0.476580
10	0.086758	0.563338
11	0.079975	0.643313
12	0.071045	0.714358
13	0.061098	0.775456
14	0.051061	0.826517
15	0.041598	0.868115
16	0.033122	0.901237
17	0.025835	0.927072
18	0.019778	0.946850
19	0.014886	0.961736
20	0.011030	0.972766
21	0.008057	0.980824
22	0.005809	0.986632
23	0.004137	0.990769
24	0.002913	0.993682
25	0.002030	0.995712
26	0.001401	0.997112
27	0.000958	0.998070
28	0.000649	0.998719
29	0.000436	0.999155
30	0.000291	0.999447
31	0.000193	0.999640
32	0.000127	0.999767
33	0.000083	0.999850
34	0.000054	0.999904

k = 10·0
Mean = 10·83
Variance = 22·57

n	P(n)	F(n)
0	0.000649	0.000649
1	0.003376	0.004025
2	0.009656	0.013681
3	0.020084	0.033765
4	0.033942	0.067706
5	0.049419	0.117125
6	0.064245	0.181370
7	0.076359	0.257729
8	0.084377	0.342106
9	0.087752	0.429858

163

n	P(n)	F(n)
10	0.086699	0.516557
11	0.081970	0.598527
12	0.074593	0.673120
13	0.065642	0.738762
14	0.056077	0.794838
15	0.046656	0.841494
16	0.037908	0.879402
17	0.030148	0.909550
18	0.023515	0.933065
19	0.018020	0.951085
20	0.013587	0.964672
21	0.010093	0.974766
22	0.007396	0.982162
23	0.005351	0.987512
24	0.003826	0.991338
25	0.002706	0.994043
26	0.001894	0.995937
27	0.001313	0.997250
28	0.000902	0.998153
29	0.000615	0.998767
30	0.000416	0.999183
31	0.000279	0.999462
32	0.000186	0.999648
33	0.000123	0.999771
34	0.000081	0.999851
35	0.000053	0.999904

k=0·1
Mean=0·10
Variance=0·20

n	P(n)	F(n)
0	0.933033	0.933033
1	0.046652	0.979685
2	0.012829	0.992514
3	0.004490	0.997004
4	0.001740	0.998744
5	0.000713	0.999457
6	0.000303	0.999761
7	0.000132	0.999893
8	0.000059	0.999951

k=0·2
Mean=0·20
Variance=0·40

n	P(n)	F(n)
0	0.870551	0.870551
1	0.087055	0.957606
2	0.026117	0.983722
3	0.009576	0.993298
4	0.003830	0.997129
5	0.001609	0.998737
6	0.000697	0.999435
7	0.000309	0.999743
8	0.000139	0.999882
9	0.000063	0.999945

k=0·3
Mean=0·30
Variance=0·60

n	P(n)	F(n)
0	0.812252	0.812252
1	0.121838	0.934090
2	0.039597	0.973688
3	0.015179	0.988867
4	0.006261	0.995128
5	0.002692	0.997820
6	0.001189	0.999009
7	0.000535	0.999544
8	0.000244	0.999789
9	0.000113	0.999901

k=0·4
Mean=0·40
Variance=0·80

n	P(n)	F(n)
0	0.757858	0.757858
1	0.151572	0.909430
2	0.053050	0.962480
3	0.021220	0.983700
4	0.009019	0.992719
5	0.003968	0.996687
6	0.001786	0.998472
7	0.000816	0.999289
8	0.000378	0.999666
9	0.000176	0.999842

| 10 | 0.000083 | 0.99992 |

k=0·5
Mean=0·50
Variance=1·00

n	P(n)	F(n)
0	0.707107	0.70710
1	0.176777	0.88388
2	0.066291	0.95017
3	0.027621	0.97779
4	0.012084	0.98988
5	0.005438	0.99531
6	0.002492	0.99781
7	0.001157	0.99896
8	0.000542	0.99951
9	0.000256	0.99976
10	0.000122	0.99988
11	0.000058	0.99994

k=0·6
Mean=0·60
Variance=1·20

n	P(n)	F(n)
0	0.659754	0.659754
1	0.197926	0.857680
2	0.079170	0.936851
3	0.034307	0.971158
4	0.015438	0.986596
5	0.007102	0.993698
6	0.003314	0.997012
7	0.001562	0.998574
8	0.000742	0.999316
9	0.000355	0.999671
10	0.000170	0.999841
11	0.000082	0.999923

k=0·7
Mean=0·70
Variance=1·40

n	P(n)	F(n)
0	0.615572	0.615572
1	0.215450	0.831022
2	0.091566	0.922589
3	0.041205	0.963794
4	0.019057	0.982851
5	0.008957	0.991808
6	0.004255	0.996062
7	0.002036	0.998098
8	0.000980	0.999078
9	0.000474	0.999552
10	0.000230	0.999782
11	0.000112	0.999893
12	0.000054	0.999948

k=0·8
Mean=0·80
Variance=1·60

n	P(n)	F(n)
0	0.574349	0.574349
1	0.229740	0.804089
2	0.103383	0.907472
3	0.048245	0.955717
4	0.022917	0.978634
5	0.011000	0.989633
6	0.005317	0.994950
7	0.002582	0.997533
8	0.001259	0.998791
9	0.000615	0.999407
10	0.000302	0.999708
11	0.000148	0.999856
12	0.000073	0.999929

k=0·9
Mean=0·90
Variance=1·80

n	P(n)	F(n)
0	0.535887	0.535887
1	0.241149	0.777036
2	0.114546	0.891582
3	0.055364	0.946945
4	0.026990	0.973935
5	0.013225	0.987160
6	0.006502	0.993663
7	0.003205	0.996867
8	0.001582	0.998450
9	0.000782	0.999232
10	0.000387	0.999619
11	0.000192	0.999811
12	0.000095	0.999906

k=1·0
Mean=1·00
Variance=2·00

n	P(n)	F(n)
0	0.500000	0.500000
1	0.250000	0.750000
2	0.125000	0.875000
3	0.062500	0.937500
4	0.031250	0.968750
5	0.015625	0.984375
6	0.007813	0.992188
7	0.003906	0.996094
8	0.001953	0.998047
9	0.000977	0.999023
10	0.000488	0.999512
11	0.000244	0.999756
12	0.000122	0.999878
13	0.000061	0.999939

k=1·1
Mean=1·10
Variance=2·20

n	P(n)	F(n)
0	0.466516	0.466516
1	0.256584	0.723101
2	0.134707	0.857807
3	0.069598	0.927406
4	0.035669	0.963075
5	0.018191	0.981266
6	0.009247	0.990513
7	0.004690	0.995203
8	0.002374	0.997577
9	0.001200	0.998777
10	0.000606	0.999384
11	0.000306	0.999689
12	0.000154	0.999844
13	0.000078	0.999921

k=1·2
Mean=1·20
Variance=2·40

n	P(n)	F(n)
0	0.435275	0.435275
1	0.261165	0.696440
2	0.143641	0.840081
3	0.076608	0.916690
4	0.040219	0.956909
5	0.020914	0.977823
6	0.010806	0.988629
7	0.005557	0.994186
8	0.002848	0.997034
9	0.001456	0.998490
10	0.000742	0.999232
11	0.000378	0.999610
12	0.000192	0.999802
13	0.000098	0.999900
14	0.000049	0.999949

k=1·3
Mean=1·30
Variance=2·60

n	P(n)	F(n)
0	0.406126	0.406126
1	0.263982	0.670108
2	0.151790	0.821898
3	0.083484	0.905382
4	0.044873	0.950255
5	0.023783	0.974038
6	0.012486	0.986523
7	0.006510	0.993034
8	0.003377	0.996411
9	0.001745	0.998156
10	0.000899	0.999055
11	0.000462	0.999516
12	0.000237	0.999753
13	0.000121	0.999874
14	0.000062	0.999936

k=1·4
Mean=1·40
Variance=2·80

n	P(n)	F(n)
0	0.378929	0.378929
1	0.265250	0.644180
2	0.159150	0.803330
3	0.090185	0.893515
4	0.049602	0.943117
5	0.026785	0.969902
6	0.014285	0.984187
7	0.007551	0.991738
8	0.003964	0.995702
9	0.002070	0.997772
10	0.001076	0.998849
11	0.000558	0.999407
12	0.000288	0.999695
13	0.000149	0.999843
14	0.000076	0.999920

k=1·5
Mean = 1·50
Variance = 3·00

n	P(n)	F(n)
0	0.353553	0.353553
1	0.265165	0.618718
2	0.165728	0.784447
3	0.096675	0.881121
4	0.054380	0.935501
5	0.029909	0.965410
6	0.016201	0.981610
7	0.008679	0.990289
8	0.004611	0.994900
9	0.002433	0.997333
10	0.001278	0.998611
11	0.000668	0.999278
12	0.000348	0.999626
13	0.000181	0.999807
14	0.000094	0.999900

k=1·6
Mean = 1·60
Variance = 3·20

n	P(n)	F(n)
0	0.329877	0.329877
1	0.263902	0.593779
2	0.171536	0.765315
3	0.102922	0.868236
4	0.059180	0.927416
5	0.033141	0.960557
6	0.018227	0.978784
7	0.009895	0.988679
8	0.005319	0.993998
9	0.002837	0.996834
10	0.001503	0.998338
11	0.000793	0.999130
12	0.000416	0.999546
13	0.000218	0.999764
14	0.000114	0.999878
15	0.000059	0.999937

k=1·7
Mean = 1·70
Variance = 3·40

n	P(n)	F(n)
0	0.307786	0.307786
1	0.261618	0.569404
2	0.176592	0.745997
3	0.108899	0.854895
4	0.063978	0.918873
5	0.036467	0.955340
6	0.020361	0.975701
7	0.011199	0.986900
8	0.006089	0.992989
9	0.003281	0.996271
10	0.001756	0.998026
11	0.000934	0.998960
12	0.000494	0.999454
13	0.000260	0.999714
14	0.000137	0.999851
15	0.000072	0.999922

k=1·8
Mean = 1·80
Variance = 3·60

n	P(n)	F(n)
0	0.287175	0.287175
1	0.258457	0.545632
2	0.180920	0.726552
3	0.114583	0.841134
4	0.068750	0.909884
5	0.039875	0.949759
6	0.022596	0.972354
7	0.012589	0.984943
8	0.006924	0.991867
9	0.003770	0.995637
10	0.002036	0.997673
11	0.001092	0.998765
12	0.000582	0.999347
13	0.000309	0.999656
14	0.000163	0.999819
15	0.000086	0.999905

k=1·9
Mean = 1·90
Variance = 3·80

n	P(n)	F(n)
0	0.267943	0.267943
1	0.254546	0.522490
2	0.184546	0.707036
3	0.119955	0.826990
4	0.073472	0.900463
5	0.043349	0.943812
6	0.024926	0.968737
7	0.014065	0.982802
8	0.007824	0.990626
9	0.004303	0.994929
10	0.002345	0.997274
11	0.001269	0.998543
12	0.000682	0.999224
13	0.000365	0.999589
14	0.000194	0.999783
15	0.000103	0.999886
16	0.000054	0.999940

k=2·0
Mean = 2·00
Variance = 4·00

n	P(n)	F(n)
0	0.250000	0.250000
1	0.250000	0.500000
2	0.187500	0.687500
3	0.125000	0.812500
4	0.078125	0.890625
5	0.046875	0.937500
6	0.027344	0.964844
7	0.015625	0.980469
8	0.008789	0.989258
9	0.004883	0.994141
10	0.002686	0.996826
11	0.001465	0.998291
12	0.000793	0.999084
13	0.000427	0.999512
14	0.000229	0.999741
15	0.000122	0.999863
16	0.000065	0.999928

k=2·1
Mean = 2·10
Variance = 4·20

n	P(n)	F(n)
0	0.233258	0.233258
1	0.244921	0.478179
2	0.189814	0.667993
3	0.129706	0.797699
4	0.082688	0.880387
5	0.050439	0.930827
6	0.029843	0.960670
7	0.017267	0.977937
8	0.009820	0.987757
9	0.005510	0.993267
10	0.003058	0.996325
11	0.001682	0.998007
12	0.000918	0.998925
13	0.000498	0.999423
14	0.000269	0.999692
15	0.000144	0.999836
16	0.000077	0.999913

k=2·2
Mean = 2·20
Variance = 4·40

n	P(n)	F(n)
0	0.217638	0.217638
1	0.239401	0.457039
2	0.191521	0.648560
3	0.134065	0.782625
4	0.087142	0.869767

n	P(n)	F(n)
5	0.054028	0.923795
6	0.032417	0.956212
7	0.018987	0.975199
8	0.010918	0.986117
9	0.006187	0.992303
10	0.003464	0.995768
11	0.001921	0.997689
12	0.001057	0.998746
13	0.000577	0.999323
14	0.000313	0.999636
15	0.000169	0.999805
16	0.000091	0.999896
17	0.000049	0.999945

k=2·3
Mean=2·30
Variance=4·60

n	P(n)	F(n)
0	0.203063	0.203063
1	0.233523	0.436586
2	0.192656	0.629242
3	0.138070	0.767312
4	0.091472	0.858784
5	0.057627	0.916411
6	0.035056	0.951467
7	0.020783	0.972251
8	0.012080	0.984331
9	0.006913	0.991244
10	0.003906	0.995149
11	0.002184	0.997333
12	0.001210	0.998543
13	0.000666	0.999208
14	0.000364	0.999572
15	0.000198	0.999770
16	0.000107	0.999877
17	0.000057	0.999934

k=2·4
Mean=2·40
Variance=4·80

n	P(n)	F(n)
0	0.189465	0.189465
1	0.227357	0.416822
2	0.193254	0.610076
3	0.141719	0.751795
4	0.095661	0.847456
5	0.061223	0.908679
6	0.037754	0.946433
7	0.022652	0.969085
8	0.013308	0.982394
9	0.007689	0.990083
10	0.004383	0.994466
11	0.002470	0.996936
12	0.001379	0.998315
13	0.000764	0.999079
14	0.000420	0.999500

n	P(n)	F(n)
15	0.000230	0.999729
16	0.000125	0.999854
17	0.000068	0.999922

k=2·5
Mean=2·50
Variance=5·00

n	P(n)	F(n)
0	0.176777	0.176777
1	0.220971	0.397748
2	0.193350	0.591097
3	0.145012	0.736109
4	0.099696	0.835805
5	0.064802	0.900607
6	0.040501	0.941109
7	0.024590	0.965699
8	0.014600	0.980299
9	0.008517	0.988816
10	0.004897	0.993713
11	0.002783	0.996496
12	0.001565	0.998061
13	0.000873	0.998934
14	0.000483	0.999417
15	0.000266	0.999683
16	0.000145	0.999828
17	0.000079	0.999907

k=3·0
Mean=3·00
Variance=6·00

n	P(n)	F(n)
0	0.125000	0.125000
1	0.187500	0.312500
2	0.187500	0.500000
3	0.156250	0.656250
4	0.117188	0.773438
5	0.082031	0.855469
6	0.054688	0.910156
7	0.035156	0.945313
8	0.021973	0.967285
9	0.013428	0.980713
10	0.008057	0.988770
11	0.004761	0.993530
12	0.002777	0.996307
13	0.001602	0.997910
14	0.000916	0.998825
15	0.000519	0.999344
16	0.000292	0.999636
17	0.000163	0.999799
18	0.000091	0.999889
19	0.000050	0.999939

k=3·5
Mean=3·50
Variance=7·00

n	P(n)	F(n)
0	0.088388	0.088388
1	0.154680	0.243068
2	0.174015	0.417083
3	0.159513	0.576596
4	0.129605	0.706200
5	0.097203	0.803404
6	0.068852	0.872256
7	0.046721	0.918978
8	0.030661	0.949639
9	0.019589	0.969227
10	0.012243	0.981470
11	0.007513	0.988983
12	0.004539	0.993522
13	0.002706	0.996228
14	0.001595	0.997823
15	0.000930	0.998753
16	0.000538	0.999291
17	0.000308	0.999599
18	0.000176	0.999775
19	0.000099	0.999874
20	0.000056	0.999930

k=4·0
Mean=4·00
Variance=8·00

n	P(n)	F(n)
0	0.062500	0.062500
1	0.125000	0.187500
2	0.156250	0.343750
3	0.156250	0.500000
4	0.136719	0.636719
5	0.109375	0.746094
6	0.082031	0.828125
7	0.058594	0.886719
8	0.040283	0.927002
9	0.026855	0.953857
10	0.017456	0.971313
11	0.011108	0.982422
12	0.006943	0.989365
13	0.004272	0.993637
14	0.002594	0.996231
15	0.001556	0.997787
16	0.000924	0.998712
17	0.000544	0.999255
18	0.000317	0.999572
19	0.000184	0.999756
20	0.000106	0.999861
21	0.000060	0.999922

25	0.000066	0.999904

k = 4·5
Mean = 4·50
Variance = 9·00

n	P(n)	F(n)
0	0.044194	0.044194
1	0.099437	0.143631
2	0.136726	0.280357
3	0.148120	0.428476
4	0.138862	0.567338
5	0.118033	0.685371
6	0.093443	0.778814
7	0.070082	0.848896
8	0.050371	0.899267
9	0.034980	0.934247
10	0.023612	0.957859
11	0.015562	0.973421
12	0.010051	0.983472
13	0.006378	0.989850
14	0.003986	0.993836
15	0.002458	0.996295
16	0.001498	0.997793
17	0.000903	0.998696
18	0.000539	0.999235
19	0.000319	0.999555
20	0.000188	0.999742
21	0.000109	0.999852
22	0.000063	0.999915

k = 5·0
Mean = 5·00
Variance = 10·00

n	P(n)	F(n)
0	0.031250	0.031250
1	0.078125	0.109375
2	0.117188	0.226563
3	0.136719	0.363281
4	0.136719	0.500000
5	0.123047	0.623047
6	0.102539	0.725586
7	0.080566	0.806152
8	0.060425	0.866577
9	0.043640	0.910217
10	0.030548	0.940765
11	0.020828	0.961594
12	0.013885	0.975479
13	0.009079	0.984558
14	0.005836	0.990395
15	0.003696	0.994091
16	0.002310	0.996401
17	0.001427	0.997828
18	0.000872	0.998700
19	0.000528	0.999228
20	0.000317	0.999545
21	0.000188	0.999733
22	0.000111	0.999845
23	0.000065	0.999910

k = 5·5
Mean = 5·50
Variance = 11·00

n	P(n)	F(n)
0	0.022097	0.022097
1	0.060767	0.082864
2	0.098746	0.181610
3	0.123433	0.305043
4	0.131148	0.436191
5	0.124590	0.560781
6	0.109016	0.669797
7	0.089549	0.759347
8	0.069960	0.829307
9	0.052470	0.881777
10	0.038041	0.919818
11	0.026802	0.946619
12	0.018426	0.965046
13	0.012402	0.977448
14	0.008194	0.985642
15	0.005326	0.990968
16	0.003412	0.994380
17	0.002158	0.996538
18	0.001349	0.997887
19	0.000834	0.998721
20	0.000511	0.999231
21	0.000310	0.999542
22	0.000187	0.999728
23	0.000112	0.999840
24	0.000066	0.999906

k = 6·0
Mean = 6·00
Variance = 12·00

n	P(n)	F(n)
0	0.015625	0.015625
1	0.046875	0.062500
2	0.082031	0.144531
3	0.109375	0.253906
4	0.123047	0.376953
5	0.123047	0.500000
6	0.112793	0.612793
7	0.096680	0.709473
8	0.078552	0.788025
9	0.061096	0.849121
10	0.045822	0.894943
11	0.033325	0.928268
12	0.023605	0.951874
13	0.016342	0.968216
14	0.011089	0.979305
15	0.007393	0.986698
16	0.004852	0.991550
17	0.003139	0.994689
18	0.002006	0.996695
19	0.001267	0.997961
20	0.000792	0.998753
21	0.000490	0.999243
22	0.000301	0.999544
23	0.000183	0.999727
24	0.000111	0.999838

k = 6·5
Mean = 6·50
Variance = 13·00

n	P(n)	F(n)
0	0.011049	0.011049
1	0.035908	0.046956
2	0.067327	0.114283
3	0.095380	0.209663
4	0.113264	0.322927
5	0.118927	0.441854
6	0.113972	0.555826
7	0.101760	0.657586
8	0.085860	0.743446
9	0.069165	0.812612
10	0.053603	0.866215
11	0.040202	0.906417
12	0.029314	0.935731
13	0.020858	0.956590
14	0.014526	0.971116
15	0.009926	0.981042
16	0.006669	0.987711
17	0.004413	0.992125
18	0.002881	0.995006
19	0.001857	0.996863
20	0.001184	0.998047
21	0.000747	0.998794
22	0.000467	0.999261
23	0.000289	0.999551
24	0.000178	0.999729
25	0.000108	0.999837
26	0.000066	0.999903

k = 7·0
Mean = 7·00
Variance = 14·00

n	P(n)	F(n)
0	0.007813	0.007813
1	0.027344	0.035156
2	0.054688	0.089844
3	0.082031	0.171875
4	0.102539	0.274414
5	0.112793	0.387207
6	0.112793	0.500000
7	0.104736	0.604736
8	0.091644	0.696381
9	0.076370	0.772751
10	0.061096	0.833847
11	0.047211	0.881058
12	0.035408	0.916466
13	0.025875	0.942341
14	0.018482	0.960823

n	P(n)	F(n)
15	0.012938	0.973761
16	0.008895	0.982655
17	0.006017	0.988672
18	0.004011	0.992683
19	0.002639	0.995322
20	0.001715	0.997038
21	0.001103	0.998140
22	0.000702	0.998842
23	0.000442	0.999285
24	0.000276	0.999561
25	0.000171	0.999732
26	0.000105	0.999838
27	0.000064	0.999902

$k = 7.5$
Mean $= 7.50$
Variance $= 15.00$

n	P(n)	F(n)
0	0.005524	0.005524
1	0.020716	0.026240
2	0.044022	0.070262
3	0.069701	0.139963
4	0.091482	0.231445
5	0.105205	0.336649
6	0.109588	0.446238
7	0.105674	0.551912
8	0.095767	0.647679
9	0.082466	0.730145
10	0.068035	0.798180
11	0.054119	0.852299
12	0.041716	0.894015
13	0.031287	0.925302
14	0.022907	0.948209
15	0.016416	0.964626
16	0.011543	0.976168
17	0.007978	0.984147
18	0.005430	0.989576
19	0.003644	0.993220
20	0.002414	0.995633
21	0.001580	0.997214
22	0.001024	0.998238
23	0.000657	0.998894
24	0.000417	0.999311
25	0.000263	0.999574
26	0.000164	0.999738
27	0.000102	0.999840
28	0.000063	0.999903

$k = 8.0$
Mean $= 8.00$
Variance $= 16.00$

n	P(n)	F(n)
0	0.003906	0.003906
1	0.015625	0.019531
2	0.035156	0.054688
3	0.058594	0.113281
4	0.080566	0.193848
5	0.096680	0.290527
6	0.104736	0.395264
7	0.104736	0.500000
8	0.098190	0.598190
9	0.087280	0.685471
10	0.074188	0.759659
11	0.060699	0.820358
12	0.048054	0.868412
13	0.036964	0.905376
14	0.027723	0.933100
15	0.020330	0.953430
16	0.014612	0.968043
17	0.010315	0.978357
18	0.007163	0.985520
19	0.004901	0.990421
20	0.003308	0.993730
21	0.002205	0.995935
22	0.001454	0.997389
23	0.000948	0.998337
24	0.000612	0.998949
25	0.000392	0.999341
26	0.000249	0.999589
27	0.000157	0.999746
28	0.000098	0.999844
29	0.000061	0.999904

$k = 8.5$
Mean $= 8.50$
Variance $= 17.00$

n	P(n)	F(n)
0	0.002762	0.002762
1	0.011739	0.014501
2	0.027880	0.042382
3	0.048791	0.091172
4	0.070136	0.161308
5	0.087671	0.248979
6	0.098629	0.347608
7	0.102152	0.449760
8	0.098960	0.548720
9	0.090713	0.639433
10	0.079374	0.718806
11	0.066746	0.785553
12	0.054231	0.839784
13	0.042759	0.882543
14	0.032833	0.915376
15	0.024625	0.940001
16	0.018084	0.958085
17	0.013031	0.971116
18	0.009230	0.980346
19	0.006437	0.986783
20	0.004425	0.991208
21	0.003003	0.994211
22	0.002013	0.996224
23	0.001335	0.997559
24	0.000876	0.998435
25	0.000569	0.999005
26	0.000367	0.999372
27	0.000234	0.999606
28	0.000149	0.999755
29	0.000093	0.999848
30	0.000058	0.999906

$k = 9.0$
Mean $= 9.00$
Variance $= 18.00$

n	P(n)	F(n)
0	0.001953	0.001953
1	0.008789	0.010742
2	0.021973	0.032715
3	0.040283	0.072998
4	0.060425	0.133423
5	0.078552	0.211975
6	0.091644	0.303619
7	0.098190	0.401810
8	0.098190	0.500000
9	0.092735	0.592735
10	0.083462	0.676197
11	0.072081	0.748278
12	0.060067	0.808345
13	0.048516	0.856861
14	0.038120	0.894980
15	0.029225	0.924205
16	0.021919	0.946124
17	0.016117	0.962241
18	0.011640	0.973881
19	0.008270	0.982151
20	0.005789	0.987940
21	0.003997	0.991938
22	0.002725	0.994663
23	0.001837	0.996500
24	0.001224	0.997724
25	0.000808	0.998532
26	0.000528	0.999061
27	0.000342	0.999403
28	0.000220	0.999624
29	0.000140	0.999764
30	0.000089	0.999853
31	0.000056	0.999909

$k = 9.5$
Mean $= 9.50$
Variance $= 19.00$

n	P(n)	F(n)
0	0.001381	0.001381
1	0.006560	0.007941
2	0.017220	0.025161
3	0.033005	0.058167
4	0.051571	0.109738
5	0.069621	0.179358
6	0.084125	0.263483
7	0.093138	0.356622
8	0.096049	0.452671
9	0.093381	0.546052

10	0.086377	0.632429				20	0.009327	0.978613
11	0.076562	0.708991				21	0.006662	0.985275
12	0.065397	0.774387				22	0.004694	0.989969
13	0.054078	0.828465				23	0.003265	0.993235
14	0.043455	0.871921				24	0.002245	0.995479

k=10·0
Mean=10·00
Variance=20·00

n	P(n)	F(n)
0	0.000977	0.000977
1	0.004883	0.005859
2	0.013428	0.019287
3	0.026855	0.046143
4	0.043640	0.089783

15	0.034040	0.905961		5	0.061096	0.150879		25	0.001527	0.997006
16	0.026062	0.932023		6	0.076370	0.227249		26	0.001027	0.998033
17	0.019546	0.951569		7	0.087280	0.314529		27	0.000685	0.998718
18	0.014388	0.965957		8	0.092735	0.407265		28	0.000453	0.999171
19	0.010413	0.976370		9	0.092735	0.500000		29	0.000297	0.999468
20	0.007419	0.983789		10	0.088099	0.588099		30	0.000193	0.999660
21	0.005211	0.989000		11	0.080090	0.668188		31	0.000124	0.999784
22	0.003612	0.992612		12	0.070078	0.738266		32	0.000080	0.999864
23	0.002474	0.995086		13	0.059297	0.797564		33	0.000051	0.999915
24	0.001675	0.996761		14	0.048708	0.846272				
25	0.001122	0.997883		15	0.038967	0.885239				
26	0.000744	0.998627		16	0.030443	0.915681				
27	0.000489	0.999117		17	0.023280	0.938961				
28	0.000319	0.999436		18	0.017460	0.956421				
29	0.000206	0.999642		19	0.012865	0.969286				
30	0.000132	0.999774								
31	0.000084	0.999858								
32	0.000053	0.999912								

k=0·1
Mean=0·09
Variance=0·18

n	P(n)	F(n)
0	0.936700	0.936700
1	0.044962	0.981661
2	0.011870	0.993531
3	0.003988	0.997519
4	0.001484	0.999003
5	0.000584	0.999587
6	0.000238	0.999825
7	0.000100	0.999925

k=0·2
Mean=0·18
Variance=0·36

n	P(n)	F(n)
0	0.877406	0.877406
1	0.084231	0.961637
2	0.024259	0.985896
3	0.008539	0.994435
4	0.003279	0.997714
5	0.001322	0.999036
6	0.000550	0.999586
7	0.000234	0.999820
8	0.000101	0.999921

k=0·3
Mean=0·28
Variance=0·53

n	P(n)	F(n)
0	0.821866	0.821866
1	0.118349	0.940215
2	0.036925	0.977139
3	0.013588	0.990728
4	0.005381	0.996109
5	0.002221	0.998330
6	0.000942	0.999272
7	0.000407	0.999679
8	0.000178	0.999857
9	0.000079	0.999936

k=0·4
Mean=0·37
Variance=0·71

n	P(n)	F(n)
0	0.769842	0.769842
1	0.147810	0.917651
2	0.049664	0.967315
3	0.019071	0.986386
4	0.007781	0.994167
5	0.003287	0.997454
6	0.001420	0.998874
7	0.000623	0.999497
8	0.000277	0.999773
9	0.000124	0.999897

| 10 | 0.000056 | 0.999953 |

k=0·5
Mean=0·46
Variance=0·89

n	P(n)	F(n)
0	0.721110	0.721110
1	0.173066	0.894177
2	0.062304	0.956481
3	0.024922	0.981402
4	0.010467	0.991869
5	0.004522	0.996391
6	0.001990	0.998381
7	0.000887	0.999267
8	0.000399	0.999666
9	0.000181	0.999847
10	0.000082	0.999930

k=0·6
Mean=0·55
Variance=1·07

n	P(n)	F(n)
0	0.675464	0.675464
1	0.194534	0.869997
2	0.074701	0.944698
3	0.031076	0.975774
4	0.013425	0.989198
5	0.005928	0.995127
6	0.002656	0.997783
7	0.001202	0.998985
8	0.000548	0.999533
9	0.000251	0.999784
10	0.000116	0.999900
11	0.000054	0.999953

k=0·7
Mean=0·65
Variance=1·24

n	P(n)	F(n)
0	0.632707	0.632707
1	0.212589	0.845296
2	0.086736	0.932032
3	0.037470	0.969503
4	0.016637	0.986139
5	0.007507	0.993646
6	0.003423	0.997069
7	0.001573	0.998641
8	0.000727	0.999368
9	0.000337	0.999705
10	0.000157	0.999862
11	0.000073	0.999935

k=0·8
Mean=0·74
Variance=1·42

n	P(n)	F(n)
0	0.592656	0.592656
1	0.227580	0.820236
2	0.098315	0.918550
3	0.044045	0.962595
4	0.020084	0.982680
5	0.009255	0.991935
6	0.004294	0.996229
7	0.002002	0.998231
8	0.000937	0.999168
9	0.000440	0.999608
10	0.000207	0.999815
11	0.000098	0.999913

k=0·9
Mean=0·83
Variance=1·60

n	P(n)	F(n)
0	0.555141	0.555141
1	0.239821	0.794961
2	0.109358	0.904320
3	0.050742	0.955062
4	0.023747	0.978809
5	0.011171	0.989980
6	0.005273	0.995253
7	0.002495	0.997747
8	0.001182	0.998930
9	0.000561	0.999491
10	0.000267	0.999758
11	0.000127	0.999885
12	0.000060	0.999945

k=1·0
Mean=0·92
Variance=1·78

n	P(n)	F(n)
0	0.520000	0.520000
1	0.249600	0.769600
2	0.119808	0.889408
3	0.057508	0.946916
4	0.027604	0.974520
5	0.013250	0.987769
6	0.006360	0.994129
7	0.003053	0.997182
8	0.001465	0.998647
9	0.000703	0.999351
10	0.000338	0.999688
11	0.000162	0.999850
12	0.000078	0.999928

k=1·1
Mean=1·02
Variance=1·95

n	P(n)	F(n)
0	0.487084	0.487084
1	0.257180	0.744264
2	0.129619	0.873883
3	0.064291	0.938174
4	0.031631	0.969805
5	0.015487	0.985292
6	0.007557	0.992849
7	0.003679	0.996528
8	0.001788	0.998317
9	0.000868	0.999185
10	0.000421	0.999605
11	0.000204	0.999809
12	0.000099	0.999908

k=1·2
Mean=1·11
Variance=2·13

n	P(n)	F(n)
0	0.456251	0.456251
1	0.262801	0.719052
2	0.138759	0.857811
3	0.071044	0.928855
4	0.035806	0.964662
5	0.017875	0.982536
6	0.008866	0.991402
7	0.004377	0.995779
8	0.002154	0.997933
9	0.001057	0.998989
10	0.000517	0.999507
11	0.000253	0.999760
12	0.000123	0.999883
13	0.000060	0.999943

k=1·3
Mean=1·20
Variance=2·31

n	P(n)	F(n)
0	0.427370	0.427370
1	0.266679	0.694049
2	0.147207	0.841256
3	0.077725	0.918981
4	0.040106	0.959088
5	0.020406	0.979494
6	0.010285	0.989778
7	0.005148	0.994927
8	0.002564	0.997490
9	0.001272	0.998762
10	0.000629	0.999391
11	0.000310	0.999701
12	0.000153	0.999853
13	0.000075	0.999928

k=1·4
Mean=1·29
Variance=2·49

n	P(n)	F(n)
0	0.400318	0.400318
1	0.269013	0.669331
2	0.154952	0.824283
3	0.084294	0.908576
4	0.044507	0.953084
5	0.023072	0.976156
6	0.011813	0.987969
7	0.005994	0.993963
8	0.003021	0.996985
9	0.001515	0.998499
10	0.000756	0.999255
11	0.000376	0.999631
12	0.000187	0.999818
13	0.000092	0.999910

5	0.041339	0.949610
6	0.023150	0.972760
7	0.012699	0.985459
8	0.006858	0.992317
9	0.003657	0.995975
10	0.001931	0.997906
11	0.001011	0.998917
12	0.000526	0.999443
13	0.000272	0.999715
14	0.000140	0.999854
15	0.000072	0.999926

k = 1·5
Mean = 1·38
Variance = 2·66

n	P(n)	F(n)
0	0.374977	0.374977
1	0.269984	0.644961
2	0.161990	0.806951
3	0.090715	0.897666
4	0.048986	0.946652
5	0.025865	0.972516
6	0.013450	0.985966
7	0.006917	0.992883
8	0.003528	0.996410
9	0.001787	0.998198
10	0.000901	0.999098
11	0.000452	0.999550
12	0.000226	0.999776
13	0.000113	0.999889
14	0.000056	0.999945

k = 1·6
Mean = 1·48
Variance = 2·84

n	P(n)	F(n)
0	0.351241	0.351241
1	0.269753	0.620994
2	0.168326	0.789320
3	0.096956	0.886276
4	0.053520	0.939796
5	0.028772	0.968568
6	0.015192	0.983759
7	0.007917	0.991676
8	0.004085	0.995762
9	0.002092	0.997853
10	0.001064	0.998918
11	0.000539	0.999456
12	0.000271	0.999728
13	0.000136	0.999864
14	0.000068	0.999932

k = 1·7
Mean = 1·57
Variance = 3·02

n	P(n)	F(n)
0	0.329007	0.329007
1	0.268470	0.597477
2	0.173969	0.771446
3	0.102989	0.874435
4	0.058086	0.932521
5	0.031785	0.964306
6	0.017037	0.981343
7	0.008995	0.990338
8	0.004696	0.995034
9	0.002429	0.997463
10	0.001248	0.998710
11	0.000637	0.999347
12	0.000324	0.999671
13	0.000164	0.999835
14	0.000082	0.999917

k = 1·8
Mean = 1·66
Variance = 3·20

n	P(n)	F(n)
0	0.308181	0.308181
1	0.266268	0.574450
2	0.178932	0.753382
3	0.108791	0.862173
4	0.062664	0.924836
5	0.034891	0.959728
6	0.018981	0.978708
7	0.010152	0.988860
8	0.005360	0.994221
9	0.002802	0.997022
10	0.001452	0.998475
11	0.000748	0.999222
12	0.000383	0.999605
13	0.000195	0.999800
14	0.000099	0.999899
15	0.000050	0.999949

k = 1·9
Mean = 1·75
Variance = 3·37

n	P(n)	F(n)
0	0.288673	0.288673
1	0.263270	0.551943
2	0.183236	0.735179
3	0.114339	0.849518
4	0.067231	0.916749
5	0.038080	0.954829
6	0.021020	0.975849
7	0.011387	0.987236
8	0.006081	0.993317
9	0.003211	0.996527
10	0.001680	0.998207
11	0.000872	0.999079
12	0.000450	0.999530
13	0.000231	0.999761
14	0.000118	0.999879
15	0.000060	0.999939

k = 2·0
Mean = 1·85
Variance = 3·55

n	P(n)	F(n)
0	0.270400	0.270400
1	0.259584	0.529984
2	0.186900	0.716884
3	0.119616	0.836501
4	0.071770	0.908271

k = 2·1
Mean = 1·94
Variance = 3·73

n	P(n)	F(n)
0	0.253284	0.253284
1	0.255310	0.508593
2	0.189951	0.698544
3	0.124608	0.823151
4	0.076260	0.899411
5	0.044658	0.944069
6	0.025366	0.969435
7	0.014089	0.983523
8	0.007692	0.991216
9	0.004144	0.995360
10	0.002208	0.997567
11	0.001166	0.998733
12	0.000611	0.999344
13	0.000318	0.999662
14	0.000165	0.999826
15	0.000085	0.999911

k = 2·2
Mean = 2·03
Variance = 3·91

n	P(n)	F(n)
0	0.237251	0.237251
1	0.250537	0.487787
2	0.192412	0.680199
3	0.129301	0.809500
4	0.080684	0.890184
5	0.048023	0.938207
6	0.027661	0.965868
7	0.015554	0.981422
8	0.008586	0.990008
9	0.004671	0.994678
10	0.002511	0.997189
11	0.001337	0.998526
12	0.000706	0.999231
13	0.000370	0.999601
14	0.000193	0.999794

n	P(n)	F(n)
15	0.000100	0.999894
16	0.000052	0.999946

k=2·3
Mean=2·12
Variance=4·08

n	P(n)	F(n)
0	0.222233	0.222233
1	0.245345	0.467577
2	0.194313	0.661890
3	0.133687	0.795578
4	0.085025	0.880603
5	0.051423	0.932026
6	0.030031	0.962057
7	0.017092	0.979149
8	0.009537	0.988687
9	0.005239	0.993926
10	0.002842	0.996768
11	0.001525	0.998293
12	0.000811	0.999104
13	0.000428	0.999533
14	0.000225	0.999757
15	0.000117	0.999875
16	0.000061	0.999935

k=2·4
Mean=2·22
Variance=4·26

n	P(n)	F(n)
0	0.208165	0.208165
1	0.239806	0.447971
2	0.195682	0.643653
3	0.137760	0.781413
4	0.089269	0.870682
5	0.054847	0.925528
6	0.032469	0.957998
7	0.018702	0.976700
8	0.010548	0.987248
9	0.005851	0.993099
10	0.003201	0.996300
11	0.001732	0.998032
12	0.000929	0.998961
13	0.000494	0.999455
14	0.000261	0.999715
15	0.000137	0.999852
16	0.000071	0.999923

k=2·5
Mean=2·31
Variance=4·44

n	P(n)	F(n)
0	0.194988	0.194988
1	0.233986	0.428974
2	0.196548	0.625522
3	0.141515	0.767037
4	0.093400	0.860436
5	0.058281	0.918718
6	0.034969	0.953687
7	0.020382	0.974069
8	0.011618	0.985686
9	0.006506	0.992192
10	0.003591	0.995783
11	0.001959	0.997742
12	0.001058	0.998800
13	0.000566	0.999366
14	0.000301	0.999667
15	0.000159	0.999826
16	0.000083	0.999910

k=3·0
Mean=2·77
Variance=5·33

n	P(n)	F(n)
0	0.140608	0.140608
1	0.202476	0.343084
2	0.194376	0.537460
3	0.155501	0.692961
4	0.111961	0.804922
5	0.075238	0.880160
6	0.048152	0.928312
7	0.029717	0.958029
8	0.017830	0.975859
9	0.010460	0.986319
10	0.006025	0.992344
11	0.003418	0.995762
12	0.001914	0.997676
13	0.001060	0.998736
14	0.000582	0.999318
15	0.000316	0.999634
16	0.000171	0.999805
17	0.000092	0.999896
18	0.000049	0.999945

k=3·5
Mean=3·23
Variance=6·21

n	P(n)	F(n)
0	0.101394	0.101394
1	0.170342	0.271736
2	0.183969	0.455705
3	0.161893	0.617597
4	0.126276	0.743874

n	P(n)	F(n)
5	0.090919	0.834793
6	0.061825	0.896618
7	0.040275	0.936892
8	0.025373	0.962265
9	0.015562	0.977827
10	0.009337	0.987164
11	0.005500	0.992665
12	0.003190	0.995855
13	0.001826	0.997681
14	0.001033	0.998714
15	0.000578	0.999292
16	0.000321	0.999613
17	0.000177	0.999790
18	0.000097	0.999887
19	0.000052	0.999939

k=4·0
Mean=3·69
Variance=7·10

n	P(n)	F(n)
0	0.073116	0.073116
1	0.140383	0.213499
2	0.168460	0.381959
3	0.161721	0.543680
4	0.135846	0.679526
5	0.104330	0.783856
6	0.075117	0.858973
7	0.051509	0.910482
8	0.033996	0.944478
9	0.021757	0.966235
10	0.013577	0.979812
11	0.008294	0.988106
12	0.004976	0.993082
13	0.002940	0.996022
14	0.001714	0.997736
15	0.000987	0.998723
16	0.000563	0.999285
17	0.000318	0.999603
18	0.000178	0.999781
19	0.000099	0.999880
20	0.000055	0.999935

k=4·5
Mean=4·15
Variance=7·99

n	P(n)	F(n)
0	0.052725	0.052725
1	0.113886	0.166610
2	0.150329	0.316939
3	0.156342	0.473282
4	0.140708	0.613989
5	0.114818	0.728807
6	0.087261	0.816069
7	0.062828	0.878897
8	0.043351	0.922248
9	0.028901	0.951149

10	0.018728	0.969877	10	0.031380	0.940911	10	0.045985	0.898463
11	0.011850	0.981727	11	0.021224	0.962135	11	0.033109	0.931573
12	0.007347	0.989073	12	0.014008	0.976143	12	0.023177	0.954749
13	0.004476	0.993549	13	0.009051	0.985194	13	0.015831	0.970581
14	0.002686	0.996235	14	0.005741	0.990935	14	0.010584	0.981165
15	0.001590	0.997825	15	0.003582	0.994518	15	0.006943	0.988109
16	0.000930	0.998755	16	0.002203	0.996721	16	0.004478	0.992587
17	0.000538	0.999293	17	0.001337	0.998059	17	0.002845	0.995432
18	0.000309	0.999602	18	0.000802	0.998861	18	0.001783	0.997215
19	0.000175	0.999777	19	0.000476	0.999337	19	0.001104	0.998319
20	0.000099	0.999876	20	0.000230	0.999618	20	0.000675	0.998994
21	0.000055	0.999932	21	0.000163	0.999781	21	0.000409	0.999403
			22	0.000094	0.999875	22	0.000245	0.999649
			23	0.000054	0.999929	23	0.000146	0.999795
						24	0.000086	0.999881
						25	0.000050	0.999931

k=5·0
Mean=4·62
Variance=8·88

n	P(n)	F(n)
0	0.038020	0.038020
1	0.091249	0.129269
2	0.131399	0.260668
3	0.147166	0.407834
4	0.141280	0.549114
5	0.122066	0.671180
6	0.097653	0.768832
7	0.073658	0.842490
8	0.053034	0.895524
9	0.036770	0.932294
10	0.024709	0.957003
11	0.016173	0.973177
12	0.010351	0.983528
13	0.006497	0.990025
14	0.004010	0.994035
15	0.002438	0.996473
16	0.001463	0.997935
17	0.000867	0.998803
18	0.000509	0.999311
19	0.000296	0.999607
20	0.000170	0.999777
21	0.000097	0.999875
22	0.000055	0.999930

k=6·0
Mean=5·54
Variance=10·65

n	P(n)	F(n)
0	0.019771	0.019771
1	0.056939	0.076710
2	0.095658	0.172368
3	0.122442	0.294810
4	0.132238	0.427048
5	0.126948	0.553997
6	0.111714	0.665711
7	0.091925	0.757636
8	0.071702	0.829338
9	0.053537	0.882875
10	0.038547	0.921422
11	0.026913	0.948334
12	0.018301	0.966635
13	0.012163	0.978798
14	0.007923	0.986721
15	0.005071	0.991792
16	0.003195	0.994986
17	0.001984	0.996971
18	0.001217	0.998188
19	0.000738	0.998926
20	0.000443	0.999369
21	0.000263	0.999632
22	0.000155	0.999787
23	0.000091	0.999877
24	0.000053	0.999930

k=7·0
Mean=6·46
Variance=12·43

n	P(n)	F(n)
0	0.010281	0.010281
1	0.034543	0.044824
2	0.066323	0.111147
3	0.095505	0.206652
4	0.114606	0.321258
5	0.121024	0.442282
6	0.116183	0.558465
7	0.103569	0.662034
8	0.086998	0.749032
9	0.069598	0.818630
10	0.053451	0.872082
11	0.039651	0.911733
12	0.028549	0.940282
13	0.020028	0.960310
14	0.013734	0.974044
15	0.009229	0.983273
16	0.006091	0.989364
17	0.003956	0.993319
18	0.002532	0.995851
19	0.001599	0.997450
20	0.000998	0.998448
21	0.000616	0.999063
22	0.000376	0.999440
23	0.000228	0.999667
24	0.000137	0.999804
25	0.000081	0.999885
26	0.000048	0.999933

k=5·5
Mean=5·08
Variance=9·76

n	P(n)	F(n)
0	0.027417	0.027417
1	0.072381	0.099798
2	0.112914	0.212711
3	0.135497	0.348208
4	0.138206	0.486414
5	0.126044	0.612459
6	0.105877	0.718336
7	0.083492	0.801827
8	0.062619	0.864446
9	0.045086	0.909532

k=6·5
Mean=6·00
Variance=11·54

n	P(n)	F(n)
0	0.014257	0.014257
1	0.044481	0.058738
2	0.080066	0.138804
3	0.108890	0.247694
4	0.124135	0.371829
5	0.125128	0.496956
6	0.115117	0.612074
7	0.098672	0.710746
8	0.079924	0.790670
9	0.061808	0.852478

= 7·5		
Mean = 6·92		
Variance = 13·31		

n	P(n)	F(n)
0	0.007414	0.007414
1	0.026689	0.034102
2	0.054445	0.088547
3	0.082756	0.171304
4	0.104273	0.275577
5	0.115117	0.390694
6	0.115117	0.505811
7	0.106566	0.612377
8	0.092712	0.705089
9	0.076642	0.781732
10	0.060701	0.842432
11	0.046353	0.888785
12	0.034301	0.923087
13	0.024697	0.947784
14	0.017358	0.965142
15	0.011943	0.977085
16	0.008061	0.985146
17	0.005349	0.990495
18	0.003495	0.993989
19	0.002251	0.996241
20	0.001432	0.997672
21	0.000900	0.998572
22	0.000560	0.999132
23	0.000345	0.999477
24	0.000210	0.999687
25	0.000127	0.999814
26	0.000076	0.999890
27	0.000045	0.999936

= 8·0		
Mean = 7·38		
Variance = 14·20		

n	P(n)	F(n)
0	0.005346	0.005346
1	0.020529	0.025875
2	0.044342	0.070216
3	0.070947	0.141163
4	0.093650	0.234812
5	0.107884	0.342697
6	0.112200	0.454896
7	0.107712	0.562608
8	0.096940	0.659548
9	0.082723	0.742271
10	0.067502	0.809772
11	0.053019	0.862792
12	0.040295	0.903087
13	0.029756	0.932843
14	0.021424	0.954267
15	0.015083	0.969350
16	0.010407	0.979757
17	0.007052	0.986810
18	0.004702	0.991511
19	0.003088	0.994599

n	P(n)	F(n)
20	0.002001	0.996600
21	0.001281	0.997881
22	0.000810	0.998692
23	0.000507	0.999199
24	0.000315	0.999513
25	0.000193	0.999707
26	0.000118	0.999824
27	0.000071	0.999896
28	0.000043	0.999938

k = 8·5		
Mean = 7·85		
Variance = 15·09		

n	P(n)	F(n)
0	0.003855	0.003855
1	0.015729	0.019584
2	0.035861	0.055445
3	0.060247	0.115691
4	0.083140	0.198832
5	0.099768	0.298600
6	0.107750	0.406350
7	0.107134	0.513484
8	0.099635	0.613119
9	0.087679	0.700797
10	0.073650	0.774447
11	0.059456	0.833903
12	0.046375	0.880279
13	0.035103	0.915381
14	0.025876	0.941257
15	0.018630	0.959887
16	0.013134	0.973022
17	0.009086	0.982108
18	0.006178	0.988286
19	0.004136	0.992422
20	0.002730	0.995152
21	0.001778	0.996931
22	0.001145	0.998075
23	0.000729	0.998804
24	0.000459	0.999263
25	0.000286	0.999549
26	0.000177	0.999727
27	0.000109	0.999835
28	0.000066	0.999901

k = 9·0		
Mean = 8·31		
Variance = 15·98		

n	P(n)	F(n)
0	0.002780	0.002780
1	0.012009	0.014789
2	0.028822	0.043611
3	0.050727	0.094338
4	0.073047	0.167385
5	0.091162	0.258547
6	0.102102	0.360649
7	0.105019	0.465667
8	0.100818	0.566485
9	0.091408	0.657894

n	P(n)	F(n)
10	0.078977	0.736871
11	0.065479	0.802350
12	0.052383	0.854733
13	0.040617	0.895350
14	0.030637	0.925987
15	0.022549	0.948536
16	0.016235	0.964771
17	0.011460	0.976231
18	0.007946	0.984177
19	0.005420	0.989596
20	0.003642	0.993239
21	0.002414	0.995653
22	0.001580	0.997233
23	0.001022	0.998255
24	0.000654	0.998910
25	0.000415	0.999324
26	0.000260	0.999584
27	0.000162	0.999746
28	0.000100	0.999846
29	0.000061	0.999907

k = 9·5		
Mean = 8·77		
Variance = 16·86		

n	P(n)	F(n)
0	0.002005	0.002005
1	0.009141	0.011146
2	0.023035	0.034181
3	0.042385	0.076566
4	0.063578	0.140144
5	0.082397	0.222541
6	0.095580	0.318122
7	0.101588	0.419710
8	0.100573	0.520283
9	0.093868	0.614150
10	0.083354	0.697505
11	0.070927	0.768432
12	0.058160	0.826592
13	0.046170	0.872762
14	0.035617	0.908380
15	0.026784	0.935164
16	0.019686	0.954850
17	0.014174	0.969024
18	0.010016	0.979040
19	0.006959	0.985999
20	0.004760	0.990759
21	0.003209	0.993968
22	0.002136	0.996104
23	0.001404	0.997508
24	0.000913	0.998421
25	0.000587	0.999008
26	0.000374	0.999382
27	0.000236	0.999617
28	0.000148	0.999765
29	0.000092	0.999857
30	0.000056	0.999913

k=10·0
Mean=9·23
Variance=17·75

n	P(n)	F(n)
0	0.001446	0.001446
1	0.006939	0.008384
2	0.018318	0.026702
3	0.035171	0.061873
4	0.054866	0.116739
5	0.073740	0.190479
6	0.088488	0.278967
7	0.097084	0.376051
8	0.099026	0.475077
9	0.095065	0.570142
10	0.086699	0.656841
11	0.075665	0.732506
12	0.063558	0.796064
13	0.051629	0.847693
14	0.040713	0.888406
15	0.031268	0.919673
16	0.023451	0.943124
17	0.017216	0.960340
18	0.012395	0.972735
19	0.008768	0.981503
20	0.006103	0.987605
21	0.004185	0.991790
22	0.002830	0.994620
23	0.001890	0.996510
24	0.001247	0.997758
25	0.000814	0.998572
26	0.000526	0.999099
27	0.000337	0.999435
28	0.000214	0.999649
29	0.000134	0.999783
30	0.000084	0.999867
31	0.000052	0.999919

k=0·1
Mean=0·09
Variance=0·16

n	P(n)	F(n)
0	0.940241	0.940241
1	0.043251	0.983493
2	0.010943	0.994435
3	0.003523	0.997959
4	0.001256	0.999215
5	0.000474	0.999688
6	0.000185	0.999874
7	0.000074	0.999948

k=0·2
Mean=0·17
Variance=0·32

n	P(n)	F(n)
0	0.884054	0.884054
1	0.081333	0.965387
2	0.022448	0.987835
3	0.007572	0.995407
4	0.002787	0.998194
5	0.001077	0.999271
6	0.000429	0.999700
7	0.000175	0.999874
8	0.000072	0.999947

k=0·3
Mean=0·26
Variance=0·47

n	P(n)	F(n)
0	0.831224	0.831224
1	0.114709	0.945933
2	0.034298	0.980231
3	0.012096	0.992327
4	0.004590	0.996917
5	0.001816	0.998733
6	0.000738	0.999471
7	0.000305	0.999776
8	0.000128	0.999905

k=0·4
Mean=0·34
Variance=0·63

n	P(n)	F(n)
0	0.781551	0.781551
1	0.143805	0.925357
2	0.046305	0.971662
3	0.017040	0.988702
4	0.006663	0.995365
5	0.002697	0.998062
6	0.001117	0.999179
7	0.000470	0.999649
8	0.000200	0.999848
9	0.000086	0.999934

k=0·5
Mean=0·43
Variance=0·79

n	P(n)	F(n)
0	0.734847	0.73484
1	0.169015	0.903862
2	0.058310	0.962173
3	0.022352	0.98452
4	0.008997	0.99352
5	0.003725	0.99724
6	0.001571	0.99881
7	0.000671	0.99948
8	0.000289	0.99977
9	0.000126	0.99990

k=0·6
Mean=0·51
Variance=0·95

n	P(n)	F(n)
0	0.690934	0.69093
1	0.190698	0.88163
2	0.070177	0.95180
3	0.027977	0.97978
4	0.011583	0.99136
5	0.004902	0.99626
6	0.002104	0.99837
7	0.000913	0.99928
8	0.000399	0.99968
9	0.000175	0.99986

0	0.000077	0.999938	10	0.000180	0.999849	10	0.000354	0.999689
			11	0.000082	0.999931	11	0.000166	0.999855
						12	0.000077	0.999932

k=0.7
Mean=0.60
Variance=1.10

n	P(n)	F(n)
0	0.649644	0.649644
1	0.209185	0.858830
2	0.081792	0.940621
3	0.033862	0.974483
4	0.014408	0.988891
5	0.006230	0.995121
6	0.002723	0.997844
7	0.001199	0.999042
8	0.000531	0.999573
9	0.000236	0.999809
10	0.000105	0.999914

k=1.0
Mean=0.85
Variance=1.58

n	P(n)	F(n)
0	0.540000	0.540000
1	0.248400	0.788400
2	0.114264	0.902664
3	0.052561	0.955225
4	0.024178	0.979404
5	0.011122	0.990526
6	0.005116	0.995642
7	0.002353	0.997995
8	0.001083	0.999078
9	0.000498	0.999576
10	0.000229	0.999805
11	0.000105	0.999910

k=1.3
Mean=1.11
Variance=2.05

n	P(n)	F(n)
0	0.448861	0.448861
1	0.268419	0.717280
2	0.141994	0.859273
3	0.071849	0.931122
4	0.035529	0.966651
5	0.017324	0.983976
6	0.008368	0.992343
7	0.004014	0.996357
8	0.001916	0.998273
9	0.000911	0.999183
10	0.000431	0.999615
11	0.000204	0.999819
12	0.000096	0.999915

k=0.8
Mean=0.68
Variance=1.26

n	P(n)	F(n)
0	0.610822	0.610822
1	0.224783	0.835605
2	0.093060	0.928665
3	0.039954	0.968619
4	0.017460	0.986079
5	0.007710	0.993789
6	0.003428	0.997217
7	0.001532	0.998750
8	0.000687	0.999437
9	0.000309	0.999746
10	0.000139	0.999885
11	0.000063	0.999948

k=1.1
Mean=0.94
Variance=1.74

n	P(n)	F(n)
0	0.507730	0.507730
1	0.256912	0.764642
2	0.124084	0.888730
3	0.058983	0.947714
4	0.027811	0.975524
5	0.013049	0.988573
6	0.006102	0.994675
7	0.002847	0.997523
8	0.001326	0.998849
9	0.000617	0.999465
10	0.000287	0.999752
11	0.000133	0.999885
12	0.000062	0.999947

k=1.4
Mean=1.19
Variance=2.21

n	P(n)	F(n)
0	0.422038	0.422038
1	0.271792	0.693830
2	0.150029	0.843859
3	0.078215	0.922075
4	0.039577	0.961652
5	0.019662	0.981313
6	0.009647	0.990961
7	0.004691	0.995652
8	0.002266	0.997918
9	0.001089	0.999007
10	0.000521	0.999528
11	0.000248	0.999776
12	0.000118	0.999894
13	0.000056	0.999950

k=0.9
Mean=0.77
Variance=1.42

n	P(n)	F(n)
0	0.574321	0.574321
1	0.237769	0.812089
2	0.103905	0.915994
3	0.046203	0.962197
4	0.020722	0.982919
5	0.009342	0.992261
6	0.004225	0.996486
7	0.001916	0.998402
8	0.000870	0.999273
9	0.000396	0.999669

k=1.2
Mean=1.02
Variance=1.89

n	P(n)	F(n)
0	0.477389	0.477389
1	0.263519	0.740908
2	0.133341	0.874248
3	0.065426	0.939674
4	0.031601	0.971275
5	0.015118	0.986393
6	0.007186	0.993579
7	0.003400	0.996978
8	0.001603	0.998582
9	0.000754	0.999335

k=1.5
Mean=1.28
Variance=2.37

n	P(n)	F(n)
0	0.396817	0.396817
1	0.273804	0.670621
2	0.157437	0.828059
3	0.084491	0.912550
4	0.043724	0.956274
5	0.022124	0.978399
6	0.011025	0.989424
7	0.005434	0.994858
8	0.002656	0.997514
9	0.001290	0.998803

n	P(n)	F(n)
10	0.000623	0.999426
11	0.000300	0.999726
12	0.000144	0.999869
13	0.000069	0.999938

k=1·6
Mean=1·36
Variance=2·52

n	P(n)	F(n)
0	0.373104	0.373104
1	0.274605	0.647709
2	0.164214	0.811922
3	0.090646	0.902568
4	0.047952	0.950520
5	0.024705	0.975225
6	0.012501	0.987725
7	0.006243	0.993968
8	0.003087	0.997055
9	0.001515	0.998570
10	0.000739	0.999309
11	0.000358	0.999667
12	0.000173	0.999840
13	0.000083	0.999924

k=1·7
Mean=1·45
Variance=2·68

n	P(n)	F(n)
0	0.350808	0.350808
1	0.274332	0.625140
2	0.170360	0.795500
3	0.096651	0.892151
4	0.052240	0.944391
5	0.027395	0.971785
6	0.014072	0.985857
7	0.007120	0.992977
8	0.003562	0.996539
9	0.001766	0.998305
10	0.000869	0.999174
11	0.000425	0.999599
12	0.000207	0.999806
13	0.000100	0.999907

k=1·8
Mean=1·53
Variance=2·84

n	P(n)	F(n)
0	0.329844	0.329844
1	0.273111	0.602955
2	0.175883	0.778839
3	0.102481	0.881320
4	0.056570	0.937890
5	0.030186	0.968075
6	0.015737	0.983812
7	0.008066	0.991878
8	0.004082	0.995960
9	0.002044	0.998004

n	P(n)	F(n)
10	0.001016	0.999020
11	0.000501	0.999521
12	0.000246	0.999767
13	0.000120	0.999887
14	0.000058	0.999945

k=1·9
Mean=1·62
Variance=3·00

n	P(n)	F(n)
0	0.310133	0.310133
1	0.271056	0.581189
2	0.180795	0.761984
3	0.108115	0.870099
4	0.060923	0.931022
5	0.033069	0.964091
6	0.017493	0.981585
7	0.009082	0.990666
8	0.004648	0.995314
9	0.002352	0.997665
10	0.001179	0.998844
11	0.000587	0.999431
12	0.000290	0.999721
13	0.000143	0.999864
14	0.000070	0.999934

k=2·0
Mean=1·70
Variance=3·16

n	P(n)	F(n)
0	0.291600	0.291600
1	0.268272	0.559872
2	0.185108	0.744980
3	0.113533	0.858512
4	0.065281	0.923794
5	0.036035	0.959829
6	0.019339	0.979168
7	0.010167	0.989335
8	0.005261	0.994596
9	0.002689	0.997285
10	0.001361	0.998646
11	0.000683	0.999329
12	0.000340	0.999669
13	0.000169	0.999837
14	0.000083	0.999920

k=2·1
Mean=1·79
Variance=3·31

n	P(n)	F(n)
0	0.274174	0.274174
1	0.264852	0.539027
2	0.188840	0.727867
3	0.118717	0.846584
4	0.069628	0.916212
5	0.039075	0.955287
6	0.021270	0.976557
7	0.011322	0.987878
8	0.005924	0.993802
9	0.003058	0.996860

n	P(n)	F(n)
10	0.001561	0.998422
11	0.000790	0.999212
12	0.000397	0.999609
13	0.000198	0.999807
14	0.000098	0.999905

k=2·2
Mean=1·87
Variance=3·47

n	P(n)	F(n)
0	0.257790	0.257790
1	0.260884	0.518674
2	0.192010	0.710684
3	0.123655	0.834339
4	0.073945	0.908284
5	0.042179	0.950463
6	0.023283	0.973745
7	0.012546	0.986291
8	0.006637	0.992928
9	0.003460	0.996388
10	0.001783	0.998171
11	0.000909	0.999080
12	0.000460	0.999540
13	0.000231	0.999771
14	0.000115	0.999887
15	0.000057	0.999944

k=2·3
Mean=1·96
Variance=3·63

n	P(n)	F(n)
0	0.242385	0.242385
1	0.256443	0.498828
2	0.194640	0.693469
3	0.128333	0.821802
4	0.078219	0.900021
5	0.045336	0.945356
6	0.025373	0.970729
7	0.013839	0.984568
8	0.007400	0.991969
9	0.003896	0.995865
10	0.002025	0.997890
11	0.001042	0.998931
12	0.000531	0.999462
13	0.000269	0.999731
14	0.000135	0.999866
15	0.000068	0.999934

k=2·4
Mean=2·04
Variance=3·79

n	P(n)	F(n)
0	0.227900	0.227900
1	0.251602	0.479502
2	0.196753	0.676255
3	0.132743	0.808998
4	0.082433	0.891431
5	0.048537	0.939967
6	0.027536	0.967504
7	0.015200	0.982704
8	0.008216	0.990920
9	0.004367	0.995287
10	0.002290	0.997577
11	0.001188	0.998764
12	0.000610	0.999374
13	0.000311	0.999685
14	0.000157	0.999842
15	0.000079	0.999921

k=2·5
Mean=2·13
Variance=3·94

n	P(n)	F(n)
0	0.214281	0.214281
1	0.246424	0.460705
2	0.198371	0.659076
3	0.136876	0.795952
4	0.086574	0.882526
5	0.051771	0.934297
6	0.029768	0.964066
7	0.016628	0.980694
8	0.009083	0.989776
9	0.004875	0.994651
10	0.002579	0.997230
11	0.001348	0.998578
12	0.000698	0.999275
13	0.000358	0.999633
14	0.000182	0.999815
15	0.000092	0.999907

k=3·0
Mean=2·56
Variance=4·73

n	P(n)	F(n)
0	0.157464	0.157464
1	0.217300	0.374764
2	0.199916	0.574681
3	0.153269	0.727950
4	0.105756	0.833705
5	0.068107	0.901812
6	0.041772	0.943584
7	0.024705	0.968289
8	0.014205	0.982495
9	0.007987	0.990482
10	0.004409	0.994890
11	0.002397	0.997287
12	0.001286	0.998573
13	0.000683	0.999256
14	0.000359	0.999615
15	0.000187	0.999802
16	0.000097	0.999899
17	0.000050	0.999948

k=3·5
Mean=2·98
Variance=5·52

n	P(n)	F(n)
0	0.115712	0.115712
1	0.186296	0.302008
2	0.192817	0.494825
3	0.162609	0.657433
4	0.121550	0.778983
5	0.083869	0.862853
6	0.054655	0.917508
7	0.034120	0.951628
8	0.020600	0.972228
9	0.012108	0.984337
10	0.006962	0.991299
11	0.003931	0.995229
12	0.002185	0.997414
13	0.001198	0.998612
14	0.000650	0.999262
15	0.000349	0.999610
16	0.000185	0.999796
17	0.000098	0.999894
18	0.000051	0.999945

k=4·0
Mean=3·41
Variance=6·31

n	P(n)	F(n)
0	0.085031	0.085031
1	0.156456	0.241487
2	0.179925	0.421411
3	0.165531	0.586942
4	0.133252	0.720194
5	0.098074	0.818268
6	0.067671	0.885939
7	0.044469	0.930408
8	0.028127	0.958535
9	0.017251	0.975786
10	0.010316	0.986102
11	0.006040	0.992142
12	0.003473	0.995615
13	0.001966	0.997581
14	0.001098	0.998679

k=4·5
Mean=3·83
Variance=7·10

n	P(n)	F(n)
0	0.062484	0.062484
1	0.129343	0.191827
2	0.163619	0.355446
3	0.163073	0.518519
4	0.140651	0.659170
5	0.109989	0.769159
6	0.080109	0.849267
7	0.055275	0.904542
8	0.036551	0.941093
9	0.023352	0.964444
10	0.014501	0.978946
11	0.008793	0.987739
12	0.005225	0.992963
13	0.003050	0.996014
14	0.001754	0.997768
15	0.000995	0.998763
16	0.000558	0.999321
17	0.000309	0.999630
18	0.000170	0.999800
19	0.000093	0.999893
20	0.000050	0.999943

k=5·0
Mean=4·26
Variance=7·89

n	P(n)	F(n)
0	0.045917	0.045917
1	0.105608	0.151524
2	0.145739	0.297263
3	0.156427	0.453690
4	0.143912	0.597602
5	0.119159	0.716762
6	0.091356	0.808117
7	0.066037	0.874154
8	0.045566	0.919720
9	0.030276	0.949996
10	0.019498	0.969493
11	0.012230	0.981724
12	0.007501	0.989225
13	0.004512	0.993737
14	0.002669	0.996406
15	0.001555	0.997961
16	0.000894	0.998855
17	0.000508	0.999363
18	0.000286	0.999649
19	0.000159	0.999808

20	0.000088	0.999896	20	0.000237	0.999694	20	0.000555	0.999221
21	0.000048	0.999944	21	0.000135	0.999829	21	0.000328	0.999549
			22	0.000076	0.999905	22	0.000192	0.999741
						23	0.000111	0.999853
						24	0.000064	0.999917

k=5·5
Mean = 4·69
Variance = 8·68

k=6·5
Mean = 5·54
Variance = 10·25

k=7·5
Mean = 6·39
Variance = 11·83

n	P(n)	F(n)	n	P(n)	F(n)	n	P(n)	F(n)
0	0.033742	0.033742	0	0.018220	0.018220	0	0.009839	0.009839
1	0.085366	0.119108	1	0.054479	0.072700	1	0.033945	0.043784
2	0.127623	0.246730	2	0.093977	0.166676	2	0.066362	0.110146
3	0.146766	0.393496	3	0.122483	0.289159	3	0.096667	0.206813
4	0.143464	0.536960	4	0.133812	0.422972	4	0.116726	0.323539
5	0.125387	0.662347	5	0.129263	0.552234	5	0.123496	0.447034
6	0.100937	0.763284	6	0.113967	0.666201	6	0.118350	0.565384
7	0.076279	0.839563	7	0.093616	0.759817	7	0.104993	0.670378
8	0.054826	0.894389	8	0.072669	0.832486	8	0.087538	0.757916
9	0.037830	0.932219	9	0.053856	0.886342	9	0.069350	0.827266
10	0.025232	0.957451	10	0.038399	0.924741	10	0.052636	0.879902
11	0.016355	0.973807	11	0.026495	0.951236	11	0.038520	0.918423
12	0.010345	0.984151	12	0.017774	0.969010	12	0.027317	0.945740
13	0.006406	0.990557	13	0.011635	0.980646	13	0.018849	0.964589
14	0.003894	0.994451	14	0.007455	0.988100	14	0.012696	0.977285
15	0.002328	0.996779	15	0.004687	0.992787	15	0.008371	0.985656
16	0.001372	0.998152	16	0.002897	0.995684	16	0.005415	0.991071
17	0.000798	0.998950	17	0.001764	0.997448	17	0.003443	0.994514
18	0.000459	0.999409	18	0.001059	0.998507	18	0.002156	0.996670
19	0.000261	0.999670	19	0.000628	0.999135	19	0.001331	0.998001
20	0.000147	0.999817	20	0.000368	0.999504	20	0.000811	0.998813
21	0.000082	0.999900	21	0.000214	0.999717	21	0.000489	0.999301
22	0.000046	0.999945	22	0.000123	0.999840	22	0.000291	0.999592
			23	0.000070	0.999911	23	0.000172	0.999764
						24	0.000100	0.999865
						25	0.000058	0.999923

k=6·0
Mean = 5·11
Variance = 9·47

k=7·0
Mean = 5·96
Variance = 11·04

k=8·0
Mean = 6·81
Variance = 12·62

n	P(n)	F(n)	n	P(n)	F(n)	n	P(n)	F(n)
0	0.024795	0.024795	0	0.013389	0.013389	0	0.007230	0.007230
1	0.068434	0.093229	1	0.043113	0.056503	1	0.026607	0.033837
2	0.110179	0.203408	2	0.079329	0.135831	2	0.055077	0.088914
3	0.135152	0.338560	3	0.109474	0.245305	3	0.084451	0.173365
4	0.139883	0.478443	4	0.125895	0.371199	4	0.106831	0.280196
5	0.128692	0.607135	5	0.127405	0.498605	5	0.117941	0.398136
6	0.108530	0.715666	6	0.117213	0.615818	6	0.117548	0.515684
7	0.085584	0.801250	7	0.100133	0.715951	7	0.108144	0.623828
8	0.063974	0.865224	8	0.080607	0.796558	8	0.093274	0.717102
9	0.045777	0.911001	9	0.061799	0.858357	9	0.076278	0.793380
10	0.031586	0.942587	10	0.045484	0.903841	10	0.059649	0.853029
11	0.021134	0.963721	11	0.032335	0.936176	11	0.044899	0.897928
12	0.013772	0.977493	12	0.022311	0.958487	12	0.032702	0.930630
13	0.008772	0.986265	13	0.015000	0.973487	13	0.023143	0.953773
14	0.005476	0.991741	14	0.009857	0.983344	14	0.015969	0.969741
15	0.003359	0.995100	15	0.006348	0.989692			
16	0.002028	0.997128	16	0.004015	0.993707			
17	0.001207	0.998335	17	0.002499	0.996206			
18	0.000710	0.999044	18	0.001533	0.997739			
19	0.000412	0.999457	19	0.000928	0.998666			

n	P(n)	F(n)
15	0.010773	0.980515
16	0.007124	0.987639
17	0.004626	0.992265
18	0.002956	0.995221
19	0.001861	0.997081
20	0.001155	0.998237
21	0.000709	0.998945
22	0.000430	0.999375
23	0.000258	0.999633
24	0.000153	0.999786
25	0.000090	0.999876
26	0.000053	0.999929

k = 8.5
Mean = 7·24
Variance = 13·41

n	P(n)	F(n)
0	0.005313	0.005313
1	0.020774	0.026087
2	0.045392	0.071479
3	0.073080	0.144559
4	0.096649	0.241208
5	0.111146	0.352354
6	0.115036	0.467391
7	0.109613	0.577004
8	0.097693	0.674696
9	0.082388	0.757084
10	0.066322	0.823406
11	0.051309	0.874715
12	0.038354	0.913069
13	0.027821	0.940890
14	0.019654	0.960543
15	0.013561	0.974104
16	0.009162	0.983266
17	0.006074	0.989340
18	0.003958	0.993299
19	0.002539	0.995838
20	0.001606	0.997444
21	0.001003	0.998447
22	0.000619	0.999066
23	0.000377	0.999443
24	0.000228	0.999671
25	0.000136	0.999807
26	0.000081	0.999888
27	0.000047	0.999935

k = 9.0
Mean = 7·67
Variance = 14·20

n	P(n)	F(n)
0	0.003904	0.003904
1	0.016164	0.020068
2	0.037177	0.057245
3	0.062705	0.119950
4	0.086533	0.206483

n	P(n)	F(n)
.5	0.103493	0.309976
6	0.111083	0.421058
7	0.109496	0.530554
8	0.100736	0.631290
9	0.087528	0.718819
10	0.072474	0.791292
11	0.057584	0.848876
12	0.044147	0.893023
13	0.032805	0.925828
14	0.023713	0.949541
15	0.016726	0.966267
16	0.011541	0.977808
17	0.007807	0.985615
18	0.005187	0.990802
19	0.003391	0.994193
20	0.002184	0.996377
21	0.001387	0.997764
22	0.000870	0.998634
23	0.000539	0.999173
24	0.000331	0.999504
25	0.000201	0.999705
26	0.000121	0.999826
27	0.000072	0.999898
28	0.000043	0.999941

k = 9.5
Mean = 8·09
Variance = 14·99

n	P(n)	F(n)
0	0.002869	0.002869
1	0.012538	0.015407
2	0.030279	0.045686
3	0.053392	0.099077
4	0.076751	0.175828
5	0.095324	0.271152
6	0.105969	0.377121
7	0.107937	0.485058
8	0.102405	0.587463
9	0.091596	0.679058
10	0.077948	0.757006
11	0.063563	0.820569
12	0.049950	0.870519
13	0.038000	0.908519
14	0.028093	0.936612
15	0.020246	0.956858
16	0.014261	0.971118
17	0.009840	0.980958
18	0.006664	0.987622
19	0.004437	0.992059
20	0.002908	0.994967
21	0.001879	0.996846
22	0.001198	0.998045
23	0.000755	0.998800
24	0.000470	0.999270
25	0.000290	0.999560
26	0.000177	0.999737
27	0.000107	0.999844
28	0.000064	0.999908

k = 10.0
Mean = 8·52
Variance = 15·78

n	P(n)	F(n)
0	0.002108	0.002108
1	0.009698	0.011807
2	0.024537	0.036343
3	0.045148	0.081491
4	0.067496	0.148986
5	0.086934	0.235921
6	0.099974	0.335895
7	0.105116	0.441011
8	0.102751	0.543762
9	0.094531	0.638292
10	0.082620	0.720912
11	0.069100	0.790012
12	0.055626	0.845638
13	0.043302	0.888941
14	0.032724	0.921665
15	0.024085	0.945750
16	0.017311	0.963061
17	0.012179	0.975240
18	0.008403	0.983644
19	0.005697	0.989340
20	0.003800	0.993140
21	0.002497	0.995637
22	0.001618	0.997255
23	0.001036	0.998291
24	0.000655	0.998946
25	0.000410	0.999356
26	0.000254	0.999610
27	0.000156	0.999766
28	0.000095	0.999860
29	0.000057	0.999917

k=0·1
Mean=0·08
Variance=0·14

n	P(n)	F(n)
0	0.943667	0.943667
1	0.041521	0.985188
2	0.010048	0.995237
3	0.003095	0.998331
4	0.001055	0.999387
5	0.000381	0.999768
6	0.000142	0.999910

k=0·2
Mean=0·16
Variance=0·28

n	P(n)	F(n)
0	0.890508	0.890508
1	0.078365	0.968872
2	0.020688	0.989560
3	0.006675	0.996236
4	0.002350	0.998586
5	0.000868	0.999454
6	0.000331	0.999785
7	0.000129	0.999914

k=0·3
Mean=0·24
Variance=0·42

n	P(n)	F(n)
0	0.840343	0.840343
1	0.110925	0.951268
2	0.031725	0.982992
3	0.010702	0.993694
4	0.003885	0.997579
5	0.001470	0.999049
6	0.000571	0.999620
7	0.000226	0.999847
8	0.000091	0.999937

k=0·4
Mean=0·31
Variance=0·56

n	P(n)	F(n)
0	0.793004	0.793004
1	0.139569	0.932572
2	0.042987	0.975559
3	0.015131	0.990691
4	0.005659	0.996350
5	0.002191	0.998541
6	0.000868	0.999409
7	0.000349	0.999758
8	0.000142	0.999900

k=0·5
Mean=0·39
Variance=0·70

n	P(n)	F(n)
0	0.748331	0.748331
1	0.164633	0.912964
2	0.054329	0.967293
3	0.019921	0.987214
4	0.007669	0.994883
5	0.003037	0.997920
6	0.001225	0.999145
7	0.000500	0.999646
8	0.000206	0.999852
9	0.000086	0.999938

k=0·6
Mean=0·47
Variance=0·84

n	P(n)	F(n)
0	0.706176	0.706176
1	0.186430	0.892606
2	0.065624	0.958230
3	0.025024	0.983254
4	0.009910	0.993164
5	0.004011	0.997175
6	0.001647	0.998823
7	0.000683	0.999506
8	0.000286	0.999792
9	0.000120	0.999912

k=0·7
Mean=0·55
Variance=0·98

n	P(n)	F(n)
0	0.666395	0.666395
1	0.205250	0.871644
2	0.076763	0.948408
3	0.030398	0.978806
4	0.012372	0.991178
5	0.005117	0.996295
6	0.002139	0.998434
7	0.000901	0.999335
8	0.000381	0.999717
9	0.000162	0.999879
10	0.000069	0.999948

k=0·8
Mean=0·63
Variance=1·12

n	P(n)	F(n)
0	0.628855	0.628855
1	0.221357	0.850212
2	0.087657	0.937869
3	0.035998	0.973867
4	0.015047	0.988914

5	0.006356	0.995270
6	0.002703	0.997973
7	0.001156	0.999129
8	0.000496	0.999625
9	0.000213	0.999838
10	0.000092	0.999930

k=0·9
Mean=0·71
Variance=1·26

n	P(n)	F(n)
0	0.593430	0.593430
1	0.234998	0.828428
2	0.098229	0.926657
3	0.041780	0.968437
4	0.017924	0.986361
5	0.007729	0.994090
6	0.003344	0.997433
7	0.001450	0.998884
8	0.000630	0.999514
9	0.000274	0.999738
10	0.000119	0.999908

k=1·0
Mean=0·79
Variance=1·40

n	P(n)	F(n)
0	0.560000	0.560000
1	0.246400	0.806400
2	0.108416	0.914816
3	0.047703	0.962519
4	0.020989	0.983508
5	0.009235	0.992744
6	0.004064	0.996807
7	0.001788	0.998595
8	0.000787	0.999382
9	0.000346	0.999728
10	0.000152	0.999880
11	0.000067	0.999947

k=1·1
Mean=0·86
Variance=1·54

n	P(n)	F(n)
0	0.528454	0.528454
1	0.255772	0.784225
2	0.118166	0.902392
3	0.053726	0.956118
4	0.024231	0.980348

n	P(n)	F(n)
5	0.010875	0.991223
6	0.004865	0.996088
7	0.002171	0.998259
8	0.000967	0.999226
9	0.000430	0.999656
10	0.000191	0.999847
11	0.000085	0.999932

n	P(n)	F(n)
5	0.016566	0.985525
6	0.007775	0.993300
7	0.003616	0.996917
8	0.001671	0.998587
9	0.000768	0.999355
10	0.000351	0.999707
11	0.000160	0.999867
12	0.000073	0.999940

n	P(n)	F(n)
5	0.023334	0.977961
6	0.011465	0.989426
7	0.005549	0.994975
8	0.002655	0.997630
9	0.001259	0.998889
10	0.000593	0.999482
11	0.000277	0.999760
12	0.000129	0.999889
13	0.000060	0.999949

k=1·2
Mean=0·94
Variance=1·68

n	P(n)	F(n)
0	0.498684	0.498684
1	0.263305	0.761989
2	0.127440	0.889429
3	0.059812	0.949241
4	0.027633	0.976874
5	0.012645	0.989519
6	0.005749	0.995268
7	0.002602	0.997870
8	0.001173	0.999043
9	0.000528	0.999571
10	0.000237	0.999808
11	0.000106	0.999914

k=1·5
Mean=1·18
Variance=2·10

n	P(n)	F(n)
0	0.419066	0.419066
1	0.276583	0.695649
2	0.152121	0.847770
3	0.078089	0.925858
4	0.038654	0.964512
5	0.018708	0.983221
6	0.008918	0.992139
7	0.004204	0.996343
8	0.001965	0.998308
9	0.000913	0.999221
10	0.000422	0.999643
11	0.000194	0.999837
12	0.000089	0.999925

k=1·8
Mean=1·41
Variance=2·53

n	P(n)	F(n)
0	0.352159	0.352159
1	0.278910	0.631068
2	0.171808	0.802877
3	0.095755	0.898631
4	0.050558	0.949190
5	0.025805	0.974995
6	0.012868	0.987863
7	0.006309	0.994172
8	0.003054	0.997225
9	0.001463	0.998688
10	0.000695	0.999384
11	0.000328	0.999712
12	0.000154	0.999866
13	0.000072	0.999938

k=1·3
Mean=1·02
Variance=1·82

n	P(n)	F(n)
0	0.470592	0.470592
1	0.269179	0.739770
2	0.136204	0.875975
3	0.065923	0.941898
4	0.031182	0.973079
5	0.014543	0.987622
6	0.006719	0.994341
7	0.003083	0.997424
8	0.001407	0.998832
9	0.000640	0.999472
10	0.000290	0.999762
11	0.000131	0.999893
12	0.000059	0.999952

k=1·6
Mean=1·26
Variance=2·24

n	P(n)	F(n)
0	0.395458	0.395458
1	0.278403	0.673861
2	0.159246	0.833108
3	0.084082	0.917190
4	0.042546	0.959735
5	0.020966	0.980702
6	0.010148	0.990849
7	0.004848	0.995697
8	0.002293	0.997990
9	0.001076	0.999066
10	0.000502	0.999568
11	0.000233	0.999801
12	0.000108	0.999909

k=1·9
Mean=1·49
Variance=2·67

n	P(n)	F(n)
0	0.332321	0.332321
1	0.277820	0.610141
2	0.177249	0.787390
3	0.101387	0.888776
4	0.054647	0.943424
5	0.028373	0.971797
6	0.014357	0.986153
7	0.007129	0.993282
8	0.003490	0.996772
9	0.001689	0.998461
10	0.000810	0.999271
11	0.000386	0.999657
12	0.000182	0.999839
13	0.000086	0.999925

k=1·4
Mean=1·10
Variance=1·96

n	P(n)	F(n)
0	0.444082	0.444082
1	0.273555	0.717637
2	0.144437	0.862073
3	0.072026	0.934099
4	0.034860	0.968960

k=1·7
Mean=1·34
Variance=2·39

n	P(n)	F(n)
0	0.373181	0.373181
1	0.279139	0.652321
2	0.165809	0.818129
3	0.089979	0.908108
4	0.046519	0.954627

k=2·0
Mean=1·57
Variance=2·81

n	P(n)	F(n)
0	0.313600	0.313600
1	0.275968	0.589568
2	0.182139	0.771707
3	0.106855	0.878562
4	0.058770	0.937332

5	0.031031	0.968362
6	0.015929	0.984292
7	0.008010	0.992302
8	0.003965	0.996267
9	0.001938	0.998205
10	0.000938	0.999143
11	0.000450	0.999594
12	0.000215	0.999808
13	0.000102	0.999910

5	0.039468	0.956612
6	0.021128	0.977740
7	0.011023	0.988763
8	0.005638	0.994402
9	0.002839	0.997241
10	0.001412	0.998652
11	0.000695	0.999347
12	0.000339	0.999686
13	0.000164	0.999850
14	0.000079	0.999928

5	0.060820	0.920575
6	0.035681	0.956256
7	0.020185	0.976442
8	0.011102	0.987544
9	0.005970	0.993514
10	0.003152	0.996666
11	0.001639	0.998306
12	0.000841	0.999147
13	0.000427	0.999574
14	0.000215	0.999789
15	0.000107	0.999896
16	0.000053	0.999949

k=2·1
Mean=1·65
Variance=2·95

n	P(n)	F(n)
0	0.295934	0.295934
1	0.273443	0.569377
2	0.186488	0.755865
3	0.112142	0.868007
4	0.062911	0.930918
5	0.033771	0.964689
6	0.017583	0.982272
7	0.008952	0.991225
8	0.004481	0.995705
9	0.002212	0.997918
10	0.001081	0.998998
11	0.000523	0.999521
12	0.000251	0.999773
13	0.000120	0.999893
14	0.000057	0.999949

k=2·4
Mean=1·89
Variance=3·37

n	P(n)	F(n)
0	0.248686	0.248686
1	0.262612	0.511298
2	0.196434	0.707732
3	0.126765	0.834498
4	0.075299	0.909796
5	0.042408	0.952205
6	0.023014	0.975218
7	0.012151	0.987369
8	0.006282	0.993652
9	0.003194	0.996846
10	0.001602	0.998448
11	0.000795	0.999242
12	0.000390	0.999633
13	0.000190	0.999823
14	0.000092	0.999915

k=3·5
Mean=2·75
Variance=4·91

n	P(n)	F(n)
0	0.131419	0.131419
1	0.202385	0.333804
2	0.200361	0.534166
3	0.161625	0.695790
4	0.115562	0.811352
5	0.076271	0.887623
6	0.047542	0.935165
7	0.028389	0.963554
8	0.016395	0.979949
9	0.009218	0.989167
10	0.005070	0.994237
11	0.002738	0.996974
12	0.001456	0.998430
13	0.000764	0.999193
14	0.000396	0.999589
15	0.000203	0.999793
16	0.000103	0.999896
17	0.000052	0.999948

k=2·2
Mean=1·73
Variance=3·09

n	P(n)	F(n)
0	0.279263	0.279263
1	0.270327	0.549590
2	0.190310	0.739900
3	0.117231	0.857131
4	0.067056	0.924187
5	0.036586	0.960773
6	0.019317	0.980090
7	0.009957	0.990047
8	0.005038	0.995085
9	0.002512	0.997597
10	0.001238	0.998835
11	0.000604	0.999440
12	0.000292	0.999732
13	0.000141	0.999872
14	0.000067	0.999940

k=2·5
Mean=1·96
Variance=3·51

n	P(n)	F(n)
0	0.234677	0.234677
1	0.258144	0.492821
2	0.198771	0.691592
3	0.131189	0.822781
4	0.079369	0.902151
5	0.045399	0.947550
6	0.024970	0.972520
7	0.013341	0.985860
8	0.006971	0.992831
9	0.003578	0.996409
10	0.001811	0.998220
11	0.000905	0.999125
12	0.000448	0.999573
13	0.000220	0.999793
14	0.000107	0.999900

k=4·0
Mean=3·14
Variance=5·61

n	P(n)	F(n)
0	0.098345	0.098345
1	0.173087	0.271432
2	0.190396	0.461828
3	0.167548	0.629376
4	0.129012	0.758388
5	0.090825	0.849213
6	0.059944	0.909157
7	0.037679	0.946837
8	0.022796	0.969633
9	0.013374	0.983006
10	0.007650	0.990656
11	0.004284	0.994940
12	0.002356	0.997296
13	0.001276	0.998572
14	0.000682	0.999253

k=2·3
Mean=1·81
Variance=3·23

n	P(n)	F(n)
0	0.263531	0.263531
1	0.266694	0.530225
2	0.193620	0.723845
3	0.122110	0.845955
4	0.071190	0.917144

k=3·0
Mean=2·36
Variance=4·21

n	P(n)	F(n)
0	0.175616	0.175616
1	0.231813	0.407429
2	0.203996	0.611425
3	0.149597	0.761021
4	0.098734	0.859755

15	0.000360	0.999613
16	0.000188	0.999801
17	0.000097	0.999899
18	0.000050	0.999949

k = 4·5
Mean = 3·54
Variance = 6·31

n	P(n)	F(n)
0	0.073595	0.073595
1	0.145717	0.219312
2	0.176318	0.395630
3	0.168090	0.563720
4	0.138674	0.702394
5	0.103728	0.806122
6	0.072264	0.878386
7	0.047694	0.926080
8	0.030167	0.956247
9	0.018435	0.974682
10	0.010950	0.985633
11	0.006351	0.991984
12	0.003610	0.995594
13	0.002016	0.997609
14	0.001109	0.998718
15	0.000602	0.999320
16	0.000323	0.999642
17	0.000171	0.999814
18	0.000090	0.999904

k = 5·0
Mean = 3·93
Variance = 7·02

n	P(n)	F(n)
0	0.055073	0.055073
1	0.121161	0.176234
2	0.159933	0.336167
3	0.164197	0.500364
4	0.144494	0.644858
5	0.114439	0.759297
6	0.083922	0.843219
7	0.058026	0.901245
8	0.038297	0.939542
9	0.024340	0.963882
10	0.014993	0.978875
11	0.008996	0.987871
12	0.005278	0.993149
13	0.003037	0.996186
14	0.001718	0.997904
15	0.000957	0.998861
16	0.000527	0.999388
17	0.000286	0.999674
18	0.000154	0.999828
19	0.000082	0.999910

k = 5·5
Mean = 4·32
Variance = 7·72

n	P(n)	F(n)
0	0.041213	0.041213
1	0.099735	0.140948
2	0.142622	0.283570
3	0.156884	0.440454
4	0.146686	0.587140
5	0.122630	0.709770
6	0.094425	0.804195
7	0.068256	0.872451
8	0.046926	0.919377
9	0.030971	0.950348
10	0.019760	0.970107
11	0.012251	0.982358
12	0.007412	0.989770
13	0.004390	0.994160
14	0.002553	0.996713
15	0.001460	0.998173
16	0.000823	0.998996
17	0.000458	0.999454
18	0.000252	0.999706
19	0.000137	0.999843
20	0.000074	0.999917

k = 6·0
Mean = 4·71
Variance = 8·42

n	P(n)	F(n)
0	0.030841	0.030841
1	0.081420	0.112261
2	0.125387	0.237648
3	0.147121	0.384769
4	0.145650	0.530419
5	0.128172	0.658590
6	0.103392	0.761982
7	0.077987	0.839969
8	0.055761	0.895730
9	0.038165	0.933895
10	0.025189	0.959084
11	0.016121	0.975205
12	0.010049	0.985254
13	0.006122	0.991376
14	0.003656	0.995031
15	0.002145	0.997176
16	0.001239	0.998415
17	0.000705	0.999120
18	0.000397	0.999516
19	0.000220	0.999737
20	0.000121	0.999858
21	0.000066	0.999924

k = 6·5
Mean = 5·11
Variance = 9·12

n	P(n)	F(n)
0	0.023079	0.023079
1	0.066007	0.089086
2	0.108911	0.197997
3	0.135776	0.333773
4	0.141886	0.475659
5	0.131102	0.606761
6	0.110563	0.717324
7	0.086871	0.804195
8	0.064502	0.868697
9	0.045725	0.914421
10	0.031184	0.945606
11	0.020582	0.966187
12	0.013206	0.979394
13	0.008269	0.987663
14	0.005068	0.992731
15	0.003047	0.995778
16	0.001802	0.997580
17	0.001049	0.998629
18	0.000603	0.999232
19	0.000342	0.999574
20	0.000192	0.999766
21	0.000107	0.999872
22	0.000059	0.999931

k = 7·0
Mean = 5·50
Variance = 9·82

n	P(n)	F(n)
0	0.017271	0.017271
1	0.053195	0.070465
2	0.093622	0.164088
3	0.123582	0.287669
4	0.135940	0.423609
5	0.131590	0.555199
6	0.115799	0.670997
7	0.094624	0.765622
8	0.072861	0.838482
9	0.053431	0.891913
10	0.037616	0.929529
11	0.025579	0.955107
12	0.016882	0.971989
13	0.010856	0.982846
14	0.006824	0.989670
15	0.004204	0.993873
16	0.002543	0.996416
17	0.001514	0.997930
18	0.000888	0.998818
19	0.000514	0.999333
20	0.000294	0.999627
21	0.000166	0.999793
22	0.000093	0.999886
23	0.000052	0.999938

k = 7·5
Mean = 5·89
Variance = 10·52

n	P(n)	F(n)
0	0.012924	0.012924
1	0.042651	0.055575
2	0.079756	0.135331
3	0.111127	0.246459
4	0.128352	0.374811
5	0.129892	0.504703
6	0.119068	0.623771
7	0.101038	0.724808
8	0.080578	0.805386
9	0.061060	0.866446
10	0.044329	0.910775
11	0.031031	0.941806
12	0.021049	0.962855
13	0.013892	0.976747
14	0.008951	0.985698
15	0.005645	0.991343
16	0.003493	0.994836
17	0.002124	0.996960
18	0.001272	0.998232
19	0.000751	0.998984
20	0.000438	0.999422
21	0.000252	0.999674
22	0.000144	0.999818
23	0.000081	0.999899
24	0.000045	0.999945

k = 8·0
Mean = 6·29
Variance = 11·22

n	P(n)	F(n)
0	0.009672	0.009672
1	0.034044	0.043716
2	0.067408	0.111124
3	0.098865	0.209990
4	0.119627	0.329616
5	0.126326	0.455942
6	0.120431	0.576373
7	0.105979	0.682352
8	0.087433	0.769785
9	0.068392	0.838177
10	0.051157	0.889334
11	0.036833	0.926167
12	0.025660	0.951828
13	0.017370	0.969198
14	0.011464	0.980662
15	0.007398	0.988060
16	0.004679	0.992740
17	0.002907	0.995646
18	0.001776	0.997423
19	0.001070	0.998492
20	0.000635	0.999128
21	0.000373	0.999500
22	0.000216	0.999716
23	0.000124	0.999841
24	0.000071	0.999911

k = 8·5
Mean = 6·68
Variance = 11·93

n	P(n)	F(n)
0	0.007238	0.007238
1	0.027069	0.034307
2	0.056574	0.090880
3	0.087124	0.178004
4	0.110212	0.288216
5	0.121233	0.409449
6	0.120020	0.529469
7	0.109390	0.638859
8	0.093255	0.732114
9	0.075226	0.807340
10	0.057924	0.865264
11	0.042864	0.908127
12	0.030647	0.938775
13	0.021265	0.960039
14	0.014369	0.974408
15	0.009483	0.983892
16	0.006129	0.990020
17	0.003886	0.993907
18	0.002422	0.996329
19	0.001487	0.997816
20	0.000899	0.998715
21	0.000537	0.999252
22	0.000317	0.999569
23	0.000185	0.999754
24	0.000107	0.999861
25	0.000061	0.999922

k = 9·0
Mean = 7·07
Variance = 12·63

n	P(n)	F(n)
0	0.005416	0.005416
1	0.021448	0.026864
2	0.047186	0.074050
3	0.076126	0.150176
4	0.100487	0.250663
5	0.114957	0.365619
6	0.118022	0.483642
7	0.111278	0.594920
8	0.097925	0.692844
9	0.081386	0.774231
10	0.064458	0.838689
11	0.048988	0.887677
12	0.035925	0.923601
13	0.025534	0.949135
14	0.017655	0.966790
15	0.011911	0.978701
16	0.007861	0.986563
17	0.005087	0.991650
18	0.003233	0.994883
19	0.002021	0.996904
20	0.001245	0.998149
21	0.000757	0.998906
22	0.000454	0.999360
23	0.000269	0.999629
24	0.000158	0.999787
25	0.000092	0.999879
26	0.000053	0.999931

k = 9·5
Mean = 7·46
Variance = 13·33

n	P(n)	F(n)
0	0.004053	0.004053
1	0.016942	0.020995
2	0.039136	0.060131
3	0.066009	0.126140
4	0.090763	0.216902
5	0.107826	0.324728
6	0.114655	0.439383
7	0.111707	0.551090
8	0.101374	0.652463
9	0.086731	0.739194
10	0.070599	0.809793
11	0.055067	0.864860
12	0.041392	0.906252
13	0.030121	0.936373
14	0.021300	0.957673
15	0.014683	0.972355
16	0.009892	0.982248
17	0.006529	0.988777
18	0.004229	0.993006
19	0.002693	0.995699
20	0.001689	0.997388
21	0.001044	0.998432
22	0.000637	0.999069
23	0.000384	0.999452
24	0.000229	0.999681
25	0.000135	0.999816
26	0.000079	0.999895
27	0.000046	0.999940

k = 10·0
Mean = 7·86
Variance = 14·03

n	P(n)	F(n)
0	0.003033	0.003033
1	0.013345	0.016378
2	0.032296	0.048674
3	0.056841	0.105515
4	0.081282	0.186798
5	0.100140	0.286938
6	0.110154	0.397092
7	0.110783	0.507875
8	0.103583	0.611458
9	0.091153	0.702611

10	0.076204	0.778814
11	0.060963	0.839777
12	0.046941	0.886719
13	0.034953	0.921672
14	0.025266	0.946938
15	0.017787	0.964726
16	0.012229	0.976954
17	0.008229	0.985184
18	0.005431	0.990615
19	0.003522	0.994137
20	0.002247	0.996384
21	0.001412	0.997796
22	0.000876	0.998672
23	0.000536	0.999208
24	0.000324	0.999532
25	0.000194	0.999726
26	0.000115	0.999841
27	0.000067	0.999909

k=0·1
Mean=0·07
Variance=0·12

n	P(n)	F(n)
0	0.946984	0.946984
1	0.039773	0.986758
2	0.009188	0.995945
3	0.002701	0.998646
4	0.000879	0.999526
5	0.000303	0.999829
6	0.000108	0.999937

k=0·2
Mean=0·14
Variance=0·25

n	P(n)	F(n)
0	0.896779	0.896779
1	0.075329	0.972109
2	0.018983	0.991092
3	0.005847	0.996939
4	0.001965	0.998903
5	0.000693	0.999596
6	0.000252	0.999848
7	0.000094	0.999942

k=0·3
Mean=0·22
Variance=0·37

n	P(n)	F(n)
0	0.849236	0.849236
1	0.107004	0.956240
2	0.029212	0.985452
3	0.009406	0.994858
4	0.003259	0.998117
5	0.001177	0.999295
6	0.000437	0.999731
7	0.000165	0.999896
8	0.000063	0.999960

k=0·4
Mean=0·29
Variance=0·50

n	P(n)	F(n)
0	0.804213	0.804213
1	0.135108	0.939321
2	0.039722	0.979043
3	0.013346	0.992389
4	0.004765	0.997154
5	0.001761	0.998915
6	0.000666	0.999581
7	0.000256	0.999836
8	0.000099	0.999936

k=0·5
Mean=0·36
Variance=0·62

n	P(n)	F(n)
0	0.761577	0.761577
1	0.159931	0.921509
2	0.050378	0.971887
3	0.017632	0.989519
4	0.006480	0.995999
5	0.002449	0.998449
6	0.000943	0.999392
7	0.000368	0.999759
8	0.000145	0.999904

k=0·6
Mean=0·43
Variance=0·75

n	P(n)	F(n)
0	0.721202	0.721202
1	0.181743	0.902945
2	0.061066	0.964010
3	0.022228	0.986238
4	0.008402	0.994640
5	0.003247	0.997887
6	0.001273	0.999160
7	0.000504	0.999663
8	0.000201	0.999865
9	0.000081	0.999945

k=0·7
Mean=0·51
Variance=0·87

n	P(n)	F(n)
0	0.682967	0.682967
1	0.200792	0.883759
2	0.071683	0.955442
3	0.027096	0.982538
4	0.010527	0.993065
5	0.004156	0.997221
6	0.001658	0.998879
7	0.000667	0.999546
8	0.000269	0.999815
9	0.000109	0.999925

k=0·8
Mean=0·58
Variance=1·00

n	P(n)	F(n)
0	0.646759	0.646759
1	0.217311	0.864070
2	0.082144	0.946213
3	0.032200	0.978414
4	0.012848	0.991262
5	0.005180	0.996442
6	0.002103	0.998545
7	0.000858	0.999403
8	0.000351	0.999755
9	0.000144	0.999899
10	0.000059	0.999958

k=0·9
Mean=0·65
Variance=1·12

n	P(n)	F(n)
0	0.612471	0.612471
1	0.231514	0.843984
2	0.092374	0.936358
3	0.037504	0.973862
4	0.015358	0.989220
5	0.006321	0.995541
6	0.002611	0.998152
7	0.001081	0.999233
8	0.000448	0.999681
9	0.000186	0.999867
10	0.000077	0.999945

k=1·0
Mean=0·72
Variance=1·25

n	P(n)	F(n)
0	0.580000	0.580000
1	0.243600	0.823600
2	0.102312	0.925912
3	0.042971	0.968883
4	0.018048	0.986931
5	0.007580	0.994511
6	0.003184	0.997695
7	0.001337	0.999032
8	0.000562	0.999593
9	0.000236	0.999829
10	0.000099	0.999928

k=1·1
Mean=0·80
Variance=1·37

n	P(n)	F(n)
0	0.549251	0.549251
1	0.253754	0.803005
2	0.111905	0.914910
3	0.048567	0.963477
4	0.020908	0.984385
5	0.008957	0.993342
6	0.003825	0.997167
7	0.001629	0.998796
8	0.000693	0.999489
9	0.000294	0.999783
10	0.000125	0.999908

k=1·2
Mean=0·87
Variance=1·50

n	P(n)	F(n)
0	0.520132	0.520132
1	0.262147	0.782279
2	0.121112	0.903390
3	0.054258	0.957648
4	0.023928	0.981576
5	0.010452	0.992028
6	0.004536	0.996564
7	0.001960	0.998523
8	0.000844	0.999367
9	0.000362	0.999729
10	0.000155	0.999884
11	0.000066	0.999951

k=1·3
Mean=0·94
Variance=1·62

n	P(n)	F(n)
0	0.492557	0.492557
1	0.268936	0.761493
2	0.129896	0.891389
3	0.060012	0.951401
4	0.027095	0.978496
5	0.012063	0.990559
6	0.005320	0.995879
7	0.002330	0.998209
8	0.001015	0.999224
9	0.000441	0.999665
10	0.000191	0.999856
11	0.000082	0.999938

k=1·4
Mean=1·01
Variance=1·75

n	P(n)	F(n)
0	0.466444	0.466444
1	0.274269	0.740713
2	0.138232	0.878944
3	0.065798	0.944742
4	0.030399	0.975141
5	0.013789	0.988930
6	0.006177	0.995107
7	0.002743	0.997850
8	0.001210	0.999060
9	0.000531	0.999590
10	0.000232	0.999822
11	0.000101	0.999923

k=1·5
Mean=1·09
Variance=1·87

n	P(n)	F(n)
0	0.441715	0.441715
1	0.278280	0.719995
2	0.146097	0.866092
3	0.071588	0.937680
4	0.033825	0.971505
5	0.015627	0.987132
6	0.007110	0.994243
7	0.003200	0.997442
8	0.001428	0.998870
9	0.000633	0.999503
10	0.000279	0.999782
11	0.000123	0.999905

k=1·6
Mean=1·16
Variance=2·00

n	P(n)	F(n)
0	0.418297	0.418297
1	0.281096	0.699393
2	0.153478	0.852871
3	0.077353	0.930224
4	0.037362	0.967585
5	0.017575	0.985160
6	0.008120	0.993280
7	0.003703	0.996982
8	0.001672	0.998654
9	0.000749	0.999403
10	0.000333	0.999736
11	0.000148	0.999884
12	0.000065	0.999949

k=1·7
Mean=1·23
Variance=2·12

n	P(n)	F(n)
0	0.396121	0.396121
1	0.282830	0.678951
2	0.160365	0.839316
3	0.083069	0.922385
4	0.040995	0.963379
5	0.019628	0.983007
6	0.009206	0.992213
7	0.004253	0.996466
8	0.001943	0.998408
9	0.000879	0.999288
10	0.000395	0.999683
11	0.000177	0.999860
12	0.000078	0.999938

k=1·8
Mean=1·30
Variance=2·25

n	P(n)	F(n)
0	0.375120	0.375120
1	0.283591	0.658711
2	0.166751	0.825462
3	0.088712	0.914174
4	0.044711	0.958885
5	0.021783	0.980668
6	0.010369	0.991037
7	0.004853	0.995889
8	0.002242	0.998131
9	0.001025	0.999156
10	0.000465	0.999621
11	0.000210	0.999831
12	0.000094	0.999925

k=1·9
Mean=1·38
Variance=2·37

n	P(n)	F(n)
0	0.355233	0.355233
1	0.283476	0.638709
2	0.172637	0.811346
3	0.094260	0.905605
4	0.048497	0.954102
5	0.024035	0.978137
6	0.011609	0.989746
7	0.005503	0.995248
8	0.002571	0.997819
9	0.001188	0.999007
10	0.000544	0.999551
11	0.000247	0.999798
12	0.000112	0.999910

k=2·0
Mean=1·45
Variance=2·50

n	P(n)	F(n)
0	0.336400	0.336400
1	0.282576	0.618976
2	0.178023	0.796999
3	0.099693	0.896692
4	0.052339	0.949030
5	0.026379	0.975409
6	0.012926	0.988335
7	0.006204	0.994539
8	0.002932	0.997471
9	0.001368	0.998839
10	0.000632	0.999471
11	0.000290	0.999760
12	0.000132	0.999892
13	0.000060	0.999952

k=2·1
Mean=1·52
Variance=2·62

n	P(n)	F(n)
0	0.318566	0.318566
1	0.280975	0.599540
2	0.182915	0.782455
3	0.104993	0.887448
4	0.056224	0.943672
5	0.028809	0.972481
6	0.014318	0.986799
7	0.006959	0.993757
8	0.003324	0.997082
9	0.001567	0.998649
10	0.000731	0.999379
11	0.000337	0.999717
12	0.000155	0.999872
13	0.000070	0.999942

k=2·2
Mean=1·59
Variance=2·75

n	P(n)	F(n)
0	0.301677	0.301677
1	0.278749	0.580426
2	0.187319	0.767745
3	0.110144	0.877889
4	0.060139	0.938028
5	0.031320	0.969348
6	0.015785	0.985133
7	0.007766	0.992899
8	0.003751	0.996651
9	0.001786	0.998436
10	0.000840	0.999276
11	0.000391	0.999667
12	0.000181	0.999848
13	0.000083	0.999931

k=2·3
Mean=1·67
Variance=2·87

n	P(n)	F(n)
0	0.285683	0.285683
1	0.275970	0.561653
2	0.191247	0.752900
3	0.115131	0.868031
4	0.064070	0.932101
5	0.033906	0.966007
6	0.017326	0.983333
7	0.008628	0.991961
8	0.004213	0.996174
9	0.002025	0.998199
10	0.000961	0.999160
11	0.000451	0.999611
12	0.000210	0.999821
13	0.000097	0.999918

k=2·4
Mean=1·74
Variance=3·00

n	P(n)	F(n)
0	0.270537	0.270537
1	0.272702	0.543239
2	0.194709	0.737948
3	0.119941	0.857889
4	0.068006	0.925895
5	0.036560	0.962455
6	0.018938	0.981393
7	0.009545	0.990938
8	0.004710	0.995649
9	0.002286	0.997935
10	0.001095	0.999029
11	0.000518	0.999548
12	0.000243	0.999791
13	0.000113	0.999904

k = 2·5
Mean = 1·81
Variance = 3·12

n	P(n)	F(n)
0	0.256195	0.256195
1	0.269004	0.525199
2	0.197718	0.722917
3	0.124562	0.847480
4	0.071935	0.919414
5	0.039276	0.958691
6	0.020620	0.979311
7	0.010516	0.989827
8	0.005245	0.995072
9	0.002570	0.997642
10	0.001241	0.998884
11	0.000592	0.999476
12	0.000280	0.999756
13	0.000131	0.999887
14	0.000061	0.999948

k = 3·0
Mean = 2·17
Variance = 3·75

n	P(n)	F(n)
0	0.195112	0.195112
1	0.245841	0.440953
2	0.206507	0.647460
3	0.144555	0.792014
4	0.091069	0.883084
5	0.053549	0.936632
6	0.029987	0.966620
7	0.016193	0.982813
8	0.008501	0.991314
9	0.004364	0.995678
10	0.002199	0.997878
11	0.001092	0.998970
12	0.000535	0.999505
13	0.000259	0.999764
14	0.000124	0.999888
15	0.000059	0.999947

k = 3·5
Mean = 2·53
Variance = 4·37

n	P(n)	F(n)
0	0.148593	0.148593
1	0.218432	0.367024
2	0.206418	0.573442
3	0.158942	0.732384
4	0.108478	0.840862
5	0.068341	0.909203
6	0.040663	0.949865
7	0.023178	0.973043
8	0.012777	0.985820
9	0.006857	0.992677

10	0.003600	0.996277
11	0.001856	0.998132
12	0.000942	0.999074
13	0.000472	0.999546
14	0.000233	0.999779
15	0.000114	0.999893
16	0.000056	0.999949

k = 4·0
Mean = 2·90
Variance = 4·99

n	P(n)	F(n)
0	0.113165	0.113165
1	0.190117	0.303282
2	0.199623	0.502905
3	0.167683	0.670588
4	0.123247	0.793836
5	0.082822	0.876658
6	0.052178	0.928836
7	0.031307	0.960142
8	0.018080	0.978222
9	0.010125	0.988347
10	0.005528	0.993875
11	0.002955	0.996830
12	0.001551	0.998381
13	0.000802	0.999183
14	0.000409	0.999592
15	0.000206	0.999798
16	0.000103	0.999901

k = 4·5
Mean = 3·26
Variance = 5·62

n	P(n)	F(n)
0	0.086184	0.086184
1	0.162888	0.249071
2	0.188135	0.437206
3	0.171203	0.608409
4	0.134822	0.743232
5	0.096263	0.839495
6	0.064015	0.903510
7	0.040329	0.943839
8	0.024349	0.968188
9	0.014204	0.982392
10	0.008053	0.990445
11	0.004459	0.994904
12	0.002419	0.997322
13	0.001289	0.998612
14	0.000677	0.999289
15	0.000351	0.999639
16	0.000179	0.999819
17	0.000091	0.999910

k = 5·0
Mean = 3·62
Variance = 6·24

n	P(n)	F(n)
0	0.065636	0.065636
1	0.137835	0.203471
2	0.173672	0.377143
3	0.170199	0.547341
4	0.142967	0.690308
5	0.108083	0.798391
6	0.075658	0.874049
7	0.049934	0.923983
8	0.031459	0.955442
9	0.019085	0.974527
10	0.011222	0.985749
11	0.006427	0.992176
12	0.003599	0.995775
13	0.001977	0.997752
14	0.001067	0.998819
15	0.000568	0.999387
16	0.000298	0.999685
17	0.000155	0.999840
18	0.000079	0.999919

k = 5·5
Mean = 3·98
Variance = 6·87

n	P(n)	F(n)
0	0.049987	0.049987
1	0.115469	0.165456
2	0.157615	0.323071
3	0.165496	0.488567
4	0.147705	0.636273
5	0.117869	0.754141
6	0.086634	0.840775
7	0.059777	0.900552
8	0.039229	0.939781
9	0.024714	0.964495
10	0.015051	0.979546
11	0.008907	0.988453
12	0.005144	0.993597
13	0.002908	0.996506
14	0.001614	0.998120
15	0.000881	0.999001
16	0.000474	0.999476
17	0.000252	0.999727
18	0.000132	0.999860
19	0.000069	0.999928

k = 6·0
Mean = 4·34
Variance = 7·49

n	P(n)	F(n)
0	0.038069	0.038069
1	0.095933	0.134002
2	0.141022	0.275023
3	0.157944	0.432968
4	0.149257	0.582225

n	P(n)	F(n)	n	P(n)	F(n)	n	P(n)	F(n)
5	0.125376	0.707601	5	0.133317	0.611062	5	0.132555	0.515074
6	0.096540	0.804141	6	0.111986	0.723048	6	0.120625	0.635698
7	0.069509	0.873649	7	0.087349	0.810397	7	0.101325	0.737023
8	0.047440	0.921089	8	0.064202	0.874598	8	0.079793	0.816817
9	0.030994	0.952083	9	0.044941	0.919539	9	0.059579	0.876396
10	0.019526	0.971609	10	0.030200	0.949740	10	0.042539	0.918935
11	0.011929	0.983538	11	0.019603	0.969342	11	0.029236	0.948171
12	0.007098	0.990635	12	0.012350	0.981692	12	0.019442	0.967614
13	0.004128	0.994763	13	0.007581	0.989273	13	0.012563	0.980176
14	0.002353	0.997115	14	0.004549	0.993822	14	0.007914	0.988091
15	0.001318	0.998433	15	0.002675	0.996496	15	0.004875	0.992966
16	0.000726	0.999159	16	0.001545	0.998041	16	0.002943	0.995909
17	0.000395	0.999554	17	0.000878	0.998918	17	0.001745	0.997655
18	0.000212	0.999766	18	0.000491	0.999410	18	0.001018	0.998673
19	0.000112	0.999878	19	0.000272	0.999681	19	0.000585	0.999258
20	0.000059	0.999937	20	0.000148	0.999830	20	0.000332	0.999590
			21	0.000080	0.999910	21	0.000186	0.999775
						22	0.000103	0.999878
						23	0.000056	0.999935

k = 6·5
Mean = 4·71
Variance = 8·12

k = 7·5
Mean = 5·43
Variance = 9·36

k = 8·5
Mean = 6·16
Variance = 10·61

n	P(n)	F(n)	n	P(n)	F(n)	n	P(n)	F(n)
0	0.028992	0.028992	0	0.016816	0.016816	0	0.009753	0.009753
1	0.079149	0.108141	1	0.052969	0.069784	1	0.034818	0.044571
2	0.124659	0.232801	2	0.094549	0.164334	2	0.069462	0.114033
3	0.148345	0.381145	3	0.125751	0.290084	3	0.102110	0.216143
4	0.147974	0.529119	4	0.138640	0.428725	4	0.123297	0.339440
5	0.130513	0.659632	5	0.133926	0.562651	5	0.129462	0.468902
6	0.105063	0.764695	6	0.117186	0.679836	6	0.122342	0.591244
7	0.078797	0.843492	7	0.094920	0.774757	7	0.106437	0.697681
8	0.055848	0.899340	8	0.072258	0.847015	8	0.086613	0.784295
9	0.037790	0.937130	9	0.052267	0.899282	9	0.066692	0.850987
10	0.024601	0.961731	10	0.036221	0.935502	10	0.049019	0.900006
11	0.015499	0.977230	11	0.024202	0.959704	11	0.034625	0.934631
12	0.009493	0.986723	12	0.015671	0.975375	12	0.023632	0.958263
13	0.005674	0.992397	13	0.009873	0.985248	13	0.015651	0.973914
14	0.003319	0.995716	14	0.006072	0.991320	14	0.010095	0.984009
15	0.001905	0.997622	15	0.003655	0.994975	15	0.006360	0.990369
16	0.001075	0.998697	16	0.002159	0.997134	16	0.003923	0.994293
17	0.000598	0.999295	17	0.001253	0.998387	17	0.002375	0.996667
18	0.000328	0.999622	18	0.000717	0.999104	18	0.001413	0.998080
19	0.000178	0.999800	19	0.000404	0.999507	19	0.000828	0.998908
20	0.000095	0.999895	20	0.000225	0.999732	20	0.000478	0.999386
21	0.000050	0.999945	21	0.000124	0.999856	21	0.000272	0.999658
			22	0.000067	0.999923	22	0.000153	0.999812
						23	0.000085	0.999897
						24	0.000047	0.999944

k = 7·0
Mean = 5·07
Variance = 8·74

k = 8·0
Mean = 5·79
Variance = 9·99

k = 9·0
Mean = 6·52
Variance = 11·24

n	P(n)	F(n)	n	P(n)	F(n)	n	P(n)	F(n)
0	0.022080	0.022080	0	0.012806	0.012806	0	0.007428	0.007428
1	0.064915	0.086995	1	0.043029	0.055836	1	0.028077	0.035504
2	0.109057	0.196051	2	0.081325	0.137161	2	0.058961	0.094465
3	0.137412	0.333463	3	0.113855	0.251016	3	0.090800	0.185265
4	0.144282	0.477745	4	0.131503	0.382519	4	0.114407	0.299672

5	0.124933	0.424605
6	0.122434	0.547039
7	0.110191	0.657230
8	0.092560	0.749790
9	0.073431	0.823222
10	0.055514	0.878735
11	0.040273	0.919008
12	0.028191	0.947199
13	0.019127	0.966326
14	0.012623	0.978949
15	0.008130	0.987079
16	0.005122	0.992201
17	0.003163	0.995364
18	0.001919	0.997283
19	0.001145	0.998428
20	0.000673	0.999102
21	0.000391	0.999492
22	0.000224	0.999716
23	0.000127	0.999843
24	0.000071	0.999914

k = 9·5
Mean = 6·88
Variance = 11·86

n	P(n)	F(n)
0	0.005657	0.005657
1	0.022570	0.028227
2	0.049768	0.077995
3	0.080126	0.158121
4	0.105165	0.263286
5	0.119257	0.382544
6	0.121046	0.503590
7	0.112573	0.616163
8	0.097516	0.713679
9	0.079638	0.793318
10	0.061879	0.855197
11	0.046072	0.901269
12	0.033057	0.934325
13	0.022962	0.957287
14	0.015499	0.972786
15	0.010198	0.982984
16	0.006559	0.989543
17	0.004132	0.993675
18	0.002555	0.996230
19	0.001553	0.997783
20	0.000930	0.998713
21	0.000548	0.999261
22	0.000319	0.999581
23	0.000184	0.999764
24	0.000104	0.999869
25	0.000059	0.999928

k = 10·0
Mean = 7·24
Variance = 12·49

n	P(n)	F(n)
0	0.004308	0.004308
1	0.018094	0.022402
2	0.041797	0.064198
3	0.070218	0.134417
4	0.095848	0.230265
5	0.112717	0.342982
6	0.118353	0.461335
7	0.113619	0.574954
8	0.101405	0.676359
9	0.085180	0.761539
10	0.067974	0.829513
11	0.051907	0.881420
12	0.038152	0.919572
13	0.027117	0.946689
14	0.018711	0.965400
15	0.012574	0.977974
16	0.008251	0.986225
17	0.005300	0.991526
18	0.003339	0.994865
19	0.002067	0.996932
20	0.001259	0.998190
21	0.000755	0.998946
22	0.000447	0.999393
23	0.000261	0.999654
24	0.000151	0.999805
25	0.000086	0.999891
26	0.000049	0.999939

k=0·1
Mean = 0·07
Variance = 0·11

n	P(n)	F(n)
0	0.950200	0.950200
1	0.038008	0.988208
2	0.008362	0.996570
3	0.002341	0.998911
4	0.000726	0.999637
5	0.000238	0.999875
6	0.000081	0.999956

k=0·2
Mean = 0·13
Variance = 0·22

n	P(n)	F(n)
0	0.902880	0.902880
1	0.072230	0.975111
2	0.017335	0.992446
3	0.005085	0.997531
4	0.001627	0.999158
5	0.000547	0.999705
6	0.000190	0.999895
7	0.000067	0.999962

k=0·3
Mean = 0·20
Variance = 0·33

n	P(n)	F(n)
0	0.857917	0.857917
1	0.102950	0.960867
2	0.026767	0.987634
3	0.008209	0.995843
4	0.002709	0.998552
5	0.000932	0.999483
6	0.000329	0.999813
7	0.000119	0.999931

k=0·4
Mean = 0·27
Variance = 0·44

n	P(n)	F(n)
0	0.815193	0.815193
1	0.130431	0.945624
2	0.036521	0.982145
3	0.011687	0.993831
4	0.003973	0.997805
5	0.001399	0.999203
6	0.000504	0.999707
7	0.000184	0.999891
8	0.000068	0.999959

k=0·5
Mean = 0·33
Variance = 0·56

n	P(n)	F(n)
0	0.774597	0.774597
1	0.154919	0.929516
2	0.046476	0.975992
3	0.015492	0.991484
4	0.005422	0.996906
5	0.001952	0.998858
6	0.000716	0.999574
7	0.000266	0.999839
8	0.000100	0.999939

k=0·6
Mean = 0·40
Variance = 0·67

n	P(n)	F(n)
0	0.736022	0.736022
1	0.176645	0.912667
2	0.056526	0.969194
3	0.019596	0.988790
4	0.007055	0.995844
5	0.002596	0.998440
6	0.000969	0.999409
7	0.000366	0.999775
8	0.000139	0.999914

k=0·7
Mean = 0·47
Variance = 0·78

n	P(n)	F(n)
0	0.699368	0.699368
1	0.195823	0.895191
2	0.066580	0.961771
3	0.023969	0.985740
4	0.008868	0.994608
5	0.003335	0.997943
6	0.001267	0.999210
7	0.000485	0.999695
8	0.000187	0.999882
9	0.000072	0.999954

k=0·8
Mean = 0·53
Variance = 0·89

n	P(n)	F(n)
0	0.664540	0.664540
1	0.212653	0.877193
2	0.076555	0.953748
3	0.028581	0.982328
4	0.010861	0.993189
5	0.004170	0.997359
6	0.001613	0.998972
7	0.000627	0.999598
8	0.000244	0.999843
9	0.000096	0.999938

k=0·9
Mean = 0·60
Variance = 1·00

n	P(n)	F(n)
0	0.631446	0.631446
1	0.227321	0.858766
2	0.086382	0.945148
3	0.033401	0.978549
4	0.013026	0.991576
5	0.005106	0.996682
6	0.002008	0.998690
7	0.000792	0.999482
8	0.000313	0.999795
9	0.000124	0.999919

k=1·0
Mean = 0·67
Variance = 1·11

n	P(n)	F(n)
0	0.600000	0.600000
1	0.240000	0.840000
2	0.096000	0.936000
3	0.038400	0.974400
4	0.015360	0.989760
5	0.006144	0.995904
6	0.002458	0.998362
7	0.000983	0.999345
8	0.000393	0.999738
9	0.000157	0.999895
10	0.000063	0.999958

k=1·1
Mean = 0·73
Variance = 1·22

n	P(n)	F(n)
0	0.570120	0.570120
1	0.250853	0.820973
2	0.105358	0.926331
3	0.043548	0.969879
4	0.017855	0.987734
5	0.007285	0.995019
6	0.002962	0.997981
7	0.001202	0.999183
8	0.000487	0.999670
9	0.000197	0.999867
10	0.000080	0.999946

k=1·2
Mean=0·80
Variance=1·33

n	P(n)	F(n)
0	0.541728	0.541728
1	0.260030	0.801758
2	0.114413	0.916171
3	0.048816	0.964987
4	0.020503	0.985490
5	0.008529	0.994019
6	0.003525	0.997544
7	0.001450	0.998995
8	0.000595	0.999590
9	0.000243	0.999833
10	0.000099	0.999932

k=1·5
Mean=1·00
Variance=1·67

n	P(n)	F(n)
0	0.464758	0.464758
1	0.278855	0.743613
2	0.139427	0.883040
3	0.065066	0.948106
4	0.029280	0.977386
5	0.012883	0.990269
6	0.005583	0.995852
7	0.002393	0.998244
8	0.001017	0.999261
9	0.000429	0.999691
10	0.000180	0.999871
11	0.000075	0.999946

k=1·8
Mean=1·20
Variance=2·00

n	P(n)	F(n)
0	0.398724	0.398724
1	0.287081	0.685805
2	0.160765	0.846571
3	0.081455	0.928025
4	0.039098	0.967123
5	0.018142	0.985265
6	0.008224	0.993489
7	0.003666	0.997155
8	0.001613	0.998767
9	0.000702	0.999470
10	0.000303	0.999773
11	0.000130	0.999904

k=1·3
Mean=0·87
Variance=1·44

n	P(n)	F(n)
0	0.514750	0.514750
1	0.267670	0.782420
2	0.123128	0.905549
3	0.054176	0.959725
4	0.023296	0.983021
5	0.009877	0.992899
6	0.004149	0.997047
7	0.001731	0.998778
8	0.000718	0.999496
9	0.000297	0.999793
10	0.000122	0.999915

k=1·6
Mean=1·07
Variance=1·78

n	P(n)	F(n)
0	0.441613	0.441613
1	0.282632	0.724246
2	0.146969	0.871214
3	0.070545	0.941759
4	0.032451	0.974210
5	0.014538	0.988748
6	0.006397	0.995145
7	0.002778	0.997923
8	0.001195	0.999117
9	0.000510	0.999627
10	0.000216	0.999843
11	0.000091	0.999934

k=1·9
Mean=1·27
Variance=2·11

n	P(n)	F(n)
0	0.378868	0.378868
1	0.287939	0.666807
2	0.167005	0.833812
3	0.086842	0.920654
4	0.042553	0.963207
5	0.020085	0.983292
6	0.009239	0.992531
7	0.004171	0.996702
8	0.001856	0.998558
9	0.000817	0.999374
10	0.000356	0.999730
11	0.000154	0.999885
12	0.000066	0.999951

k=1·4
Mean=0·93
Variance=1·56

n	P(n)	F(n)
0	0.489116	0.489116
1	0.273905	0.763021
2	0.131474	0.894495
3	0.059602	0.954097
4	0.026225	0.980322
5	0.011329	0.991651
6	0.004834	0.996484
7	0.002044	0.998528
8	0.000858	0.999387
9	0.000359	0.999745
10	0.000149	0.999895
11	0.000062	0.999957

k=1·7
Mean=1·13
Variance=1·89

n	P(n)	F(n)
0	0.419621	0.419621
1	0.285342	0.704963
2	0.154085	0.859048
3	0.076015	0.935063
4	0.035727	0.970790
5	0.016292	0.987082
6	0.007277	0.994359
7	0.003202	0.997561
8	0.001393	0.998953
9	0.000600	0.999554
10	0.000257	0.999811
11	0.000109	0.999920

k=2·0
Mean=1·33
Variance=2·22

n	P(n)	F(n)
0	0.360000	0.360000
1	0.288000	0.648000
2	0.172800	0.820800
3	0.092160	0.912960
4	0.046080	0.959040
5	0.022118	0.981158
6	0.010322	0.991480
7	0.004719	0.996199
8	0.002123	0.998322
9	0.000944	0.999266
10	0.000415	0.999681
11	0.000181	0.999862
12	0.000079	0.999941

k=2·1
Mean = 1·40
Variance = 2·33

n	P(n)	F(n)
0	0.342072	0.342072
1	0.287341	0.629413
2	0.178151	0.807564
3	0.097389	0.904953
4	0.049669	0.954622
5	0.024238	0.978860
6	0.011473	0.990333
7	0.005310	0.995643
8	0.002416	0.998059
9	0.001085	0.999144
10	0.000482	0.999625
11	0.000212	0.999837
12	0.000093	0.999930

k=2·2
Mean = 1·47
Variance = 2·44

n	P(n)	F(n)
0	0.325037	0.325037
1	0.236033	0.611069
2	0.183061	0.794130
3	0.102514	0.896644
4	0.053307	0.949952
5	0.026440	0.976392
6	0.012691	0.989084
7	0.005947	0.995030
8	0.002736	0.997766
9	0.001240	0.999006
10	0.000556	0.999562
11	0.000246	0.999808
12	0.000108	0.999916

k=2·3
Mean = 1·53
Variance = 2·56

n	P(n)	F(n)
0	0.308850	0.308850
1	0.284142	0.592992
2	0.187534	0.780526
3	0.107519	0.888046
4	0.056985	0.945031
5	0.028721	0.973751
6	0.013977	0.987729
7	0.006629	0.994358
8	0.003083	0.997441
9	0.001411	0.998852
10	0.000638	0.999490
11	0.000285	0.999775
12	0.000126	0.999901

k=2·4
Mean = 1·60
Variance = 2·67

n	P(n)	F(n)
0	0.293470	0.293470
1	0.281731	0.575200
2	0.191577	0.766777
3	0.112392	0.879169
4	0.060692	0.939861
5	0.031074	0.970935
6	0.015330	0.986264
7	0.007358	0.993623
8	0.003458	0.997081
9	0.001599	0.998680
10	0.000729	0.999409
11	0.000329	0.999737
12	0.000147	0.999884
13	0.000065	0.999949

k=2·5
Mean = 1·67
Variance = 2·78

n	P(n)	F(n)
0	0.278855	0.278855
1	0.278855	0.557710
2	0.195158	0.752908
3	0.117119	0.870027
4	0.064415	0.934442
5	0.033496	0.967938
6	0.016748	0.984686
7	0.008135	0.992821
8	0.003864	0.996685
9	0.001803	0.998488
10	0.000829	0.999318
11	0.000377	0.999695
12	0.000170	0.999865
13	0.000076	0.999940

k=3·0
Mean = 2·00
Variance = 3·33

n	P(n)	F(n)
0	0.216000	0.216000
1	0.259200	0.475200
2	0.207360	0.682560
3	0.138240	0.820800
4	0.082944	0.903744
5	0.046449	0.950193
6	0.024773	0.974965
7	0.012740	0.987705
8	0.006370	0.994076
9	0.003114	0.997190
10	0.001495	0.998685
11	0.000707	0.999391
12	0.000330	0.999721
13	0.000152	0.999873
14	0.000070	0.999943

k=3·5
Mean = 2·33
Variance = 3·89

n	P(n)	F(n)
0	0.167313	0.167313
1	0.234238	0.401551
2	0.210814	0.612365
3	0.154597	0.766962
4	0.100488	0.867450
5	0.060293	0.927743
6	0.034166	0.961909
7	0.018547	0.980456
8	0.009737	0.990194
9	0.004977	0.995171
10	0.002488	0.997659
11	0.001222	0.998881
12	0.000590	0.999471
13	0.000282	0.999753
14	0.000133	0.999885
15	0.000062	0.999947

k=4·0
Mean = 2·67
Variance = 4·44

n	P(n)	F(n)
0	0.129600	0.129600
1	0.207360	0.336960
2	0.207360	0.544320
3	0.165888	0.710208
4	0.116122	0.826330
5	0.074318	0.900647
6	0.044591	0.945238
7	0.025480	0.970719
8	0.014014	0.984733
9	0.007474	0.992207
10	0.003887	0.996094
11	0.001979	0.998072
12	0.000989	0.999062
13	0.000487	0.999549
14	0.000237	0.999785
15	0.000114	0.999899
16	0.000054	0.999953

k=4·5
Mean = 3·00
Variance = 5·00

n	P(n)	F(n)
0	0.100388	0.100388
1	0.180698	0.281086
2	0.198768	0.479853
3	0.172265	0.652119
4	0.129199	0.781318

5	0.087855	0.869173
6	0.055642	0.924815
7	0.033385	0.958200
8	0.019196	0.977396
9	0.010665	0.988061
10	0.005759	0.993820
11	0.003037	0.996856
12	0.001569	0.998425
13	0.000797	0.999222
14	0.000398	0.999620
15	0.000196	0.999816
16	0.000096	0.999912

k = 5·0
Mean = 3·33
Variance = 5·56

n	P(n)	F(n)
0	0.077760	0.077760
1	0.155520	0.233280
2	0.186624	0.419904
3	0.174182	0.594086
4	0.139346	0.733432
5	0.100329	0.833761
6	0.066886	0.900647
7	0.042043	0.942690
8	0.025226	0.967916
9	0.014575	0.982490
10	0.008162	0.990652
11	0.004452	0.995104
12	0.002374	0.997479
13	0.001242	0.998721
14	0.000639	0.999359
15	0.000324	0.999683
16	0.000162	0.999845
17	0.000080	0.999925

k = 5·5
Mean = 3·67
Variance = 6·11

n	P(n)	F(n)
0	0.060233	0.060233
1	0.132512	0.192744
2	0.172265	0.365010
3	0.172265	0.537275
4	0.146426	0.683701
5	0.111283	0.794984
6	0.077898	0.872882
7	0.051190	0.924073
8	0.031994	0.956067
9	0.019196	0.975263
10	0.011134	0.986397
11	0.006275	0.992673
12	0.003452	0.996124
13	0.001859	0.997983
14	0.000982	0.998965

15	0.000511	0.999476
16	0.000262	0.999738
17	0.000132	0.999870
18	0.000066	0.999936

k = 6·0
Mean = 4·00
Variance = 6·67

n	P(n)	F(n)
0	0.046656	0.046656
1	0.111974	0.158630
2	0.156764	0.315395
3	0.167215	0.482610
4	0.150494	0.633103
5	0.120395	0.753498
6	0.088290	0.841788
7	0.060541	0.902329
8	0.039352	0.941681
9	0.024486	0.966167
10	0.014691	0.980858
11	0.008548	0.989406
12	0.004844	0.994250
13	0.002683	0.996932
14	0.001456	0.998388
15	0.000777	0.999165
16	0.000408	0.999573
17	0.000211	0.999784
18	0.000108	0.999892
19	0.000055	0.999946

k = 6·5
Mean = 4·33
Variance = 7·22

n	P(n)	F(n)
0	0.036140	0.036140
1	0.093963	0.130102
2	0.140944	0.271047
3	0.159737	0.430784
4	0.151750	0.582534
5	0.127470	0.710004
6	0.097727	0.807731
7	0.069805	0.877536
8	0.047118	0.924655
9	0.030365	0.955020
10	0.018826	0.973846
11	0.011296	0.985142
12	0.006589	0.991731
13	0.003751	0.995482
14	0.002090	0.997572
15	0.001142	0.998714
16	0.000614	0.999328
17	0.000325	0.999653
18	0.000170	0.999823
19	0.000088	0.999911

k = 7·0
Mean = 4·67
Variance = 7·78

n	P(n)	F(n)
0	0.027994	0.02799
1	0.078382	0.10637
2	0.125411	0.23178
3	0.150494	0.38228
4	0.150494	0.53277
5	0.132434	0.66520
6	0.105947	0.77115
7	0.078704	0.84986
8	0.055093	0.90495
9	0.036728	0.94168
10	0.023506	0.96518
11	0.014531	0.97971
12	0.008719	0.98843
13	0.005097	0.99353
14	0.002913	0.99644
15	0.001631	0.99807
16	0.000897	0.99897
17	0.000485	0.99946
18	0.000259	0.99971
19	0.000136	0.99985
20	0.000071	0.99992

k = 7·5
Mean = 5·00
Variance = 8·33

n	P(n)	F(n)
0	0.021684	0.02168
1	0.065051	0.08673
2	0.110587	0.19732
3	0.140077	0.33739
4	0.147081	0.48448
5	0.135314	0.61979
6	0.112762	0.73255
7	0.086988	0.81954
8	0.063066	0.88261
9	0.043446	0.92605
10	0.028674	0.95473
11	0.018247	0.97297
12	0.011252	0.98423
13	0.006751	0.99098
14	0.003954	0.99493
15	0.002267	0.99720
16	0.001275	0.99847
17	0.000705	0.99918
18	0.000384	0.99956
19	0.000206	0.99977
20	0.000109	0.99988
21	0.000057	0.99994

k=8·0
Mean=5·33
Variance=8·89

n	P(n)	F(n)
0	0.016796	0.016796
1	0.053748	0.070544
2	0.096746	0.167290
3	0.128995	0.296284
4	0.141894	0.438178
5	0.136218	0.574396
6	0.118056	0.692452
7	0.094445	0.786897
8	0.070833	0.857730
9	0.050370	0.908101
10	0.034252	0.942353
11	0.022419	0.964772
12	0.014199	0.978971
13	0.008738	0.987709
14	0.005243	0.992952
15	0.003076	0.996027
16	0.001769	0.997796
17	0.000999	0.998795
18	0.000555	0.999349
19	0.000304	0.999653
20	0.000164	0.999817
21	0.000087	0.999905

k=9·0
Mean=6·00
Variance=10·00

n	P(n)	F(n)
0	0.010078	0.010078
1	0.036280	0.046357
2	0.072559	0.118917
3	0.106420	0.225337
4	0.127705	0.353042
5	0.132813	0.485855
6	0.123959	0.609813
7	0.106250	0.716063
8	0.085000	0.801063
9	0.064222	0.865286
10	0.046240	0.911526
11	0.031948	0.943474
12	0.021298	0.964772
13	0.013762	0.978534
14	0.008650	0.987185
15	0.005306	0.992490
16	0.003183	0.995674
17	0.001873	0.997546
18	0.001082	0.998628
19	0.000615	0.999243
20	0.000344	0.999587
21	0.000190	0.999778
22	0.000104	0.999881
23	0.000056	0.999937

k=10·0
Mean=6·67
Variance=11·11

n	P(n)	F(n)
0	0.006047	0.006047
1	0.024186	0.030233
2	0.053210	0.083443
3	0.085136	0.168580
4	0.110677	0.279257
5	0.123959	0.403216
6	0.123959	0.527174
7	0.113334	0.640508
8	0.096334	0.736841
9	0.077067	0.813908
10	0.058571	0.872479
11	0.042597	0.915076
12	0.029818	0.944894
13	0.020184	0.965078
14	0.013264	0.978342
15	0.008489	0.986831
16	0.005306	0.992137
17	0.003246	0.995382
18	0.001947	0.997330
19	0.001148	0.998478
20	0.000666	0.999144
21	0.000380	0.999524
22	0.000214	0.999739
23	0.000119	0.999858
24	0.000066	0.999924

k=8·5
Mean=5·67
Variance=9·44

n	P(n)	F(n)
0	0.013010	0.013010
1	0.044235	0.057245
2	0.084046	0.141291
3	0.117665	0.258956
4	0.135314	0.394270
5	0.135314	0.529585
6	0.121783	0.651368
7	0.100906	0.752274
8	0.078202	0.830476
9	0.057348	0.887824
10	0.040144	0.927968
11	0.027006	0.954973
12	0.017554	0.972527
13	0.011072	0.983600
14	0.006802	0.990401
15	0.004081	0.994482
16	0.002398	0.996880
17	0.001382	0.998262
18	0.000783	0.999045
19	0.000437	0.999482
20	0.000240	0.999722
21	0.000130	0.999853
22	0.000070	0.999923

k=9·5
Mean=6·33
Variance=10·56

n	P(n)	F(n)
0	0.007806	0.007806
1	0.029663	0.037470
2	0.062293	0.099763
3	0.095516	0.195279
4	0.119395	0.314674
5	0.128947	0.443620
6	0.124648	0.568269
7	0.110403	0.678672
8	0.091082	0.769754
9	0.070842	0.840596
10	0.052423	0.893019
11	0.037173	0.930192
12	0.025401	0.955593
13	0.016804	0.972397
14	0.010803	0.983199
15	0.006770	0.989969
16	0.004146	0.994115
17	0.002488	0.996603
18	0.001465	0.998068
19	0.000848	0.998916
20	0.000483	0.999400
21	0.000272	0.999672
22	0.000151	0.999822
23	0.000083	0.999905

P=0·62

k=0·2
Mean = 0·12
Variance = 0·20

n	P(n)	F(n)
0	0.908821	0.908821
1	0.069070	0.977891
2	0.015748	0.993639
3	0.004388	0.998028
4	0.001334	0.999362
5	0.000426	0.999788
6	0.000140	0.999928

k=0·4
Mean = 0·25
Variance = 0·40

n	P(n)	F(n)
0	0.825956	0.825956
1	0.125545	0.951501
2	0.033395	0.984896
3	0.010152	0.995048
4	0.003279	0.998327
5	0.001097	0.999424
6	0.000375	0.999799
7	0.000130	0.999929

k=0·6
Mean = 0·37
Variance = 0·59

n	P(n)	F(n)
0	0.750646	0.750646
1	0.171147	0.921793
2	0.052029	0.973822
3	0.017135	0.990957
4	0.005860	0.996817
5	0.002049	0.998865
6	0.000727	0.999592
7	0.000260	0.999852
8	0.000094	0.999946

k=0·8
Mean = 0·49
Variance = 0·79

n	P(n)	F(n)
0	0.682203	0.682203
1	0.207390	0.889592
2	0.070927	0.960519
3	0.025156	0.985675
4	0.009081	0.994756
5	0.003313	0.998069
6	0.001217	0.999286
7	0.000449	0.999735
8	0.000166	0.999901

k=1·0
Mean = 0·61
Variance = 0·99

n	P(n)	F(n)
0	0.620000	0.620000
1	0.235600	0.855600
2	0.089528	0.945128
3	0.034021	0.979149
4	0.012928	0.992076
5	0.004913	0.996989
6	0.001867	0.998856
7	0.000709	0.999565
8	0.000270	0.999835
9	0.000102	0.999937

k=1·2
Mean = 0·74
Variance = 1·19

n	P(n)	F(n)
0	0.563469	0.563469
1	0.256942	0.820411
2	0.107402	0.927813
3	0.043533	0.971346
4	0.017370	0.988716
5	0.006865	0.995580
6	0.002695	0.998276
7	0.001054	0.999330
8	0.000410	0.999740
9	0.000159	0.999899
10	0.000062	0.999961

k=1·4
Mean = 0·86
Variance = 1·38

n	P(n)	F(n)
0	0.512092	0.512092
1	0.272433	0.784526
2	0.124230	0.908755
3	0.053502	0.962257
4	0.022364	0.984620
5	0.009178	0.993798
6	0.003720	0.997518
7	0.001494	0.999013
8	0.000596	0.999609
9	0.000237	0.999846
10	0.000094	0.999939

k=1·6
Mean = 0·98
Variance = 1·58

n	P(n)	F(n)
0	0.465400	0.465400
1	0.282963	0.748364
2	0.139784	0.888148
3	0.063741	0.951889
4	0.027855	0.979744
5	0.011855	0.991599
6	0.004955	0.996555
7	0.002044	0.998599
8	0.000835	0.999434
9	0.000339	0.999773
10	0.000136	0.999909

k=1·8
Mean = 1·10
Variance = 1·78

n	P(n)	F(n)
0	0.422966	0.422966
1	0.289308	0.712274
2	0.153912	0.866186
3	0.074083	0.940269
4	0.033782	0.974051
5	0.014891	0.988942
6	0.006413	0.995355
7	0.002715	0.998071
8	0.001135	0.999206
9	0.000470	0.999675
10	0.000193	0.999868
11	0.000079	0.999947

k=2·0
Mean = 1·23
Variance = 1·98

n	P(n)	F(n)
0	0.384400	0.384400
1	0.292144	0.676544
2	0.166522	0.843066
3	0.084371	0.927437
4	0.040076	0.967514
5	0.018275	0.985788
6	0.008102	0.993890
7	0.003519	0.997409
8	0.001504	0.998913
9	0.000635	0.999548
10	0.000265	0.999813
11	0.000110	0.999923

k=2·2
Mean=1·35
Variance=2·17

n	P(n)	F(n)
0	0.349351	0.349351
1	0.292057	0.641408
2	0.177571	0.818979
3	0.094468	0.913447
4	0.046667	0.960114
5	0.021990	0.982103
6	0.010027	0.992130
7	0.004464	0.996594
8	0.001951	0.998544
9	0.000840	0.999384
10	0.000358	0.999742
11	0.000151	0.999893
12	0.000063	0.999956

k=2·4
Mean=1·47
Variance=2·37

n	P(n)	F(n)
0	0.317497	0.317497
1	0.289558	0.607055
2	0.187054	0.794109
3	0.104252	0.898361
4	0.053481	0.951842
5	0.026013	0.977855
6	0.012192	0.990046
7	0.005559	0.995606
8	0.002482	0.998088
9	0.001090	0.999178
10	0.000472	0.999650
11	0.000202	0.999852
12	0.000086	0.999938

k=2·6
Mean=1·59
Variance=2·57

n	P(n)	F(n)
0	0.288548	0.288548
1	0.285086	0.573634
2	0.194999	0.768632
3	0.113619	0.882252
4	0.060445	0.942697
5	0.030319	0.973016
6	0.014594	0.987610
7	0.006813	0.994423
8	0.003107	0.997530
9	0.001390	0.998921
10	0.000613	0.999534
11	0.000267	0.999800
12	0.000115	0.999915

k=2·8
Mean=1·72
Variance=2·77

n	P(n)	F(n)
0	0.262239	0.262239
1	0.279022	0.541261
2	0.201454	0.742714
3	0.122484	0.865198
4	0.067489	0.932687
5	0.034878	0.967565
6	0.017230	0.984795
7	0.008231	0.993026
8	0.003831	0.996857
9	0.001747	0.998605
10	0.000783	0.999388
11	0.000346	0.999734
12	0.000151	0.999886
13	0.000065	0.999951

k=3·0
Mean=1·84
Variance=2·97

n	P(n)	F(n)
0	0.238328	0.238328
1	0.271694	0.510022
2	0.206487	0.716509
3	0.130775	0.847285
4	0.074542	0.921827
5	0.039656	0.961483
6	0.020093	0.981575
7	0.009817	0.991392
8	0.004663	0.996055
9	0.002166	0.998221
10	0.000988	0.999208
11	0.000443	0.999652
12	0.000197	0.999848
13	0.000086	0.999934

k=3·2
Mean=1·96
Variance=3·16

n	P(n)	F(n)
0	0.216597	0.216597
1	0.263383	0.479980
2	0.210179	0.690159
3	0.138438	0.828597
4	0.081540	0.910137
5	0.044619	0.954756
6	0.023172	0.977928
7	0.011573	0.989501
8	0.005607	0.995108
9	0.002651	0.997759
10	0.001229	0.998989
11	0.000561	0.999549
12	0.000252	0.999801
13	0.000112	0.999913

k=3·4
Mean=2·08
Variance=3·36

n	P(n)	F(n)
0	0.196848	0.196848
1	0.254328	0.451176
2	0.212618	0.663795
3	0.145431	0.809226
4	0.088422	0.897647
5	0.049729	0.947376
6	0.026456	0.973832
7	0.013500	0.987331
8	0.006669	0.994000
9	0.003210	0.997210
10	0.001513	0.998723
11	0.000700	0.999423
12	0.000319	0.999742
13	0.000144	0.999886
14	0.000064	0.999950

k=3·6
Mean=2·21
Variance=3·56

n	P(n)	F(n)
0	0.178900	0.178900
1	0.244735	0.423635
2	0.213898	0.637533
3	0.151725	0.789259
4	0.095132	0.884390
5	0.054948	0.939339
6	0.029928	0.969267
7	0.015597	0.984864
8	0.007853	0.992717
9	0.003846	0.996563
10	0.001842	0.998405
11	0.000865	0.999270
12	0.000400	0.999670
13	0.000182	0.999852
14	0.000082	0.999935

k=3·8
Mean=2·33
Variance=3·76

n	P(n)	F(n)
0	0.162588	0.162588
1	0.234777	0.397365
2	0.214117	0.611482
3	0.157304	0.768786
4	0.101619	0.870405
5	0.060240	0.930644
6	0.033573	0.964218
7	0.017861	0.982079
8	0.009163	0.991242
9	0.004565	0.995807
10	0.002220	0.998027
11	0.001059	0.999086
12	0.000496	0.999582
13	0.000229	0.999811
14	0.000104	0.999915

k=4·0
Mean=2·45
Variance=3·95

n	P(n)	F(n)
0	0.147763	0.147763
1	0.224600	0.372364
2	0.213370	0.585734
3	0.162161	0.747895
4	0.107837	0.855733
5	0.065565	0.921298
6	0.037372	0.958670
7	0.020288	0.978958
8	0.010600	0.989558
9	0.005371	0.994929
10	0.002653	0.997582
11	0.001283	0.998865
12	0.000610	0.999475
13	0.000285	0.999760
14	0.000132	0.999891
15	0.000060	0.999951

k=4·2
Mean=2·57
Variance=4·15

n	P(n)	F(n)
0	0.134290	0.134290
1	0.214328	0.348618
2	0.211756	0.560374
3	0.166299	0.726672
4	0.113748	0.840421
5	0.070888	0.911309
6	0.041304	0.952613
7	0.022871	0.975483
8	0.012167	0.987651
9	0.006267	0.993918
10	0.003144	0.997062
11	0.001542	0.998604
12	0.000742	0.999346
13	0.000352	0.999698
14	0.000164	0.999862
15	0.000076	0.999937

k=4·4
Mean=2·70
Variance=4·35

n	P(n)	F(n)
0	0.122046	0.122046
1	0.204061	0.326107
2	0.209366	0.535473
3	0.169726	0.705200
4	0.119318	0.824517
5	0.076172	0.900690
6	0.045348	0.946038
7	0.025602	0.971640
8	0.013864	0.985503
9	0.007258	0.992762
10	0.003696	0.996458
11	0.001839	0.998296
12	0.000897	0.999193
13	0.000430	0.999623
14	0.000203	0.999826
15	0.000095	0.999920

k=4·6
Mean=2·82
Variance=4·55

n	P(n)	F(n)
0	0.110918	0.110918
1	0.193885	0.304802
2	0.206293	0.511096
3	0.172461	0.683557
4	0.124517	0.808074
5	0.081384	0.889458
6	0.049482	0.938939
7	0.028473	0.967413
8	0.015689	0.983101
9	0.008346	0.991448
10	0.004313	0.995761
11	0.002176	0.997937
12	0.001075	0.999011
13	0.000521	0.999533
14	0.000249	0.999782
15	0.000117	0.999899
16	0.000055	0.999954

k=4·8
Mean=2·94
Variance=4·75

n	P(n)	F(n)
0	0.100805	0.100805
1	0.183867	0.284672
2	0.202622	0.487294
3	0.174525	0.661819
4	0.129323	0.791142
5	0.086491	0.877633
6	0.053682	0.931316
7	0.031473	0.962789
8	0.017641	0.980429
9	0.009534	0.989963
10	0.005000	0.994963
11	0.002556	0.997519
12	0.001279	0.998798
13	0.000628	0.999426
14	0.000303	0.999729

k=5·0
Mean=3·06
Variance=4·94

n	P(n)	F(n)
0	0.091613	0.091613
1	0.174065	0.265679
2	0.198434	0.464113
3	0.175945	0.640058
4	0.133718	0.773776
5	0.091463	0.865240
6	0.057927	0.923166
7	0.034591	0.957757
8	0.019717	0.977474
9	0.010822	0.988296
10	0.005757	0.994053
11	0.002983	0.997037
12	0.001512	0.998548
13	0.000751	0.999299
14	0.000367	0.999666
15	0.000177	0.999843
16	0.000084	0.999927

k=6·0
Mean=3·68
Variance=5·93

n	P(n)	F(n)
0	0.056800	0.056800
1	0.129505	0.186305
2	0.172241	0.358546
3	0.174538	0.533083
4	0.149230	0.682313
5	0.113415	0.795728
6	0.079012	0.874740
7	0.051471	0.926210
8	0.031783	0.957994
9	0.018787	0.976781
10	0.010709	0.987490
11	0.005919	0.993409
12	0.003186	0.996595
13	0.001677	0.998272
14	0.000865	0.999136
15	0.000438	0.999575
16	0.000218	0.999793
17	0.000107	0.999900

k=7·0
Mean=4·29
Variance=6·92

n	P(n)	F(n)
0	0·035216	0·035216
1	0·093675	0·128891
2	0·142386	0·271277
3	0·162320	0·433597
4	0·154204	0·587801
5	0·128915	0·716715
6	0·097975	0·814690
7	0·069142	0·883833
8	0·045980	0·929813
9	0·029120	0·958933
10	0·017705	0·976638
11	0·010398	0·987036
12	0·005927	0·992963
13	0·003292	0·996254
14	0·001787	0·998041
15	0·000951	0·998992
16	0·000497	0·999489
17	0·000255	0·999744
18	0·000129	0·999873
19	0·000065	0·999938

k=8·0
Mean=4·90
Variance=7·91

n	P(n)	F(n)
0	0·021834	0·021834
1	0·066375	0·088209
2	0·113502	0·201711
3	0·143769	0·345480
4	0·150239	0·495719
5	0·137018	0·632737
6	0·112811	0·745548
7	0·085737	0·831285
8	0·061087	0·892372
9	0·041268	0·933640
10	0·026659	0·960299
11	0·016577	0·976876
12	0·009974	0·986850
13	0·005831	0·992681
14	0·003324	0·996004
15	0·001852	0·997857
16	0·001012	0·998868
17	0·000543	0·999411
18	0·000286	0·999698
19	0·000149	0·999847
20	0·000076	0·999923

k=9·0
Mean=5·52
Variance=8·90

n	P(n)	F(n)
0	0·013537	0·013537
1	0·046297	0·059834
2	0·087964	0·147798
3	0·122563	0·270361
4	0·139722	0·410083
5	0·138045	0·548128
6	0·122400	0·670529
7	0·099669	0·770197
8	0·075748	0·845946
9	0·054370	0·900316
10	0·037189	0·937505
11	0·024410	0·961915
12	0·015460	0·977375
13	0·009490	0·986864
14	0·005667	0·992531
15	0·003302	0·995833
16	0·001882	0·997715
17	0·001052	0·998767
18	0·000577	0·999344
19	0·000312	0·999656
20	0·000166	0·999821
21	0·000087	0·999909

k=10·0
Mean=6·13
Variance=9·89

n	P(n)	F(n)
0	0·008393	0·008393
1	0·031893	0·040286
2	0·066657	0·106944
3	0·101319	0·208262
4	0·125129	0·333391
5	0·133137	0·466528
6	0·126480	0·593008
7	0·109857	0·702866
8	0·088710	0·791575
9	0·067419	0·858994
10	0·048677	0·907671
11	0·033631	0·941302
12	0·022365	0·963667
13	0·014382	0·978049
14	0·008979	0·987028
15	0·005459	0·992487
16	0·003241	0·995728
17	0·001884	0·997612
18	0·001074	0·998686
19	0·000601	0·999287
20	0·000331	0·999618
21	0·000180	0·999798
22	0·000096	0·999895
23	0·000051	0·999946

k=11·0
Mean=6·74
Variance=10·87

n	P(n)	F(n)
0	0·005204	0·005204
1	0·021751	0·026955
2	0·049593	0·076548
3	0·081663	0·158211
4	0·108612	0·266823
5	0·123817	0·390640
6	0·125468	0·516109
7	0·115789	0·631898
8	0·099000	0·730898
9	0·079420	0·810318
10	0·060359	0·870677
11	0·043788	0·914465
12	0·030506	0·944970
13	0·020509	0·965479
14	0·013360	0·978840
15	0·008461	0·987301
16	0·005225	0·992526
17	0·003153	0·995679
18	0·001864	0·997543
19	0·001081	0·998624
20	0·000616	0·999241
21	0·000346	0·999586
22	0·000191	0·999777
23	0·000104	0·999882
24	0·000056	0·999938

k=12·0
Mean=7·35
Variance=11·86

n	P(n)	F(n)
0	0·003226	0·003226
1	0·014712	0·017938
2	0·036338	0·054276
3	0·064440	0·118716
4	0·091826	0·210542
5	0·111661	0·322203
6	0·120222	0·442424
7	0·117474	0·559898
8	0·106020	0·665918
9	0·089528	0·755446
10	0·071443	0·826889
11	0·054297	0·881186
12	0·039546	0·920732
13	0·027743	0·948475
14	0·018826	0·967301
15	0·012400	0·979701
16	0·007951	0·987652
17	0·004977	0·992629
18	0·003047	0·995676
19	0·001828	0·997504
20	0·001077	0·998581
21	0·000623	0·999204
22	0·000355	0·999560
23	0·000200	0·999759
24	0·000111	0·999870

25	0.000061	0.999930

k=13.0
Mean = 7.97
Variance = 12.85

n	P(n)	F(n)
0	0.002000	0.002000
1	0.009881	0.011882
2	0.026285	0.038166
3	0.049941	0.088107
4	0.075910	0.164017
5	0.098075	0.262092
6	0.111806	0.373898
7	0.115320	0.489218
8	0.109554	0.598772
9	0.097138	0.695910
10	0.081207	0.777117
11	0.064523	0.841640
12	0.049037	0.890677
13	0.035835	0.926512
14	0.025289	0.951801
15	0.017298	0.969099
16	0.011503	0.980602
17	0.007457	0.988059
18	0.004723	0.992781
19	0.002928	0.995709
20	0.001780	0.997490
21	0.001063	0.998553
22	0.000624	0.999177
23	0.000361	0.999538
24	0.000206	0.999744
25	0.000116	0.999860
26	0.000064	0.999924

k=14.0
Mean = 8.58
Variance = 13.84

n	P(n)	F(n)
0	0.001240	0.001240
1	0.006598	0.007838
2	0.018804	0.026641
3	0.038109	0.064750
4	0.061545	0.126295
5	0.084194	0.210489
6	0.101313	0.311803
7	0.109997	0.421800
8	0.109722	0.531523
9	0.101920	0.633443
10	0.089078	0.722521
11	0.073854	0.796374
12	0.058468	0.854842
13	0.044435	0.899277
14	0.032565	0.931842

15	0.023099	0.954942
16	0.015910	0.970851
17	0.010669	0.981520
18	0.006982	0.988502
19	0.004469	0.992971
20	0.002802	0.995772
21	0.001724	0.997496
22	0.001042	0.998538
23	0.000620	0.999158
24	0.000363	0.999521
25	0.000210	0.999731
26	0.000120	0.999851
27	0.000067	0.999918

k=15.0
Mean = 9.19
Variance = 14.83

n	P(n)	F(n)
0	0.000769	0.000769
1	0.004383	0.005152
2	0.013324	0.018475
3	0.028690	0.047166
4	0.049060	0.096226
5	0.070843	0.167069
6	0.089735	0.256804
7	0.102298	0.359102
8	0.106901	0.466003
9	0.103813	0.569815
10	0.094677	0.664493
11	0.081767	0.746259
12	0.067321	0.813581
13	0.053132	0.866713
14	0.040380	0.907093
15	0.029666	0.936759
16	0.021137	0.957896
17	0.014647	0.972543
18	0.009895	0.982438
19	0.006530	0.988968
20	0.004219	0.993187
21	0.002672	0.995859
22	0.001661	0.997520
23	0.001016	0.998536
24	0.000611	0.999147
25	0.000362	0.999509
26	0.000212	0.999721
27	0.000122	0.999843
28	0.000070	0.999913

k=16.0
Mean = 9.81
Variance = 15.82

n	P(n)	F(n)
0	0.000477	0.000477
1	0.002898	0.003375
2	0.009362	0.012737
3	0.021346	0.034083
4	0.038529	0.072612

5	0.058564	0.131175
6	0.077890	0.209065
7	0.093023	0.302088
8	0.101627	0.403715
9	0.102982	0.506697
10	0.097833	0.604530
11	0.087872	0.692402
12	0.075131	0.767533
13	0.061491	0.829024
14	0.048403	0.877427
15	0.036786	0.914213
16	0.027084	0.941296
17	0.019373	0.960669
18	0.013496	0.974166
19	0.009178	0.983343
20	0.006103	0.989446
21	0.003976	0.993422
22	0.002541	0.995963
23	0.001595	0.997558
24	0.000985	0.998543
25	0.000599	0.999142
26	0.000359	0.999501
27	0.000212	0.999713
28	0.000124	0.999837
29	0.000071	0.999908

k=17.0
Mean = 10.42
Variance = 16.81

n	P(n)	F(n)
0	0.000296	0.000296
1	0.001909	0.002205
2	0.006530	0.008735
3	0.015716	0.024451
4	0.029860	0.054310
5	0.047656	0.101967
6	0.066401	0.168368
7	0.082906	0.251274
8	0.094513	0.345787
9	0.099764	0.445552
10	0.098567	0.544118
11	0.091936	0.636054
12	0.081517	0.717571
13	0.069101	0.786672
14	0.056268	0.842940
15	0.044189	0.887129
16	0.033584	0.920713
17	0.024773	0.945486
18	0.017781	0.963267
19	0.012447	0.975714
20	0.008514	0.984228
21	0.005700	0.989928
22	0.003741	0.993670
23	0.002411	0.996080
24	0.001527	0.997607
25	0.000952	0.998559
26	0.000584	0.999143
27	0.000353	0.999496
28	0.000211	0.999707
29	0.000124	0.999832

30	0.000073	0.999904

k=18·0
Mean = 11·03
Variance = 17·79

n	P(n)	F(n)
0	0.000183	0.000183
1	0.001253	0.001437
2	0.004525	0.005962
3	0.011463	0.017425
4	0.022869	0.040294
5	0.038237	0.078531
6	0.055699	0.134230
7	0.072568	0.206797
8	0.086174	0.292971
9	0.094600	0.387571
10	0.097059	0.484630
11	0.093883	0.578513
12	0.086216	0.664729
13	0.075605	0.740334
14	0.063616	0.803950
15	0.051571	0.855521
16	0.040419	0.895940
17	0.030718	0.926658
18	0.022698	0.949356
19	0.016342	0.965698
20	0.011489	0.977187
21	0.007900	0.985086
22	0.005322	0.990408
23	0.003517	0.993925
24	0.002283	0.996208
25	0.001457	0.997665
26	0.000916	0.998581
27	0.000567	0.999149
28	0.000346	0.999495
2	0.000209	0.999704
30	0.000124	0.999828
31	0.000073	0.999901

k=19·0
Mean = 11·65
Variance = 18·78

n	P(n)	F(n)
0	0.000114	0.000114
1	0.000820	0.000934
2	0.003117	0.004051
3	0.008292	0.012343
4	0.017330	0.029673
5	0.030292	0.059965
6	0.046044	0.106009
7	0.062489	0.168498
8	0.077174	0.245671
9	0.087978	0.333649

10	0.093608	0.427258
11	0.093779	0.521036
12	0.089090	0.610126
13	0.080729	0.690855
14	0.070119	0.760974
15	0.058619	0.819593
16	0.047335	0.866928
17	0.037033	0.903961
18	0.028145	0.932106
19	0.020827	0.952933
20	0.015037	0.967970
21	0.010612	0.978582
22	0.007332	0.985914
23	0.004967	0.990881
24	0.003303	0.994184
25	0.002159	0.996342
26	0.001388	0.997730
27	0.000879	0.998610
28	0.000549	0.999159
29	0.000338	0.999497
30	0.000206	0.999702
31	0.000123	0.999826
32	0.000073	0.999899
33	0.000043	0.999942

k=20·0
Mean = 12·26
Variance = 19·77

n	P(n)	F(n)
0	0.000070	0.000070
1	0.000535	0.000606
2	0.002136	0.002742
3	0.005953	0.008694
4	0.013006	0.021701
5	0.023724	0.045425
6	0.037562	0.082987
7	0.053017	0.136004
8	0.067994	0.203998
9	0.080384	0.284382
10	0.088583	0.372965
11	0.091804	0.464769
12	0.090121	0.554890
13	0.084298	0.639188
14	0.075507	0.714695
15	0.065037	0.779732
16	0.054062	0.833793
17	0.043504	0.877297
18	0.033981	0.911278
19	0.025826	0.937104
20	0.019137	0.956241
21	0.013851	0.970093
22	0.009809	0.979902
23	0.006807	0.986709
24	0.004634	0.991343
25	0.003099	0.994443
26	0.002038	0.996481
27	0.001320	0.997801
28	0.000842	0.998643
29	0.000529	0.999172

30	0.000329	0.999501
31	0.000201	0.999702
32	0.000122	0.999824
33	0.000073	0.999897
34	0.000043	0.999940

k=0·2
Mean=0·11
Variance=0·18

n	P(n)	F(n)
0	0.914610	0.914610
1	0.065852	0.980462
2	0.014224	0.994686
3	0.003755	0.998441
4	0.001081	0.999523
5	0.000327	0.999850
6	0.000102	0.999952

k=0·4
Mean=0·23
Variance=0·35

n	P(n)	F(n)
0	0.836512	0.836512
1	0.120458	0.956969
2	0.030355	0.987325
3	0.008742	0.996067
4	0.002675	0.998742
5	0.000847	0.999590
6	0.000275	0.999864
7	0.000090	0.999955

k=0·6
Mean=0·35
Variance=0·53

n	P(n)	F(n)
0	0.765082	0.765082
1	0.165258	0.930340
2	0.047594	0.977934
3	0.014849	0.992783
4	0.004811	0.997595
5	0.001593	0.999188
6	0.000535	0.999723
7	0.000182	0.999905

k=0·8
Mean=0·45
Variance=0·70

n	P(n)	F(n)
0	0.699752	0.699752
1	0.201528	0.901280
2	0.065295	0.966575
3	0.021939	0.988515
4	0.007503	0.996018
5	0.002593	0.998611
6	0.000902	0.999513
7	0.000316	0.999829
8	0.000111	0.999940

k=1·0
Mean=0·56
Variance=0·88

n	P(n)	F(n)
0	0.640000	0.640000
1	0.230400	0.870400
2	0.082944	0.953344
3	0.029860	0.983204
4	0.010750	0.993953
5	0.003870	0.997823
6	0.001393	0.999216
7	0.000502	0.999718
8	0.000181	0.999898
9	0.000065	0.999963

k=1·2
Mean=0·68
Variance=1·05

n	P(n)	F(n)
0	0.585350	0.585350
1	0.252871	0.838222
2	0.100137	0.938359
3	0.038453	0.976812
4	0.014535	0.991347
5	0.005442	0.996789
6	0.002024	0.998813
7	0.000750	0.999563
8	0.000277	0.999839
9	0.000102	0.999941

k=1·4
Mean=0·79
Variance=1·23

n	P(n)	F(n)
0	0.535367	0.535367
1	0.269825	0.805193
2	0.116564	0.921757
3	0.047558	0.969315
4	0.018833	0.988149
5	0.007322	0.995471
6	0.002812	0.998283
7	0.001070	0.999353
8	0.000404	0.999757
9	0.000152	0.999909

k=1·6
Mean=0·90
Variance=1·41

n	P(n)	F(n)
0	0.489652	0.489652
1	0.282040	0.771692
2	0.131995	0.903687
3	0.057022	0.960709
4	0.023607	0.984316
5	0.009518	0.993834
6	0.003769	0.997603
7	0.001473	0.999076
8	0.000570	0.999647
9	0.000219	0.999866

| 10 | 0.000084 | 0.999949 |

k=1·8
Mean=1·01
Variance=1·58

n	P(n)	F(n)
0	0.447841	0.447841
1	0.290201	0.738042
2	0.146261	0.884303
3	0.066695	0.950999
4	0.028812	0.979811
5	0.012032	0.991843
6	0.004909	0.996752
7	0.001969	0.998721
8	0.000780	0.999501
9	0.000306	0.999807
10	0.000119	0.999926

k=2·0
Mean=1·12
Variance=1·76

n	P(n)	F(n)
0	0.409600	0.409600
1	0.294912	0.704512
2	0.159252	0.863764
3	0.076441	0.940206
4	0.034399	0.974604
5	0.014860	0.989464
6	0.006241	0.995706
7	0.002568	0.998273
8	0.001040	0.999313
9	0.000416	0.999729
10	0.000165	0.999894
11	0.000065	0.999959

k=2·2
Mean=1·24
Variance=1·93

n	P(n)	F(n)
0	0.374624	0.374624
1	0.296702	0.671327
2	0.170901	0.842227
3	0.086134	0.928361
4	0.040311	0.968672
5	0.017995	0.986667
6	0.007774	0.994440
7	0.003278	0.997719
8	0.001357	0.999076
9	0.000554	0.999630

10	0.000223	0.999853	10	0.000499	0.999645	10	0.000981	0.999247
11	0.000089	0.999942	11	0.000209	0.999854	11	0.000430	0.999678
			12	0.000086	0.999940	12	0.000186	0.999864
						13	0.000079	0.999943

k=2·4
Mean=1·35
Variance=2·11

n	P(n)	F(n)
0	0.342635	0.342635
1	0.296037	0.638672
2	0.181175	0.819846
3	0.095660	0.915507
4	0.046491	0.961997
5	0.021423	0.983420
6	0.009512	0.992932
7	0.004109	0.997041
8	0.001738	0.998779
9	0.000723	0.999503
10	0.000297	0.999799
11	0.000120	0.999920

k=3·0
Mean=1·69
Variance=2·64

n	P(n)	F(n)
0	0.262144	0.262144
1	0.283116	0.545260
2	0.203843	0.749103
3	0.122306	0.871409
4	0.066045	0.937454
5	0.033287	0.970741
6	0.015978	0.986718
7	0.007395	0.994114
8	0.003328	0.997442
9	0.001464	0.998906
10	0.000633	0.999538
11	0.000269	0.999807
12	0.000113	0.999921

k=3·6
Mean=2·03
Variance=3·16

n	P(n)	F(n)
0	0.200562	0.200562
1	0.259928	0.460490
2	0.215220	0.675710
3	0.144628	0.820338
4	0.085909	0.906247
5	0.047009	0.953256
6	0.024257	0.977513
7	0.011976	0.989489
8	0.005713	0.995202
9	0.002651	0.997852
10	0.001202	0.999055
11	0.000535	0.999590
12	0.000234	0.999824
13	0.000101	0.999926

k=2·6
Mean=1·46
Variance=2·29

n	P(n)	F(n)
0	0.313378	0.313378
1	0.293321	0.606699
2	0.190072	0.796771
3	0.104920	0.901691
4	0.052880	0.954571
5	0.025128	0.979699
6	0.011459	0.991158
7	0.005068	0.996226
8	0.002189	0.998415
9	0.000928	0.999343
10	0.000388	0.999731
11	0.000160	0.999891
12	0.000065	0.999956

k=3·2
Mean=1·80
Variance=2·81

n	P(n)	F(n)
0	0.239760	0.239760
1	0.276203	0.515963
2	0.208809	0.724772
3	0.130297	0.855069
4	0.072706	0.927775
5	0.037691	0.965466
6	0.018544	0.984009
7	0.008774	0.992783
8	0.004027	0.996811
9	0.001804	0.998615
10	0.000792	0.999407
11	0.000342	0.999749
12	0.000146	0.999895
13	0.000061	0.999957

k=3·8
Mean=2·14
Variance=3·34

n	P(n)	F(n)
0	0.183436	0.183436
1	0.250940	0.434376
2	0.216812	0.651188
3	0.150901	0.802089
4	0.092352	0.894441
5	0.051865	0.946306
6	0.027385	0.973690
7	0.013802	0.987492
8	0.006708	0.994200
9	0.003166	0.997366
10	0.001459	0.998824
11	0.000659	0.999483
12	0.000293	0.999776
13	0.000128	0.999904

k=2·8
Mean=1·58
Variance=2·46

n	P(n)	F(n)
0	0.286618	0.286618
1	0.288911	0.575530
2	0.197615	0.773145
3	0.113826	0.886971
4	0.059417	0.946389
5	0.029091	0.975479
6	0.013614	0.989094
7	0.006162	0.995255
8	0.002717	0.997973
9	0.001174	0.999146

k=3·4
Mean=1·91
Variance=2·99

n	P(n)	F(n)
0	0.219287	0.219287
1	0.268407	0.487693
2	0.212578	0.700271
3	0.137751	0.838022
4	0.079344	0.917366
5	0.042275	0.959641
6	0.021306	0.980947
7	0.010300	0.991247
8	0.004820	0.996068
9	0.002198	0.998266

k=4·0
Mean=2·25
Variance=3·52

n	P(n)	F(n)
0	0.167772	0.167772
1	0.241592	0.409364
2	0.217433	0.626797
3	0.156552	0.783348
4	0.098627	0.881976
5	0.056809	0.938785
6	0.030677	0.969462
7	0.015777	0.985239
8	0.007810	0.993049
9	0.003749	0.996797

n	P(n)	F(n)
10	0.001754	0.998552
11	0.000804	0.999355
12	0.000362	0.999717
13	0.000160	0.999877
14	0.000070	0.999947

k = 4·2
Mean = 2·36
Variance = 3·69

n	P(n)	F(n)
0	0.153446	0.153446
1	0.232011	0.385457
2	0.217162	0.602618
3	0.161568	0.764187
4	0.104696	0.868883
5	0.061813	0.930696
6	0.034121	0.964817
7	0.017899	0.982715
8	0.009021	0.991736
9	0.004402	0.996138
10	0.002092	0.998230
11	0.000972	0.999203
12	0.000443	0.999646
13	0.000199	0.999845
14	0.000088	0.999933

k = 4·4
Mean = 2·47
Variance = 3·87

n	P(n)	F(n)
0	0.140343	0.140343
1	0.222304	0.362647
2	0.216079	0.578727
3	0.165949	0.744676
4	0.110522	0.855198
5	0.066844	0.922041
6	0.037700	0.959741
7	0.020164	0.979905
8	0.010344	0.990249
9	0.005131	0.995380
10	0.002475	0.997855
11	0.001166	0.999022
12	0.000539	0.999560
13	0.000245	0.999805
14	0.000110	0.999915

k = 4·6
Mean = 2·59
Variance = 4·04

n	P(n)	F(n)
0	0.128359	0.128359
1	0.212563	0.340923
2	0.214264	0.555186
3	0.169697	0.724883
4	0.116073	0.840956
5	0.071872	0.912828
6	0.041398	0.954227
7	0.022568	0.976795
8	0.011781	0.988575
9	0.005937	0.994513

n	P(n)	F(n)
10	0.002907	0.997420
11	0.001389	0.998809
12	0.000650	0.999459
13	0.000299	0.999757
14	0.000135	0.999893
15	0.000060	0.999953

k = 4·8
Mean = 2·70
Variance = 4·22

n	P(n)	F(n)
0	0.117399	0.117399
1	0.202865	0.320264
2	0.211791	0.532055
3	0.172822	0.704877
4	0.121321	0.826198
5	0.076869	0.903067
6	0.045199	0.948266
7	0.025105	0.973370
8	0.013331	0.986701
9	0.006825	0.993526
10	0.003391	0.996917
11	0.001642	0.998560
12	0.000778	0.999338
13	0.000362	0.999700
14	0.000166	0.999866
15	0.000075	0.999941

k = 5·0
Mean = 2·81
Variance = 4·39

n	P(n)	F(n)
0	0.107374	0.107374
1	0.193274	0.300648
2	0.208735	0.509383
3	0.175338	0.684721
4	0.126243	0.810964
5	0.081806	0.892770
6	0.049083	0.941853
7	0.027767	0.969620
8	0.014994	0.984614
9	0.007797	0.992411
10	0.003930	0.996341
11	0.001929	0.998270
12	0.000926	0.999196
13	0.000436	0.999632
14	0.000202	0.999834
15	0.000092	0.999926

k = 6·0
Mean = 3·37
Variance = 5·27

n	P(n)	F(n)
0	0.068719	0.068719
1	0.148434	0.217154
2	0.187027	0.404180
3	0.179546	0.583726
4	0.145432	0.729158
5	0.104711	0.833870
6	0.069109	0.902979
7	0.042650	0.945629
8	0.024950	0.970580
9	0.013972	0.984552
10	0.007545	0.992097
11	0.003951	0.996048
12	0.002015	0.998063
13	0.001004	0.999067
14	0.000491	0.999558
15	0.000236	0.999793
16	0.000111	0.999905

k = 7·0
Mean = 3·94
Variance = 6·15

n	P(n)	F(n)
0	0.043980	0.043980
1	0.110831	0.154811
2	0.159596	0.314408
3	0.172364	0.486772
4	0.155128	0.641899
5	0.122861	0.764760
6	0.088460	0.853220
7	0.059142	0.912362
8	0.037259	0.949621
9	0.022356	0.971977
10	0.012877	0.984854
11	0.007164	0.992018
12	0.003869	0.995887
13	0.002036	0.997922
14	0.001047	0.998969
15	0.000528	0.999497
16	0.000261	0.999758
17	0.000127	0.999885
18	0.000061	0.999946

k = 8·0
Mean = 4·50
Variance = 7·03

n	P(n)	F(n)
0	0.028147	0.028147
1	0.081065	0.109212
2	0.131325	0.240537
3	0.157590	0.398127
4	0.156014	0.554141

n	P(n)	F(n)
5	0.134796	0.688937
6	0.105141	0.794078
7	0.075702	0.869780
8	0.051099	0.920878
9	0.032703	0.953582
10	0.020014	0.973596
11	0.011790	0.985386
12	0.006720	0.992106
13	0.003722	0.995829
14	0.002010	0.997838
15	0.001061	0.998900
16	0.000549	0.999449
17	0.000279	0.999728
18	0.000140	0.999868
19	0.000069	0.999936

n	P(n)	F(n)
10	0.038940	0.935481
11	0.025488	0.960968
12	0.016057	0.977026
13	0.009783	0.986808
14	0.005786	0.992594
15	0.003333	0.995927
16	0.001875	0.997801
17	0.001032	0.998833
18	0.000557	0.999391
19	0.000296	0.999686
20	0.000154	0.999841
21	0.000079	0.999920

n	P(n)	F(n)
10	0.060899	0.873188
11	0.043847	0.917036
12	0.030255	0.947290
13	0.020108	0.967398
14	0.012926	0.980324
15	0.008066	0.988390
16	0.004900	0.993290
17	0.002905	0.996196
18	0.001685	0.997881
19	0.000958	0.998839
20	0.000535	0.999373
21	0.000293	0.999667
22	0.000158	0.999825
23	0.000084	0.999909

k=9·0
Mean=5·06
Variance=7·91

n	P(n)	F(n)
0	0.018014	0.018014
1	0.058367	0.076381
2	0.105060	0.181441
3	0.138679	0.320120
4	0.149773	0.469894
5	0.140188	0.610082
6	0.117758	0.727840
7	0.090842	0.818681
8	0.065406	0.884088
9	0.044476	0.928564
10	0.028821	0.957384
11	0.017921	0.975305
12	0.010753	0.986058
13	0.006253	0.992311
14	0.003537	0.995849
15	0.001953	0.997801
16	0.001054	0.998856
17	0.000558	0.999414
18	0.000290	0.999704
19	0.000149	0.999853
20	0.000075	0.999928

k=11·0
Mean=6·19
Variance=9·67

n	P(n)	F(n)
0	0.007379	0.007379
1	0.029220	0.036598
2	0.063114	0.099713
3	0.098459	0.198171
4	0.124058	0.322229
5	0.133982	0.456211
6	0.128623	0.584834
7	0.112453	0.697288
8	0.091087	0.788375
9	0.069226	0.857601
10	0.049843	0.907444
11	0.034256	0.941700
12	0.022609	0.964308
13	0.014400	0.978708
14	0.008887	0.987595
15	0.005332	0.992927
16	0.003119	0.996047
17	0.001784	0.997830
18	0.000999	0.998829
19	0.000549	0.999378
20	0.000296	0.999674
21	0.000157	0.999832
22	0.000082	0.999914

k=13·0
Mean=7·31
Variance=11·43

n	P(n)	F(n)
0	0.003022	0.003022
1	0.014144	0.017167
2	0.035644	0.052811
3	0.064159	0.116970
4	0.092389	0.209359
5	0.113084	0.322443
6	0.122131	0.444574
7	0.119340	0.563914
8	0.107406	0.671320
9	0.090221	0.761540
10	0.071455	0.832995
11	0.053786	0.886781
12	0.038726	0.925507
13	0.026810	0.952317
14	0.017925	0.970242
15	0.011615	0.981857
16	0.007318	0.989174
17	0.004494	0.993668
18	0.002696	0.996364
19	0.001584	0.997948
20	0.000912	0.998860
21	0.000516	0.999376
22	0.000287	0.999664
23	0.000157	0.999821
24	0.000085	0.999906

k=10·0
Mean=5·62
Variance=8·79

n	P(n)	F(n)
0	0.011529	0.011529
1	0.041505	0.053034
2	0.082180	0.135215
3	0.118340	0.253554
4	0.138457	0.392011
5	0.139565	0.531576
6	0.125608	0.657185
7	0.103358	0.760543
8	0.079069	0.839611
9	0.056929	0.896541

k=12·0
Mean=6·75
Variance=10·55

n	P(n)	F(n)
0	0.004722	0.004722
1	0.020401	0.025123
2	0.047737	0.072860
3	0.080199	0.153059
4	0.108269	0.261328
5	0.124725	0.386053
6	0.127220	0.513273
7	0.117769	0.631042
8	0.100693	0.731735
9	0.080554	0.812289

k=14·0
Mean=7·87
Variance=12·30

n	P(n)	F(n)
0	0.001934	0.001934
1	0.009749	0.011683
2	0.026322	0.038005
3	0.050538	0.088542
4	0.077323	0.165865
5	0.100210	0.266075
6	0.114240	0.380315
7	0.117504	0.497818
8	0.111041	0.608859
9	0.097716	0.706575

10	0.080909	0.787484
11	0.063550	0.851034
12	0.047663	0.898697
13	0.034317	0.933014
14	0.023826	0.956840
15	0.016011	0.972851
16	0.010447	0.983298
17	0.006637	0.989935
18	0.004115	0.994050
19	0.002495	0.996545
20	0.001482	0.998027
21	0.000864	0.998890
22	0.000495	0.999385
23	0.000279	0.999664
24	0.000155	0.999819
25	0.000085	0.999903

k=15·0
Mean=8·44
Variance=13·18

n	P(n)	F(n)
0	0.001238	0.001238
1	0.006685	0.007923
2	0.019252	0.027175
3	0.039275	0.066450
4	0.063625	0.130076
5	0.087040	0.217115
6	0.104448	0.321563
7	0.112803	0.434366
8	0.111675	0.546042
9	0.102741	0.648783
10	0.088769	0.737552
11	0.072629	0.810180
12	0.056650	0.866831
13	0.042357	0.909188
14	0.030497	0.939685
15	0.021226	0.960911
16	0.014328	0.975238
17	0.009406	0.984644
18	0.006020	0.990664
19	0.003764	0.994428
20	0.002303	0.996731
21	0.001382	0.998113
22	0.000814	0.998927
23	0.000472	0.999399
24	0.000269	0.999668
25	0.000151	0.999818
26	0.000084	0.999902

k=16·0
Mean=9·00
Variance=14·06

n	P(n)	F(n)
0	0.000792	0.000792
1	0.004564	0.005356
2	0.013964	0.019320
3	0.030163	0.049483
4	0.051579	0.101063
5	0.074274	0.175336
6	0.093585	0.268921
7	0.105885	0.374806
8	0.109591	0.484397
9	0.105207	0.589604
10	0.094686	0.684290
11	0.080570	0.764860
12	0.065261	0.830121
13	0.050603	0.880724
14	0.037735	0.918459
15	0.027169	0.945628
16	0.018951	0.964579
17	0.012842	0.977421
18	0.008476	0.985896
19	0.005460	0.991356
20	0.003440	0.994796
21	0.002123	0.996919
22	0.001285	0.998204
23	0.000764	0.998969
24	0.000447	0.999416
25	0.000258	0.999674
26	0.000146	0.999820
27	0.000082	0.999902

k=17·0
Mean=9·56
Variance=14·94

n	P(n)	F(n)
0	0.000507	0.000507
1	0.003103	0.003610
2	0.010054	0.013665
3	0.022924	0.036589
4	0.041263	0.077852
5	0.062390	0.140242
6	0.082355	0.222597
7	0.097414	0.320011
8	0.105207	0.425218
9	0.105207	0.530425
10	0.098474	0.628899
11	0.087015	0.715914
12	0.073093	0.789007
13	0.058699	0.847706
14	0.045282	0.892988
15	0.033690	0.926678
16	0.024257	0.950934
17	0.016951	0.967886
18	0.011527	0.979412
19	0.007644	0.987056

20	0.004953	0.992010
21	0.003142	0.995152
22	0.001954	0.997105
23	0.001193	0.998298
24	0.000716	0.999013
25	0.000422	0.999436
26	0.000246	0.999682
27	0.000141	0.999822
28	0.000080	0.999902

k=18·0
Mean=10·12
Variance=15·82

n	P(n)	F(n)
0	0.000325	0.000325
1	0.002103	0.002427
2	0.007192	0.009619
3	0.017260	0.026880
4	0.032622	0.059502
5	0.051674	0.111176
6	0.071310	0.182485
7	0.088016	0.270502
8	0.099018	0.369520
9	0.102979	0.472439
10	0.100096	0.572595
11	0.091724	0.664319
12	0.079800	0.744119
13	0.066295	0.810414
14	0.052847	0.863261
15	0.040586	0.903848
16	0.030135	0.933983
17	0.021697	0.955681
18	0.015188	0.970869
19	0.010360	0.981229
20	0.006900	0.988129
21	0.004495	0.992623
22	0.002868	0.995492
23	0.001796	0.997288
24	0.001104	0.998392
25	0.000668	0.999060
26	0.000398	0.999458
27	0.000233	0.999691
28	0.000135	0.999826
29	0.000077	0.999903

k=19·0
Mean=10·69
Variance=16·70

n	P(n)	F(n)
0	0.000208	0.000208
1	0.001421	0.001628
2	0.005114	0.006743
3	0.012888	0.019630
4	0.025518	0.045148
5	0.042258	0.087406
6	0.060851	0.148257
7	0.078237	0.226493
8	0.091537	0.318030
9	0.098860	0.416890

10	0.099651	0.516541
11	0.094578	0.611119
12	0.085120	0.696239
13	0.073072	0.769311
14	0.060128	0.829439
15	0.047621	0.877061
16	0.036430	0.913491
17	0.027001	0.940492
18	0.019441	0.959933
19	0.013629	0.973563
20	0.009322	0.982885
21	0.006233	0.989117
22	0.004080	0.993197
23	0.002618	0.995815
24	0.001649	0.997464
25	0.001021	0.998486
26	0.000622	0.999108
27	0.000373	0.999481
28	0.000221	0.999702
29	0.000129	0.999831
30	0.000074	0.999905

k=20·0
Mean=11·25
Variance=17·58

n	P(n)	F(n)
0	0.000133	0.000133
1	0.000957	0.001090
2	0.003618	0.004708
3	0.009551	0.014258
4	0.019770	0.034028
5	0.034162	0.068190
6	0.051243	0.119432
7	0.068519	0.187951
8	0.083251	0.271202
9	0.093241	0.364443
10	0.097343	0.461786
11	0.095573	0.557359
12	0.088883	0.646242
13	0.078764	0.725006
14	0.066837	0.791843
15	0.054539	0.846383
16	0.042949	0.889332
17	0.032743	0.922075
18	0.024230	0.946304
19	0.017445	0.963750

20	0.012247	0.975996
21	0.008398	0.984394
22	0.005634	0.990028
23	0.003704	0.993732
24	0.002389	0.996121
25	0.001514	0.997634
26	0.000943	0.998577
27	0.000578	0.999156
28	0.000350	0.999505
29	0.000208	0.999714
30	0.000122	0.999836
31	0.000071	0.999907

k=0·2
Mean=0·10
Variance=0·16

n	P(n)	F(n)
0	0.920256	0.920256
1	0.062577	0.982834
2	0.012766	0.995599
3	0.003183	0.998782
4	0.000866	0.999648
5	0.000247	0.999895
6	0.000073	0.999968

k=0·6
Mean=0·31
Variance=0·47

n	P(n)	F(n)
0	0.779339	0.779339
1	0.158985	0.938324
2	0.043244	0.981568
3	0.012743	0.994311
4	0.003899	0.998210
5	0.001220	0.999429
6	0.000387	0.999817
7	0.000124	0.999941

k=1·0
Mean=0·52
Variance=0·78

n	P(n)	F(n)
0	0.660000	0.660000
1	0.224400	0.884400
2	0.076296	0.960696
3	0.025941	0.986637
4	0.008820	0.995456
5	0.002999	0.998455
6	0.001020	0.999475
7	0.000347	0.999821
8	0.000118	0.999939

k=0·4
Mean=0·21
Variance=0·31

n	P(n)	F(n)
0	0.846872	0.846872
1	0.115175	0.962046
2	0.027412	0.989458
3	0.007456	0.996914
4	0.002155	0.999068
5	0.000645	0.999713
6	0.000197	0.999910

k=0·8
Mean=0·41
Variance=0·62

n	P(n)	F(n)
0	0.717192	0.717192
1	0.195076	0.912268
2	0.059693	0.971961
3	0.018943	0.990904
4	0.006118	0.997022
5	0.001997	0.999019
6	0.000656	0.999675
7	0.000217	0.999892
8	0.000072	0.999964

k=1·2
Mean=0·62
Variance=0·94

n	P(n)	F(n)
0	0.607369	0.607369
1	0.247807	0.855176
2	0.092680	0.947855
3	0.033612	0.981467
4	0.011999	0.993467
5	0.004243	0.997710
6	0.001491	0.999200
7	0.000521	0.999722
8	0.000182	0.999903

k=1·4
Mean = 0·72
Variance = 1·09

n	P(n)	F(n)
0	0.558935	0.558935
1	0.266053	0.824988
2	0.108550	0.933538
3	0.041328	0.975366
4	0.015644	0.991010
5	0.005744	0.996754
6	0.002083	0.998837
7	0.000749	0.999586
8	0.000267	0.999853
9	0.000095	0.999948

k=1·6
Mean = 0·82
Variance = 1·25

n	P(n)	F(n)
0	0.514364	0.514364
1	0.279814	0.794178
2	0.123678	0.917855
3	0.050461	0.968316
4	0.019730	0.988046
5	0.007513	0.995559
6	0.002810	0.998369
7	0.001037	0.999406
8	0.000379	0.999785
9	0.000137	0.999923

k=1·8
Mean = 0·93
Variance = 1·40

n	P(n)	F(n)
0	0.473346	0.473346
1	0.289688	0.763034
2	0.137891	0.900926
3	0.059385	0.960311
4	0.024229	0.984540
5	0.009556	0.994096
6	0.003682	0.997779
7	0.001395	0.999174
8	0.000522	0.999695
9	0.000193	0.999889
10	0.000071	0.999959

k=2·0
Mean = 1·03
Variance = 1·56

n	P(n)	F(n)
0	0.435600	0.435600
1	0.296208	0.731808
2	0.151066	0.882874
3	0.068483	0.951357
4	0.029105	0.980463
5	0.011875	0.992338
6	0.004710	0.997048
7	0.001830	0.998879
8	0.000700	0.999579
9	0.000264	0.999843
10	0.000099	0.999942

k=2·2
Mean = 1·13
Variance = 1·72

n	P(n)	F(n)
0	0.400864	0.400864
1	0.299846	0.700710
2	0.163116	0.863826
3	0.077643	0.941469
4	0.034318	0.975788
5	0.014469	0.990256
6	0.005903	0.996159
7	0.002351	0.998510
8	0.000919	0.999430
9	0.000354	0.999784
10	0.000135	0.999919

k=2·4
Mean = 1·24
Variance = 1·87

n	P(n)	F(n)
0	0.368897	0.368897
1	0.301020	0.669917
2	0.173990	0.843907
3	0.086763	0.930670
4	0.039824	0.970494
5	0.017331	0.987826
6	0.007268	0.995093
7	0.002965	0.998058
8	0.001185	0.999243
9	0.000465	0.999708
10	0.000180	0.999889
11	0.000069	0.999958

k=2·6
Mean = 1·34
Variance = 2·03

n	P(n)	F(n)
0	0.339480	0.339480
1	0.300100	0.639580
2	0.183661	0.823242
3	0.095749	0.918991
4	0.045576	0.964567
5	0.020455	0.985022
6	0.008809	0.993831
7	0.003680	0.997511
8	0.001501	0.999012
9	0.000601	0.999613
10	0.000237	0.999850
11	0.000092	0.999943

k=2·8
Mean = 1·44
Variance = 2·19

n	P(n)	F(n)
0	0.312409	0.312409
1	0.297413	0.609822
2	0.192129	0.801950
3	0.104518	0.906469
4	0.051527	0.957996
5	0.023826	0.981822
6	0.010531	0.992353
7	0.004501	0.996855
8	0.001875	0.998730
9	0.000765	0.999494
10	0.000307	0.999801
11	0.000121	0.999923

k=3·0
Mean = 1·55
Variance = 2·34

n	P(n)	F(n)
0	0.287496	0.287496
1	0.293246	0.580742
2	0.199407	0.780149
3	0.112997	0.893147
4	0.057629	0.950775
5	0.027431	0.978207
6	0.012436	0.990642
7	0.005436	0.996078
8	0.002310	0.998388
9	0.000960	0.999349
10	0.000392	0.999740
11	0.000157	0.999898
12	0.000062	0.999960

k=3·2
Mean = 1·65
Variance = 2·50

n	P(n)	F(n)
0	0.264570	0.264570
1	0.287852	0.552422
2	0.205526	0.757949
3	0.121124	0.879072
4	0.063832	0.942904

5	0.031252	0.974157
6	0.014522	0.988678
7	0.006489	0.995168
8	0.002813	0.997981
9	0.001190	0.999171
10	0.000494	0.999665
11	0.000201	0.999866
12	0.000081	0.999947

5	0.043806	0.959255
6	0.021845	0.981100
7	0.010398	0.991498
8	0.004773	0.996271
9	0.002128	0.998398
10	0.000926	0.999324
11	0.000395	0.999719
12	0.000166	0.999885
13	0.000068	0.999953

5	0.057510	0.940030
6	0.030634	0.970664
7	0.015474	0.986138
8	0.007497	0.993635
9	0.003512	0.997148
10	0.001600	0.998748
11	0.000712	0.999460
12	0.000311	0.999771
13	0.000133	0.999904

k=3·4
Mean=1·75
Variance=2·65

n	P(n)	F(n)
0	0.243472	0.243472
1	0.281454	0.524926
2	0.210527	0.735454
3	0.128843	0.864296
4	0.070090	0.934387
5	0.035270	0.969656
6	0.016788	0.986445
7	0.007665	0.994110
8	0.003388	0.997498
9	0.001459	0.998957
10	0.000615	0.999572
11	0.000255	0.999827
12	0.000104	0.999931

k=4·0
Mean=2·06
Variance=3·12

n	P(n)	F(n)
0	0.189747	0.189747
1	0.258056	0.447804
2	0.219348	0.667152
3	0.149157	0.816308
4	0.088748	0.905057
5	0.048279	0.953336
6	0.024622	0.977958
7	0.011959	0.989917
8	0.005591	0.995508
9	0.002535	0.998043
10	0.001120	0.999163
11	0.000485	0.999648
12	0.000206	0.999854
13	0.000086	0.999940

k=4·6
Mean=2·37
Variance=3·59

n	P(n)	F(n)
0	0.147878	0.147878
1	0.231280	0.379158
2	0.220179	0.599337
3	0.164694	0.764031
4	0.106392	0.870423
5	0.062218	0.932641
6	0.033847	0.966488
7	0.017426	0.983914
8	0.008591	0.992505
9	0.004089	0.996595
10	0.001891	0.998485
11	0.000853	0.999339
12	0.000377	0.999716
13	0.000164	0.999880
14	0.000070	0.999950

k=3·6
Mean=1·85
Variance=2·81

n	P(n)	F(n)
0	0.224057	0.224057
1	0.274246	0.498302
2	0.214460	0.712762
3	0.136111	0.848873
4	0.076358	0.925231
5	0.039462	0.964693
6	0.019231	0.983924
7	0.008967	0.992891
8	0.004040	0.996931
9	0.001770	0.998701
10	0.000758	0.999460
11	0.000319	0.999778
12	0.000132	0.999910

k=4·2
Mean=2·16
Variance=3·28

n	P(n)	F(n)
0	0.174616	0.174616
1	0.249352	0.423968
2	0.220427	0.644395
3	0.154887	0.799282
4	0.094791	0.894073
5	0.052855	0.946928
6	0.027555	0.974483
7	0.013652	0.988135
8	0.006498	0.994633
9	0.002995	0.997628
10	0.001344	0.998972
11	0.000590	0.999562
12	0.000254	0.999816
13	0.000108	0.999924

k=4·8
Mean=2·47
Variance=3·75

n	P(n)	F(n)
0	0.136085	0.136085
1	0.222091	0.358176
2	0.218982	0.577158
3	0.168762	0.745920
4	0.111889	0.857809
5	0.066954	0.924764
6	0.037182	0.961946
7	0.019505	0.981450
8	0.009782	0.991232
9	0.004730	0.995962
10	0.002219	0.998181
11	0.001015	0.999196
12	0.000454	0.999651
13	0.000200	0.999851
14	0.000086	0.999937

k=3·8
Mean=1·96
Variance=2·97

n	P(n)	F(n)
0	0.206190	0.206190
1	0.266397	0.472587
2	0.217380	0.689967
3	0.142891	0.832858
4	0.082591	0.915449

k=4·4
Mean=2·27
Variance=3·43

n	P(n)	F(n)
0	0.160692	0.160692
1	0.240395	0.401086
2	0.220682	0.621769
3	0.160068	0.781837
4	0.100683	0.882520

k=5·0
Mean=2·58
Variance=3·90

n	P(n)	F(n)
0	0.125233	0.125233
1	0.212897	0.338130
2	0.217154	0.555284
3	0.172276	0.727560
4	0.117148	0.844708

P = 0·66

5	0.071694	0.916402
6	0.040627	0.957029
7	0.021706	0.978735
8	0.011070	0.989805
9	0.005437	0.995242
10	0.002588	0.997830
11	0.001200	0.999030
12	0.000544	0.999574
13	0.000242	0.999816
14	0.000106	0.999921

k = 6·0
Mean = 3·09
Variance = 4·68

n	P(n)	F(n)
0	0.082654	0.082654
1	0.168614	0.251268
2	0.200651	0.451919
3	0.181923	0.633842
4	0.139171	0.773013
5	0.094637	0.867650
6	0.058990	0.926640
7	0.034383	0.961023
8	0.018996	0.980019
9	0.010047	0.990066
10	0.005124	0.995190
11	0.002534	0.997724
12	0.001221	0.998945
13	0.000575	0.999520
14	0.000265	0.999785
15	0.000120	0.999905

k = 7·0
Mean = 3·61
Variance = 5·46

n	P(n)	F(n)
0	0.054552	0.054552
1	0.129833	0.184384
2	0.176573	0.360957
3	0.180104	0.541061
4	0.153088	0.694150
5	0.114510	0.808660
6	0.077867	0.886527
7	0.049167	0.935694
8	0.029255	0.964949
9	0.016578	0.981526
10	0.009018	0.990545
11	0.004739	0.995283
12	0.002417	0.997700
13	0.001201	0.998901
14	0.000583	0.999484
15	0.000278	0.999762
16	0.000130	0.999892
17	0.000060	0.999951

k = 8·0
Mean = 4·12
Variance = 6·24

n	P(n)	F(n)
0	0.036004	0.036004
1	0.097931	0.133935
2	0.149834	0.283770
3	0.169812	0.453582
4	0.158775	0.612357
5	0.129560	0.741917
6	0.095443	0.837359
7	0.064901	0.902260
8	0.041374	0.943635
9	0.025009	0.968643
10	0.014455	0.983098
11	0.008042	0.991140
12	0.004329	0.995470
13	0.002265	0.997734
14	0.001155	0.998889
15	0.000576	0.999465
16	0.000281	0.999747
17	0.000135	0.999882
18	0.000064	0.999946

k = 9·0
Mean = 4·64
Variance = 7·02

n	P(n)	F(n)
0	0.023763	0.023763
1	0.072714	0.096476
2	0.123613	0.220090
3	0.154105	0.374195
4	0.157187	0.531382
5	0.138953	0.670335
6	0.110236	0.780571
7	0.080315	0.860886
8	0.054614	0.915500
9	0.035074	0.950575
10	0.021466	0.972040
11	0.012606	0.984646
12	0.007143	0.991790
13	0.003923	0.995713
14	0.002096	0.997809
15	0.001093	0.998902
16	0.000557	0.999460
17	0.000279	0.999738
18	0.000137	0.999875
19	0.000066	0.999941

k = 10·0
Mean = 5·15
Variance = 7·81

n	P(n)	F(n)
0	0.015683	0.015683
1	0.053323	0.069007
2	0.099715	0.168722
3	0.135612	0.304334
4	0.149851	0.454185
5	0.142659	0.596844
6	0.121260	0.718104
7	0.094236	0.812340
8	0.068086	0.880426
9	0.046298	0.926724
10	0.029909	0.956633
11	0.018489	0.975122
12	0.011001	0.986123
13	0.006330	0.992452
14	0.003536	0.995988
15	0.001923	0.997911
16	0.001022	0.998933
17	0.000531	0.999464
18	0.000271	0.999735
19	0.000136	0.999871
20	0.000067	0.999938

k = 11·0
Mean = 5·67
Variance = 8·59

n	P(n)	F(n)
0	0.010351	0.010351
1	0.038713	0.049064
2	0.078974	0.128038
3	0.116355	0.244393
4	0.138463	0.382856
5	0.141232	0.524088
6	0.128050	0.652138
7	0.105733	0.757871
8	0.080886	0.838757
9	0.058058	0.896815
10	0.039479	0.936295
11	0.025626	0.961920
12	0.015973	0.977894
13	0.009609	0.987502
14	0.005600	0.993103
15	0.003174	0.996276
16	0.001753	0.998030
17	0.000947	0.998977
18	0.000501	0.999477
19	0.000260	0.999737
20	0.000133	0.999870
21	0.000067	0.999936

k = 12·0
Mean = 6·18
Variance = 9·37

n	P(n)	F(n)
0	0.006832	0.006832
1	0.027873	0.034705
2	0.061600	0.096305
3	0.097738	0.194043
4	0.124617	0.318660

n	P(n)	F(n)
5	0.135583	0.454242
6	0.130611	0.584854
7	0.114192	0.699046
8	0.092210	0.791255
9	0.069670	0.860925
10	0.049744	0.910669
11	0.033826	0.944495
12	0.022043	0.966538
13	0.013836	0.980375
14	0.008401	0.988775
15	0.004951	0.993726
16	0.002841	0.996567
17	0.001591	0.998157
18	0.000871	0.999029
19	0.000468	0.999496
20	0.000247	0.999743
21	0.000128	0.999871
22	0.000065	0.999936

k = 13·0
Mean = 6·70
Variance = 10·15

n	P(n)	F(n)
0	0.004509	0.004509
1	0.019929	0.024438
2	0.047432	0.071870
3	0.080634	0.152504
4	0.109663	0.262167
5	0.126770	0.388937
6	0.129305	0.518242
7	0.119330	0.637572
8	0.101431	0.739003
9	0.080468	0.819471
10	0.060190	0.879662
11	0.042790	0.922452
12	0.029097	0.951549
13	0.019025	0.970574
14	0.012013	0.982587
15	0.007352	0.989939
16	0.004374	0.994313
17	0.002537	0.996850
18	0.001438	0.998288
19	0.000798	0.999086
20	0.000434	0.999519
21	0.000232	0.999751
22	0.000122	0.999873
23	0.000063	0.999936

k = 14·0
Mean = 7·21
Variance = 10·93

n	P(n)	F(n)
0	0.002976	0.002976
1	0.014165	0.017141
2	0.036121	0.053262
3	0.065500	0.118762
4	0.094647	0.213409

n	P(n)	F(n)
5	0.115848	0.329257
6	0.124730	0.453987
7	0.121165	0.575153
8	0.108141	0.683294
9	0.089877	0.773171
10	0.070284	0.843455
11	0.052138	0.895593
12	0.036931	0.932524
13	0.025113	0.957637
14	0.016467	0.974104
15	0.010451	0.984555
16	0.006440	0.990995
17	0.003864	0.994860
18	0.002263	0.997122
19	0.001296	0.998418
20	0.000727	0.999145
21	0.000400	0.999545
22	0.000216	0.999762
23	0.000115	0.999877
24	0.000060	0.999937

k = 15·0
Mean = 7·73
Variance = 11·71

n	P(n)	F(n)
0	0.001964	0.001964
1	0.010017	0.011981
2	0.027246	0.039227
3	0.052493	0.091720
4	0.080315	0.172035
5	0.103767	0.275802
6	0.117602	0.393404
7	0.119954	0.513359
8	0.112157	0.625516
9	0.097452	0.722968
10	0.079521	0.802490
11	0.061448	0.863938
12	0.045267	0.909205
13	0.031965	0.941170
14	0.021736	0.962906
15	0.014288	0.977194
16	0.009109	0.986303
17	0.005647	0.991950
18	0.003414	0.995364
19	0.002016	0.997380
20	0.001165	0.998545
21	0.000660	0.999205
22	0.000367	0.999572
23	0.000201	0.999773
24	0.000108	0.999881
25	0.000057	0.999939

k = 16·0
Mean = 8·24
Variance = 12·49

n	P(n)	F(n)
0	0.001296	0.001296
1	0.007052	0.008348
2	0.020380	0.028728
3	0.041575	0.070303
4	0.067143	0.137446
5	0.091315	0.228761
6	0.108665	0.337425
7	0.116116	0.453541
8	0.113503	0.567045
9	0.102910	0.669954
10	0.087473	0.757428
11	0.070297	0.827724
12	0.053777	0.881501
13	0.039381	0.920883
14	0.027736	0.948618
15	0.018860	0.967478
16	0.012424	0.979903
17	0.007951	0.987854
18	0.004956	0.992811
19	0.003016	0.995826
20	0.001794	0.997620
21	0.001046	0.998666
22	0.000598	0.999264
23	0.000336	0.999600
24	0.000186	0.999786
25	0.000101	0.999887
26	0.000054	0.999941

k = 17·0
Mean = 8·76
Variance = 13·27

n	P(n)	F(n)
0	0.000856	0.000856
1	0.004945	0.005801
2	0.015132	0.020933
3	0.032584	0.053517
4	0.055393	0.108910
5	0.079101	0.188012
6	0.098613	0.286625
7	0.110165	0.396790
8	0.112368	0.509158
9	0.106126	0.615284
10	0.093815	0.709099
11	0.078293	0.787392
12	0.062112	0.849504
13	0.047110	0.896614
14	0.034323	0.930937
15	0.024118	0.955054
16	0.016400	0.971454
17	0.010824	0.982278
18	0.006951	0.989230
19	0.004354	0.993583

20	0.002665	0.996248
21	0.001596	0.997844
22	0.000937	0.998781
23	0.000540	0.999322
24	0.000306	0.999628
25	0.000171	0.999799
26	0.000094	0.999893
27	0.000051	0.999943

k = 18·0
Mean = 9·27
Variance = 14·05

n	P(n)	F(n)
0	0.000565	0.000565
1	0.003456	0.004020
2	0.011162	0.015182
3	0.025301	0.040483
4	0.045162	0.085645
5	0.067562	0.153207
6	0.088056	0.241263
7	0.102648	0.343910
8	0.109063	0.452974
9	0.107124	0.560098
10	0.098340	0.658439
11	0.085109	0.743548
12	0.069931	0.813479
13	0.054869	0.868348
14	0.041309	0.909656
15	0.029963	0.939619
16	0.021011	0.960630
17	0.014288	0.974918
18	0.009446	0.984364
19	0.006085	0.990449
20	0.003827	0.994276
21	0.002355	0.996631
22	0.001419	0.998050
23	0.000839	0.998889
24	0.000487	0.999377
25	0.000278	0.999655
26	0.000157	0.999812
27	0.000087	0.999899
28	0.000047	0.999946

k = 19·0
Mean = 9·79
Variance = 14·83

n	P(n)	F(n)
0	0.000373	0.000373
1	0.002408	0.002780
2	0.008186	0.010966
3	0.019482	0.030447
4	0.036430	0.066878
5	0.056977	0.123855
6	0.077489	0.201344
7	0.094094	0.295438
8	0.103974	0.399412
9	0.106053	0.505465

10	0.100963	0.606427
11	0.090499	0.696927
12	0.076924	0.773851
13	0.062368	0.836219
14	0.048469	0.884688
15	0.036255	0.920942
16	0.026194	0.947136
17	0.018336	0.965472
18	0.012468	0.977940
19	0.008255	0.986196
20	0.005333	0.991529
21	0.003367	0.994896
22	0.002082	0.996978
23	0.001262	0.998239
24	0.000751	0.998990
25	0.000439	0.999429
26	0.000253	0.999682
27	0.000143	0.999825
28	0.000080	0.999905

k = 20·0
Mean = 10·30
Variance = 15·61

n	P(n)	F(n)
0	0.000246	0.000246
1	0.001673	0.001919
2	0.005971	0.007890
3	0.014888	0.022778
4	0.029106	0.051884
5	0.047501	0.099385
6	0.067293	0.166678
7	0.084982	0.251659
8	0.097516	0.349176
9	0.103151	0.452327
10	0.101707	0.554033
11	0.094310	0.648343
12	0.082835	0.731178
13	0.069327	0.800505
14	0.055561	0.856066
15	0.042819	0.898884
16	0.031846	0.930731
17	0.022929	0.953660
18	0.016025	0.969685
19	0.010897	0.980582
20	0.007225	0.987807
21	0.004679	0.992486
22	0.002965	0.995450
23	0.001841	0.997291
24	0.001121	0.998412
25	0.000671	0.999083
26	0.000395	0.999478
27	0.000229	0.999707
28	0.000131	0.999838
29	0.000073	0.999911

k=0·2
Mean=0·09
Variance=0·14

n	P(n)	F(n)
0	0.925767	0.925767
1	0.059249	0.985016
2	0.011376	0.996392
3	0.002670	0.999062
4	0.000683	0.999745
5	0.000184	0.999929

k=0·4
Mean=0·19
Variance=0·28

n	P(n)	F(n)
0	0.857045	0.857045
1	0.109702	0.966747
2	0.024573	0.991320
3	0.006291	0.997611
4	0.001711	0.999322
5	0.000482	0.999803
6	0.000139	0.999942

k=0·6
Mean=0·28
Variance=0·42

n	P(n)	F(n)
0	0.793424	0.793424
1	0.152337	0.945761
2	0.038998	0.984760
3	0.010816	0.995575
4	0.003115	0.998690
5	0.000917	0.999607
6	0.000274	0.999881
7	0.000083	0.999964

k=0·8
Mean=0·38
Variance=0·55

n	P(n)	F(n)
0	0.734526	0.734526
1	0.188039	0.922565
2	0.054155	0.976720
3	0.016174	0.992894
4	0.004917	0.997811
5	0.001511	0.999322
6	0.000467	0.999789
7	0.000145	0.999934

k=1·0
Mean=0·47
Variance=0·69

n	P(n)	F(n)
0	0.680000	0.680000
1	0.217600	0.897600
2	0.069632	0.967232
3	0.022282	0.989514
4	0.007130	0.996645
5	0.002282	0.998926
6	0.000730	0.999656
7	0.000234	0.999890
8	0.000075	0.999965

k=1·2
Mean=0·56
Variance=0·83

n	P(n)	F(n)
0	0.629522	0.629522
1	0.241736	0.871258
2	0.085091	0.956349
3	0.029044	0.985394
4	0.009759	0.995153
5	0.003248	0.998400
6	0.001074	0.999474
7	0.000353	0.999828
8	0.000116	0.999944

k=1·4
Mean=0·66
Variance=0·97

n	P(n)	F(n)
0	0.582791	0.582791
1	0.261090	0.843881
2	0.100259	0.944139
3	0.036360	0.980500
4	0.012799	0.993299
5	0.004423	0.997722
6	0.001510	0.999232
7	0.000511	0.999742
8	0.000172	0.999914

k=1·6
Mean=0·75
Variance=1·11

n	P(n)	F(n)
0	0.539528	0.539528
1	0.276239	0.815767
2	0.114915	0.930682
3	0.044127	0.974810
4	0.016239	0.991048
5	0.005820	0.996868
6	0.002049	0.998917
7	0.000712	0.999629
8	0.000245	0.999874
9	0.000084	0.999957

k=1·8
Mean=0·85
Variance=1·25

n	P(n)	F(n)
0	0.499478	0.499478
1	0.287699	0.787177
2	0.128889	0.916066
3	0.052243	0.968309
4	0.020061	0.988370
5	0.007447	0.995817
6	0.002701	0.998518
7	0.000963	0.999481
8	0.000339	0.999820
9	0.000118	0.999938

k=2·0
Mean=0·94
Variance=1·38

n	P(n)	F(n)
0	0.462400	0.462400
1	0.295936	0.758336
2	0.142049	0.900385
3	0.060608	0.960993
4	0.024243	0.985236
5	0.009309	0.994545
6	0.003475	0.998021
7	0.001271	0.999292
8	0.000458	0.999749
9	0.000163	0.999912

k=2·2
Mean=1·04
Variance=1·52

n	P(n)	F(n)
0	0.428075	0.428075
1	0.301365	0.729439
2	0.154299	0.883738
3	0.069126	0.952864
4	0.028756	0.981620
5	0.011411	0.993031
6	0.004382	0.997412
7	0.001642	0.999055
8	0.000604	0.999659
9	0.000219	0.999878
10	0.000079	0.999957

k=2·4
Mean=1·13
Variance=1·66

n	P(n)	F(n)
0	0.396298	0.396298
1	0.304357	0.700654
2	0.165570	0.866224
3	0.077707	0.943932
4	0.033570	0.977501

n	P(n)	F(n)		n	P(n)	F(n)		n	P(n)	F(n)
5	0.013750	0.991251		5	0.022156	0.984119		5	0.032449	0.973916
6	0.005427	0.996678		6	0.009453	0.993572		6	0.014883	0.988799
7	0.002084	0.998762		7	0.003889	0.997462		7	0.006532	0.995331
8	0.000784	0.999545		8	0.001556	0.999017		8	0.002769	0.998100
9	0.000290	0.999835		9	0.000608	0.999626		9	0.001142	0.999243
10	0.000106	0.999941		10	0.000234	0.999859		10	0.000461	0.999703
				11	0.000088	0.999948		11	0.000182	0.999885
								12	0.000071	0.999956

k=2·6
Mean=1·22
Variance=1·80

n	P(n)	F(n)
0	0.366879	0.366879
1	0.305244	0.672123
2	0.175820	0.847943
3	0.086269	0.934212
4	0.038649	0.972861
5	0.016325	0.989186
6	0.006617	0.995803
7	0.002601	0.998405
8	0.000999	0.999404
9	0.000376	0.999780
10	0.000140	0.999920

k=3·2
Mean=1·51
Variance=2·21

n	P(n)	F(n)
0	0.291091	0.291091
1	0.298077	0.589168
2	0.200308	0.789476
3	0.111104	0.900580
4	0.055108	0.955687
5	0.025394	0.981081
6	0.011105	0.992186
7	0.004671	0.996857
8	0.001906	0.998763
9	0.000759	0.999521
10	0.000296	0.999818
11	0.000114	0.999931

k=3·8
Mean=1·79
Variance=2·63

n	P(n)	F(n)
0	0.230958	0.230958
1	0.280845	0.511804
2	0.215689	0.727493
3	0.133440	0.860933
4	0.072591	0.933524
5	0.036238	0.969762
6	0.017007	0.986769
7	0.007619	0.994389
8	0.003292	0.997680
9	0.001381	0.999061
10	0.000566	0.999627
11	0.000227	0.999854
12	0.000090	0.999944

k=2·8
Mean=1·32
Variance=1·94

n	P(n)	F(n)
0	0.339645	0.339645
1	0.304322	0.643967
2	0.185028	0.828994
3	0.094734	0.923728
4	0.043957	0.967685
5	0.019130	0.986815
6	0.007958	0.994773
7	0.003201	0.997974
8	0.001255	0.999229
9	0.000482	0.999711
10	0.000182	0.999893
11	0.000068	0.999961

k=3·4
Mean=1·60
Variance=2·35

n	P(n)	F(n)
0	0.269482	0.269482
1	0.293197	0.562679
2	0.206411	0.769090
3	0.118892	0.887982
4	0.060873	0.948855
5	0.028829	0.977684
6	0.012916	0.990600
7	0.005550	0.996150
8	0.002309	0.998459
9	0.000936	0.999395
10	0.000371	0.999766
11	0.000145	0.999911

k=4·0
Mean=1·88
Variance=2·77

n	P(n)	F(n)
0	0.213814	0.213814
1	0.273682	0.487495
2	0.218945	0.706441
3	0.140125	0.846566
4	0.078470	0.925036
5	0.040177	0.965212
6	0.019285	0.984497
7	0.008816	0.993313
8	0.003879	0.997192
9	0.001655	0.998847
10	0.000688	0.999535
11	0.000280	0.999816
12	0.000112	0.999928

k=3·0
Mean=1·41
Variance=2·08

n	P(n)	F(n)
0	0.314432	0.314432
1	0.301855	0.616287
2	0.193187	0.809474
3	0.103033	0.912507
4	0.049456	0.961963

k=3·6
Mean=1·69
Variance=2·49

n	P(n)	F(n)
0	0.249478	0.249478
1	0.287399	0.536876
2	0.211525	0.748402
3	0.126351	0.874753
4	0.066713	0.941466

k=4·2
Mean=1·98
Variance=2·91

n	P(n)	F(n)
0	0.197942	0.197942
1	0.266034	0.463975
2	0.221340	0.685316
3	0.146380	0.831695
4	0.084315	0.916010

n	P(n)	F(n)
5	0.044248	0.960258
6	0.021711	0.981969
7	0.010124	0.992093
8	0.004535	0.996628
9	0.001967	0.998596
10	0.000831	0.999427
11	0.000343	0.999770
12	0.000139	0.999909

n	P(n)	F(n)
5	0.057065	0.942908
6	0.029826	0.972734
7	0.014725	0.987459
8	0.006950	0.994410
9	0.003163	0.997573
10	0.001397	0.998970
11	0.000601	0.999571
12	0.000253	0.999824
13	0.000105	0.999929

n	P(n)	F(n)
5	0.104221	0.847899
6	0.066701	0.914600
7	0.039640	0.954240
8	0.022198	0.976438
9	0.011839	0.988277
10	0.006062	0.994339
11	0.002998	0.997337
12	0.001439	0.998775
13	0.000673	0.999448
14	0.000308	0.999756
15	0.000138	0.999894
16	0.000061	0.999955

k=4·4
Mean=2·07
Variance=3·04

n	P(n)	F(n)
0	0.183248	0.183248
1	0.258013	0.441261
2	0.222923	0.664185
3	0.152182	0.816367
4	0.090092	0.906459
5	0.048433	0.954892
6	0.024281	0.979174
7	0.011544	0.990718
8	0.005264	0.995982
9	0.002321	0.998303
10	0.000995	0.999298
11	0.000417	0.999715
12	0.000171	0.999886
13	0.000069	0.999955

k=5·0
Mean=2·35
Variance=3·46

n	P(n)	F(n)
0	0.145393	0.145393
1	0.232629	0.378023
2	0.223324	0.601347
3	0.166749	0.768096
4	0.106719	0.874815
5	0.061470	0.936285
6	0.032784	0.969069
7	0.016486	0.985555
8	0.007913	0.993468
9	0.003658	0.997126
10	0.001639	0.998764
11	0.000715	0.999479
12	0.000305	0.999784
13	0.000128	0.999912

k=8·0
Mean=3·76
Variance=5·54

n	P(n)	F(n)
0	0.045716	0.045716
1	0.117034	0.162750
2	0.168529	0.331279
3	0.179764	0.511043
4	0.158192	0.669235
5	0.121492	0.790727
6	0.084234	0.874961
7	0.053910	0.928871
8	0.032346	0.961217
9	0.018401	0.979618
10	0.010010	0.989628
11	0.005242	0.994870
12	0.002656	0.997526
13	0.001307	0.998833
14	0.000628	0.999461
15	0.000295	0.999755
16	0.000135	0.999891
17	0.000061	0.999952

k=4·6
Mean=2·16
Variance=3·18

n	P(n)	F(n)
0	0.169645	0.169645
1	0.249717	0.419362
2	0.223747	0.643109
3	0.157518	0.800627
4	0.095771	0.896398
5	0.052712	0.949110
6	0.026989	0.976099
7	0.013078	0.989177
8	0.006068	0.995245
9	0.002719	0.997963
10	0.001183	0.999146
11	0.000502	0.999649
12	0.000209	0.999858
13	0.000085	0.999943

k=6·0
Mean=2·82
Variance=4·15

n	P(n)	F(n)
0	0.098867	0.098867
1	0.189826	0.288693
2	0.212605	0.501298
3	0.181423	0.682720
4	0.130624	0.813345
5	0.083600	0.896944
6	0.049045	0.945989
7	0.026905	0.972894
8	0.013990	0.986884
9	0.006964	0.993849
10	0.003343	0.997191
11	0.001556	0.998747
12	0.000705	0.999453
13	0.000313	0.999765
14	0.000136	0.999901

k=9·0
Mean=4·24
Variance=6·23

n	P(n)	F(n)
0	0.031087	0.031087
1	0.089531	0.120618
2	0.143249	0.263867
3	0.168079	0.431947
4	0.161356	0.593303
5	0.134248	0.727551
6	0.100239	0.827790
7	0.068735	0.896525
8	0.043990	0.940515
9	0.026590	0.967105
10	0.015316	0.982421
11	0.008465	0.990886
12	0.004515	0.995401
13	0.002334	0.997735
14	0.001174	0.998908

k=4·8
Mean=2·26
Variance=3·32

n	P(n)	F(n)
0	0.157052	0.157052
1	0.241231	0.398283
2	0.223863	0.622146
3	0.162375	0.784521
4	0.101322	0.885843

k=7·0
Mean=3·29
Variance=4·84

n	P(n)	F(n)
0	0.067230	0.067230
1	0.150595	0.217825
2	0.192762	0.410586
3	0.185051	0.595637
4	0.148041	0.743678

15	0.000576	0.999484
16	0.000276	0.999761
17	0.000130	0.999891
18	0.000060	0.999951

k = 10·0
Mean = 4·71
Variance = 6·92

n	P(n)	F(n)
0	0.021139	0.021139
1	0.067646	0.088785
2	0.119056	0.207841
3	0.152392	0.360233
4	0.158488	0.518720
5	0.142005	0.660725
6	0.113604	0.774329
7	0.083093	0.857422
8	0.056503	0.913925
9	0.036162	0.950087
10	0.021987	0.972074
11	0.012792	0.984866
12	0.007164	0.992030
13	0.003879	0.995909
14	0.002039	0.997949
15	0.001044	0.998993
16	0.000522	0.999515
17	0.000256	0.999771
18	0.000123	0.999893
19	0.000058	0.999951

k = 11·0
Mean = 5·18
Variance = 7·61

n	P(n)	F(n)
0	0.014375	0.014375
1	0.050599	0.064974
2	0.097150	0.162123
3	0.134714	0.296838
4	0.150880	0.447718
5	0.144845	0.592563
6	0.123601	0.716164
7	0.096056	0.812219
8	0.069160	0.881379
9	0.046721	0.928101
10	0.029902	0.958003
11	0.018267	0.976270
12	0.010717	0.986987
13	0.006067	0.993054
14	0.003328	0.996382
15	0.001775	0.998158
16	0.000923	0.999081
17	0.000469	0.999550
18	0.000234	0.999783
19	0.000114	0.999897
20	0.000055	0.999952

k = 12·0
Mean = 5·65
Variance = 8·30

n	P(n)	F(n)
0	0.009775	0.009775
1	0.037535	0.047310
2	0.078073	0.125383
3	0.116589	0.241972
4	0.139907	0.381879
5	0.143265	0.525144
6	0.129893	0.655037
7	0.106884	0.761921
8	0.081232	0.843153
9	0.057765	0.900918
10	0.038818	0.939735
11	0.024843	0.964579
12	0.015237	0.979816
13	0.009002	0.988818
14	0.005144	0.993962
15	0.002853	0.996815
16	0.001541	0.998356
17	0.000812	0.999168
18	0.000419	0.999586
19	0.000212	0.999798
20	0.000105	0.999903

k = 13·0
Mean = 6·12
Variance = 9·00

n	P(n)	F(n)
0	0.006647	0.006647
1	0.027651	0.034298
2	0.061938	0.096236
3	0.099101	0.195337
4	0.126849	0.322186
5	0.138012	0.460197
6	0.132491	0.592689
7	0.115078	0.707767
8	0.092063	0.799829
9	0.068740	0.868569
10	0.048393	0.916962
11	0.032379	0.949342
12	0.020723	0.970064
13	0.012752	0.982817
14	0.007579	0.990395
15	0.004365	0.994761
16	0.002445	0.997205
17	0.001334	0.998540
18	0.000712	0.999251
19	0.000372	0.999623
20	0.000190	0.999813
21	0.000096	0.999909

k = 14·0
Mean = 6·59
Variance = 9·69

n	P(n)	F(n)
0	0.004520	0.004520
1	0.020249	0.024769
2	0.048598	0.073366
3	0.082040	0.156306
4	0.112793	0.269104
5	0.129943	0.399048
6	0.131676	0.530723
7	0.120389	0.651113
8	0.101127	0.752240
9	0.079104	0.831344
10	0.058220	0.889564
11	0.040648	0.930213
12	0.027099	0.957312
13	0.017343	0.974655
14	0.010703	0.985358
15	0.006393	0.991752
16	0.003708	0.995460
17	0.002034	0.997554
18	0.001154	0.998708
19	0.000622	0.999330
20	0.000328	0.999659
21	0.000170	0.999829
22	0.000087	0.999915

k = 15·0
Mean = 7·06
Variance = 10·38

n	P(n)	F(n)
0	0.003074	0.003074
1	0.014753	0.017826
2	0.037767	0.055594
3	0.068485	0.124078
4	0.098618	0.222696
5	0.119919	0.342615
6	0.127914	0.470529
7	0.122797	0.593326
8	0.108062	0.701388
9	0.088370	0.789758
10	0.067868	0.857626
11	0.049359	0.906985
12	0.034222	0.941207
13	0.022745	0.963952
14	0.014557	0.978508
15	0.009006	0.987514
16	0.005403	0.992917
17	0.003153	0.996070
18	0.001794	0.997864
19	0.000997	0.998861
20	0.000542	0.999403
21	0.000289	0.999693
22	0.000151	0.999844
23	0.000078	0.999922

25	0.000062	0.999935

k = 16·0
Mean = 7·53
Variance = 11·07

n	P(n)	F(n)
0	0.002090	0.002090
1	0.010701	0.012791
2	0.029106	0.041897
3	0.055883	0.097780
4	0.084943	0.182723
5	0.108727	0.291449
6	0.121774	0.413223
7	0.122470	0.535693
8	0.112672	0.648365
9	0.096147	0.744512
10	0.076918	0.821430
11	0.058178	0.879607
12	0.041888	0.921495
13	0.028870	0.950366
14	0.019137	0.969503
15	0.012248	0.981750
16	0.007594	0.989344
17	0.004574	0.993918
18	0.002683	0.996601
19	0.001537	0.998138
20	0.000860	0.998998
21	0.000472	0.999471
22	0.000254	0.999725
23	0.000134	0.999859
24	0.000070	0.999929

k = 17·0
Mean = 8·00
Variance = 11·76

n	P(n)	F(n)
0	0.001421	0.001421
1	0.007731	0.009152
2	0.022266	0.031418
3	0.045126	0.076544
4	0.072201	0.148746
5	0.097039	0.245784
6	0.113859	0.359643
7	0.119714	0.479357
8	0.114926	0.594283
9	0.102156	0.696439
10	0.084994	0.781433
11	0.066759	0.848192
12	0.049847	0.898038
13	0.035583	0.933621
14	0.024400	0.958021
15	0.016136	0.974157
16	0.010327	0.984484
17	0.006415	0.990899
18	0.003878	0.994777
19	0.002286	0.997062
20	0.001317	0.998379
21	0.000742	0.999121
22	0.000410	0.999531
23	0.000223	0.999754
24	0.000119	0.999873

k = 18·0
Mean = 8·47
Variance = 12·46

n	P(n)	F(n)
0	0.000966	0.000966
1	0.005567	0.006533
2	0.016922	0.023455
3	0.036101	0.059556
4	0.060649	0.120205
5	0.085394	0.205599
6	0.104750	0.310349
7	0.114926	0.425274
8	0.114926	0.540200
9	0.106242	0.646442
10	0.091793	0.738236
11	0.074770	0.813006
12	0.057822	0.870828
13	0.042699	0.913527
14	0.030256	0.943783
15	0.020654	0.964437
16	0.013632	0.978069
17	0.008724	0.986793
18	0.005429	0.992222
19	0.003291	0.995513
20	0.001949	0.997462
21	0.001128	0.998590
22	0.000640	0.999230
23	0.000356	0.999586
24	0.000195	0.999781
25	0.000105	0.999886
26	0.000055	0.999941

k = 19·0
Mean = 8·94
Variance = 13·15

n	P(n)	F(n)
0	0.000657	0.000657
1	0.003996	0.004653
2	0.012786	0.017438
3	0.028640	0.046078
4	0.050406	0.096484
5	0.074198	0.170682
6	0.094973	0.265655
7	0.108541	0.374196
8	0.112883	0.487079
9	0.108367	0.595446
10	0.097097	0.692543
11	0.081915	0.774458
12	0.065532	0.839989
13	0.050006	0.889995
14	0.036576	0.926571

15	0.025749	0.952320
16	0.017509	0.969829
17	0.011536	0.981365
18	0.007383	0.988748
19	0.004601	0.993348
20	0.002797	0.996146
21	0.001662	0.997808
22	0.000967	0.998775
23	0.000552	0.999327
24	0.000309	0.999636
25	0.000170	0.999806
26	0.000092	0.999898
27	0.000049	0.999947

k = 20·0
Mean = 9·41
Variance = 13·84

n	P(n)	F(n)
0	0.000447	0.000447
1	0.002860	0.003307
2	0.009609	0.012916
3	0.022550	0.035466
4	0.041492	0.076959
5	0.063732	0.140691
6	0.084976	0.225667
7	0.101000	0.326667
8	0.109080	0.435747
9	0.108595	0.544342
10	0.100776	0.645119
11	0.087950	0.733069
12	0.072706	0.805775
13	0.057270	0.863045
14	0.043198	0.906242
15	0.031333	0.937575
16	0.021933	0.959508
17	0.014863	0.974371
18	0.009776	0.984147
19	0.006257	0.990404
20	0.003904	0.994308
21	0.002380	0.996688
22	0.001419	0.998107
23	0.000829	0.998937
24	0.000475	0.999412
25	0.000268	0.999680
26	0.000148	0.999828
27	0.000081	0.999909

k = 0·2
Mean = 0·09
Variance = 0·12

n	P(n)	F(n)
0	0.931150	0.931150
1	0.055869	0.987019
2	0.010056	0.997075
3	0.002212	0.999288
4	0.000531	0.999819
5	0.000134	0.999953

k = 1·0
Mean = 0·43
Variance = 0·61

n	P(n)	F(n)
0	0.700000	0.700000
1	0.210000	0.910000
2	0.063000	0.973000
3	0.018900	0.991900
4	0.005670	0.997570
5	0.001701	0.999271
6	0.000510	0.999781
7	0.000153	0.999934

k = 1·8
Mean = 0·77
Variance = 1·10

n	P(n)	F(n)
0	0.526231	0.52623
1	0.284165	0.81039
2	0.119349	0.92974
3	0.045353	0.97509
4	0.016327	0.99142
5	0.005682	0.99710
6	0.001932	0.99903
7	0.000646	0.99968
8	0.000213	0.99989
9	0.000070	0.99996

k = 0·4
Mean = 0·17
Variance = 0·24

n	P(n)	F(n)
0	0.867040	0.867040
1	0.104045	0.971085
2	0.021849	0.992934
3	0.005244	0.998178
4	0.001337	0.999515
5	0.000353	0.999868
6	0.000095	0.999964

k = 1·2
Mean = 0·51
Variance = 0·73

n	P(n)	F(n)
0	0.651805	0.651805
1	0.234650	0.886455
2	0.077434	0.963889
3	0.024779	0.988668
4	0.007805	0.996474
5	0.002435	0.998909
6	0.000755	0.999664
7	0.000233	0.999897
8	0.000072	0.999968

k = 2·0
Mean = 0·86
Variance = 1·22

n	P(n)	F(n)
0	0.490000	0.49000
1	0.294000	0.78400
2	0.132300	0.91630
3	0.052920	0.96922
4	0.019845	0.98906
5	0.007144	0.99620
6	0.002500	0.99871
7	0.000857	0.99956
8	0.000289	0.99985
9	0.000096	0.99995

k = 0·6
Mean = 0·26
Variance = 0·37

n	P(n)	F(n)
0	0.807344	0.807344
1	0.145322	0.952666
2	0.034877	0.987544
3	0.009068	0.996612
4	0.002448	0.999060
5	0.000676	0.999736
6	0.000189	0.999925

k = 1·4
Mean = 0·60
Variance = 0·86

n	P(n)	F(n)
0	0.606928	0.606928
1	0.254910	0.861838
2	0.091768	0.953605
3	0.031201	0.984806
4	0.010296	0.995103
5	0.003336	0.998439
6	0.001068	0.999506
7	0.000339	0.999845
8	0.000107	0.999951

k = 2·2
Mean = 0·94
Variance = 1·35

n	P(n)	F(n)
0	0.456263	0.45626
1	0.301134	0.75739
2	0.144544	0.90194
3	0.060709	0.96265
4	0.023676	0.98632
5	0.008808	0.99513
6	0.003171	0.99830
7	0.001114	0.99941
8	0.000384	0.99980
9	0.000131	0.99993

k = 0·8
Mean = 0·34
Variance = 0·49

n	P(n)	F(n)
0	0.751759	0.751759
1	0.180422	0.932181
2	0.048714	0.980895
3	0.013640	0.994535
4	0.003887	0.998422
5	0.001120	0.999542
6	0.000325	0.999866
7	0.000095	0.999961

k = 1·6
Mean = 0·69
Variance = 0·98

n	P(n)	F(n)
0	0.565141	0.565141
1	0.271268	0.836409
2	0.105794	0.942203
3	0.038086	0.980289
4	0.013140	0.993429
5	0.004415	0.997844
6	0.001457	0.999301
7	0.000475	0.999775
8	0.000153	0.999928

k = 2·4
Mean = 1·03
Variance = 1·47

n	P(n)	F(n)
0	0.424850	0.42485
1	0.305892	0.73074
2	0.156005	0.88674
3	0.068642	0.95538
4	0.027800	0.98318
5	0.010675	0.99386
6	0.003950	0.99781
7	0.001422	0.99923
8	0.000501	0.99973
9	0.000174	0.99999

=2·6
Mean=1·11
Variance=1·59

n	P(n)	F(n)
0	0.395599	0.395599
1	0.308567	0.704166
2	0.166626	0.870792
3	0.076648	0.947440
4	0.032192	0.979632
5	0.012748	0.992380
6	0.004844	0.997225
7	0.001785	0.999010
8	0.000643	0.999653
9	0.000227	0.999880
10	0.000079	0.999959

k=3·2
Mean=1·37
Variance=1·96

n	P(n)	F(n)
0	0.319384	0.319384
1	0.306609	0.625993
2	0.193164	0.819157
3	0.100445	0.919602
4	0.046707	0.966309
5	0.020177	0.986487
6	0.008273	0.994759
7	0.003262	0.998021
8	0.001248	0.999269
9	0.000466	0.999735
10	0.000170	0.999905

k=3·8
Mean=1·63
Variance=2·33

n	P(n)	F(n)
0	0.257853	0.257853
1	0.293953	0.551806
2	0.211646	0.763452
3	0.122755	0.886206
4	0.062605	0.948811
5	0.029299	0.978110
6	0.012892	0.991002
7	0.005414	0.996416
8	0.002193	0.998609
9	0.000863	0.999472
10	0.000331	0.999803
11	0.000125	0.999928

=2·8
Mean=1·20
Variance=1·71

n	P(n)	F(n)
0	0.368362	0.368362
1	0.309424	0.677786
2	0.176372	0.854157
3	0.084658	0.938816
4	0.036826	0.975642
5	0.015025	0.990667
6	0.005860	0.996527
7	0.002210	0.998737
8	0.000812	0.999549
9	0.000292	0.999841
10	0.000104	0.999945

k=3·4
Mean=1·46
Variance=2·08

n	P(n)	F(n)
0	0.297395	0.297395
1	0.303343	0.600737
2	0.200206	0.800944
3	0.108111	0.909055
4	0.051893	0.960948
5	0.023041	0.983989
6	0.009677	0.993666
7	0.003898	0.997565
8	0.001520	0.999085
9	0.000578	0.999663
10	0.000215	0.999878
11	0.000079	0.999956

k=4·0
Mean=1·71
Variance=2·45

n	P(n)	F(n)
0	0.240100	0.240100
1	0.288120	0.528220
2	0.216090	0.744310
3	0.129654	0.873964
4	0.068068	0.942032
5	0.032673	0.974705
6	0.014703	0.989408
7	0.006301	0.995709
8	0.002599	0.998308
9	0.001040	0.999348
10	0.000405	0.999754
11	0.000155	0.999908

=3·0
Mean=1·29
Variance=1·84

n	P(n)	F(n)
0	0.343000	0.343000
1	0.308700	0.651700
2	0.185220	0.836920
3	0.092610	0.929530
4	0.041675	0.971204
5	0.017503	0.988708
6	0.007001	0.995709
7	0.002701	0.998410
8	0.001013	0.999422
9	0.000371	0.999794
10	0.000134	0.999927

k=3·6
Mean=1·54
Variance=2·20

n	P(n)	F(n)
0	0.276919	0.276919
1	0.299073	0.575992
2	0.206360	0.782352
3	0.115562	0.897914
4	0.057203	0.955117
5	0.026085	0.981201
6	0.011216	0.992418
7	0.004615	0.997032
8	0.001834	0.998867
9	0.000709	0.999576
10	0.000268	0.999844
11	0.000099	0.999943

k=4·2
Mean=1·80
Variance=2·57

n	P(n)	F(n)
0	0.223569	0.223569
1	0.281697	0.505266
2	0.219724	0.724990
3	0.136229	0.861219
4	0.073563	0.934782
5	0.036193	0.970975
6	0.016649	0.987624
7	0.007278	0.994902
8	0.003057	0.997959
9	0.001243	0.999202
10	0.000492	0.999694
11	0.000191	0.999885
12	0.000072	0.999957

P=0·70

| 15 | 0.000064 | 0.999956 |

k = 4·4
Mean = 1·89
Variance = 2·69

n	P(n)	F(n)
0	0.208176	0.208176
1	0.274793	0.482969
2	0.222582	0.705551
3	0.142453	0.848004
4	0.079061	0.927065
5	0.039847	0.966912
6	0.018728	0.985640
7	0.008347	0.993987
8	0.003568	0.997556
9	0.001475	0.999031
10	0.000593	0.999624
11	0.000233	0.999856
12	0.000090	0.999946

k = 5·0
Mean = 2·14
Variance = 3·06

n	P(n)	F(n)
0	0.168070	0.168070
1	0.252105	0.420175
2	0.226895	0.647070
3	0.158826	0.805896
4	0.095296	0.901191
5	0.051460	0.952651
6	0.025730	0.978381
7	0.012130	0.990511
8	0.005458	0.995969
9	0.002365	0.998334
10	0.000993	0.999328
11	0.000406	0.999734
12	0.000163	0.999897
13	0.000064	0.999961

k = 8·0
Mean = 3·43
Variance = 4·90

n	P(n)	F(n)
0	0.057648	0.057648
1	0.138355	0.196003
2	0.186780	0.382783
3	0.186780	0.569562
4	0.154093	0.723655
5	0.110947	0.834603
6	0.072116	0.906718
7	0.043269	0.949987
8	0.024339	0.974326
9	0.012981	0.987307
10	0.006620	0.993927
11	0.003250	0.997177
12	0.001544	0.998721
13	0.000712	0.999437
14	0.000321	0.999754
15	0.000141	0.999895
16	0.000061	0.999956

k = 4·6
Mean = 1·97
Variance = 2·82

n	P(n)	F(n)
0	0.193843	0.193843
1	0.267504	0.461347
2	0.224703	0.686051
3	0.148304	0.834355
4	0.084533	0.918888
5	0.043619	0.962507
6	0.020937	0.983444
7	0.009511	0.992956
8	0.004137	0.997093
9	0.001738	0.998831
10	0.000709	0.999540
11	0.000282	0.999822
12	0.000110	0.999933

k = 6·0
Mean = 2·57
Variance = 3·67

n	P(n)	F(n)
0	0.117649	0.117649
1	0.211768	0.329417
2	0.222357	0.551774
3	0.177885	0.729659
4	0.120073	0.849732
5	0.072044	0.921775
6	0.039624	0.961399
7	0.020378	0.981777
8	0.009934	0.991711
9	0.004636	0.996347
10	0.002086	0.998434
11	0.000910	0.999344
12	0.000387	0.999731
13	0.000161	0.999892
14	0.000065	0.999957

k = 9·0
Mean = 3·86
Variance = 5·51

n	P(n)	F(n)
0	0.040354	0.040354
1	0.108955	0.149308
2	0.163432	0.312740
3	0.179775	0.492516
4	0.161798	0.654314
5	0.126202	0.780516
6	0.088342	0.868857
7	0.056791	0.925648
8	0.034075	0.959723
9	0.019309	0.979032
10	0.010427	0.989459
11	0.005403	0.994862
12	0.002701	0.997563
13	0.001309	0.998877
14	0.000617	0.999490
15	0.000284	0.999774
16	0.000128	0.999901

k = 4·8
Mean = 2·06
Variance = 2·94

n	P(n)	F(n)
0	0.180497	0.180497
1	0.259916	0.440413
2	0.226127	0.666540
3	0.153766	0.820307
4	0.089953	0.910260
5	0.047495	0.957755
6	0.023273	0.981028
7	0.010772	0.991800
8	0.004767	0.996566
9	0.002034	0.998600
10	0.000842	0.999442
11	0.000340	0.999782
12	0.000134	0.999916

k = 7·0
Mean = 3·00
Variance = 4·29

n	P(n)	F(n)
0	0.082354	0.082354
1	0.172944	0.255298
2	0.207533	0.462831
3	0.186780	0.649611
4	0.140085	0.789695
5	0.092456	0.882151
6	0.055474	0.937625
7	0.030907	0.968531
8	0.016226	0.984757
9	0.008113	0.992870
10	0.003894	0.996765
11	0.001806	0.998570
12	0.000812	0.999383
13	0.000356	0.999739
14	0.000153	0.999892

k = 10·0
Mean = 4·29
Variance = 6·12

n	P(n)	F(n)
0	0.028248	0.028248
1	0.084743	0.112990
2	0.139825	0.252815
3	0.167790	0.420606
4	0.163596	0.584201
5	0.137420	0.721621
6	0.103065	0.824687
7	0.070673	0.895360
8	0.045054	0.940414
9	0.027033	0.967447
10	0.015409	0.982855
11	0.008405	0.991260
12	0.004412	0.995672
13	0.002240	0.997912
14	0.001104	0.999017
15	0.000530	0.999546
16	0.000248	0.999795
17	0.000114	0.999909

k = 11·0
Mean = 4·71
Variance = 6·73

n	P(n)	F(n)
0	0.019773	0.019773
1	0.065252	0.085025
2	0.117453	0.202478
3	0.152689	0.355167
4	0.160324	0.515491
5	0.144291	0.659782
6	0.115433	0.775215
7	0.084101	0.859317
8	0.056768	0.916085
9	0.035953	0.952038
10	0.021572	0.973610
11	0.012355	0.985965
12	0.006795	0.992760
13	0.003607	0.996367
14	0.001855	0.998222
15	0.000927	0.999149
16	0.000452	0.999601
17	0.000215	0.999817
18	0.000101	0.999917

k = 12·0
Mean = 5·14
Variance = 7·35

n	P(n)	F(n)
0	0.013841	0.013841
1	0.049829	0.063670
2	0.097166	0.160836
3	0.136032	0.296868
4	0.153036	0.449904
5	0.146915	0.596819
6	0.124878	0.721696
7	0.096334	0.818030
8	0.068638	0.886669
9	0.045759	0.932427
10	0.028828	0.961255
11	0.017297	0.978552
12	0.009946	0.988498
13	0.005508	0.994006
14	0.002951	0.996957
15	0.001534	0.998491
16	0.000777	0.999268
17	0.000384	0.999652
18	0.000186	0.999838
19	0.000088	0.999925

k = 13·0
Mean = 5·57
Variance = 7·96

n	P(n)	F(n)
0	0.009689	0.009689
1	0.037787	0.047476
2	0.079352	0.126828
3	0.119028	0.245856
4	0.142834	0.388690
5	0.145690	0.534380
6	0.131121	0.665502
7	0.106770	0.772272
8	0.080078	0.852350
9	0.056054	0.908404
10	0.036996	0.945400
11	0.023207	0.968606
12	0.013924	0.982530
13	0.008033	0.990563
14	0.004476	0.995039
15	0.002417	0.997456
16	0.001269	0.998724
17	0.000649	0.999374
18	0.000325	0.999698
19	0.000159	0.999857
20	0.000076	0.999934

k = 14·0
Mean = 6·00
Variance = 8·57

n	P(n)	F(n)
0	0.006782	0.006782
1	0.028485	0.035268
2	0.064092	0.099360
3	0.102547	0.201907
4	0.130748	0.332655
5	0.141208	0.473863
6	0.134147	0.608010
7	0.114983	0.722993
8	0.090549	0.813543
9	0.066403	0.879946
10	0.045818	0.925764
11	0.029990	0.955753
12	0.018744	0.974497
13	0.011246	0.985743
14	0.006507	0.992250
15	0.003644	0.995894
16	0.001981	0.997875
17	0.001049	0.998924
18	0.000542	0.999466
19	0.000274	0.999740
20	0.000136	0.999876
21	0.000066	0.999941

k = 15·0
Mean = 6·43
Variance = 9·18

n	P(n)	F(n)
0	0.004748	0.004748
1	0.021364	0.026112
2	0.051274	0.077385
3	0.087165	0.164550
4	0.117673	0.282224
5	0.134147	0.416371
6	0.134147	0.550518
7	0.120733	0.671251
8	0.099604	0.770855
9	0.076363	0.847218
10	0.054982	0.902200
11	0.037487	0.939687
12	0.024367	0.964054
13	0.015182	0.979237
14	0.009109	0.988346
15	0.005283	0.993630
16	0.002972	0.996602
17	0.001626	0.998227
18	0.000867	0.999095
19	0.000452	0.999546
20	0.000230	0.999777
21	0.000115	0.999892
22	0.000057	0.999949

k = 16·0
Mean = 6·86
Variance = 9·80

n	P(n)	F(n)
0	0.003323	0.003323
1	0.015952	0.019275
2	0.040677	0.059952
3	0.073219	0.133171
4	0.104337	0.237508
5	0.125204	0.362712
6	0.131464	0.494176
7	0.123952	0.618128
8	0.106909	0.725037
9	0.085527	0.810564

10	0.064145	0.874709
11	0.045485	0.920194
12	0.030702	0.950896
13	0.019838	0.970735
14	0.012328	0.983063
15	0.007397	0.990460
16	0.004299	0.994759
17	0.002428	0.997187
18	0.001335	0.998522
19	0.000717	0.999239
20	0.000376	0.999615
21	0.000194	0.999809
22	0.000098	0.999907

k=17·0
Mean=7·29
Variance=10·41

n	P(n)	F(n)
0	0.002326	0.002326
1	0.011864	0.014190
2	0.032033	0.046224
3	0.060863	0.107087
4	0.091295	0.198381
5	0.115031	0.313413
6	0.126534	0.439947
7	0.124727	0.564674
8	0.112254	0.676928
9	0.093545	0.770473
10	0.072965	0.843438
11	0.053729	0.897167
12	0.037610	0.934778
13	0.025170	0.959947
14	0.016181	0.976128
15	0.010032	0.986160
16	0.006019	0.992179
17	0.003505	0.995685
18	0.001986	0.997671
19	0.001098	0.998769
20	0.000593	0.999361
21	0.000313	0.999675
22	0.000162	0.999837
23	0.000083	0.999920

k=18·0
Mean=7·71
Variance=11·02

n	P(n)	F(n)
0	0.001628	0.001628
1	0.008793	0.010422
2	0.025061	0.035483
3	0.050123	0.085606
4	0.078943	0.164549
5	0.104205	0.268754
6	0.119836	0.388589
7	0.123259	0.511849
8	0.115556	0.627404
9	0.100148	0.727553

10	0.081120	0.808673
11	0.061946	0.870619
12	0.044911	0.915530
13	0.031092	0.946622
14	0.020654	0.967276
15	0.013219	0.980495
16	0.008179	0.988674
17	0.004907	0.993581
18	0.002863	0.996444
19	0.001627	0.998071
20	0.000903	0.998974
21	0.000490	0.999465
22	0.000261	0.999725
23	0.000136	0.999861
24	0.000070	0.999931

k=19·0
Mean=8·14
Variance=11·63

n	P(n)	F(n)
0	0.001140	0.001140
1	0.006497	0.007637
2	0.019492	0.027129
3	0.040933	0.068063
4	0.067540	0.135603
5	0.093205	0.228808
6	0.111847	0.340655
7	0.119836	0.460490
8	0.116840	0.577330
9	0.105156	0.682486
10	0.088331	0.770817
11	0.069862	0.840678
12	0.052396	0.893074
13	0.037483	0.930558
14	0.025703	0.956261
15	0.016964	0.973225
16	0.010815	0.984039
17	0.006680	0.990719
18	0.004008	0.994727
19	0.002341	0.997068
20	0.001335	0.998402
21	0.000744	0.999146
22	0.000406	0.999552
23	0.000217	0.999768
24	0.000114	0.999882
25	0.000059	0.999941

k=20·0
Mean=8·57
Variance=12·24

n	P(n)	F(n)
0	0.000798	0.000798
1	0.004788	0.005585
2	0.015081	0.020666
3	0.033178	0.053844
4	0.057231	0.111075
5	0.082413	0.193488
6	0.103017	0.296505
7	0.114790	0.411295
8	0.116225	0.527520
9	0.108476	0.635996
10	0.094374	0.730370
11	0.077215	0.807586
12	0.059842	0.867428
13	0.044191	0.911619
14	0.031249	0.942868
15	0.021250	0.964118
16	0.013945	0.978063
17	0.008859	0.986922
18	0.005463	0.992385
19	0.003278	0.995663
20	0.001918	0.997581
21	0.001096	0.998676
22	0.000613	0.999289
23	0.000336	0.999625
24	0.000180	0.999805
25	0.000095	0.999900

k=0·2
Mean=0·08
Variance=0·11

n	P(n)	F(n)
0	0.936411	0.936411
1	0.052439	0.988850
2	0.008810	0.997660
3	0.001809	0.999469
4	0.000405	0.999874
5	0.000095	0.999969

k=1·0
Mean=0·39
Variance=0·54

n	P(n)	F(n)
0	0.720000	0.720000
1	0.201600	0.921600
2	0.056448	0.978048
3	0.015805	0.993853
4	0.004426	0.998279
5	0.001239	0.999518
6	0.000347	0.999865
7	0.000097	0.999962

k=1·8
Mean=0·70
Variance=0·97

n	P(n)	F(n)
0	0.553603	0.553603
1	0.279016	0.832619
2	0.109374	0.941993
3	0.038791	0.980785
4	0.013034	0.993819
5	0.004233	0.998052
6	0.001343	0.999395
7	0.000419	0.999815
8	0.000129	0.999944

k=0·4
Mean=0·16
Variance=0·22

n	P(n)	F(n)
0	0.876866	0.876866
1	0.098209	0.975074
2	0.019249	0.994323
3	0.004312	0.998635
4	0.001026	0.999661
5	0.000253	0.999914

k=1·2
Mean=0·47
Variance=0·65

n	P(n)	F(n)
0	0.674216	0.674216
1	0.226537	0.900752
2	0.069773	0.970526
3	0.020839	0.991365
4	0.006127	0.997491
5	0.001784	0.999275
6	0.000516	0.999792
7	0.000149	0.999940

k=2·0
Mean=0·78
Variance=1·08

n	P(n)	F(n)
0	0.518400	0.518400
1	0.290304	0.808704
2	0.121928	0.930632
3	0.045520	0.976151
4	0.015932	0.992083
5	0.005353	0.997436
6	0.001749	0.999185
7	0.000560	0.999745
8	0.000176	0.999921

k=0·6
Mean=0·23
Variance=0·32

n	P(n)	F(n)
0	0.821107	0.821107
1	0.137946	0.959052
2	0.030900	0.989952
3	0.007498	0.997451
4	0.001890	0.999340
5	0.000487	0.999827
6	0.000127	0.999954

k=1·4
Mean=0·54
Variance=0·76

n	P(n)	F(n)
0	0.631343	0.631343
1	0.247487	0.878830
2	0.083155	0.961985
3	0.026388	0.988373
4	0.008128	0.996501
5	0.002458	0.998958
6	0.000734	0.999692
7	0.000217	0.999910

k=2·2
Mean=0·86
Variance=1·19

n	P(n)	F(n)
0	0.485435	0.485435
1	0.299028	0.784464
2	0.133965	0.918428
3	0.052514	0.970942
4	0.019115	0.990058
5	0.006637	0.996694
6	0.002230	0.998924
7	0.000731	0.999656
8	0.000236	0.999891
9	0.000075	0.999966

k=0·8
Mean=0·31
Variance=0·43

n	P(n)	F(n)
0	0.768893	0.768893
1	0.172232	0.941125
2	0.043402	0.984528
3	0.011343	0.995870
4	0.003017	0.998887
5	0.000811	0.999698
6	0.000220	0.999918

k=1·6
Mean=0·62
Variance=0·86

n	P(n)	F(n)
0	0.591197	0.591197
1	0.264856	0.856053
2	0.096408	0.952460
3	0.032393	0.984853
4	0.010431	0.995284
5	0.003271	0.998555
6	0.001007	0.999562
7	0.000306	0.999869
8	0.000092	0.999961

k=2·4
Mean=0·93
Variance=1·30

n	P(n)	F(n)
0	0.454567	0.454567
1	0.305469	0.760036
2	0.145403	0.905439
3	0.059712	0.965152
4	0.022571	0.987723
5	0.008090	0.995813
6	0.002794	0.998606
7	0.000939	0.999545
8	0.000309	0.999854
9	0.000100	0.999953

k=2·6
Mean=1·01
Variance=1·40

n	P(n)	F(n)
0	0.425662	0.425662
1	0.309882	0.735543
2	0.156180	0.891724
3	0.067053	0.958777
4	0.026285	0.985062
5	0.009715	0.994777
6	0.003446	0.998222
7	0.001185	0.999408
8	0.000398	0.999806
9	0.000131	0.999937

k=2·8
Mean=1·09
Variance=1·51

n	P(n)	F(n)
0	0.398594	0.398594
1	0.312498	0.711092
2	0.166249	0.877341
3	0.074479	0.951820
4	0.030239	0.982059
5	0.011515	0.993574
6	0.004191	0.997765
7	0.001475	0.999241
8	0.000506	0.999747
9	0.000170	0.999917

k=3·0
Mean=1·17
Variance=1·62

n	P(n)	F(n)
0	0.373248	0.373248
1	0.313528	0.686776
2	0.175576	0.862352
3	0.081935	0.944288
4	0.034413	0.978700
5	0.013490	0.992190
6	0.005036	0.997227
7	0.001813	0.999040
8	0.000635	0.999674
9	0.000217	0.999891
10	0.000073	0.999964

k=3·2
Mean=1·24
Variance=1·73

n	P(n)	F(n)
0	0.349514	0.349514
1	0.313164	0.662678
2	0.184141	0.846818
3	0.089370	0.936188
4	0.038786	0.974974

5	0.015639	0.990613
6	0.005984	0.996597
7	0.002202	0.998799
8	0.000786	0.999586
9	0.000274	0.999860
10	0.000094	0.999953

k=3·4
Mean=1·32
Variance=1·84

n	P(n)	F(n)
0	0.327288	0.327288
1	0.311578	0.638867
2	0.191932	0.830799
3	0.096734	0.927533
4	0.043337	0.970870
5	0.017959	0.988829
6	0.007040	0.995868
7	0.002647	0.998515
8	0.000964	0.999479
9	0.000342	0.999821
10	0.000119	0.999939

k=3·6
Mean=1·40
Variance=1·94

n	P(n)	F(n)
0	0.306476	0.306476
1	0.308928	0.615405
2	0.198950	0.814354
3	0.103984	0.918339
4	0.048041	0.966379
5	0.020446	0.986826
6	0.008206	0.995031
7	0.003151	0.998182
8	0.001169	0.999351
9	0.000422	0.999773
10	0.000149	0.999922

k=3·8
Mean=1·48
Variance=2·05

n	P(n)	F(n)
0	0.286988	0.286988
1	0.305355	0.592343
2	0.205199	0.797541
3	0.111081	0.908622
4	0.052874	0.961497

5	0.023096	0.984592
6	0.009485	0.994077
7	0.003718	0.997795
8	0.001405	0.999200
9	0.000516	0.999716
10	0.000185	0.999901

k=4·0
Mean=1·56
Variance=2·16

n	P(n)	F(n)
0	0.268739	0.268739
1	0.300987	0.569726
2	0.210691	0.780417
3	0.117987	0.898404
4	0.057814	0.956217
5	0.025901	0.982118
6	0.010878	0.992996
7	0.004351	0.997347
8	0.001675	0.999023
9	0.000625	0.999648
10	0.000228	0.999876
11	0.000081	0.999957

k=4·2
Mean=1·63
Variance=2·27

n	P(n)	F(n)
0	0.251650	0.251650
1	0.295940	0.547590
2	0.215444	0.763034
3	0.124670	0.887705
4	0.062834	0.950539
5	0.028853	0.979392
6	0.012388	0.991780
7	0.005054	0.996834
8	0.001981	0.998815
9	0.000752	0.999567
10	0.000278	0.999845
11	0.000100	0.999945

k=4·4
Mean=1·71
Variance=2·38

n	P(n)	F(n)
0	0.235648	0.235648
1	0.290318	0.525965
2	0.219480	0.745446
3	0.131103	0.876549
4	0.067911	0.944460

5	0.031945	0.976405
6	0.014013	0.990419
7	0.005830	0.996248
8	0.002326	0.998574
9	0.000897	0.999472
10	0.000337	0.999808
11	0.000123	0.999932

5	0.041959	0.965801
6	0.019581	0.985381
7	0.008616	0.993997
8	0.003619	0.997615
9	0.001463	0.999079
10	0.000574	0.999653
11	0.000219	0.999872
12	0.000082	0.999953

5	0.098441	0.873005
6	0.059721	0.932726
7	0.033444	0.966170
8	0.017558	0.983727
9	0.008740	0.992467
10	0.004160	0.996628
11	0.001906	0.998534
12	0.000845	0.999379
13	0.000364	0.999743
14	0.000153	0.999896
15	0.000063	0.999958

k=4·6
Mean=1·79
Variance=2·48

n	P(n)	F(n)
0	0.220663	0.220663
1	0.284214	0.504877
2	0.222824	0.727701
3	0.137259	0.864960
4	0.073022	0.937982
5	0.035167	0.973149
6	0.015755	0.988904
7	0.006680	0.995585
8	0.002712	0.998297
9	0.001063	0.999360
10	0.000405	0.999765
11	0.000150	0.999915

k=6·0
Mean=2·33
Variance=3·24

n	P(n)	F(n)
0	0.139314	0.139314
1	0.234048	0.373362
2	0.229367	0.602728
3	0.171260	0.773989
4	0.107894	0.881883
5	0.060421	0.942304
6	0.031016	0.973320
7	0.014888	0.988207
8	0.006774	0.994981
9	0.002950	0.997932
10	0.001239	0.999171
11	0.000505	0.999675
12	0.000200	0.999876
13	0.000078	0.999953

k=9·0
Mean=3·50
Variance=4·86

n	P(n)	F(n)
0	0.051999	0.051999
1	0.131037	0.183035
2	0.183451	0.366487
3	0.188343	0.554830
4	0.158208	0.713039
5	0.115176	0.828215
6	0.075248	0.903463
7	0.045149	0.948612
8	0.025283	0.973895
9	0.013372	0.987267
10	0.006740	0.994007
11	0.003259	0.997266
12	0.001521	0.998787
13	0.000688	0.999475
14	0.000303	0.999778
15	0.000130	0.999908

k=4·8
Mean=1·87
Variance=2·59

n	P(n)	F(n)
0	0.206631	0.206631
1	0.277712	0.484344
2	0.225502	0.709846
3	0.143119	0.852965
4	0.078143	0.931108
5	0.038509	0.969617
6	0.017611	0.987228
7	0.007608	0.994836
8	0.003142	0.997978
9	0.001251	0.999230
10	0.000483	0.999713
11	0.000182	0.999895
12	0.000067	0.999962

k=7·0
Mean=2·72
Variance=3·78

n	P(n)	F(n)
0	0.100306	0.100306
1	0.196600	0.296906
2	0.220192	0.517098
3	0.184961	0.702059
4	0.129473	0.831532
5	0.079755	0.911288
6	0.044663	0.955951
7	0.023225	0.979175
8	0.011380	0.990556
9	0.005311	0.995866
10	0.002379	0.998245
11	0.001030	0.999275
12	0.000432	0.999707
13	0.000177	0.999884
14	0.000071	0.999955

k=10·0
Mean=3·89
Variance=5·40

n	P(n)	F(n)
0	0.037439	0.037439
1	0.104829	0.142268
2	0.161437	0.303706
3	0.180810	0.484515
4	0.164537	0.649052
5	0.128997	0.778049
6	0.090298	0.868347
7	0.057791	0.926137
8	0.034385	0.960523
9	0.019256	0.979779
10	0.010244	0.990023
11	0.005215	0.995238
12	0.002555	0.997793
13	0.001211	0.999004
14	0.000557	0.999561

k=5·0
Mean=1·94
Variance=2·70

n	P(n)	F(n)
0	0.193492	0.193492
1	0.270888	0.464380
2	0.227546	0.691927
3	0.148664	0.840590
4	0.083252	0.923842

k=8·0
Mean=3·11
Variance=4·32

n	P(n)	F(n)
0	0.072220	0.072220
1	0.161774	0.233994
2	0.203835	0.437829
3	0.190246	0.628075
4	0.146489	0.774564

n	P(n)	F(n)
15	0.000250	0.999811
16	0.000109	0.999920

k=11·0
Mean=4·28
Variance=5·94

n	P(n)	F(n)
0	0.026956	0.026956
1	0.083025	0.109981
2	0.139482	0.249463
3	0.169238	0.418701
4	0.165853	0.584554
5	0.139317	0.723870
6	0.104023	0.827893
7	0.070736	0.898629
8	0.044563	0.943193
9	0.026342	0.969535
10	0.014752	0.984286
11	0.007885	0.992171
12	0.004048	0.996219
13	0.002005	0.998225
14	0.000963	0.999187
15	0.000449	0.999636
16	0.000204	0.999841
17	0.000091	0.999931

k=12·0
Mean=4·67
Variance=6·48

n	P(n)	F(n)
0	0.019408	0.019408
1	0.065212	0.084621
2	0.118686	0.203307
3	0.155083	0.358390
4	0.162838	0.521228
5	0.145903	0.667131
6	0.115749	0.782880
7	0.083340	0.866219
8	0.055421	0.921640
9	0.034484	0.956124
10	0.020277	0.976401
11	0.011355	0.987756
12	0.006094	0.993850
13	0.003150	0.997000
14	0.001575	0.998575
15	0.000764	0.999339
16	0.000361	0.999700
17	0.000167	0.999867
18	0.000075	0.999942

k=13·0
Mean=5·06
Variance=7·02

n	P(n)	F(n)
0	0.013974	0.013974
1	0.050866	0.064840
2	0.099696	0.164536
3	0.139575	0.304111
4	0.156324	0.460435
5	0.148821	0.609256
6	0.125009	0.734265
7	0.095007	0.829272
8	0.066505	0.895777
9	0.043450	0.939227
10	0.026765	0.965992
11	0.015670	0.981662
12	0.008775	0.990437
13	0.004725	0.995162
14	0.002457	0.997619
15	0.001238	0.998857
16	0.000607	0.999464
17	0.000290	0.999754
18	0.000135	0.999889
19	0.000062	0.999951

k=14·0
Mean=5·44
Variance=7·56

n	P(n)	F(n)
0	0.010061	0.010061
1	0.039440	0.049502
2	0.082825	0.132326
3	0.123685	0.256011
4	0.147185	0.403197
5	0.148363	0.551559
6	0.131548	0.683108
7	0.105239	0.788346
8	0.077350	0.865696
9	0.052942	0.918638
10	0.034095	0.952733
11	0.020829	0.973562
12	0.012150	0.985712
13	0.006804	0.992516
14	0.003674	0.996190
15	0.001920	0.998111
16	0.000975	0.999085
17	0.000482	0.999567
18	0.000232	0.999799
19	0.000110	0.999908

k=15·0
Mean=5·83
Variance=8·10

n	P(n)	F(n)
0	0.007244	0.007244
1	0.030425	0.037670
2	0.068153	0.105823
3	0.108136	0.213959
4	0.136251	0.350210
5	0.144971	0.495181
6	0.135307	0.630488
7	0.113658	0.744146
8	0.087516	0.831662
9	0.062623	0.894285
10	0.042083	0.936368
11	0.026780	0.963147
12	0.016246	0.979394
13	0.009448	0.988842
14	0.005291	0.994133
15	0.002864	0.996997
16	0.001504	0.998500
17	0.000768	0.999268
18	0.000382	0.999650
19	0.000186	0.999836
20	0.000088	0.999925

k=16·0
Mean=6·22
Variance=8·64

n	P(n)	F(n)
0	0.005216	0.005216
1	0.023367	0.028583
2	0.055613	0.084195
3	0.093430	0.177625
4	0.124261	0.301886
5	0.139173	0.441059
6	0.136389	0.577448
7	0.120022	0.697470
8	0.096618	0.794089
9	0.072142	0.866230
10	0.050499	0.916729
11	0.033421	0.950150
12	0.021055	0.971206
13	0.012698	0.983904
14	0.007365	0.991269
15	0.004124	0.995393
16	0.002237	0.997630
17	0.001179	0.998810
18	0.000605	0.999415
19	0.000303	0.999718
20	0.000149	0.999867
21	0.000071	0.999938

k=17·0
Mean=6·61
Variance=9·18

n	P(n)	F(n)
0	0.003755	0.003755
1	0.017876	0.021631
2	0.045046	0.066677
3	0.079882	0.146560
4	0.111835	0.258395

n	P(n)	F(n)		n	P(n)	F(n)
5	0.131518	0.389913		5	0.112740	0.298413
6	0.135025	0.524938		6	0.126269	0.424683
7	0.124223	0.649161		7	0.126269	0.550952
8	0.104348	0.753509		8	0.114905	0.665857
9	0.081159	0.834668		9	0.096520	0.762377
10	0.059084	0.893752		10	0.075672	0.838049
11	0.040607	0.934359		11	0.055860	0.893909
12	0.026530	0.960889		12	0.039102	0.933010
13	0.016571	0.977459		13	0.026108	0.959118
14	0.009943	0.987402		14	0.016709	0.975827
15	0.005753	0.993155		15	0.010293	0.986120
16	0.003222	0.996377		16	0.006124	0.992244
17	0.001751	0.998129		17	0.003530	0.995775
18	0.000926	0.999055		18	0.001977	0.997752
19	0.000478	0.999532		19	0.001078	0.998830
20	0.000241	0.999773		20	0.000573	0.999403
21	0.000119	0.999892		21	0.000298	0.999702
22	0.000057	0.999949		22	0.000152	0.999853
				23	0.000076	0.999929

k=18·0
Mean = 7·00
Variance = 9·72

n	P(n)	F(n)
0	0.002704	0.002704
1	0.013627	0.016331
2	0.036249	0.052580
3	0.067665	0.120245
4	0.099468	0.219713
5	0.122544	0.342257
6	0.131531	0.473787
7	0.126269	0.600057
8	0.110486	0.710542
9	0.089371	0.799913
10	0.067564	0.867477
11	0.048155	0.915632
12	0.032585	0.948217
13	0.021055	0.969271
14	0.013054	0.982325
15	0.007798	0.990123
16	0.004503	0.994626
17	0.002522	0.997148
18	0.001373	0.998521
19	0.000728	0.999249
20	0.000377	0.999626
21	0.000191	0.999818
22	0.000095	0.999913

k=20·0
Mean = 7·78
Variance = 10·80

n	P(n)	F(n)
0	0.001402	0.001402
1	0.007849	0.009251
2	0.023077	0.032328
3	0.047385	0.079714
4	0.076291	0.156004
5	0.102534	0.258539
6	0.119624	0.378162
7	0.124408	0.502571
8	0.117566	0.620137
9	0.102413	0.722550
10	0.083159	0.805709
11	0.063504	0.869213
12	0.045934	0.915147
13	0.031659	0.946806
14	0.020895	0.967702
15	0.013261	0.980963
16	0.008123	0.989086
17	0.004816	0.993902
18	0.002772	0.996674
19	0.001552	0.998226
20	0.000848	0.999074
21	0.000452	0.999526
22	0.000236	0.999762
23	0.000121	0.999882
24	0.000061	0.999943

k=19·0
Mean = 7·39
Variance = 10·26

n	P(n)	F(n)
0	0.001947	0.001947
1	0.010357	0.012304
2	0.028999	0.041303
3	0.056839	0.098142
4	0.087531	0.185673

P = 0·74

k = 0·2
Mean = 0·07
Variance = 0·09

n	P(n)	F(n)
0	0.941556	0.941556
1	0.048961	0.990517
2	0.007638	0.998155
3	0.001456	0.999612
4	0.000303	0.999914

k = 0·4
Mean = 0·14
Variance = 0·19

n	P(n)	F(n)
0	0.886528	0.886528
1	0.092199	0.978727
2	0.016780	0.995508
3	0.003490	0.998998
4	0.000771	0.999769
5	0.000176	0.999946

k = 0·6
Mean = 0·21
Variance = 0·28

n	P(n)	F(n)
0	0.834717	0.834717
1	0.130216	0.964932
2	0.027085	0.992017
3	0.006103	0.998120
4	0.001428	0.999548
5	0.000342	0.999890
6	0.000083	0.999973

k = 0·8
Mean = 0·28
Variance = 0·38

n	P(n)	F(n)
0	0.785933	0.785933
1	0.163474	0.949407
2	0.038253	0.987660
3	0.009283	0.996942
4	0.002293	0.999235
5	0.000572	0.999807
6	0.000144	0.999951

k = 1·0
Mean = 0·35
Variance = 0·47

n	P(n)	F(n)
0	0.740000	0.740000
1	0.192400	0.932400
2	0.050024	0.982424
3	0.013006	0.995430
4	0.003382	0.998812
5	0.000879	0.999691
6	0.000229	0.999920

k = 1·2
Mean = 0·42
Variance = 0·57

n	P(n)	F(n)
0	0.696752	0.696752
1	0.217387	0.914138
2	0.062173	0.976311
3	0.017243	0.993553
4	0.004707	0.998261
5	0.001273	0.999533
6	0.000342	0.999875
7	0.000091	0.999967

k = 1·4
Mean = 0·49
Variance = 0·66

n	P(n)	F(n)
0	0.656031	0.656031
1	0.238795	0.894826
2	0.074504	0.969331
3	0.021954	0.991284
4	0.006279	0.997563
5	0.001763	0.999326
6	0.000489	0.999815
7	0.000134	0.999950

k = 1·6
Mean = 0·56
Variance = 0·76

n	P(n)	F(n)
0	0.617690	0.617690
1	0.256959	0.874649
2	0.086852	0.961502
3	0.027098	0.988599
4	0.008102	0.996702
5	0.002359	0.999061
6	0.000675	0.999736
7	0.000190	0.999926

k = 1·8
Mean = 0·63
Variance = 0·85

n	P(n)	F(n)
0	0.581590	0.581590
1	0.272184	0.853774
2	0.099075	0.952850
3	0.032629	0.985478
4	0.010180	0.995658
5	0.003070	0.998729
6	0.000905	0.999633
7	0.000262	0.999896
8	0.000075	0.999971

k = 2·0
Mean = 0·70
Variance = 0·95

n	P(n)	F(n)
0	0.547600	0.547600
1	0.284752	0.832352
2	0.111053	0.943405
3	0.038498	0.981904
4	0.012512	0.994416
5	0.003904	0.998319
6	0.001184	0.999504
7	0.000352	0.999855
8	0.000103	0.999958

k = 2·2
Mean = 0·77
Variance = 1·04

n	P(n)	F(n)
0	0.515596	0.515596
1	0.294921	0.810517
2	0.122687	0.933205
3	0.044658	0.977863
4	0.015094	0.992957
5	0.004866	0.997824
6	0.001518	0.999342
7	0.000462	0.999804
8	0.000138	0.999943

k = 2·4
Mean = 0·84
Variance = 1·14

n	P(n)	F(n)
0	0.485463	0.485463
1	0.302929	0.788392
2	0.133895	0.922286
3	0.051058	0.973345
4	0.017922	0.991266
5	0.005964	0.997231
6	0.001913	0.999143
7	0.000597	0.999740
8	0.000182	0.999922

k=2·6
Mean=0·91
Variance=1·23

n	P(n)	F(n)
0	0.457091	0.457091
1	0.308993	0.766084
2	0.144609	0.910693
3	0.057651	0.968344
4	0.020985	0.989329
5	0.007202	0.996531
6	0.002372	0.998903
7	0.000758	0.999660
8	0.000236	0.999897
9	0.000072	0.999969

k=2·8
Mean=0·98
Variance=1·33

n	P(n)	F(n)
0	0.430377	0.430377
1	0.313314	0.743691
2	0.154777	0.898468
3	0.064387	0.962856
4	0.024274	0.987130
5	0.008583	0.995713
6	0.002901	0.998614
7	0.000948	0.999562
8	0.000302	0.999864
9	0.000094	0.999959

k=3·0
Mean=1·05
Variance=1·42

n	P(n)	F(n)
0	0.405224	0.405224
1	0.316075	0.721299
2	0.164359	0.885658
3	0.071222	0.956880
4	0.027777	0.984656
5	0.010111	0.994767
6	0.003505	0.998272
7	0.001172	0.999444
8	0.000381	0.999825
9	0.000121	0.999946

k=3·2
Mean=1·12
Variance=1·52

n	P(n)	F(n)
0	0.381541	0.381541
1	0.317442	0.698984
2	0.173324	0.872307
3	0.078111	0.950418
4	0.031479	0.981897
5	0.011786	0.993683
6	0.004188	0.997870
7	0.001431	0.999302
8	0.000474	0.999776
9	0.000153	0.999929

k=3·4
Mean=1·19
Variance=1·61

n	P(n)	F(n)
0	0.359243	0.359243
1	0.317570	0.676813
2	0.181650	0.858463
3	0.085012	0.943476
4	0.035365	0.978841
5	0.013609	0.992449
6	0.004953	0.997403
7	0.001729	0.999132
8	0.000585	0.999717
9	0.000193	0.999909

k=3·6
Mean=1·26
Variance=1·71

n	P(n)	F(n)
0	0.338247	0.338247
1	0.316599	0.654847
2	0.189326	0.844173
3	0.091886	0.936059
4	0.039419	0.975479
5	0.015578	0.991057
6	0.005806	0.996863
7	0.002070	0.998933
8	0.000713	0.999646
9	0.000239	0.999885
10	0.000078	0.999963

k=3·8
Mean=1·34
Variance=1·80

n	P(n)	F(n)
0	0.318479	0.318479
1	0.314657	0.633136
2	0.196346	0.829482
3	0.098697	0.928178
4	0.043624	0.971802
5	0.017694	0.989496
6	0.006747	0.996243
7	0.002456	0.998699
8	0.000862	0.999562
9	0.000294	0.999855
10	0.000098	0.999953

k=4·0
Mean=1·41
Variance=1·90

n	P(n)	F(n)
0	0.299866	0.299866
1	0.311860	0.611726
2	0.202709	0.814435
3	0.105409	0.919844
4	0.047961	0.967805
5	0.019952	0.987757
6	0.007781	0.995538
7	0.002890	0.998428
8	0.001033	0.999462
9	0.000358	0.999820
10	0.000121	0.999941

k=4·2
Mean=1·48
Variance=1·99

n	P(n)	F(n)
0	0.282341	0.282341
1	0.308316	0.590656
2	0.208422	0.799078
3	0.111992	0.911070
4	0.052412	0.963482
5	0.022349	0.985830
6	0.008910	0.994740
7	0.003375	0.998116
8	0.001229	0.999344
9	0.000433	0.999777
10	0.000149	0.999926

k=4·4
Mean=1·55
Variance=2·09

n	P(n)	F(n)
0	0.265840	0.265840
1	0.304120	0.569960
2	0.213493	0.783452
3	0.118417	0.901870
4	0.056959	0.958828
5	0.024880	0.983708
6	0.010134	0.993842
7	0.003915	0.997757
8	0.001450	0.999207
9	0.000520	0.999727
10	0.000181	0.999908

k=4·6
Mean=1·62
Variance=2·18

n	P(n)	F(n)
0	0.250303	0.250303
1	0.299362	0.549665
2	0.217936	0.767601
3	0.124659	0.892260
4	0.061582	0.953842
5	0.027539	0.981381
6	0.011456	0.992838
7	0.004511	0.997348
8	0.001700	0.999049
9	0.000619	0.999668
10	0.000219	0.999886
11	0.000076	0.999962

k=6·0
Mean=2·11
Variance=2·85

n	P(n)	F(n)
0	0.164206	0.164206
1	0.256162	0.420369
2	0.233108	0.653476
3	0.161621	0.815097
4	0.094548	0.909646
5	0.049165	0.958811
6	0.023435	0.982246
7	0.010445	0.992692
8	0.004413	0.997105
9	0.001785	0.998890
10	0.000696	0.999586
11	0.000263	0.999849
12	0.000097	0.999946

k=9·0
Mean=3·16
Variance=4·27

n	P(n)	F(n)
0	0.066540	0.066540
1	0.155705	0.222245
2	0.202416	0.424661
3	0.192970	0.617631
4	0.150516	0.768147
5	0.101749	0.869896
6	0.061728	0.931624
7	0.034391	0.966015
8	0.017883	0.983899
9	0.008783	0.992682
10	0.004110	0.996792
11	0.001846	0.998638
12	0.000800	0.999438
13	0.000336	0.999774
14	0.000137	0.999911

k=4·8
Mean=1·69
Variance=2·28

n	P(n)	F(n)
0	0.235674	0.235674
1	0.294122	0.529796
2	0.221768	0.751564
3	0.130695	0.882259
4	0.066262	0.948521
5	0.030322	0.978843
6	0.012877	0.991719
7	0.005165	0.996885
8	0.001981	0.998866
9	0.000732	0.999598
10	0.000263	0.999861
11	0.000092	0.999953

k=7·0
Mean=2·46
Variance=3·32

n	P(n)	F(n)
0	0.121513	0.121513
1	0.221153	0.342666
2	0.229999	0.572666
3	0.179400	0.752065
4	0.116610	0.868675
5	0.066701	0.935376
6	0.034684	0.970060
7	0.016748	0.986808
8	0.007620	0.994428
9	0.003302	0.997730
10	0.001374	0.999103
11	0.000552	0.999655
12	0.000215	0.999871
13	0.000082	0.999952

k=10·0
Mean=3·51
Variance=4·75

n	P(n)	F(n)
0	0.049240	0.049240
1	0.128024	0.177264
2	0.183074	0.360338
3	0.190397	0.550735
4	0.160885	0.711620
5	0.117125	0.828745
6	0.076131	0.904875
7	0.045244	0.950119
8	0.024997	0.975116
9	0.012998	0.988115
10	0.006421	0.994536
11	0.003035	0.997571
12	0.001381	0.998952
13	0.000608	0.999560
14	0.000260	0.999820
15	0.000108	0.999928

k=5·0
Mean=1·76
Variance=2·37

n	P(n)	F(n)
0	0.221901	0.221901
1	0.288471	0.510372
2	0.225007	0.735379
3	0.136504	0.871883
4	0.070982	0.942865
5	0.033220	0.976085
6	0.014395	0.990480
7	0.005881	0.996362
8	0.002294	0.998656
9	0.000861	0.999517
10	0.000314	0.999831
11	0.000111	0.999942

k=8·0
Mean=2·81
Variance=3·80

n	P(n)	F(n)
0	0.089919	0.089919
1	0.187033	0.276952
2	0.218828	0.495780
3	0.189651	0.685431
4	0.135600	0.821031
5	0.084615	0.905646
6	0.047666	0.953312
7	0.024786	0.978099
8	0.012083	0.990182
9	0.005585	0.995767
10	0.002469	0.998236
11	0.001050	0.999286
12	0.000432	0.999719
13	0.000173	0.999892
14	0.000067	0.999959

k=11·0
Mean=3·86
Variance=5·22

n	P(n)	F(n)
0	0.036438	0.036438
1	0.104211	0.140649
2	0.162570	0.303219
3	0.183162	0.486380
4	0.166677	0.653058
5	0.130008	0.783066
6	0.090139	0.873205
7	0.056916	0.930121
8	0.033296	0.963417
9	0.018276	0.981693

10	0.009503	0.991197
11	0.004717	0.995914
12	0.002249	0.998162
13	0.001034	0.999197
14	0.000461	0.999658
15	0.000200	0.999858
16	0.000084	0.999942

k=12·0
Mean=4·22
Variance=5·70

n	P(n)	F(n)
0	0.026964	0.026964
1	0.084127	0.111091
2	0.142175	0.253265
3	0.172505	0.425770
4	0.168193	0.593963
5	0.139936	0.733899
6	0.103086	0.836985
7	0.068921	0.905906
8	0.042558	0.948464
9	0.024589	0.973054
10	0.013426	0.986480
11	0.006981	0.993461
12	0.003479	0.996940
13	0.001670	0.998610
14	0.000775	0.999385
15	0.000349	0.999735
16	0.000153	0.999888
17	0.000066	0.999954

k=13·0
Mean=4·57
Variance=6·17

n	P(n)	F(n)
0	0.019953	0.019953
1	0.067442	0.087395
2	0.122744	0.210139
3	0.159567	0.369706
4	0.165950	0.535656
5	0.146700	0.682356
6	0.114426	0.796782
7	0.080752	0.877534
8	0.052489	0.930022
9	0.031843	0.961866
10	0.018214	0.980080
11	0.009902	0.989982
12	0.005149	0.995131
13	0.002575	0.997705
14	0.001243	0.998949
15	0.000582	0.999530
16	0.000265	0.999795
17	0.000117	0.999912

k=14·0
Mean=4·92
Variance=6·65

n	P(n)	F(n)
0	0.014765	0.014765
1	0.053746	0.068511
2	0.104805	0.173316
3	0.145329	0.318645
4	0.160588	0.479233
5	0.150311	0.629544
6	0.123756	0.753300
7	0.091933	0.845233
8	0.062744	0.907977
9	0.039877	0.947855
10	0.023847	0.971701
11	0.013528	0.985229
12	0.007327	0.992556
13	0.003810	0.996367
14	0.001911	0.998277
15	0.000927	0.999205
16	0.000437	0.999642
17	0.000200	0.999842
18	0.000090	0.999932

k=15·0
Mean=5·27
Variance=7·12

n	P(n)	F(n)
0	0.010926	0.010926
1	0.042613	0.053539
2	0.088635	0.142174
3	0.130588	0.272762
4	0.152788	0.425551
5	0.150955	0.576506
6	0.130828	0.707334
7	0.102046	0.809379
8	0.072963	0.882342
9	0.048480	0.930821
10	0.030251	0.961073
11	0.017876	0.978948
12	0.010070	0.989018
13	0.005438	0.994456
14	0.002828	0.997284
15	0.001421	0.998705
16	0.000693	0.999398
17	0.000329	0.999727
18	0.000152	0.999878
19	0.000069	0.999947

k=16·0
Mean=5·62
Variance=7·60

n	P(n)	F(n)
0	0.008086	0.008086
1	0.033636	0.041721
2	0.074335	0.116056
3	0.115963	0.232019
4	0.143214	0.375232

5	0.148942	0.524175
6	0.135537	0.659712
7	0.110753	0.770466
8	0.082788	0.853254
9	0.057400	0.910654
10	0.037310	0.947964
11	0.022929	0.970892
12	0.013413	0.984306
13	0.007511	0.991817
14	0.004045	0.995862
15	0.002104	0.997966
16	0.001060	0.999026
17	0.000519	0.999544
18	0.000247	0.999792
19	0.000115	0.999907

k=17·0
Mean=5·97
Variance=8·07

n	P(n)	F(n)
0	0.005983	0.005983
1	0.026446	0.032429
2	0.061884	0.094313
3	0.101902	0.196215
4	0.132473	0.328688
5	0.144660	0.473348
6	0.137909	0.611258
7	0.117814	0.729072
8	0.091895	0.820967
9	0.066369	0.887335
10	0.044865	0.932200
11	0.028632	0.960832
12	0.017370	0.978203
13	0.010075	0.988277
14	0.005613	0.993890
15	0.003016	0.996906
16	0.001568	0.998475
17	0.000792	0.999266
18	0.000389	0.999655
19	0.000186	0.999841
20	0.000087	0.999928

k=18·0
Mean=6·32
Variance=8·55

n	P(n)	F(n)
0	0.004428	0.004428
1	0.020721	0.025149
2	0.051182	0.076331
3	0.088715	0.165045
4	0.121096	0.286141
5	0.138533	0.424674
6	0.138072	0.562746
7	0.123081	0.685827
8	0.100003	0.785830
9	0.075114	0.860944

10	0.052730	0.913674		10	0.068557	0.868260
11	0.034898	0.948571		11	0.048613	0.916873
12	0.021927	0.970498		12	0.032652	0.949524
13	0.013156	0.983655		13	0.020897	0.970421
14	0.007574	0.991229		14	0.012807	0.983228
15	0.004201	0.995430		15	0.007548	0.990776
16	0.002253	0.997683		16	0.004293	0.995068
17	0.001172	0.998855		17	0.002363	0.997432
18	0.000592	0.999447		18	0.001263	0.998695
19	0.000292	0.999739		19	0.000657	0.999352
20	0.000140	0.999879		20	0.000333	0.999685
21	0.000066	0.999945		21	0.000165	0.999850
				22	0.000080	0.999930

k = 19·0
Mean = 6·68
Variance = 9·02

n	P(n)	F(n)
0	0.003276	0.003276
1	0.016186	0.019462
2	0.042083	0.061545
3	0.076590	0.138135
4	0.109524	0.247659
5	0.130991	0.378650
6	0.136231	0.514881
7	0.126500	0.641381
8	0.106892	0.748273
9	0.083376	0.831650
10	0.060698	0.892347
11	0.041606	0.933953
12	0.027044	0.960997
13	0.016767	0.977764
14	0.009964	0.987728
15	0.005700	0.993428
16	0.003149	0.996577
17	0.001686	0.998262
18	0.000877	0.999139
19	0.000444	0.999583
20	0.000219	0.999802
21	0.000106	0.999908

k = 20·0
Mean = 7·03
Variance = 9·50

n	P(n)	F(n)
0	0.002425	0.002425
1	0.012608	0.015032
2	0.034419	0.049451
3	0.065626	0.115077
4	0.098111	0.213188
5	0.122442	0.335630
6	0.132646	0.468276
7	0.128098	0.596374
8	0.112406	0.708779
9	0.090924	0.799703

k=0·2
Mean=0·06
Variance=0·08

n	P(n)	F(n)
0	0.946592	0.946592
1	0.045436	0.992028
2	0.006543	0.998571
3	0.001152	0.999723
4	0.000221	0.999944

k=0·4
Mean=0·13
Variance=0·17

n	P(n)	F(n)
0	0.896036	0.896036
1	0.086019	0.982055
2	0.014451	0.996507
3	0.002775	0.999281
4	0.000566	0.999847
5	0.000120	0.999967

k=0·6
Mean=0·19
Variance=0·25

n	P(n)	F(n)
0	0.848180	0.848180
1	0.122138	0.970318
2	0.023450	0.993769
3	0.004878	0.998646
4	0.001054	0.999700
5	0.000233	0.999933

k=0·8
Mean=0·25
Variance=0·33

n	P(n)	F(n)
0	0.802880	0.802880
1	0.154153	0.957033
2	0.033297	0.990331
3	0.007459	0.997789
4	0.001701	0.999490
5	0.000392	0.999881
6	0.000091	0.999972

k=1·0
Mean=0·32
Variance=0·42

n	P(n)	F(n)
0	0.760000	0.760000
1	0.182400	0.942400
2	0.043776	0.986176
3	0.010506	0.996682
4	0.002521	0.999204
5	0.000605	0.999809
6	0.000145	0.999954

k=1·2
Mean=0·38
Variance=0·50

n	P(n)	F(n)
0	0.719410	0.719410
1	0.207190	0.926600
2	0.054698	0.981298
3	0.014003	0.995301
4	0.003529	0.998829
5	0.000881	0.999710
6	0.000218	0.999929

k=1·4
Mean=0·44
Variance=0·58

n	P(n)	F(n)
0	0.680987	0.680987
1	0.228812	0.909799
2	0.065898	0.975697
3	0.017924	0.993621
4	0.004732	0.998353
5	0.001227	0.999580
6	0.000314	0.999894
7	0.000080	0.999973

k=1·6
Mean=0·51
Variance=0·66

n	P(n)	F(n)
0	0.644617	0.644617
1	0.247533	0.892150
2	0.077230	0.969380
3	0.022242	0.991623
4	0.006139	0.997761
5	0.001650	0.999412
6	0.000436	0.999847
7	0.000114	0.999961

k=1·8
Mean=0·57
Variance=0·75

n	P(n)	F(n)
0	0.610189	0.610189
1	0.263602	0.873791
2	0.088570	0.962361
3	0.026925	0.989286
4	0.007754	0.997041
5	0.002159	0.999200
6	0.000587	0.999787
7	0.000157	0.999944

k=2·0
Mean=0·63
Variance=0·83

n	P(n)	F(n)
0	0.577600	0.577600
1	0.277248	0.854848
2	0.099809	0.954657
3	0.031939	0.986596
4	0.009582	0.996178
5	0.002760	0.998937
6	0.000773	0.999710
7	0.000212	0.999922

k=2·2
Mean=0·69
Variance=0·91

n	P(n)	F(n)
0	0.546751	0.546751
1	0.288685	0.835436
2	0.110855	0.946291
3	0.037247	0.983538
4	0.011621	0.995159
5	0.003458	0.998618
6	0.000996	0.999614
7	0.000280	0.999894
8	0.000077	0.999971

k=2·4
Mean=0·76
Variance=1·00

n	P(n)	F(n)
0	0.517550	0.517550
1	0.298109	0.815659
2	0.121628	0.937288
3	0.042813	0.980101
4	0.013871	0.993973
5	0.004261	0.998234
6	0.001261	0.999495
7	0.000363	0.999859
8	0.000102	0.999961

k=2·6
Mean = 0·82
Variance = 1·08

n	P(n)	F(n)
0	0.489909	0.489909
1	0.305703	0.795612
2	0.132064	0.927676
3	0.048599	0.976275
4	0.016329	0.992605
5	0.005173	0.997778
6	0.001573	0.999351
7	0.000464	0.999814
8	0.000134	0.999948

k=2·8
Mean = 0·88
Variance = 1·16

n	P(n)	F(n)
0	0.463744	0.463744
1	0.311636	0.775380
2	0.142106	0.917485
3	0.054569	0.972054
4	0.018990	0.991044
5	0.006198	0.997242
6	0.001934	0.999176
7	0.000583	0.999760
8	0.000172	0.999931

k=3·0
Mean = 0·95
Variance = 1·25

n	P(n)	F(n)
0	0.438976	0.438976
1	0.316063	0.755039
2	0.151710	0.906749
3	0.060684	0.967433
4	0.021846	0.989279
5	0.007340	0.996619
6	0.002349	0.998968
7	0.000725	0.999693
8	0.000217	0.999911

k=3·2
Mean = 1·01
Variance = 1·33

n	P(n)	F(n)
0	0.415531	0.415531
1	0.319128	0.734659
2	0.160840	0.895499
3	0.066910	0.962409
4	0.024890	0.987299
5	0.008602	0.995901
6	0.002821	0.998723
7	0.000890	0.999613
8	0.000272	0.999885
9	0.000081	0.999967

k=3·4
Mean = 1·07
Variance = 1·41

n	P(n)	F(n)
0	0.393338	0.393338
1	0.320964	0.714302
2	0.169469	0.883771
3	0.073211	0.956982
4	0.028113	0.985095
5	0.009986	0.995081
6	0.003355	0.998436
7	0.001081	0.999517
8	0.000337	0.999854
9	0.000103	0.999957

k=3·6
Mean = 1·14
Variance = 1·50

n	P(n)	F(n)
0	0.372331	0.372331
1	0.321694	0.694025
2	0.177575	0.871600
3	0.079554	0.951153
4	0.031503	0.982656
5	0.011492	0.994149
6	0.003953	0.998102
7	0.001301	0.999403
8	0.000414	0.999817
9	0.000128	0.999945

k=3·8
Mean = 1·20
Variance = 1·58

n	P(n)	F(n)
0	0.352445	0.352445
1	0.321430	0.673875
2	0.185144	0.859019
3	0.085907	0.944926
4	0.035050	0.979976
5	0.013123	0.993098
6	0.004619	0.997717
7	0.001552	0.999270
8	0.000503	0.999772
9	0.000158	0.999931

k=4·0
Mean = 1·26
Variance = 1·66

n	P(n)	F(n)
0	0.333622	0.333622
1	0.320277	0.653899
2	0.192166	0.846065
3	0.092240	0.938305
4	0.038741	0.977045
5	0.014876	0.991922
6	0.005356	0.997277
7	0.001836	0.999113
8	0.000606	0.999719
9	0.000194	0.999913

k=4·2
Mean = 1·33
Variance = 1·75

n	P(n)	F(n)
0	0.315804	0.315804
1	0.318330	0.634134
2	0.198638	0.832772
3	0.098524	0.931296
4	0.042563	0.973859
5	0.016753	0.990611
6	0.006165	0.996776
7	0.002156	0.998932
8	0.000724	0.999657
9	0.000236	0.999892
10	0.000075	0.999967

k=4·4
Mean = 1·39
Variance = 1·83

n	P(n)	F(n)
0	0.298937	0.298937
1	0.315678	0.614615
2	0.204559	0.819174
3	0.104734	0.923908
4	0.046502	0.970410
5	0.018750	0.989160
6	0.007050	0.996209
7	0.002514	0.998723
8	0.000860	0.999583
9	0.000284	0.999867
10	0.000091	0.999959

k=4·6
Mean = 1·45
Variance = 1·91

n	P(n)	F(n)
0	0.282971	0.282971
1	0.312400	0.595372
2	0.209933	0.805305
3	0.110845	0.916150
4	0.050545	0.966695
5	0.020865	0.987560
6	0.008012	0.995572
7	0.002912	0.998484
8	0.001013	0.999497
9	0.000340	0.999838
10	0.000111	0.999949

k=4·8
Mean=1·52
Variance=1·99

n	P(n)	F(n)
0	0.267858	0.267858
1	0.308573	0.576431
2	0.214767	0.791198
3	0.116833	0.908031
4	0.054678	0.962709
5	0.023096	0.985805
6	0.009054	0.994858
7	0.003352	0.998211
8	0.001187	0.999398
9	0.000405	0.999803
10	0.000134	0.999937

k=5·0
Mean=1·58
Variance=2·08

n	P(n)	F(n)
0	0.253553	0.253553
1	0.304263	0.557816
2	0.219069	0.776885
3	0.122679	0.899564
4	0.058886	0.958450
5	0.025439	0.983888
6	0.010175	0.994064
7	0.003838	0.997901
8	0.001382	0.999283
9	0.000479	0.999762
10	0.000161	0.999923

k=6·0
Mean=1·89
Variance=2·49

n	P(n)	F(n)
0	0.192700	0.192700
1	0.277488	0.470188
2	0.233090	0.703278
3	0.149177	0.852455
4	0.080556	0.933011
5	0.038667	0.971678
6	0.017013	0.988691
7	0.007000	0.995691
8	0.002730	0.998421
9	0.001019	0.999440
10	0.000367	0.999807
11	0.000128	0.999935

k=7·0
Mean=2·21
Variance=2·91

n	P(n)	F(n)
0	0.146452	0.146452
1	0.246039	0.392491
2	0.236198	0.628689
3	0.170062	0.798751
4	0.102037	0.900789
5	0.053876	0.954664
6	0.025860	0.980525
7	0.011526	0.992051
8	0.004841	0.996892
9	0.001936	0.998829
10	0.000744	0.999572
11	0.000276	0.999848
12	0.000099	0.999947

k=8·0
Mean=2·53
Variance=3·32

n	P(n)	F(n)
0	0.111303	0.111303
1	0.213703	0.325006
2	0.230799	0.555805
3	0.184639	0.740444
4	0.121862	0.862306
5	0.070192	0.932498
6	0.036500	0.968998
7	0.017520	0.986518
8	0.007884	0.994402
9	0.003364	0.997766
10	0.001372	0.999139
11	0.000539	0.999678
12	0.000205	0.999883
13	0.000076	0.999958

k=9·0
Mean=2·84
Variance=3·74

n	P(n)	F(n)
0	0.084591	0.084591
1	0.182716	0.267306
2	0.219259	0.486565
3	0.192948	0.679513
4	0.138922	0.818436
5	0.086688	0.905123
6	0.048545	0.953668
7	0.024966	0.978634
8	0.011984	0.990618
9	0.005433	0.996051
10	0.002347	0.998398
11	0.000973	0.999371
12	0.000389	0.999760
13	0.000151	0.999911

k=10·0
Mean=3·16
Variance=4·16

n	P(n)	F(n)
0	0.064289	0.064289
1	0.154293	0.218582
2	0.203667	0.422249
3	0.195521	0.617770
4	0.152506	0.770276
5	0.102484	0.872760
6	0.061490	0.934250
7	0.033732	0.967982
8	0.017203	0.985186
9	0.008258	0.993443
10	0.003765	0.997209
11	0.001643	0.998852
12	0.000690	0.999542
13	0.000280	0.999822
14	0.000111	0.999933

k=11·0
Mean=3·47
Variance=4·57

n	P(n)	F(n)
0	0.048860	0.048860
1	0.128989	0.177849
2	0.185744	0.363593
3	0.193174	0.556768
4	0.162266	0.719034
5	0.116832	0.835866
6	0.074772	0.910638
7	0.043582	0.954220
8	0.023534	0.977754
9	0.011924	0.989678
10	0.005723	0.995401
11	0.002622	0.998024
12	0.001154	0.999177
13	0.000490	0.999667
14	0.000202	0.999869
15	0.000081	0.999950

k=12·0
Mean=3·79
Variance=4·99

n	P(n)	F(n)
0	0.037133	0.037133
1	0.106944	0.144077
2	0.166832	0.310909
3	0.186852	0.497762
4	0.168167	0.665929
5	0.129152	0.795081
6	0.087824	0.882904
7	0.054220	0.937104
8	0.030894	0.967998
9	0.016477	0.984474

n	P(n)	F(n)
10	0.008304	0.992779
11	0.003986	0.996765
12	0.001834	0.998598
13	0.000812	0.999411
14	0.000348	0.999759
15	0.000145	0.999904

k=13.0
Mean=4.11
Variance=5.40

n	P(n)	F(n)
0	0.028221	0.028221
1	0.088050	0.116272
2	0.147925	0.264196
3	0.177510	0.441706
4	0.170409	0.612115
5	0.139054	0.751169
6	0.100119	0.851288
7	0.065220	0.916508
8	0.039132	0.955640
9	0.021914	0.977554
10	0.011571	0.989125
11	0.005806	0.994931
12	0.002787	0.997718
13	0.001286	0.999005
14	0.000573	0.999578
15	0.000248	0.999826
16	0.000104	0.999930

k=14.0
Mean=4.42
Variance=5.82

n	P(n)	F(n)
0	0.021448	0.021448
1	0.072066	0.093514
2	0.129719	0.223233
3	0.166040	0.389272
4	0.169361	0.558633
5	0.146327	0.704960
6	0.111209	0.816169
7	0.076258	0.892427
8	0.048042	0.940469
9	0.028185	0.968654
10	0.015558	0.984212
11	0.008147	0.992359
12	0.004073	0.996432
13	0.001955	0.998387
14	0.000905	0.999292
15	0.000405	0.999698
16	0.000176	0.999874
17	0.000075	0.999949

k=15.0
Mean=4.74
Variance=6.23

n	P(n)	F(n)
0	0.016301	0.016301
1	0.058682	0.074983
2	0.112670	0.187653
3	0.153231	0.340884
4	0.165489	0.506373
5	0.150926	0.657299
6	0.120741	0.778040
7	0.086934	0.864974
8	0.057376	0.922350
9	0.035191	0.957541
10	0.020270	0.977811
11	0.011056	0.988867
12	0.005749	0.994616
13	0.002866	0.997482
14	0.001376	0.998858
15	0.000638	0.999496
16	0.000287	0.999783
17	0.000126	0.999909

k=16.0
Mean=5.05
Variance=6.65

n	P(n)	F(n)
0	0.012388	0.012388
1	0.047572	0.059960
2	0.097046	0.157006
3	0.139747	0.296753
4	0.159311	0.456064
5	0.152939	0.609003
6	0.128469	0.737471
7	0.096902	0.834373
8	0.066862	0.901236
9	0.042792	0.944028
10	0.025675	0.969703
11	0.014565	0.984268
12	0.007865	0.992133
13	0.004066	0.996198
14	0.002021	0.998219
15	0.000970	0.999190
16	0.000451	0.999641
17	0.000204	0.999845
18	0.000090	0.999934

k=17.0
Mean=5.37
Variance=7.06

n	P(n)	F(n)
0	0.009415	0.009415
1	0.038414	0.047829
2	0.082975	0.130804
3	0.126121	0.256925
4	0.151346	0.408271
5	0.152556	0.560827
6	0.134250	0.695077
7	0.105865	0.800942
8	0.076223	0.877165
9	0.050815	0.927981
10	0.031709	0.959690
11	0.018679	0.978369
12	0.010460	0.988829
13	0.005600	0.994430
14	0.002880	0.997310
15	0.001429	0.998738
16	0.000686	0.999424
17	0.000319	0.999744
18	0.000145	0.999888
19	0.000064	0.999953

k=18.0
Mean=5.68
Variance=7.48

n	P(n)	F(n)
0	0.007156	0.007156
1	0.030912	0.038068
2	0.070480	0.108547
3	0.112767	0.221315
4	0.142087	0.363401
5	0.150044	0.513445
6	0.138040	0.651485
7	0.113587	0.765073
8	0.085191	0.850263
9	0.059065	0.909329
10	0.038274	0.947603
11	0.023382	0.970985
12	0.013562	0.984547
13	0.007511	0.992058
14	0.003992	0.996049
15	0.002044	0.998093
16	0.001012	0.999105
17	0.000486	0.999590
18	0.000227	0.999817
19	0.000103	0.999920

k=19.0
Mean=6.00
Variance=7.89

n	P(n)	F(n)
0	0.005438	0.005438
1	0.024798	0.030237
2	0.059516	0.089753
3	0.099987	0.189740
4	0.131983	0.321723
5	0.145709	0.467432
6	0.139881	0.607312
7	0.119898	0.727210
8	0.093520	0.820730
9	0.067335	0.888065
10	0.045249	0.933314
11	0.028630	0.961944
12	0.017178	0.979122
13	0.009831	0.988953
14	0.005393	0.994346

15	0.002848	0.997194
16	0.001452	0.998646
17	0.000718	0.999364
18	0.000344	0.999708
19	0.000161	0.999869
20	0.000073	0.999943

k = 20·0
Mean = 6·32
Variance = 8·31

n	P(n)	F(n)
0	0.004133	0.004133
1	0.019839	0.023972
2	0.049994	0.073965
3	0.087989	0.161954
4	0.121424	0.283378
5	0.139881	0.423259
6	0.139881	0.563140
7	0.124694	0.687833
8	0.101002	0.788835
9	0.075415	0.864250
10	0.052489	0.916738
11	0.034356	0.951095
12	0.021301	0.972395
13	0.012584	0.984979
14	0.007119	0.992098
15	0.003873	0.995971
16	0.002033	0.998004
17	0.001033	0.999037
18	0.000510	0.999547
19	0.000245	0.999792
20	0.000115	0.999906

k=0·2
Mean=0·06
Variance=0·07

n	P(n)	F(n)
0	0.951522	0.951522
1	0.041867	0.993389
2	0.005526	0.998916
3	0.000892	0.999807
4	0.000157	0.999964

k=0·4
Mean=0·11
Variance=0·14

n	P(n)	F(n)
0	0.905394	0.905394
1	0.079675	0.985069
2	0.012270	0.997339
3	0.002160	0.999499
4	0.000404	0.999902

k=0·6
Mean=0·17
Variance=0·22

n	P(n)	F(n)
0	0.861503	0.861503
1	0.113718	0.975221
2	0.020014	0.995236
3	0.003816	0.999052
4	0.000756	0.999807
5	0.000153	0.999960

k=0·8
Mean=0·23
Variance=0·29

n	P(n)	F(n)
0	0.819739	0.819739
1	0.144274	0.964013
2	0.028566	0.992580
3	0.005866	0.998445
4	0.001226	0.999671
5	0.000259	0.999930

k=1·0
Mean=0·28
Variance=0·36

n	P(n)	F(n)
0	0.780000	0.780000
1	0.171600	0.951600
2	0.037752	0.989352
3	0.008305	0.997657
4	0.001827	0.999485

| 5 | 0.000402 | 0.999887 |
| 6 | 0.000088 | 0.999975 |

k=1·2
Mean=0·34
Variance=0·43

n	P(n)	F(n)
0	0.742187	0.742187
1	0.195937	0.938125
2	0.047417	0.985542
3	0.011127	0.996669
4	0.002570	0.999239
5	0.000588	0.999827
6	0.000134	0.999961

k=1·4
Mean=0·39
Variance=0·51

n	P(n)	F(n)
0	0.706208	0.706208
1	0.217512	0.923720
2	0.057423	0.981143
3	0.014318	0.995460
4	0.003465	0.998925
5	0.000823	0.999748
6	0.000193	0.999942

k=1·6
Mean=0·45
Variance=0·58

n	P(n)	F(n)
0	0.671972	0.671972
1	0.236534	0.908507
2	0.067649	0.976155
3	0.017859	0.994015
4	0.004518	0.998533
5	0.001113	0.999646
6	0.000269	0.999916

k=1·8
Mean=0·51
Variance=0·65

n	P(n)	F(n)
0	0.639397	0.639397
1	0.253201	0.892598
2	0.077986	0.970583
3	0.021732	0.992316
4	0.005737	0.998053

5	0.001464	0.999517
6	0.000365	0.999882
7	0.000089	0.999972

k=2·0
Mean=0·56
Variance=0·72

n	P(n)	F(n)
0	0.608400	0.608400
1	0.267696	0.876096
2	0.088340	0.964436
3	0.025913	0.990349
4	0.007126	0.997475
5	0.001881	0.999356
6	0.000483	0.999839
7	0.000121	0.999960

k=2·2
Mean=0·62
Variance=0·80

n	P(n)	F(n)
0	0.578906	0.578906
1	0.280191	0.859097
2	0.098627	0.957724
3	0.030377	0.988101
4	0.008688	0.996789
5	0.002370	0.999159
6	0.000626	0.999784
7	0.000161	0.999946

k=2·4
Mean=0·68
Variance=0·87

n	P(n)	F(n)
0	0.550842	0.550842
1	0.290845	0.841687
2	0.108776	0.950462
3	0.035098	0.985561
4	0.010424	0.995985
5	0.002935	0.998920
6	0.000796	0.999717
7	0.000210	0.999927

k=2·6
Mean=0·73
Variance=0·94

n	P(n)	F(n)
0	0.524138	0.524138
1	0.299807	0.823946
2	0.118724	0.942669
3	0.040049	0.982719
4	0.012335	0.995054

n	P(n)	F(n)
5	0.003582	0.998636
6	0.000998	0.999634
7	0.000270	0.999904

n	P(n)	F(n)
5	0.007060	0.996929
6	0.002174	0.999104
7	0.000642	0.999746
8	0.000184	0.999930

n	P(n)	F(n)
5	0.012093	0.994042
6	0.004079	0.998121
7	0.001308	0.999429
8	0.000403	0.999831
9	0.000120	0.999951

k=2·8
Mean=0·79
Variance=1·01

n	P(n)	F(n)
0	0.498729	0.498729
1	0.307217	0.805947
2	0.128417	0.934363
3	0.045203	0.979566
4	0.014420	0.993986
5	0.004314	0.998300
6	0.001234	0.999534
7	0.000341	0.999875
8	0.000092	0.999967

k=3·6
Mean=1·02
Variance=1·30

n	P(n)	F(n)
0	0.408828	0.408828
1	0.323792	0.732620
2	0.163839	0.896458
3	0.067283	0.963741
4	0.024424	0.988165
5	0.008167	0.996332
6	0.002575	0.998908
7	0.000777	0.999685
8	0.000227	0.999911

k=4·4
Mean=1·24
Variance=1·59

n	P(n)	F(n)
0	0.335132	0.335132
1	0.324408	0.659540
2	0.192698	0.852239
3	0.090440	0.942678
4	0.036809	0.979487
5	0.013605	0.993092
6	0.004689	0.997781
7	0.001533	0.999314
8	0.000480	0.999794
9	0.000146	0.999940

k=3·0
Mean=0·85
Variance=1·08

n	P(n)	F(n)
0	0.474552	0.474552
1	0.313204	0.787756
2	0.137810	0.925566
3	0.050530	0.976097
4	0.016675	0.992772
5	0.005136	0.997907
6	0.001507	0.999414
7	0.000426	0.999840
8	0.000117	0.999957

k=3·8
Mean=1·07
Variance=1·37

n	P(n)	F(n)
0	0.389009	0.389009
1	0.325211	0.714220
2	0.171712	0.885932
3	0.073035	0.958967
4	0.027315	0.986282
5	0.009374	0.995656
6	0.003025	0.998681
7	0.000932	0.999613
8	0.000277	0.999889
9	0.000080	0.999969

k=4·6
Mean=1·30
Variance=1·66

n	P(n)	F(n)
0	0.318886	0.318886
1	0.322712	0.641598
2	0.198791	0.840389
3	0.096215	0.936604
4	0.040218	0.976822
5	0.015218	0.992040
6	0.005357	0.997397
7	0.001785	0.999182
8	0.000569	0.999751
9	0.000175	0.999926

k=3·2
Mean=0·90
Variance=1·16

n	P(n)	F(n)
0	0.451547	0.451547
1	0.317889	0.769436
2	0.146865	0.916300
3	0.056004	0.972305
4	0.019097	0.991402
5	0.006050	0.997452
6	0.001819	0.999271
7	0.000526	0.999797
8	0.000148	0.999945

k=4·0
Mean=1·13
Variance=1·45

n	P(n)	F(n)
0	0.370151	0.370151
1	0.325732	0.695883
2	0.179153	0.875036
3	0.078827	0.953863
4	0.030348	0.984212
5	0.010683	0.994894
6	0.003525	0.998420
7	0.001108	0.999528
8	0.000335	0.999863
9	0.000098	0.999961

k=4·8
Mean=1·35
Variance=1·74

n	P(n)	F(n)
0	0.303427	0.303427
1	0.320419	0.623846
2	0.204427	0.828273
3	0.101941	0.930214
4	0.043733	0.973947
5	0.016933	0.990880
6	0.006085	0.996965
7	0.002065	0.999030
8	0.000670	0.999700
9	0.000210	0.999910

k=3·4
Mean=0·96
Variance=1·23

n	P(n)	F(n)
0	0.429657	0.429657
1	0.321383	0.751040
2	0.155549	0.906590
3	0.061598	0.968187
4	0.021682	0.989869

k=4·2
Mean=1·18
Variance=1·52

n	P(n)	F(n)
0	0.352206	0.352206
1	0.325439	0.677645
2	0.186151	0.863796
3	0.084637	0.948433
4	0.033516	0.981949

k=5·0
Mean=1·41
Variance=1·81

n	P(n)	F(n)
0	0.288717	0.288717
1	0.317589	0.606307
2	0.209609	0.815915
3	0.107599	0.923515
4	0.047344	0.970858

5	0.018748	0.989606
6	0.006874	0.996481
7	0.002377	0.998857
8	0.000784	0.999642
9	0.000249	0.999891
10	0.000077	0.999968

5	0.055924	0.953788
6	0.026657	0.980445
7	0.011729	0.992174
8	0.004838	0.997012
9	0.001892	0.998904
10	0.000708	0.999612
11	0.000255	0.999867
12	0.000089	0.999955

5	0.100626	0.881156
6	0.059034	0.940189
7	0.031541	0.971730
8	0.015613	0.987343
9	0.007251	0.994594
10	0.003191	0.997785
11	0.001340	0.999125
12	0.000540	0.999665
13	0.000210	0.999876
14	0.000079	0.999955

k=6·0
Mean=1·69
Variance=2·17

n	P(n)	F(n)
0	0.225200	0.225200
1	0.297263	0.522463
2	0.228893	0.751356
3	0.134284	0.885640
4	0.066470	0.952110
5	0.029247	0.981357
6	0.011796	0.993154
7	0.004449	0.997602
8	0.001590	0.999193
9	0.000544	0.999737
10	0.000180	0.999917

k=9·0
Mean=2·54
Variance=3·25

n	P(n)	F(n)
0	0.106869	0.106869
1	0.211600	0.318469
2	0.232761	0.551230
3	0.187760	0.738990
4	0.123922	0.862912
5	0.070883	0.933795
6	0.036387	0.970182
7	0.017154	0.987335
8	0.007548	0.994883
9	0.003136	0.998020
10	0.001242	0.999262
11	0.000472	0.999734
12	0.000173	0.999907

k=12·0
Mean=3·38
Variance=4·34

n	P(n)	F(n)
0	0.050715	0.050715
1	0.133887	0.184602
2	0.191459	0.376061
3	0.196564	0.572625
4	0.162166	0.734791
5	0.114165	0.848955
6	0.071163	0.920118
7	0.040258	0.960375
8	0.021035	0.981410
9	0.010284	0.991694
10	0.004751	0.996445
11	0.002090	0.998535
12	0.000881	0.999415
13	0.000358	0.999775
14	0.000141	0.999915

k=7·0
Mean=1·97
Variance=2·53

n	P(n)	F(n)
0	0.175656	0.175656
1	0.270510	0.446165
2	0.238049	0.684214
3	0.157112	0.841326
4	0.086412	0.927738
5	0.041823	0.969561
6	0.018402	0.987963
7	0.007519	0.995482
8	0.002895	0.998376
9	0.001061	0.999438
10	0.000374	0.999811
11	0.000127	0.999938

k=10·0
Mean=2·82
Variance=3·62

n	P(n)	F(n)
0	0.083358	0.083358
1	0.183387	0.266745
2	0.221898	0.488643
3	0.195271	0.683914
4	0.139618	0.823532
5	0.086005	0.909537
6	0.047303	0.956840
7	0.023787	0.980626
8	0.011120	0.991747
9	0.004893	0.996639
10	0.002045	0.998685
11	0.000818	0.999503
12	0.000315	0.999818
13	0.000117	0.999935

k=13·0
Mean=3·67
Variance=4·70

n	P(n)	F(n)
0	0.039558	0.039558
1	0.113135	0.152692
2	0.174227	0.326920
3	0.191650	0.518570
4	0.168652	0.687222
5	0.126152	0.813374
6	0.083260	0.896634
7	0.049718	0.946352
8	0.027345	0.973697
9	0.014037	0.987735
10	0.006794	0.994529
11	0.003125	0.997654
12	0.001375	0.999029
13	0.000582	0.999611
14	0.000238	0.999848
15	0.000094	0.999942

k=8·0
Mean=2·26
Variance=2·89

n	P(n)	F(n)
0	0.137011	0.137011
1	0.241140	0.378152
2	0.238729	0.616880
3	0.175068	0.791948
4	0.105916	0.897864

k=11·0
Mean=3·10
Variance=3·98

n	P(n)	F(n)
0	0.065019	0.065019
1	0.157346	0.222365
2	0.207697	0.430062
3	0.198004	0.628066
4	0.152463	0.780530

k=14·0
Mean=3·95
Variance=5·06

n	P(n)	F(n)
0	0.030855	0.030855
1	0.095033	0.125888
2	0.156805	0.282693
3	0.183984	0.466677
4	0.172025	0.638702
5	0.136244	0.774946
6	0.094917	0.869863
7	0.059662	0.929525
8	0.034455	0.963979
9	0.018529	0.982508
10	0.009376	0.991884
11	0.004500	0.996384
12	0.002063	0.998447
13	0.000908	0.999355
14	0.000385	0.999740
15	0.000158	0.999898
16	0.000063	0.999961

k=15·0
Mean=4·23
Variance=5·42

n	P(n)	F(n)
0	0.024067	0.024067
1	0.079421	0.103487
2	0.139780	0.243268
3	0.174259	0.417527
4	0.172517	0.590044
5	0.144224	0.734268
6	0.105764	0.840032
7	0.069804	0.909836
8	0.042232	0.952068
9	0.023744	0.975812
10	0.012537	0.988348
11	0.006268	0.994616
12	0.002988	0.997604
13	0.001365	0.998970
14	0.000601	0.999570
15	0.000255	0.999826
16	0.000105	0.999931

k=16·0
Mean=4·51
Variance=5·79

n	P(n)	F(n)
0	0.018772	0.018772
1	0.066078	0.084850
2	0.123566	0.208416
3	0.163107	0.371522
4	0.170447	0.541969
5	0.149993	0.691962
6	0.115495	0.807456
7	0.079856	0.887313
8	0.050509	0.937822
9	0.029632	0.967454
10	0.016298	0.983751
11	0.008475	0.992226
12	0.004195	0.996421
13	0.001988	0.998409
14	0.000906	0.999315
15	0.000399	0.999713
16	0.000170	0.999883
17	0.000070	0.999954

k=17·0
Mean=4·79
Variance=6·15

n	P(n)	F(n)
0	0.014642	0.014642
1	0.054762	0.069404
2	0.108429	0.177833
3	0.151078	0.328911
4	0.166185	0.495096
5	0.153555	0.648651
6	0.123868	0.772519
7	0.089539	0.862058
8	0.059096	0.921154
9	0.036114	0.957268
10	0.020657	0.977925
11	0.011155	0.989080
12	0.005726	0.994806
13	0.002810	0.997616
14	0.001325	0.998941
15	0.000602	0.999543
16	0.000265	0.999808
17	0.000113	0.999922

k=18·0
Mean=5·08
Variance=6·51

n	P(n)	F(n)
0	0.011421	0.011421
1	0.045227	0.056648
2	0.094524	0.151172
3	0.138636	0.289808
4	0.160124	0.449933
5	0.155000	0.604933
6	0.130717	0.735650
7	0.098598	0.834248
8	0.067786	0.902035
9	0.043082	0.945116
10	0.025591	0.970707
11	0.014331	0.985038
12	0.007619	0.992657
13	0.003868	0.996525
14	0.001884	0.998410
15	0.000884	0.999294
16	0.000401	0.999695
17	0.000177	0.999872
18	0.000076	0.999947

k=19·0
Mean=5·36
Variance=6·87

n	P(n)	F(n)
0	0.008908	0.008908
1	0.037237	0.046145
2	0.081921	0.128066
3	0.126159	0.254225
4	0.152652	0.406877
5	0.154484	0.561361
6	0.135946	0.697307
7	0.106815	0.804121
8	0.076372	0.880494
9	0.050406	0.930899
10	0.031050	0.961949
11	0.018009	0.979958
12	0.009905	0.989863
13	0.005196	0.995060
14	0.002613	0.997673
15	0.001265	0.998937
16	0.000591	0.999529
17	0.000268	0.999796
18	0.000118	0.999914

k=20·0
Mean=5·64
Variance=7·23

n	P(n)	F(n)
0	0.006949	0.006949
1	0.030573	0.037522
2	0.070625	0.108147
3	0.113941	0.222088
4	0.144136	0.366224
5	0.152207	0.518431
6	0.139523	0.657954
7	0.114010	0.771964
8	0.084653	0.856617
9	0.057940	0.914557
10	0.036966	0.951523
11	0.022179	0.973703
12	0.012605	0.986308
13	0.006826	0.993134
14	0.003540	0.996674
15	0.001765	0.998439
16	0.000850	0.999289
17	0.000396	0.999685
18	0.000179	0.999864
19	0.000079	0.999942

k=0·2
Mean=0·05
Variance=0·06

n	P(n)	F(n)
0	0.956352	0.956352
1	0.038254	0.994607
2	0.004590	0.999197
3	0.000673	0.999870
4	0.000108	0.999978

k=0·4
Mean=0·10
Variance=0·12

n	P(n)	F(n)
0	0.914610	0.914610
1	0.073169	0.987779
2	0.010244	0.998023
3	0.001639	0.999662
4	0.000279	0.999940

k=0·6
Mean=0·15
Variance=0·19

n	P(n)	F(n)
0	0.874690	0.874690
1	0.104963	0.979652
2	0.016794	0.996446
3	0.002911	0.999357
4	0.000524	0.999881
5	0.000096	0.999978

k=0·8
Mean=0·20
Variance=0·25

n	P(n)	F(n)
0	0.836512	0.836512
1	0.133842	0.970354
2	0.024092	0.994445
3	0.004497	0.998942
4	0.000854	0.999797
5	0.000164	0.999961

k=1·0
Mean=0·25
Variance=0·31

n	P(n)	F(n)
0	0.800000	0.800000
1	0.160000	0.960000
2	0.032000	0.992000
3	0.006400	0.998400
4	0.001280	0.999680

5	0.000256	0.999936

k=1·2
Mean=0·30
Variance=0·37

n	P(n)	F(n)
0	0.765082	0.765082
1	0.183620	0.948702
2	0.040396	0.989098
3	0.008618	0.997716
4	0.001810	0.999526
5	0.000376	0.999902

k=1·4
Mean=0·35
Variance=0·44

n	P(n)	F(n)
0	0.731688	0.731688
1	0.204873	0.936561
2	0.049169	0.985730
3	0.011145	0.996875
4	0.002452	0.999327
5	0.000530	0.999857
6	0.000113	0.999970

k=1·6
Mean=0·40
Variance=0·50

n	P(n)	F(n)
0	0.699752	0.699752
1	0.223921	0.923672
2	0.058219	0.981892
3	0.013973	0.995864
4	0.003214	0.999078
5	0.000720	0.999798
6	0.000158	0.999956

k=1·8
Mean=0·45
Variance=0·56

n	P(n)	F(n)
0	0.669209	0.669209
1	0.240915	0.910125
2	0.067456	0.977581
3	0.017089	0.994670
4	0.004101	0.998771

5	0.000952	0.999723
6	0.000216	0.999938

k=2·0
Mean=0·50
Variance=0·63

n	P(n)	F(n)
0	0.640000	0.640000
1	0.256000	0.896000
2	0.076800	0.972800
3	0.020480	0.993280
4	0.005120	0.998400
5	0.001229	0.999629
6	0.000287	0.999916

k=2·2
Mean=0·55
Variance=0·69

n	P(n)	F(n)
0	0.612066	0.612066
1	0.269309	0.881374
2	0.086179	0.967553
3	0.024130	0.991683
4	0.006274	0.997957
5	0.001556	0.999513
6	0.000373	0.999887
7	0.000087	0.999974

k=2·4
Mean=0·60
Variance=0·75

n	P(n)	F(n)
0	0.585350	0.585350
1	0.280968	0.866319
2	0.095529	0.961848
3	0.028022	0.989870
4	0.007566	0.997436
5	0.001937	0.999373
6	0.000478	0.999850
7	0.000115	0.999965

k=2·6
Mean=0·65
Variance=0·81

n	P(n)	F(n)
0	0.559801	0.559801
1	0.291097	0.850898
2	0.104795	0.955693
3	0.032137	0.987830
4	0.008998	0.996828

5	0.002376	0.999204
6	0.000602	0.999806
7	0.000148	0.999954

5	0.004778	0.998178
6	0.001338	0.999516
7	0.000359	0.999875
8	0.000093	0.999969

5	0.008351	0.996407
6	0.002561	0.998968
7	0.000746	0.999714
8	0.000209	0.999923

k=2·8
Mean=0·70
Variance=0·88

n	P(n)	F(n)
0	0.535367	0.535367
1	0.299806	0.835173
2	0.113926	0.949099
3	0.036456	0.985556
4	0.010572	0.996128
5	0.002876	0.999004
6	0.000748	0.999752
7	0.000188	0.999939

k=3·6
Mean=0·90
Variance=1·13

n	P(n)	F(n)
0	0.447841	0.447841
1	0.322446	0.770287
2	0.148325	0.918612
3	0.055375	0.973986
4	0.018274	0.992260
5	0.005555	0.997815
6	0.001592	0.999408
7	0.000437	0.999844
8	0.000116	0.999960

k=4·4
Mean=1·10
Variance=1·37

n	P(n)	F(n)
0	0.374624	0.374624
1	0.329669	0.704294
2	0.178021	0.882315
3	0.075956	0.958271
4	0.028104	0.986375
5	0.009443	0.995817
6	0.002959	0.998776
7	0.000879	0.999655
8	0.000251	0.999906

k=3·0
Mean=0·75
Variance=0·94

n	P(n)	F(n)
0	0.512000	0.512000
1	0.307200	0.819200
2	0.122880	0.942080
3	0.040960	0.983040
4	0.012288	0.995328
5	0.003441	0.998769
6	0.000918	0.999686
7	0.000236	0.999922

k=3·8
Mean=0·95
Variance=1·19

n	P(n)	F(n)
0	0.428294	0.428294
1	0.325503	0.753797
2	0.156242	0.910039
3	0.060413	0.970452
4	0.020541	0.990993
5	0.006409	0.997402
6	0.001880	0.999282
7	0.000526	0.999808
8	0.000142	0.999950

k=4·6
Mean=1·15
Variance=1·44

n	P(n)	F(n)
0	0.358273	0.358273
1	0.329611	0.687884
2	0.184582	0.872466
3	0.081216	0.953682
4	0.030862	0.984544
5	0.010617	0.995161
6	0.003397	0.998558
7	0.001029	0.999587
8	0.000298	0.999886
9	0.000084	0.999969

k=3·2
Mean=0·80
Variance=1·00

n	P(n)	F(n)
0	0.489652	0.489652
1	0.313378	0.803030
2	0.131619	0.934649
3	0.045628	0.980276
4	0.014145	0.994421
5	0.004074	0.998495
6	0.001113	0.999608
7	0.000293	0.999901

k=4·0
Mean=1·00
Variance=1·25

n	P(n)	F(n)
0	0.409600	0.409600
1	0.327680	0.737280
2	0.163840	0.901120
3	0.065536	0.966656
4	0.022938	0.989594
5	0.007340	0.996934
6	0.002202	0.999136
7	0.000629	0.999765
8	0.000173	0.999938

k=4·8
Mean=1·20
Variance=1·50

n	P(n)	F(n)
0	0.342635	0.342635
1	0.328930	0.671565
2	0.190779	0.862344
3	0.086487	0.948831
4	0.033730	0.982561
5	0.011873	0.994433
6	0.003878	0.998312
7	0.001197	0.999509
8	0.000353	0.999862
9	0.000100	0.999962

k=3·4
Mean=0·85
Variance=1·06

n	P(n)	F(n)
0	0.468280	0.468280
1	0.318431	0.786711
2	0.140109	0.926821
3	0.050439	0.977260
4	0.016141	0.993401

k=4·2
Mean=1·05
Variance=1·31

n	P(n)	F(n)
0	0.391722	0.391722
1	0.329046	0.720768
2	0.171104	0.891873
3	0.070723	0.962596
4	0.025460	0.988056

k=5·0
Mean=1·25
Variance=1·56

n	P(n)	F(n)
0	0.327680	0.327680
1	0.327680	0.655360
2	0.196608	0.851968
3	0.091750	0.943718
4	0.036700	0.980419

245

5	0.013212	0.993631
6	0.004404	0.998035
7	0.001384	0.999419
8	0.000415	0.999834
9	0.000120	0.999954

10	0.000334	0.999841
11	0.000109	0.999950

10	0.001625	0.999030
11	0.000621	0.999651
12	0.000228	0.999878
13	0.000081	0.999959

k=6·0
Mean=1·50
Variance=1·87

n	P(n)	F(n)
0	0.262144	0.262144
1	0.314573	0.576717
2	0.220201	0.796918
3	0.117441	0.914358
4	0.052848	0.967207
5	0.021139	0.988346
6	0.007751	0.996097
7	0.002658	0.998754
8	0.000864	0.999618
9	0.000269	0.999887
10	0.000081	0.999967

k=9·0
Mean=2·25
Variance=2·81

n	P(n)	F(n)
0	0.134218	0.134218
1	0.241592	0.375810
2	0.241592	0.617402
3	0.177167	0.794569
4	0.106300	0.900869
5	0.055276	0.956146
6	0.025796	0.981941
7	0.011055	0.992996
8	0.004422	0.997419
9	0.001671	0.999089
10	0.000601	0.999691
11	0.000208	0.999898
12	0.000069	0.999968

k=12·0
Mean=3·00
Variance=3·75

n	P(n)	F(n)
0	0.068719	0.068719
1	0.164927	0.233646
2	0.214405	0.448051
3	0.200111	0.648162
4	0.150083	0.798245
5	0.096053	0.894299
6	0.054430	0.948729
7	0.027993	0.976722
8	0.013297	0.990018
9	0.005910	0.995928
10	0.002482	0.998410
11	0.000993	0.999403
12	0.000381	0.999783
13	0.000141	0.999924

k=7·0
Mean=1·75
Variance=2·19

n	P(n)	F(n)
0	0.209715	0.209715
1	0.293601	0.503316
2	0.234881	0.738198
3	0.140929	0.879126
4	0.070464	0.949590
5	0.031004	0.980595
6	0.012402	0.992996
7	0.004606	0.997603
8	0.001612	0.999215
9	0.000537	0.999752
10	0.000172	0.999924

k=10·0
Mean=2·50
Variance=3·12

n	P(n)	F(n)
0	0.107374	0.107374
1	0.214748	0.322123
2	0.236223	0.558346
3	0.188979	0.747324
4	0.122836	0.870160
5	0.068788	0.938949
6	0.034394	0.973343
7	0.015723	0.989066
8	0.006682	0.995748
9	0.002673	0.998421
10	0.001016	0.999437
11	0.000369	0.999806
12	0.000129	0.999935

k=13·0
Mean=3·25
Variance=4·06

n	P(n)	F(n)
0	0.054976	0.054976
1	0.142937	0.197912
2	0.200111	0.398023
3	0.200111	0.598134
4	0.160089	0.758223
5	0.108860	0.867084
6	0.065316	0.932400
7	0.035457	0.967857
8	0.017729	0.985586
9	0.008273	0.993859
10	0.003640	0.997500
11	0.001522	0.999022
12	0.000609	0.999631
13	0.000234	0.999865
14	0.000087	0.999952

k=8·0
Mean=2·00
Variance=2·50

n	P(n)	F(n)
0	0.167772	0.167772
1	0.268435	0.436208
2	0.241592	0.677800
3	0.161061	0.838861
4	0.088584	0.927444
5	0.042520	0.969965
6	0.018425	0.988390
7	0.007370	0.995760
8	0.002764	0.998524
9	0.000983	0.999507

k=11·0
Mean=2·75
Variance=3·44

n	P(n)	F(n)
0	0.085899	0.085899
1	0.188979	0.274878
2	0.226774	0.501652
3	0.196538	0.698190
4	0.137576	0.835766
5	0.082546	0.918312
6	0.044024	0.962337
7	0.021383	0.983720
8	0.009622	0.993342
9	0.004063	0.997405

k=14·0
Mean=3·50
Variance=4·37

n	P(n)	F(n)
0	0.043980	0.043980
1	0.123145	0.167126
2	0.184718	0.351844
3	0.197032	0.548876
4	0.167478	0.716354
5	0.120584	0.836938
6	0.076370	0.913307
7	0.043640	0.956947
8	0.022911	0.979858
9	0.011201	0.991059

n	P(n)	F(n)
10	0.005152	0.996212
11	0.002248	0.998460
12	0.000937	0.999397
13	0.000375	0.999771
14	0.000145	0.999916

k = 15·0
Mean = 3·75
Variance = 4·69

n	P(n)	F(n)
0	0.035184	0.035184
1	0.105553	0.140737
2	0.168885	0.309622
3	0.191403	0.501025
4	0.172263	0.673288
5	0.130920	0.804208
6	0.087280	0.891488
7	0.052368	0.943855
8	0.028802	0.972658
9	0.014721	0.987379
10	0.007066	0.994445
11	0.003212	0.997657
12	0.001392	0.999049
13	0.000578	0.999627
14	0.000231	0.999858
15	0.000089	0.999948

k = 16·0
Mean = 4·00
Variance = 5·00

n	P(n)	F(n)
0	0.028147	0.028147
1	0.090072	0.118219
2	0.153122	0.271342
3	0.183747	0.455089
4	0.174560	0.629648
5	0.139648	0.769296
6	0.097753	0.867049
7	0.061445	0.928494
8	0.035331	0.963825
9	0.018843	0.982668
10	0.009422	0.992090
11	0.004454	0.996544
12	0.002004	0.998548
13	0.000863	0.999411
14	0.000358	0.999769
15	0.000143	0.999912

k = 17·0
Mean = 4·25
Variance = 5·31

n	P(n)	F(n)
0	0.022518	0.022518
1	0.076561	0.099079
2	0.137810	0.236889
3	0.174560	0.411449
4	0.174560	0.586008
5	0.146630	0.732638
6	0.107529	0.840167
7	0.070662	0.910829
8	0.042397	0.953226
9	0.023554	0.976780
10	0.012248	0.989028
11	0.006013	0.995040
12	0.002806	0.997846
13	0.001252	0.999098
14	0.000537	0.999635
15	0.000222	0.999856
16	0.000089	0.999945

k = 18·0
Mean = 4·50
Variance = 5·62

n	P(n)	F(n)
0	0.018014	0.018014
1	0.064852	0.082866
2	0.123218	0.206085
3	0.164291	0.370376
4	0.172506	0.542882
5	0.151805	0.694687
6	0.116384	0.811071
7	0.079806	0.890877
8	0.049879	0.940756
9	0.028819	0.969575
10	0.015562	0.985137
11	0.007923	0.993060
12	0.003829	0.996889
13	0.001767	0.998656
14	0.000783	0.999439
15	0.000334	0.999773
16	0.000138	0.999911

k = 19·0
Mean = 4·75
Variance = 5·94

n	P(n)	F(n)
0	0.014412	0.014412
1	0.054764	0.069175
2	0.109528	0.178703
3	0.153339	0.332041
4	0.168672	0.500714
5	0.155179	0.655892
6	0.124143	0.780035
7	0.088673	0.868709
8	0.057638	0.926347
9	0.034583	0.960929
10	0.019366	0.980296
11	0.010211	0.990507
12	0.005106	0.995613
13	0.002435	0.998048
14	0.001113	0.999161
15	0.000490	0.999650
16	0.000208	0.999859
17	0.000086	0.999944

k = 20·0
Mean = 5·00
Variance = 6·25

n	P(n)	F(n)
0	0.011529	0.011529
1	0.046117	0.057646
2	0.096845	0.154491
3	0.142040	0.296531
4	0.163346	0.459877
5	0.156812	0.616689
6	0.130677	0.747366
7	0.097074	0.844440
8	0.065525	0.909965
9	0.040771	0.950736
10	0.023647	0.974384
11	0.012899	0.987282
12	0.006664	0.993946
13	0.003281	0.997227
14	0.001547	0.998774
15	0.000701	0.999475
16	0.000307	0.999782
17	0.000130	0.999912

k=0·5
Mean=0·11
Variance=0·13

n	P(n)	F(n)
0	0.905539	0.905539
1	0.081498	0.987037
2	0.011002	0.998039
3	0.001650	0.999690
4	0.000260	0.999950

k=1·0
Mean=0·22
Variance=0·27

n	P(n)	F(n)
0	0.820000	0.820000
1	0.147600	0.967600
2	0.026568	0.994168
3	0.004782	0.998950
4	0.000861	0.999811
5	0.000155	0.999966

k=1·5
Mean=0·33
Variance=0·40

n	P(n)	F(n)
0	0.742542	0.742542
1	0.200486	0.943028
2	0.045109	0.988137
3	0.009473	0.997610
4	0.001918	0.999528
5	0.000380	0.999908

k=2·0
Mean=0·44
Variance=0·54

n	P(n)	F(n)
0	0.672400	0.672400
1	0.242064	0.914464
2	0.065357	0.979821
3	0.015686	0.995507
4	0.003529	0.999036
5	0.000762	0.999799
6	0.000160	0.999959

k=2·5
Mean=0·55
Variance=0·67

n	P(n)	F(n)
0	0.608884	0.608884
1	0.273998	0.882882
2	0.086309	0.969191
3	0.023304	0.992495
4	0.005768	0.998262
5	0.001350	0.999612
6	0.000304	0.999916

k=3·0
Mean=0·66
Variance=0·80

n	P(n)	F(n)
0	0.551368	0.551368
1	0.297739	0.849107
2	0.107186	0.956293
3	0.032156	0.988448
4	0.008682	0.997131
5	0.002188	0.999318
6	0.000525	0.999843
7	0.000122	0.999965

k=3·5
Mean=0·77
Variance=0·94

n	P(n)	F(n)
0	0.499285	0.499285
1	0.314550	0.813834
2	0.127393	0.941227
3	0.042040	0.983267
4	0.012297	0.995563
5	0.003320	0.998883
6	0.000847	0.999730
7	0.000207	0.999937

k=4·0
Mean=0·88
Variance=1·07

n	P(n)	F(n)
0	0.452122	0.452122
1	0.325528	0.777649
2	0.146487	0.924137
3	0.052735	0.976872
4	0.016612	0.993484
5	0.004784	0.998268
6	0.001292	0.999560
7	0.000332	0.999892
8	0.000082	0.999974

k=4·5
Mean=0·99
Variance=1·20

n	P(n)	F(n)
0	0.409414	0.409414
1	0.331625	0.741039
2	0.164154	0.905193
3	0.064020	0.969213
4	0.021607	0.990820
5	0.006612	0.997432
6	0.001884	0.999316
7	0.000509	0.999825
8	0.000132	0.999957

k=5·0
Mean=1·10
Variance=1·34

n	P(n)	F(n)
0	0.370740	0.370740
1	0.333666	0.704406
2	0.180180	0.884585
3	0.075675	0.960261
4	0.027243	0.987504
5	0.008827	0.996331
6	0.002648	0.998979
7	0.000749	0.999728
8	0.000202	0.999930

k=5·5
Mean=1·21
Variance=1·47

n	P(n)	F(n)
0	0.335719	0.335719
1	0.332362	0.668081
2	0.194432	0.862513
3	0.087494	0.950007
4	0.033467	0.983474
5	0.011446	0.994919
6	0.003605	0.998525
7	0.001066	0.999591
8	0.000300	0.999891
9	0.000081	0.999972

k=6·0
Mean=1·32
Variance=1·61

n	P(n)	F(n)
0	0.304007	0.304007
1	0.328327	0.632334
2	0.206846	0.839180
3	0.099286	0.938466
4	0.040211	0.978677
5	0.014476	0.993153
6	0.004777	0.997930
7	0.001474	0.999404
8	0.000431	0.999835
9	0.000121	0.999956

k = 6·5
Mean = 1·43
Variance = 1·74

n	P(n)	F(n)
0	0.275290	0.275290
1	0.322089	0.597379
2	0.217410	0.814789
3	0.110879	0.925668
4	0.047401	0.973069
5	0.017918	0.990986
6	0.006182	0.997168
7	0.001987	0.999155
8	0.000604	0.999758
9	0.000175	0.999933

k = 7·0
Mean = 1·54
Variance = 1·87

n	P(n)	F(n)
0	0.249285	0.249285
1	0.314100	0.563385
2	0.226152	0.789537
3	0.122122	0.911659
4	0.054955	0.966614
5	0.021762	0.988376
6	0.007834	0.996210
7	0.002619	0.998829
8	0.000825	0.999654
9	0.000247	0.999902

k = 7·5
Mean = 1·65
Variance = 2·01

n	P(n)	F(n)
0	0.225738	0.225738
1	0.304746	0.530483
2	0.233131	0.763614
3	0.132884	0.896498
4	0.062788	0.959286
5	0.025994	0.985280
6	0.009748	0.995028
7	0.003384	0.998412
8	0.001104	0.999516
9	0.000342	0.999858
10	0.000102	0.999960

k = 8·0
Mean = 1·76
Variance = 2·14

n	P(n)	F(n)
0	0.204414	0.204414
1	0.294356	0.498770
2	0.238429	0.737199
3	0.143057	0.880256
4	0.070813	0.951069

5	0.030591	0.981661
6	0.011931	0.993591
7	0.004295	0.997886
8	0.001450	0.999336
9	0.000464	0.999800
10	0.000142	0.999942

k = 8·5
Mean = 1·87
Variance = 2·28

n	P(n)	F(n)
0	0.185105	0.185105
1	0.283210	0.468315
2	0.242145	0.710460
3	0.152551	0.863011
4	0.078945	0.941957
5	0.035525	0.977482
6	0.014388	0.991870
7	0.005365	0.997234
8	0.001871	0.999105
9	0.000617	0.999723
10	0.000194	0.999917

k = 9·0
Mean = 1·98
Variance = 2·41

n	P(n)	F(n)
0	0.167620	0.167620
1	0.271544	0.439163
2	0.244389	0.683553
3	0.161297	0.844849
4	0.087100	0.931950
5	0.040763	0.972713
6	0.017120	0.989833
7	0.006604	0.996437
8	0.002377	0.998814
9	0.000808	0.999622
10	0.000262	0.999884
11	0.000081	0.999966

k = 9·5
Mean = 2·09
Variance = 2·54

n	P(n)	F(n)
0	0.151786	0.151786
1	0.259554	0.411340
2	0.245279	0.656618
3	0.169242	0.825861
4	0.095199	0.921059

5	0.046267	0.967326
6	0.020126	0.987452
7	0.008022	0.995474
8	0.002978	0.998452
9	0.001042	0.999494
10	0.000347	0.999841
11	0.000111	0.999952

k = 10·0
Mean = 2·20
Variance = 2·68

n	P(n)	F(n)
0	0.137448	0.137448
1	0.247406	0.384854
2	0.244932	0.629787
3	0.176351	0.806138
4	0.103166	0.909304
5	0.051995	0.961299
6	0.023398	0.984697
7	0.009627	0.994324
8	0.003682	0.998006
9	0.001326	0.999331
10	0.000453	0.999785
11	0.000148	0.999933

k = 12·0
Mean = 2·63
Variance = 3·21

n	P(n)	F(n)
0	0.092420	0.092420
1	0.199627	0.292047
2	0.233564	0.525611
3	0.196194	0.721805
4	0.132431	0.854236
5	0.076280	0.930516
6	0.038903	0.969419
7	0.018006	0.987425
8	0.007698	0.995123
9	0.003079	0.998202
10	0.001164	0.999366
11	0.000419	0.999785
12	0.000145	0.999930

k = 14·0
Mean = 3·07
Variance = 3·75

n	P(n)	F(n)
0	0.062143	0.062143
1	0.156601	0.218744
2	0.211411	0.430156
3	0.202955	0.633110
4	0.155260	0.788371

5	0.100609	0.888980
6	0.057347	0.946327
7	0.029493	0.975819
8	0.013935	0.989755
9	0.006132	0.995886
10	0.002538	0.998425
11	0.000997	0.999422
12	0.000374	0.999796
13	0.000135	0.999930

k = 16·0
Mean = 3·51
Variance = 4·28

n	P(n)	F(n)
0	0.041785	0.041785
1	0.120341	0.162126
2	0.184122	0.346248
3	0.198852	0.545100
4	0.170018	0.715118
5	0.122413	0.837531
6	0.077120	0.914651
7	0.043628	0.958280
8	0.022578	0.980857
9	0.010837	0.991694
10	0.004877	0.996571
11	0.002075	0.998646
12	0.000840	0.999486
13	0.000326	0.999812
14	0.000121	0.999933

k = 18·0
Mean = 3·95
Variance = 4·82

n	P(n)	F(n)
0	0.028096	0.028096
1	0.091032	0.119128
2	0.155665	0.274793
3	0.186798	0.461591
4	0.176524	0.638115
5	0.139807	0.777922
6	0.096467	0.874389
7	0.059534	0.933922
8	0.033488	0.967410
9	0.017414	0.984824
10	0.008463	0.993287
11	0.003878	0.997164
12	0.001687	0.998851
13	0.000701	0.999552
14	0.000279	0.999831
15	0.000107	0.999938

k = 20·0
Mean = 4·39
Variance = 5·35

n	P(n)	F(n)
0	0.018892	0.018892
1	0.068011	0.086903
2	0.128541	0.215444
3	0.169674	0.385118
4	0.175613	0.560731
5	0.151729	0.712460
6	0.113797	0.826257
7	0.076081	0.902338
8	0.046219	0.948558
9	0.025883	0.974440
10	0.013511	0.987951
11	0.006633	0.994584
12	0.003084	0.997668
13	0.001367	0.999035
14	0.000580	0.999614
15	0.000237	0.999851
16	0.000093	0.999944

k = 22·0
Mean = 4·83
Variance = 5·89

n	P(n)	F(n)
0	0.012703	0.012703
1	0.050304	0.063007
2	0.104129	0.167135
3	0.149945	0.317081
4	0.168688	0.485769
5	0.157892	0.643661
6	0.127893	0.771554
7	0.092083	0.863637
8	0.060084	0.923721
9	0.036050	0.959772
10	0.020116	0.979888
11	0.010534	0.990421
12	0.005214	0.995635
13	0.002455	0.998090
14	0.001105	0.999195
15	0.000477	0.999672
16	0.000199	0.999870
17	0.000080	0.999950

k = 24·0
Mean = 5·27
Variance = 6·42

n	P(n)	F(n)
0	0.008541	0.008541
1	0.036899	0.045441
2	0.083023	0.128464
3	0.129516	0.257980
4	0.157362	0.415342

5	0.158621	0.573962
6	0.138000	0.711962
7	0.106457	0.818420
8	0.074254	0.892674
9	0.047523	0.940196
10	0.028228	0.968424
11	0.015705	0.984130
12	0.008245	0.992375
13	0.004110	0.996485
14	0.001955	0.998440
15	0.000892	0.999332
16	0.000391	0.999723
17	0.000166	0.999888
18	0.000068	0.999956

k = 26·0
Mean = 5·71
Variance = 6·96

n	P(n)	F(n)
0	0.005743	0.005743
1	0.026879	0.032622
2	0.065315	0.097937
3	0.109729	0.207666
4	0.143196	0.350862
5	0.154652	0.505514
6	0.143826	0.649341
7	0.118349	0.767689
8	0.087874	0.855563
9	0.059754	0.915317
10	0.037645	0.952963
11	0.022176	0.975139
12	0.012308	0.987447
13	0.006476	0.993923
14	0.003247	0.997170
15	0.001559	0.998729
16	0.000719	0.999448
17	0.000320	0.999767
18	0.000137	0.999905

k = 28·0
Mean = 6·15
Variance = 7·50

n	P(n)	F(n)
0	0.003862	0.003862
1	0.019463	0.023325
2	0.050799	0.074125
3	0.091439	0.165564
4	0.127557	0.293121
5	0.146946	0.440067
6	0.145477	0.585544
7	0.127188	0.712732
8	0.100161	0.812893
9	0.072116	0.885008
10	0.048029	0.933037
11	0.029865	0.962903
12	0.017471	0.980374
13	0.009676	0.990050
14	0.005101	0.995151

n	P(n)	F(n)
15	0.002571	0.997722
16	0.001244	0.998966
17	0.000579	0.999545
18	0.000261	0.999806
19	0.000114	0.999919

n	P(n)	F(n)
20	0.000173	0.999866
21	0.000077	0.999943

n	P(n)	F(n)
20	0.000508	0.999551
21	0.000244	0.999795
22	0.000114	0.999909

k = 30·0
Mean = 6·59
Variance = 8·03

n	P(n)	F(n)
0	0.002597	0.002597
1	0.014022	0.016619
2	0.039121	0.055740
3	0.075113	0.130853
4	0.111543	0.242396
5	0.136528	0.378924
6	0.143355	0.522279
7	0.132705	0.654984
8	0.110477	0.765461
9	0.083963	0.849424
10	0.058942	0.908366
11	0.038580	0.946946
12	0.023727	0.970673
13	0.013798	0.984471
14	0.007628	0.992099
15	0.004028	0.996127
16	0.002039	0.998166
17	0.000993	0.999159
18	0.000467	0.999626
19	0.000212	0.999838
20	0.000094	0.999932

k = 34·0
Mean = 7·46
Variance = 9·10

n	P(n)	F(n)
0	0.001174	0.001174
1	0.007185	0.008359
2	0.022633	0.030991
3	0.048886	0.079878
4	0.081396	0.161273
5	0.111349	0.272622
6	0.130279	0.402901
7	0.134001	0.536902
8	0.123616	0.660518
9	0.103837	0.764355
10	0.080370	0.844725
11	0.057866	0.902591
12	0.039060	0.941651
13	0.024878	0.966529
14	0.015033	0.981563
15	0.008659	0.990222
16	0.004773	0.994995
17	0.002527	0.997522
18	0.001289	0.998811
19	0.000635	0.999446
20	0.000303	0.999749
21	0.000140	0.999889
22	0.000063	0.999952

k = 38·0
Mean = 8·34
Variance = 10·17

n	P(n)	F(n)
0	0.000531	0.000531
1	0.003631	0.004161
2	0.012744	0.016905
3	0.030584	0.047489
4	0.056428	0.103918
5	0.085320	0.189237
6	0.110062	0.299300
7	0.124528	0.423827
8	0.126084	0.549912
9	0.115998	0.665909
10	0.098134	0.764043
11	0.077080	0.841123
12	0.056654	0.897776
13	0.039222	0.936998
14	0.025718	0.962716
15	0.016048	0.978765
16	0.009569	0.988333
17	0.005471	0.993804
18	0.003009	0.996813
19	0.001596	0.998410
20	0.000819	0.999229
21	0.000407	0.999636
22	0.000197	0.999832
23	0.000092	0.999925

k = 32·0
Mean = 7·02
Variance = 8·57

n	P(n)	F(n)
0	0.001746	0.001746
1	0.010057	0.011803
2	0.029869	0.041672
3	0.060933	0.102605
4	0.095969	0.198574
5	0.124376	0.322951
6	0.138058	0.461009
7	0.134902	0.595911
8	0.118377	0.714287
9	0.094701	0.808989
10	0.069890	0.878878
11	0.048033	0.926912
12	0.030981	0.957893
13	0.018875	0.976768
14	0.010920	0.987688
15	0.006028	0.993716
16	0.003187	0.996904
17	0.001620	0.998524
18	0.000794	0.999317
19	0.000376	0.999693

k = 36·0
Mean = 7·90
Variance = 9·64

n	P(n)	F(n)
0	0.000789	0.000789
1	0.005115	0.005905
2	0.017034	0.022939
3	0.038838	0.061776
4	0.068160	0.129936
5	0.098150	0.228087
6	0.120725	0.348812
7	0.130383	0.479195
8	0.126146	0.605341
9	0.111008	0.716349
10	0.089917	0.806266
11	0.067683	0.873948
12	0.047716	0.921664
13	0.031713	0.953377
14	0.019979	0.973357
15	0.011988	0.985344
16	0.006878	0.992222
17	0.003787	0.996009
18	0.002007	0.998016
19	0.001027	0.999043

k = 40·0
Mean = 8·78
Variance = 10·71

n	P(n)	F(n)
0	0.000357	0.000357
1	0.002570	0.002927
2	0.009482	0.012409
3	0.023895	0.036304
4	0.046238	0.082542
5	0.073240	0.155782
6	0.098874	0.254656
7	0.116954	0.371610
8	0.123679	0.495289
9	0.118732	0.614021
10	0.104722	0.718743
11	0.085681	0.804424
12	0.065546	0.869970
13	0.047193	0.917163
14	0.032159	0.949322
15	0.020839	0.970161
16	0.012894	0.983055
17	0.007645	0.990701
18	0.004358	0.995059
19	0.002395	0.997453

n	P(n)	F(n)
20	0.001272	0.998725
21	0.000654	0.999379
22	0.000326	0.999705
23	0.000158	0.999863
24	0.000075	0.999938

k=42·0
Mean=9·22
Variance=11·24

n	P(n)	F(n)
0	0.000240	0.000240
1	0.001814	0.002054
2	0.007021	0.009076
3	0.018536	0.027612
4	0.037536	0.065147
5	0.062159	0.127306
6	0.087644	0.214950
7	0.108178	0.323128
8	0.119266	0.442394
9	0.119266	0.561661
10	0.109486	0.671147
11	0.093163	0.764310
12	0.074065	0.838374
13	0.055377	0.893752
14	0.039160	0.932912
15	0.026315	0.959227
16	0.016875	0.976102
17	0.010363	0.986465
18	0.006114	0.992579
19	0.003475	0.996055
20	0.001908	0.997963
21	0.001014	0.998977
22	0.000523	0.999499
23	0.000262	0.999761
24	0.000128	0.999889
25	0.000061	0.999949

k=44·0
Mean=9·66
Variance=11·78

n	P(n)	F(n)
0	0.000161	0.000161
1	0.001278	0.001439
2	0.005176	0.006615
3	0.014286	0.020901
4	0.030214	0.051115
5	0.052210	0.103325
6	0.076749	0.180073
7	0.098677	0.278750
8	0.113232	0.391982
9	0.117761	0.509742
10	0.112344	0.622086
11	0.099271	0.721357
12	0.081899	0.803256
13	0.063503	0.866759
14	0.046539	0.913298
15	0.032391	0.945688
16	0.021499	0.967188
17	0.013658	0.980846
18	0.008332	0.989178
19	0.004894	0.994072
20	0.002775	0.996846
21	0.001522	0.998369
22	0.000810	0.999178
23	0.000418	0.999596
24	0.000210	0.999806
25	0.000103	0.999909

k=46·0
Mean=10·10
Variance=12·31

n	P(n)	F(n)
0	0.000109	0.000109
1	0.000898	0.001007
2	0.003800	0.004807
3	0.010945	0.015752
4	0.024133	0.039885
5	0.043439	0.083324
6	0.066462	0.149786
7	0.088869	0.238655
8	0.105976	0.344631
9	0.114455	0.459086
10	0.113310	0.572396
11	0.103833	0.676229
12	0.088777	0.765006
13	0.071295	0.836301
14	0.054082	0.890383
15	0.038939	0.929323
16	0.026722	0.956045
17	0.017542	0.973587
18	0.011052	0.984639
19	0.006701	0.991340
20	0.003920	0.995259
21	0.002218	0.997477
22	0.001216	0.998693
23	0.000647	0.999340
24	0.000335	0.999674
25	0.000169	0.999843
26	0.000083	0.999926

k=48·0
Mean=10·54
Variance=12·85

n	P(n)	F(n)
0	0.000073	0.000073
1	0.000630	0.000703
2	0.002780	0.003483
3	0.008339	0.011823
4	0.019139	0.030962
5	0.035828	0.066790
6	0.056967	0.123757
7	0.079103	0.202860
8	0.097890	0.300750
9	0.109637	0.410386
10	0.112487	0.522874
11	0.106761	0.629634
12	0.094483	0.724117
13	0.078494	0.802611
14	0.061561	0.864172
15	0.045802	0.909974
16	0.032462	0.942436
17	0.021998	0.964434
18	0.014299	0.978732
19	0.008940	0.987673
20	0.005391	0.993064
21	0.003142	0.996206
22	0.001774	0.997980
23	0.000972	0.998952
24	0.000517	0.999469
25	0.000268	0.999737
26	0.000136	0.999873
27	0.000067	0.999940

k=50·0
Mean=10·98
Variance=13·38

n	P(n)	F(n)
0	0.000049	0.000049
1	0.000442	0.000491
2	0.002027	0.002517
3	0.006323	0.008840
4	0.015080	0.023919
5	0.029315	0.053234
6	0.048369	0.101604
7	0.069652	0.171256
8	0.089329	0.260584
9	0.103621	0.364205
10	0.110046	0.474251
11	0.108045	0.582296
12	0.098861	0.681157
13	0.084468	0.766026
14	0.068743	0.834769
15	0.052795	0.887564
16	0.038606	0.926170
17	0.026979	0.953149
18	0.018076	0.971225
19	0.011645	0.982870
20	0.007231	0.990101
21	0.004339	0.994440
22	0.002520	0.996961
23	0.001420	0.998381
24	0.000778	0.999158
25	0.000414	0.999573
26	0.000215	0.999788
27	0.000109	0.999897
28	0.000054	0.999951

k=0·5
Mean=0·10
Variance=0·11

n	P(n)	F(n)
0	0.916515	0.916515
1	0.073321	0.989836
2	0.008799	0.998635
3	0.001173	0.999808
4	0.000164	0.999972

k=1·0
Mean=0·19
Variance=0·23

n	P(n)	F(n)
0	0.840000	0.840000
1	0.134400	0.974400
2	0.021504	0.995904
3	0.003441	0.999345
4	0.000551	0.999895
5	0.000088	0.999983

k=1·5
Mean=0·29
Variance=0·34

n	P(n)	F(n)
0	0.769873	0.769873
1	0.184769	0.954642
2	0.036954	0.991596
3	0.006898	0.998494
4	0.001242	0.999736
5	0.000219	0.999954

k=2·0
Mean=0·38
Variance=0·45

n	P(n)	F(n)
0	0.705600	0.705600
1	0.225792	0.931392
2	0.054190	0.985582
3	0.011561	0.997143
4	0.002312	0.999455
5	0.000444	0.999899
6	0.000083	0.999982

k=2·5
Mean=0·48
Variance=0·57

n	P(n)	F(n)
0	0.646693	0.646693
1	0.258677	0.905370
2	0.072430	0.977800
3	0.017383	0.995183
4	0.003824	0.999007
5	0.000795	0.999803
6	0.000159	0.999962

k=3·0
Mean=0·57
Variance=0·68

n	P(n)	F(n)
0	0.592704	0.592704
1	0.284498	0.877202
2	0.091039	0.968241
3	0.024277	0.992518
4	0.005827	0.998345
5	0.001305	0.999650
6	0.000278	0.999928

k=3·5
Mean=0·67
Variance=0·79

n	P(n)	F(n)
0	0.543222	0.543222
1	0.304204	0.847427
2	0.109514	0.956940
3	0.032124	0.989064
4	0.008352	0.997416
5	0.002005	0.999421
6	0.000454	0.999875
7	0.000099	0.999974

k=4·0
Mean=0·76
Variance=0·91

n	P(n)	F(n)
0	0.497871	0.497871
1	0.318638	0.816509
2	0.127455	0.943964
3	0.040786	0.984750
4	0.011420	0.996170
5	0.002924	0.999093
6	0.000702	0.999795
7	0.000160	0.999955

k=4·5
Mean=0·86
Variance=1·02

n	P(n)	F(n)
0	0.456307	0.456307
1	0.328541	0.784847
2	0.144558	0.929405
3	0.050113	0.979519
4	0.015034	0.994553
5	0.004089	0.998642
6	0.001036	0.999678
7	0.000249	0.999927

k=5·0
Mean=0·95
Variance=1·13

n	P(n)	F(n)
0	0.418212	0.418212
1	0.334570	0.752781
2	0.160593	0.913375
3	0.059955	0.973330
4	0.019186	0.992515
5	0.005525	0.998041
6	0.001473	0.999514
7	0.000370	0.999885
8	0.000089	0.999974

k=5·5
Mean=1·05
Variance=1·25

n	P(n)	F(n)
0	0.383298	0.383298
1	0.337302	0.720599
2	0.175397	0.895996
3	0.070159	0.966155
4	0.023854	0.990009
5	0.007252	0.997261
6	0.002030	0.999291
7	0.000534	0.999825
8	0.000133	0.999958

k=6·0
Mean=1·14
Variance=1·36

n	P(n)	F(n)
0	0.351298	0.351298
1	0.337246	0.688544
2	0.188858	0.877402
3	0.080579	0.957981
4	0.029009	0.986990
5	0.009283	0.996273
6	0.002723	0.998996
7	0.000747	0.999742
8	0.000194	0.999937

k=6·5
Mean=1·24
Variance=1·47

n	P(n)	F(n)
0	0.321970	0.321970
1	0.334849	0.656819
2	0.200909	0.857728
3	0.091079	0.948807
4	0.034610	0.983417
5	0.011629	0.995046
6	0.003566	0.998612
7	0.001019	0.999631
8	0.000275	0.999906

k=7·0
Mean=1·33
Variance=1·59

n	P(n)	F(n)
0	0.295090	0.295090
1	0.330501	0.625592
2	0.211521	0.837112
3	0.101530	0.938642
4	0.040612	0.979254
5	0.014295	0.993550
6	0.004575	0.998124
7	0.001359	0.999483
8	0.000381	0.999864
9	0.000101	0.999966

k=7·5
Mean=1·43
Variance=1·70

n	P(n)	F(n)
0	0.270455	0.270455
1	0.324546	0.595000
2	0.220691	0.815692
3	0.111817	0.927508
4	0.046963	0.974471
5	0.017282	0.991754
6	0.005761	0.997515
7	0.001778	0.999292
8	0.000516	0.999808
9	0.000142	0.999950

k=8·0
Mean=1·52
Variance=1·81

n	P(n)	F(n)
0	0.247876	0.247876
1	0.317281	0.565157
2	0.228442	0.793599
3	0.121836	0.915435
4	0.053608	0.969043
5	0.020585	0.989629
6	0.007136	0.996765
7	0.002284	0.999049
8	0.000685	0.999734
9	0.000195	0.999928

k=8·5
Mean=1·62
Variance=1·93

n	P(n)	F(n)
0	0.227182	0.227182
1	0.308968	0.536150
2	0.234815	0.770965
3	0.131497	0.902461
4	0.060488	0.962950
5	0.024195	0.987145
6	0.008710	0.995856
7	0.002887	0.998742
8	0.000895	0.999637
9	0.000263	0.999900
10	0.000074	0.999973

k=9·0
Mean=1·71
Variance=2·04

n	P(n)	F(n)
0	0.208216	0.208216
1	0.299831	0.508046
2	0.239865	0.747911
3	0.140721	0.888632
4	0.067546	0.956177
5	0.028099	0.984276
6	0.010490	0.994767
7	0.003597	0.998363
8	0.001151	0.999514
9	0.000348	0.999862
10	0.000100	0.999962

k=9·5
Mean=1·81
Variance=2·15

n	P(n)	F(n)
0	0.190833	0.190833
1	0.290066	0.480899
2	0.243655	0.724554
3	0.149442	0.873996
4	0.074721	0.948717
5	0.032279	0.980997
6	0.012481	0.993478
7	0.004422	0.997900
8	0.001459	0.999359
9	0.000454	0.999813
10	0.000134	0.999948

k=10·0
Mean=1·90
Variance=2·27

n	P(n)	F(n)
0	0.174901	0.174901
1	0.279842	0.454743
2	0.246261	0.701004
3	0.157607	0.858611
4	0.081956	0.940567
5	0.036716	0.977283
6	0.014686	0.991969
7	0.005371	0.997340
8	0.001826	0.999167
9	0.000584	0.999751
10	0.000178	0.999929

k=12·0
Mean=2·29
Variance=2·72

n	P(n)	F(n)
0	0.123410	0.123410
1	0.236948	0.360358
2	0.246426	0.606784
3	0.183998	0.790782
4	0.110399	0.901180
5	0.056524	0.957705
6	0.025624	0.983329
7	0.010543	0.993871
8	0.004006	0.997878
9	0.001424	0.999302
10	0.000479	0.999781
11	0.000153	0.999934

k=14·0
Mean=2·67
Variance=3·17

n	P(n)	F(n)
0	0.087078	0.087078
1	0.195055	0.282134
2	0.234067	0.516200
3	0.199737	0.715937
4	0.135821	0.851758
5	0.078233	0.929991
6	0.039638	0.969629
7	0.018120	0.987749
8	0.007610	0.995360
9	0.002977	0.998336
10	0.001095	0.999432
11	0.000382	0.999814
12	0.000127	0.999941

k = 16·0
Mean = 3·05
Variance = 3·63

n	P(n)	F(n)
0	0.061442	0.061442
1	0.157293	0.218735
2	0.213918	0.432653
3	0.205361	0.638015
4	0.156075	0.794089
5	0.099888	0.893977
6	0.055937	0.949914
7	0.028128	0.978042
8	0.012939	0.990982
9	0.005521	0.996502
10	0.002208	0.998710
11	0.000835	0.999546
12	0.000301	0.999846
13	0.000104	0.999950

k = 18·0
Mean = 3·43
Variance = 4·08

n	P(n)	F(n)
0	0.043354	0.043354
1	0.124859	0.168213
2	0.189786	0.357998
3	0.202438	0.560436
4	0.170048	0.730484
5	0.119714	0.850198
6	0.073424	0.923622
7	0.040279	0.963901
8	0.020139	0.984040
9	0.009309	0.993349
10	0.004021	0.997370
11	0.001638	0.999008
12	0.000633	0.999641
13	0.000234	0.999875
14	0.000083	0.999958

k = 20·0
Mean = 3·81
Variance = 4·54

n	P(n)	F(n)
0	0.030590	0.030590
1	0.097889	0.128480
2	0.164454	0.292934
3	0.192960	0.485894
4	0.177523	0.663416
5	0.136338	0.799754
6	0.090892	0.890646
7	0.054016	0.944661
8	0.029168	0.973830
9	0.014519	0.988349
10	0.006737	0.995086
11	0.002940	0.998026
12	0.001215	0.999241
13	0.000479	0.999720
14	0.000180	0.999900

k = 22·0
Mean = 4·19
Variance = 4·99

n	P(n)	F(n)
0	0.021585	0.021585
1	0.075978	0.097562
2	0.139799	0.237362
3	0.178943	0.416305
4	0.178943	0.595248
5	0.148881	0.744128
6	0.107194	0.851322
7	0.068604	0.919927
8	0.039790	0.959717
9	0.021222	0.980938
10	0.010526	0.991464
11	0.004899	0.996364
12	0.002156	0.998519
13	0.000902	0.999421
14	0.000361	0.999782
15	0.000139	0.999921

k = 24·0
Mean = 4·57
Variance = 5·44

n	P(n)	F(n)
0	0.015230	0.015230
1	0.058484	0.073714
2	0.116967	0.190681
3	0.162195	0.352875
4	0.175170	0.528045
5	0.156952	0.684998
6	0.121377	0.806374
7	0.083230	0.889604
8	0.051602	0.941206
9	0.029356	0.970562
10	0.015500	0.986062
11	0.007665	0.993728
12	0.003577	0.997305
13	0.001585	0.998890
14	0.000670	0.999560
15	0.000272	0.999832
16	0.000106	0.999938

k = 26·0
Mean = 4·95
Variance = 5·90

n	P(n)	F(n)
0	0.010746	0.010746
1	0.044705	0.055451
2	0.096563	0.152014
3	0.144200	0.296214
4	0.167272	0.463486
5	0.160581	0.624067
6	0.132747	0.756814
7	0.097095	0.853909
8	0.064083	0.917992
9	0.038734	0.956726
10	0.021691	0.978417
11	0.011358	0.989776
12	0.005603	0.995379
13	0.002621	0.998000
14	0.001168	0.999168
15	0.000498	0.999666
16	0.000204	0.999871
17	0.000081	0.999951

k = 28·0
Mean = 5·33
Variance = 6·35

n	P(n)	F(n)
0	0.007583	0.007583
1	0.033970	0.041553
2	0.078811	0.120364
3	0.126097	0.246461
4	0.156361	0.402822
5	0.160113	0.562935
6	0.140900	0.703835
7	0.109499	0.813334
8	0.076649	0.889984
9	0.049056	0.939039
10	0.029041	0.968080
11	0.016052	0.984132
12	0.008347	0.992479
13	0.004109	0.996588
14	0.001925	0.998514
15	0.000863	0.999376
16	0.000371	0.999747
17	0.000154	0.999901

k = 30·0
Mean = 5·71
Variance = 6·80

n	P(n)	F(n)
0	0.005350	0.005350
1	0.025681	0.031032
2	0.063690	0.094722
3	0.108698	0.203419
4	0.143481	0.346900
5	0.156107	0.503008
6	0.145700	0.648708
7	0.119890	0.768598
8	0.088719	0.857317
9	0.059935	0.917251
10	0.037399	0.954651
11	0.021760	0.976410
12	0.011895	0.988305
13	0.006149	0.994454
14	0.003022	0.997476

15	0.001418	0.998894
16	0.000638	0.999532
17	0.000276	0.999809
18	0.000115	0.999924

k=32·0
Mean=6·10
Variance=7·26

n	P(n)	F(n)
0	0.003775	0.003775
1	0.019329	0.023104
2	0.051028	0.074132
3	0.092531	0.166664
4	0.129544	0.296207
5	0.149234	0.445442
6	0.147245	0.592687
7	0.127893	0.720579
8	0.099756	0.820335
9	0.070938	0.891273
10	0.046535	0.937808
11	0.028429	0.966237
12	0.016299	0.982536
13	0.008827	0.991363
14	0.004539	0.995902
15	0.002227	0.998130
16	0.001047	0.999176
17	0.000473	0.999649
18	0.000206	0.999855
19	0.000087	0.999942

k=34·0
Mean=6·48
Variance=7·71

n	P(n)	F(n)
0	0.002664	0.002664
1	0.014491	0.017155
2	0.040574	0.057729
3	0.077903	0.135632
4	0.115296	0.250928
5	0.140200	0.391129
6	0.145808	0.536937
7	0.133311	0.670248
8	0.109315	0.779562
9	0.081622	0.861184
10	0.056156	0.917340
11	0.035940	0.953279
12	0.021564	0.974843
13	0.012208	0.987051
14	0.006558	0.993609
15	0.003358	0.996967
16	0.001645	0.998612
17	0.000774	0.999386
18	0.000351	0.999737
19	0.000154	0.999891
20	0.000065	0.999956

k=36·0
Mean=6·86
Variance=8·16

n	P(n)	F(n)
0	0.001880	0.001880
1	0.010826	0.012706
2	0.032046	0.044751
3	0.064946	0.109697
4	0.101315	0.211013
5	0.129684	0.340696
6	0.141788	0.482484
7	0.136116	0.618600
8	0.117060	0.735660
9	0.091567	0.827226
10	0.065928	0.893154
11	0.044112	0.937266
12	0.027643	0.964910
13	0.016331	0.981241
14	0.009145	0.990386
15	0.004877	0.995263
16	0.002488	0.997751
17	0.001217	0.998968
18	0.000574	0.999542
19	0.000261	0.999803
20	0.000115	0.999917

k=38·0
Mean=7·24
Variance=8·62

n	P(n)	F(n)
0	0.001326	0.001326
1	0.008063	0.009390
2	0.025158	0.034547
3	0.053670	0.088217
4	0.088018	0.176235
5	0.118297	0.294532
6	0.135647	0.430179
7	0.136422	0.566601
8	0.122780	0.689381
9	0.100407	0.789788
10	0.075506	0.865294
11	0.052717	0.918010
12	0.034442	0.952452
13	0.021195	0.973647
14	0.012354	0.986000
15	0.006852	0.992853
16	0.003632	0.996484
17	0.001846	0.998330
18	0.000902	0.999232
19	0.000426	0.999658
20	0.000194	0.999852
21	0.000086	0.999938

k=40·0
Mean=7·62
Variance=9·07

n	P(n)	F(n)
0	0.000936	0.000936
1	0.005989	0.006925
2	0.019644	0.026569
3	0.044002	0.070571
4	0.075684	0.146254
5	0.106562	0.252817
6	0.127875	0.380692
7	0.134451	0.515143
8	0.126384	0.641527
9	0.107848	0.749375
10	0.084553	0.833928
11	0.061493	0.895421
12	0.041815	0.937236
13	0.026762	0.963998
14	0.016210	0.980208
15	0.009337	0.989545
16	0.005135	0.994680
17	0.002707	0.997387
18	0.001371	0.998758
19	0.000670	0.999428
20	0.000316	0.999744
21	0.000145	0.999889
22	0.000064	0.999953

k=42·0
Mean=8·00
Variance=9·52

n	P(n)	F(n)
0	0.000660	0.000660
1	0.004437	0.005097
2	0.015264	0.020361
3	0.035819	0.056180
4	0.064474	0.120653
5	0.094905	0.215558
6	0.118948	0.334506
7	0.130503	0.465009
8	0.127893	0.592901
9	0.113682	0.706583
10	0.092765	0.799348
11	0.070164	0.869512
12	0.049582	0.919095
13	0.032953	0.952048
14	0.020713	0.972761
15	0.012373	0.985134
16	0.007053	0.992187
17	0.003850	0.996037
18	0.002019	0.998056
19	0.001020	0.999076
20	0.000498	0.999574
21	0.000235	0.999809
22	0.000108	0.999916

k=44·0
Mean = 8·38
Variance = 9·98

n	P(n)	F(n)
0	0.000466	0.000466
1	0.003280	0.003746
2	0.011808	0.015553
3	0.028968	0.044522
4	0.054460	0.098982
5	0.083651	0.182632
6	0.109304	0.291936
7	0.124918	0.416854
8	0.127417	0.544271
9	0.117790	0.662060
10	0.099886	0.761946
11	0.078456	0.840402
12	0.057534	0.897936
13	0.039654	0.937590
14	0.025832	0.963422
15	0.015981	0.979403
16	0.009429	0.988832
17	0.005325	0.994157
18	0.002887	0.997044
19	0.001507	0.998552
20	0.000760	0.999311
21	0.000370	0.999682
22	0.000175	0.999857
23	0.000080	0.999937

k=46·0
Mean = 8·76
Variance = 10·43

n	P(n)	F(n)
0	0.000329	0.000329
1	0.002419	0.002748
2	0.009097	0.011846
3	0.023289	0.035135
4	0.045647	0.080781
5	0.073035	0.153816
6	0.099327	0.253143
7	0.118057	0.371200
8	0.125141	0.496341
9	0.120135	0.616476
10	0.105719	0.722195
11	0.086113	0.808308
12	0.065446	0.873754
13	0.046718	0.920472
14	0.031501	0.951974
15	0.020161	0.972134
16	0.012298	0.984433
17	0.007176	0.991609
18	0.004019	0.995628
19	0.002166	0.997794
20	0.001126	0.998920
21	0.000566	0.999486
22	0.000276	0.999762
23	0.000131	0.999893
24	0.000060	0.999953

k=48·0
Mean = 9·14·
Variance = 10·88

n	P(n)	F(n)
0	0.000232	0.000232
1	0.001781	0.002013
2	0.006983	0.008997
3	0.018622	0.027618
4	0.037988	0.065607
5	0.063213	0.128820
6	0.089341	0.218160
7	0.110272	0.328433
8	0.121299	0.449732
9	0.120760	0.570492
10	0.110133	0.680625
11	0.092912	0.773538
12	0.073091	0.846629
13	0.053975	0.900604
14	0.037628	0.938232
15	0.024885	0.963117
16	0.015677	0.978794
17	0.009443	0.988238
18	0.005456	0.993694
19	0.003032	0.996726
20	0.001625	0.998352
21	0.000842	0.999194
22	0.000423	0.999616
23	0.000206	0.999822
24	0.000097	0.999920
25	0.000073	0.999940

k=50·0
Mean = 9·52
Variance = 11·34

n	P(n)	F(n)
0	0.000164	0.000164
1	0.001309	0.001473
2	0.005342	0.006815
3	0.014816	0.021631
4	0.031409	0.053040
5	0.054275	0.107314
6	0.079603	0.186917
7	0.101891	0.288808
8	0.116156	0.404964
9	0.119770	0.524734
10	0.113063	0.637797
11	0.098673	0.736470
12	0.080254	0.816724
13	0.061240	0.877964
14	0.044093	0.922057
15	0.030101	0.952158
16	0.019565	0.971723
17	0.012154	0.983877
18	0.007238	0.991115
19	0.004145	0.995260
20	0.002288	0.997547
21	0.001220	0.998768
22	0.000630	0.999398
23	0.000316	0.999713
24	0.000154	0.999867

k = 0·5
Mean = 0·08
Variance = 0·09

n	P(n)	F(n)
0	0.927362	0.927362
1	0.064915	0.992277
2	0.006816	0.999093
3	0.000795	0.999889
4	0.000097	0.999986

k = 1·0
Mean = 0·16
Variance = 0·19

n	P(n)	F(n)
0	0.860000	0.860000
1	0.120400	0.980400
2	0.016856	0.997256
3	0.002360	0.999616
4	0.000330	0.999946

k = 1·5
Mean = 0·24
Variance = 0·28

n	P(n)	F(n)
0	0.797531	0.797531
1	0.167482	0.965013
2	0.029309	0.994322
3	0.004787	0.999109
4	0.000754	0.999863
5	0.000116	0.999979

k = 2·0
Mean = 0·33
Variance = 0·38

n	P(n)	F(n)
0	0.739600	0.739600
1	0.207088	0.946688
2	0.043488	0.990176
3	0.008118	0.998294
4	0.001421	0.999715
5	0.000239	0.999954

k = 2·5
Mean = 0·41
Variance = 0·47

n	P(n)	F(n)
0	0.685877	0.685877
1	0.240057	0.925934
2	0.058814	0.984748
3	0.012351	0.997099
4	0.002378	0.999476

5	0.000433	0.999909

k = 3·0
Mean = 0·49
Variance = 0·57

n	P(n)	F(n)
0	0.636056	0.636056
1	0.267144	0.903200
2	0.074800	0.978000
3	0.017453	0.995453
4	0.003665	0.999118
5	0.000718	0.999837
6	0.000134	0.999971

k = 3·5
Mean = 0·57
Variance = 0·66

n	P(n)	F(n)
0	0.589854	0.589854
1	0.289028	0.878883
2	0.091044	0.969927
3	0.023368	0.993294
4	0.005316	0.998611
5	0.001116	0.999727
6	0.000221	0.999949

k = 4·0
Mean = 0·65
Variance = 0·76

n	P(n)	F(n)
0	0.547008	0.547008
1	0.306325	0.853333
2	0.107214	0.960546
3	0.030020	0.990566
4	0.007355	0.997921
5	0.001647	0.999568
6	0.000346	0.999914

k = 4·5
Mean = 0·73
Variance = 0·85

n	P(n)	F(n)
0	0.507274	0.507274
1	0.319583	0.826857
2	0.123039	0.949897
3	0.037322	0.987219
4	0.009797	0.997016

5	0.002332	0.999348
6	0.000517	0.999864
7	0.000109	0.999973

k = 5·0
Mean = 0·81
Variance = 0·95

n	P(n)	F(n)
0	0.470427	0.470427
1	0.329299	0.799726
2	0.138306	0.938031
3	0.045180	0.983211
4	0.012650	0.995862
5	0.003188	0.999050
6	0.000744	0.999793
7	0.000164	0.999957

k = 5·5
Mean = 0·90
Variance = 1·04

n	P(n)	F(n)
0	0.436256	0.436256
1	0.335917	0.772173
2	0.152842	0.925016
3	0.053495	0.978510
4	0.015915	0.994425
5	0.004233	0.998658
6	0.001037	0.999696
7	0.000239	0.999934

k = 6·0
Mean = 0·98
Variance = 1·14

n	P(n)	F(n)
0	0.404567	0.404567
1	0.339836	0.744404
2	0.166520	0.910924
3	0.062167	0.973091
4	0.019583	0.992674
5	0.005483	0.998157
6	0.001407	0.999564
7	0.000338	0.999902

k = 6·5
Mean = 1·06
Variance = 1·23

n	P(n)	F(n)
0	0.375180	0.375180
1	0.341414	0.716594
2	0.179242	0.895837
3	0.071099	0.966936
4	0.023641	0.990577

5	0.006950	0.997527
6	0.001865	0.999392
7	0.000466	0.999858
8	0.000110	0.999968

k=7·0
Mean=1·14
Variance=1·33

n	P(n)	F(n)
0	0.347928	0.347928
1	0.340969	0.688897
2	0.190943	0.879840
3	0.080196	0.960036
4	0.028069	0.988104
5	0.008645	0.996750
6	0.002421	0.999170
7	0.000629	0.999800
8	0.000154	0.999954

k=7·5
Mean=1·22
Variance=1·42

n	P(n)	F(n)
0	0.322655	0.322655
1	0.338788	0.661443
2	0.201579	0.863021
3	0.089367	0.952388
4	0.032842	0.985230
5	0.010575	0.995805
6	0.003084	0.998890
7	0.000833	0.999723
8	0.000211	0.999934

k=8·0
Mean=1·30
Variance=1·51

n	P(n)	F(n)
0	0.299218	0.299218
1	0.335124	0.634342
2	0.211128	0.845470
3	0.098526	0.943997
4	0.037933	0.981929
5	0.012745	0.994675
6	0.003866	0.998541
7	0.001083	0.999623
8	0.000284	0.999908

k=8·5
Mean=1·38
Variance=1·61

n	P(n)	F(n)
0	0.277483	0.277483
1	0.330205	0.607688
2	0.219586	0.827275
3	0.107597	0.934872
4	0.043308	0.978180

5	0.015158	0.993338
6	0.004775	0.998113
7	0.001385	0.999497
8	0.000376	0.999873
9	0.000096	0.999969

k=9·0
Mean=1·47
Variance=1·70

n	P(n)	F(n)
0	0.257327	0.257327
1	0.324233	0.581560
2	0.226963	0.808523
3	0.116508	0.925030
4	0.048933	0.973963
5	0.017812	0.991775
6	0.005818	0.997594
7	0.001746	0.999339
8	0.000489	0.999828
9	0.000129	0.999957

k=9·5
Mean=1·55
Variance=1·80

n	P(n)	F(n)
0	0.238636	0.238636
1	0.317385	0.556021
2	0.233278	0.789299
3	0.125193	0.914492
4	0.054772	0.969264
5	0.020704	0.989967
6	0.007005	0.996972
7	0.002171	0.999144
8	0.000627	0.999771
9	0.000171	0.999941

k=10·0
Mean=1·63
Variance=1·89

n	P(n)	F(n)
0	0.221302	0.221302
1	0.309822	0.531124
2	0.238563	0.769687
3	0.133595	0.903282
4	0.060786	0.964068
5	0.023828	0.987896
6	0.008340	0.996236
7	0.002669	0.998905
8	0.000794	0.999699
9	0.000222	0.999921

k=12·0
Mean=1·95
Variance=2·27

n	P(n)	F(n)
0	0.163675	0.163675
1	0.274973	0.438648
2	0.250226	0.688874
3	0.163481	0.852355
4	0.085827	0.938182

5	0.038451	0.976633
6	0.015252	0.991885
7	0.005491	0.997376
8	0.001826	0.999201
9	0.000568	0.999769
10	0.000167	0.999936

k=14·0
Mean=2·28
Variance=2·65

n	P(n)	F(n)
0	0.121054	0.121054
1	0.237265	0.358319
2	0.249129	0.607448
3	0.186016	0.793464
4	0.110680	0.904143
5	0.055782	0.959926
6	0.024730	0.984656
7	0.009892	0.994548
8	0.003635	0.998184
9	0.001244	0.999428
10	0.000401	0.999828
11	0.000122	0.999951

k=16·0
Mean=2·60
Variance=3·03

n	P(n)	F(n)
0	0.089531	0.089531
1	0.200550	0.290082
2	0.238655	0.528736
3	0.200470	0.729206
4	0.133313	0.862519
5	0.074655	0.937174
6	0.036581	0.973755
7	0.016096	0.989851
8	0.006478	0.996329
9	0.002419	0.998748
10	0.000847	0.999594
11	0.000280	0.999874
12	0.000088	0.999963

k=18·0
Mean=2·93
Variance=3·41

n	P(n)	F(n)
0	0.066217	0.066217
1	0.166868	0.233085
2	0.221934	0.455019
3	0.207139	0.662158
4	0.152247	0.814405

n	P(n)	F(n)
5	0.093784	0.908189
6	0.050331	0.958520
7	0.024159	0.982679
8	0.010569	0.993248
9	0.004275	0.997523
10	0.001616	0.999139
11	0.000576	0.999715
12	0.000195	0.999909

k=20·0
Mean=3·26
Variance=3·79

n	P(n)	F(n)
0	0.048974	0.048974
1	0.137128	0.186103
2	0.201579	0.387681
3	0.206954	0.594635
4	0.166598	0.761233
5	0.111954	0.873187
6	0.065306	0.938494
7	0.033959	0.972453
8	0.016046	0.988499
9	0.006989	0.995487
10	0.002837	0.998325
11	0.001083	0.999408
12	0.000392	0.999800
13	0.000135	0.999935

k=22·0
Mean=3·58
Variance=4·16

n	P(n)	F(n)
0	0.036221	0.036221
1	0.111562	0.147784
2	0.179615	0.327399
3	0.201169	0.528567
4	0.176023	0.704590
5	0.128145	0.832734
6	0.080731	0.913465
7	0.045209	0.958675
8	0.022944	0.981619
9	0.010707	0.992326
10	0.004647	0.996973
11	0.001893	0.998865
12	0.000729	0.999594
13	0.000267	0.999861
14	0.000093	0.999954

k=24·0
Mean=3·91
Variance=4·54

n	P(n)	F(n)
0	0.026789	0.026789
1	0.090012	0.116802
2	0.157522	0.274323
3	0.191126	0.465450
4	0.180614	0.646064
5	0.141602	0.787665
6	0.095817	0.883483
7	0.057490	0.940973
8	0.031188	0.972161
9	0.015525	0.987686
10	0.007173	0.994859
11	0.003104	0.997962
12	0.001267	0.999230
13	0.000491	0.999721
14	0.000182	0.999903

k=26·0
Mean=4·23
Variance=4·92

n	P(n)	F(n)
0	0.019813	0.019813
1	0.072121	0.091934
2	0.136308	0.228243
3	0.178110	0.406353
4	0.180781	0.587134
5	0.151856	0.738990
6	0.109843	0.848833
7	0.070299	0.919133
8	0.040598	0.959730
9	0.021472	0.981202
10	0.010521	0.991723
11	0.004821	0.996544
12	0.002081	0.998625
13	0.000852	0.999476
14	0.000332	0.999809
15	0.000124	0.999933

k=28·0
Mean=4·56
Variance=5·30

n	P(n)	F(n)
0	0.014654	0.014654
1	0.057444	0.072098
2	0.116611	0.188709
3	0.163255	0.351964
4	0.177132	0.529095
5	0.158710	0.687806
6	0.122207	0.810012
7	0.083101	0.893113
8	0.050899	0.944012
9	0.028504	0.972516
10	0.014765	0.987280
11	0.007141	0.994421
12	0.003249	0.997670
13	0.001400	0.999070
14	0.000574	0.999644
15	0.000225	0.999869
16	0.000085	0.999953

k=30·0
Mean=4·88
Variance=5·68

n	P(n)	F(n)
0	0.010838	0.010838
1	0.045520	0.056358
2	0.098779	0.155137
3	0.147509	0.302646
4	0.170373	0.473019
5	0.162195	0.635214
6	0.132459	0.767674
7	0.095371	0.863045
8	0.061753	0.924797
9	0.036503	0.961300
10	0.019930	0.981231
11	0.010146	0.991377
12	0.004853	0.996230
13	0.002195	0.998426
14	0.000944	0.999369
15	0.000388	0.999757
16	0.000153	0.999910

k=32·0
Mean=5·21
Variance=6·06

n	P(n)	F(n)
0	0.008016	0.008016
1	0.035911	0.043927
2	0.082955	0.126882
3	0.131621	0.258503
4	0.161236	0.419739
5	0.162526	0.582265
6	0.140314	0.722579
7	0.106639	0.829218
8	0.072781	0.901999
9	0.045286	0.947284
10	0.025994	0.973279
11	0.013895	0.987174
12	0.006971	0.994144
13	0.003303	0.997447
14	0.001486	0.998934
15	0.000638	0.999572
16	0.000262	0.999834
17	0.000104	0.999938

k=34·0
Mean=5·53
Variance=6·44

n	P(n)	F(n)
0	0.005929	0.005929
1	0.028220	0.034148
2	0.069139	0.103287
3	0.116153	0.219440
4	0.150418	0.369858

n	P(n)	F(n)
5	0.160045	0.529902
6	0.145641	0.675543
7	0.116512	0.792055
8	0.083598	0.875653
9	0.054617	0.930270
10	0.032880	0.963150
11	0.018413	0.981562
12	0.009667	0.991229
13	0.004789	0.996017
14	0.002251	0.998268
15	0.001008	0.999276
16	0.000432	0.999709
17	0.000178	0.999887
18	0.000071	0.999957

k=36·0
Mean=5·86
Variance=6·81

n	P(n)	F(n)
0	0.004385	0.004385
1	0.022099	0.026484
2	0.057237	0.083721
3	0.101500	0.185220
4	0.138547	0.323767
5	0.155173	0.478940
6	0.148449	0.627389
7	0.124697	0.752086
8	0.093834	0.845920
9	0.064224	0.910145
10	0.040461	0.950606
11	0.023688	0.974294
12	0.012989	0.987283
13	0.006714	0.993998
14	0.003290	0.997288
15	0.001535	0.998823
16	0.000685	0.999508
17	0.000293	0.999802
18	0.000121	0.999923

k=38·0
Mean=6·19
Variance=7·19

n	P(n)	F(n)
0	0.003243	0.003243
1	0.017253	0.020495
2	0.047099	0.067595
3	0.087919	0.155514
4	0.126164	0.281677
5	0.148368	0.430046
6	0.148863	0.578909
7	0.130999	0.709908
8	0.103162	0.813070
9	0.073818	0.886888
10	0.048572	0.935461
11	0.029673	0.965134
12	0.016963	0.982097
13	0.009134	0.991231
14	0.004658	0.995890

n	P(n)	F(n)
15	0.002261	0.998151
16	0.001048	0.999199
17	0.000466	0.999665
18	0.000199	0.999865
19	0.000082	0.999947

k=40·0
Mean=6·51
Variance=7·57

n	P(n)	F(n)
0	0.002398	0.002398
1	0.013432	0.015830
2	0.038549	0.054379
3	0.075555	0.129934
4	0.113710	0.243644
5	0.140091	0.383736
6	0.147096	0.530831
7	0.135328	0.666160
8	0.111307	0.777467
9	0.083110	0.860577
10	0.057013	0.917590
11	0.036281	0.953871
12	0.021587	0.975458
13	0.012089	0.987547
14	0.006407	0.993954
15	0.003229	0.997183
16	0.001554	0.998737
17	0.000717	0.999454
18	0.000318	0.999772
19	0.000136	0.999908

k=42·0
Mean=6·84
Variance=7·95

n	P(n)	F(n)
0	0.001774	0.001774
1	0.010431	0.012205
2	0.031396	0.043601
3	0.064467	0.108068
4	0.101536	0.209604
5	0.130778	0.340382
6	0.143420	0.483802
7	0.137683	0.621485
8	0.118063	0.739548
9	0.091827	0.831375
10	0.065564	0.896939
11	0.043392	0.940331
12	0.026831	0.967162
13	0.015603	0.982765
14	0.008582	0.991346
15	0.004485	0.995832
16	0.002237	0.998069
17	0.001069	0.999137
18	0.000490	0.999628
19	0.000217	0.999844
20	0.000093	0.999937

k=44·0
Mean=7·16
Variance=8·33

n	P(n)	F(n)
0	0.001312	0.001312
1	0.008082	0.009394
2	0.025458	0.034852
3	0.054650	0.089502
4	0.089899	0.179400
5	0.120824	0.300224
6	0.138142	0.438366
7	0.138142	0.576508
8	0.123292	0.699800
9	0.099729	0.799529
10	0.073999	0.873528
11	0.050858	0.924386
12	0.032634	0.957020
13	0.019681	0.976700
14	0.011218	0.987918
15	0.006073	0.993991
16	0.003135	0.997126
17	0.001549	0.998675
18	0.000735	0.999410
19	0.000336	0.999746
20	0.000148	0.999894
21	0.000063	0.999957

k=46·0
Mean=7·49
Variance=8·71

n	P(n)	F(n)
0	0.000970	0.000970
1	0.006249	0.007219
2	0.020559	0.027779
3	0.046053	0.073832
4	0.078981	0.152813
5	0.110573	0.263386
6	0.131582	0.394969
7	0.136846	0.531814
8	0.126924	0.658739
9	0.106616	0.765355
10	0.082095	0.847450
11	0.058511	0.905961
12	0.038910	0.944871
13	0.024304	0.969174
14	0.014339	0.983514
15	0.008030	0.991544
16	0.004286	0.995830
17	0.002188	0.998018
18	0.001072	0.999090
19	0.000506	0.999596
20	0.000230	0.999826
21	0.000101	0.999927

k = 48·0
Mean = 7·81
Variance = 9·09

n	P(n)	F(n)
0	0.000718	0.000718
1	0.004823	0.005540
2	0.016542	0.022082
3	0.038598	0.060681
4	0.068898	0.129578
5	0.100315	0.229893
6	0.124056	0.353949
7	0.133981	0.487930
8	0.128956	0.616886
9	0.112335	0.729221
10	0.089644	0.818865
11	0.066173	0.885038
12	0.045549	0.930587
13	0.029432	0.960019
14	0.017953	0.977973
15	0.010389	0.988362
16	0.005727	0.994089
17	0.003018	0.997107
18	0.001526	0.998633
19	0.000742	0.999375
20	0.000348	0.999723
21	0.000158	0.999881
22	0.000069	0.999950

k = 50·0
Mean = 8·14
Variance = 9·46

n	P(n)	F(n)
0	0.000531	0.000531
1	0.003716	0.004246
2	0.013264	0.017511
3	0.032188	0.049699
4	0.059709	0.109409
5	0.090281	0.199689
6	0.115860	0.315549
7	0.129763	0.445313
8	0.129439	0.574752
9	0.116783	0.691534
10	0.096463	0.787997
11	0.073662	0.861659
12	0.052423	0.914082
13	0.035002	0.949085
14	0.022052	0.971136
15	0.013172	0.984308
16	0.007492	0.991800
17	0.004072	0.995872
18	0.002122	0.997994
19	0.001063	0.999057
20	0.000514	0.999571
21	0.000240	0.999810
22	0.000108	0.999918

k = 0·5
Mean = 0·07
Variance = 0·08

n	P(n)	F(n)
0	0.938083	0.938083
1	0.056285	0.994368
2	0.005066	0.999434
3	0.000507	0.999940

k = 1·0
Mean = 0·14
Variance = 0·15

n	P(n)	F(n)
0	0.880000	0.880000
1	0.105600	0.985600
2	0.012672	0.998272
3	0.001521	0.999793
4	0.000182	0.999975

k = 1·5
Mean = 0·20
Variance = 0·23

n	P(n)	F(n)
0	0.825513	0.825513
1	0.148592	0.974106
2	0.022289	0.996394
3	0.003120	0.999515
4	0.000421	0.999936

k = 2·0
Mean = 0·27
Variance = 0·31

n	P(n)	F(n)
0	0.774400	0.774400
1	0.185856	0.960256
2	0.033454	0.993710
3	0.005353	0.999063
4	0.000803	0.999866
5	0.000116	0.999981

k = 2·5
Mean = 0·34
Variance = 0·39

n	P(n)	F(n)
0	0.726452	0.726452
1	0.217935	0.944387
2	0.045766	0.990154
3	0.008238	0.998391
4	0.001359	0.999751
5	0.000212	0.999963

k = 3·0
Mean = 0·41
Variance = 0·46

n	P(n)	F(n)
0	0.681472	0.681472
1	0.245330	0.926802
2	0.058879	0.985681
3	0.011776	0.997457
4	0.002120	0.999577
5	0.000356	0.999933

k = 3·5
Mean = 0·48
Variance = 0·54

n	P(n)	F(n)
0	0.639277	0.639277
1	0.268497	0.907774
2	0.072494	0.980268
3	0.015949	0.996217
4	0.003110	0.999327
5	0.000560	0.999886
6	0.000095	0.999982

k=4·0
Mean=0·55
Variance=0·62

n	P(n)	F(n)
0	0.599695	0.599695
1	0.287854	0.887549
2	0.086356	0.973905
3	0.020725	0.994631
4	0.004352	0.998983
5	0.000836	0.999819
6	0.000150	0.999969

k=6·0
Mean=0·82
Variance=0·93

n	P(n)	F(n)
0	0.464404	0.464404
1	0.334371	0.798775
2	0.140436	0.939211
3	0.044939	0.984150
4	0.012134	0.996284
5	0.002912	0.999196
6	0.000641	0.999837
7	0.000132	0.999968

k=8·0
Mean=1·09
Variance=1·24

n	P(n)	F(n)
0	0.359635	0.359635
1	0.345249	0.704884
2	0.186435	0.891318
3	0.074574	0.965892
4	0.024609	0.990501
5	0.007087	0.997589
6	0.001843	0.999432
7	0.000442	0.999874
8	0.000100	0.999973

k=4·5
Mean=0·61
Variance=0·70

n	P(n)	F(n)
0	0.562564	0.562564
1	0.303785	0.866349
2	0.100249	0.966598
3	0.026065	0.992662
4	0.005865	0.998527
5	0.001196	0.999723
6	0.000227	0.999951

k=6·5
Mean=0·89
Variance=1·01

n	P(n)	F(n)
0	0.435650	0.435650
1	0.339807	0.775456
2	0.152913	0.928369
3	0.051990	0.980360
4	0.014817	0.995177
5	0.003734	0.998911
6	0.000859	0.999770
7	0.000184	0.999954

k=8·5
Mean=1·16
Variance=1·32

n	P(n)	F(n)
0	0.337367	0.337367
1	0.344114	0.681482
2	0.196145	0.877627
3	0.082381	0.960008
4	0.028421	0.988429
5	0.008526	0.996956
6	0.002302	0.999258
7	0.000572	0.999830
8	0.000133	0.999963

k=5·0
Mean=0·68
Variance=0·77

n	P(n)	F(n)
0	0.527732	0.527732
1	0.316639	0.844371
2	0.113990	0.958361
3	0.031917	0.990278
4	0.007660	0.997939
5	0.001655	0.999593
6	0.000331	0.999924

k=7·0
Mean=0·95
Variance=1·08

n	P(n)	F(n)
0	0.408676	0.408676
1	0.343288	0.751963
2	0.164778	0.916741
3	0.059320	0.976061
4	0.017796	0.993857
5	0.004698	0.998555
6	0.001128	0.999683
7	0.000251	0.999934

k=9·0
Mean=1·23
Variance=1·39

n	P(n)	F(n)
0	0.316478	0.316478
1	0.341797	0.658275
2	0.205078	0.863353
3	0.090234	0.953587
4	0.032484	0.986072
5	0.010135	0.996207
6	0.002838	0.999045
7	0.000730	0.999774
8	0.000175	0.999950

k=5·5
Mean=0·75
Variance=0·85

n	P(n)	F(n)
0	0.495056	0.495056
1	0.326737	0.821794
2	0.127428	0.949221
3	0.038228	0.987449
4	0.009748	0.997198
5	0.002223	0.999420
6	0.000467	0.999887
7	0.000092	0.999979

k=7·5
Mean=1·02
Variance=1·16

n	P(n)	F(n)
0	0.383372	0.383372
1	0.345035	0.728406
2	0.175968	0.904374
3	0.066868	0.971242
4	0.021063	0.992305
5	0.005813	0.998118
6	0.001453	0.999572
7	0.000336	0.999908

k=9·5
Mean=1·30
Variance=1·47

n	P(n)	F(n)
0	0.296883	0.296883
1	0.338447	0.635330
2	0.213221	0.848551
3	0.098082	0.946633
4	0.036781	0.983414
5	0.011917	0.995331
6	0.003456	0.998786
7	0.000918	0.999705
8	0.000227	0.999932

k = 10·0
Mean = 1·36
Variance = 1·55

n	P(n)	F(n)
0	0.278501	0.278501
1	0.334201	0.612702
2	0.220573	0.833275
3	0.105875	0.939150
4	0.041291	0.980441
5	0.013874	0.994315
6	0.004162	0.998477
7	0.001142	0.999619
8	0.000291	0.999910

k = 12·0
Mean = 1·64
Variance = 1·86

n	P(n)	F(n)
0	0.215671	0.215671
1	0.910566	0.526238
2	0.242242	0.768479
3	0.135655	0.904135
4	0.061045	0.965180
5	0.023441	0.988621
6	0.007970	0.996591
7	0.002459	0.999050
8	0.000701	0.999751
9	0.000187	0.999938

k = 14·0
Mean = 1·91
Variance = 2·17

n	P(n)	F(n)
0	0.167016	0.167016
1	0.280586	0.447602
2	0.252528	0.700130
3	0.161618	0.861748
4	0.082425	0.944173
5	0.035608	0.979780
6	0.013531	0.993311
7	0.004639	0.997951
8	0.001461	0.999412
9	0.000429	0.999841
10	0.000118	0.999959

k = 16·0
Mean = 2·18
Variance = 2·48

n	P(n)	F(n)
0	0.129337	0.129337
1	0.248327	0.377664
2	0.253294	0.630958
3	0.182371	0.813329
4	0.103952	0.917281
5	0.049897	0.967177
6	0.020957	0.988134
7	0.007904	0.996038
8	0.002727	0.998764
9	0.000873	0.999637
10	0.000262	0.999899
11	0.000074	0.999973

k = 18·0
Mean = 2·45
Variance = 2·79

n	P(n)	F(n)
0	0.100159	0.100159
1	0.216342	0.316501
2	0.246630	0.563132
3	0.197304	0.760436
4	0.124302	0.884738
5	0.065631	0.950369
6	0.030190	0.980559
7	0.012421	0.992981
8	0.004658	0.997639
9	0.001615	0.999253
10	0.000523	0.999776
11	0.000160	0.999936

k = 20·0
Mean = 2·73
Variance = 3·10

n	P(n)	F(n)
0	0.077563	0.077563
1	0.186151	0.263713
2	0.234550	0.498263
3	0.206404	0.704667
4	0.142419	0.847086
5	0.082033	0.929119
6	0.041017	0.970136
7	0.018282	0.988417
8	0.007404	0.995821
9	0.002764	0.998586
10	0.000962	0.999548
11	0.000315	0.999862
12	0.000098	0.999960

k = 22·0
Mean = 3·00
Variance = 3·41

n	P(n)	F(n)
0	0.060065	0.060065
1	0.158571	0.218635
2	0.218827	0.437463
3	0.210074	0.647537
4	0.157556	0.805093

k = 24·0
Mean = 3·27
Variance = 3·72

n	P(n)	F(n)
0	0.046514	0.046514
1	0.133960	0.180475
2	0.200941	0.381415
3	0.208978	0.590393
4	0.169272	0.759666
5	0.113751	0.873417
6	0.065976	0.939393
7	0.033930	0.973323
8	0.015778	0.989101
9	0.006732	0.995832
10	0.002666	0.998498
11	0.000989	0.999487
12	0.000346	0.999833
13	0.000115	0.999948

k = 26·0
Mean = 3·55
Variance = 4·03

n	P(n)	F(n)
0	0.036020	0.036020
1	0.112384	0.148404
2	0.182062	0.330466
3	0.203909	0.534376
4	0.177401	0.711777
5	0.127729	0.839506
6	0.079192	0.918697
7	0.043442	0.962140
8	0.021504	0.983644
9	0.009748	0.993392
10	0.004094	0.997487
11	0.001608	0.999095
12	0.000595	0.999690
13	0.000209	0.999898
14	0.000070	0.999968

k = 28·0
Mean = 3·82
Variance = 4·34

n	P(n)	F(n)
0	0.027894	0.027894
1	0.093725	0.121619
2	0.163081	0.284700
3	0.195697	0.480397
4	0.181998	0.662396

5	0.139775	0.802170
6	0.092251	0.894422
7	0.053769	0.948191
8	0.028229	0.976420
9	0.013550	0.989970
10	0.006016	0.995986
11	0.002494	0.998480
12	0.000973	0.999453
13	0.000359	0.999812
14	0.000126	0.999938

k = 30·0
Mean = 4·09
Variance = 4·65

n	P(n)	F(n)
0	0.021601	0.021601
1	0.077765	0.099366
2	0.144642	0.244008
3	0.185142	0.429151
4	0.183291	0.612442
5	0.149565	0.762007
6	0.104696	0.866703
7	0.064612	0.931315
8	0.035860	0.967175
9	0.018169	0.985344
10	0.008503	0.993847
11	0.003710	0.997557
12	0.001521	0.999078
13	0.000590	0.999668
14	0.000217	0.999886
15	0.000077	0.999962

k = 32·0
Mean = 4·36
Variance = 4·96

n	P(n)	F(n)
0	0.016728	0.016728
1	0.064236	0.080964
2	0.127187	0.208151
3	0.172974	0.381125
4	0.181623	0.562747
5	0.156922	0.719669
6	0.116122	0.835792
7	0.075645	0.911437
8	0.044253	0.955689
9	0.023601	0.979291
10	0.011612	0.990903
11	0.005320	0.996223
12	0.002288	0.998511
13	0.000929	0.999440
14	0.000358	0.999798
15	0.000132	0.999930

k = 34·0
Mean = 4·64
Variance = 5·27

n	P(n)	F(n)
0	0.012954	0.012954
1	0.052853	0.065807
2	0.110992	0.176799
3	0.159828	0.336627
4	0.177409	0.514036
5	0.161797	0.675833
6	0.126202	0.802035
7	0.086538	0.888573
8	0.053221	0.941794
9	0.029804	0.971598
10	0.015379	0.986977
11	0.007382	0.994359
12	0.003322	0.997680
13	0.001410	0.999091
14	0.000568	0.999659
15	0.000218	0.999877
16	0.000080	0.999957

k = 36·0
Mean = 4·91
Variance = 5·58

n	P(n)	F(n)
0	0.010032	0.010032
1	0.043337	0.053369
2	0.096208	0.149577
3	0.146237	0.295814
4	0.171097	0.466911
5	0.164253	0.631164
6	0.134688	0.765852
7	0.096975	0.862827
8	0.062549	0.925376
9	0.036695	0.962071
10	0.019815	0.981886
11	0.009944	0.991830
12	0.004674	0.996504
13	0.002071	0.998574
14	0.000870	0.999444
15	0.000348	0.999792
16	0.000133	0.999925

k = 38·0
Mean = 5·18
Variance = 5·89

n	P(n)	F(n)
0	0.007769	0.007769
1	0.035425	0.043193
2	0.082894	0.126087
3	0.132630	0.258717
4	0.163135	0.421852

5	0.164440	0.586292
6	0.141419	0.727711
7	0.106670	0.834381
8	0.072002	0.906383
9	0.044161	0.950545
10	0.024907	0.975452
11	0.013042	0.988494
12	0.006391	0.994885
13	0.002950	0.997834
14	0.001289	0.999123
15	0.000536	0.999660
16	0.000213	0.999873
17	0.000081	0.999954

k = 40·0
Mean = 5·45
Variance = 6·20

n	P(n)	F(n)
0	0.006016	0.006016
1	0.028877	0.034893
2	0.071037	0.105929
3	0.119342	0.225271
4	0.153951	0.379222
5	0.162572	0.541794
6	0.146315	0.688109
7	0.115380	0.803489
8	0.081343	0.884832
9	0.052059	0.936891
10	0.030611	0.967502
11	0.016697	0.984199
12	0.008515	0.992714
13	0.004087	0.996802
14	0.001857	0.998658
15	0.000802	0.999461
16	0.000331	0.999792
17	0.000131	0.999922

k = 42·0
Mean = 5·73
Variance = 6·51

n	P(n)	F(n)
0	0.004659	0.004659
1	0.023480	0.028139
2	0.060579	0.088718
3	0.106619	0.195337
4	0.143936	0.339273
5	0.158905	0.498178
6	0.149371	0.647549
7	0.122911	0.770460
8	0.090339	0.860799
9	0.060226	0.921026
10	0.036859	0.957884
11	0.020909	0.978793
12	0.011082	0.989875
13	0.005524	0.995399
14	0.002604	0.998003

15	0.001167	0.999169
16	0.000499	0.999668
17	0.000204	0.999872
18	0.000080	0.999952

k = 44·0
Mean = 6·00
Variance = 6·82

n	P(n)	F(n)
0	0.003608	0.003608
1	0.019049	0.022657
2	0.051432	0.074089
3	0.094635	0.168724
4	0.133436	0.302160
5	0.153718	0.455878
6	0.150644	0.606522
7	0.129123	0.735645
8	0.098779	0.834424
9	0.068487	0.902911
10	0.043558	0.946468
11	0.025659	0.972128
12	0.014113	0.986241
13	0.007295	0.993536
14	0.003564	0.997100
15	0.001654	0.998754
16	0.000732	0.999485
17	0.000310	0.999795
18	0.000126	0.999921

k = 46·0
Mean = 6·27
Variance = 7·13

n	P(n)	F(n)
0	0.002794	0.002794
1	0.015422	0.018216
2	0.043490	0.061706
3	0.083501	0.145207
4	0.122747	0.267954
5	0.147296	0.415250
6	0.150242	0.565492
7	0.133930	0.699422
8	0.106474	0.805896
9	0.076661	0.882557
10	0.050597	0.933154
11	0.030910	0.964064
12	0.017619	0.981683
13	0.009433	0.991115
14	0.004770	0.995886
15	0.002290	0.998175
16	0.001048	0.999223
17	0.000458	0.999681
18	0.000193	0.999874
19	0.000078	0.999952

k = 48·0
Mean = 6·55
Variance = 7·44

n	P(n)	F(n)
0	0.002164	0.002164
1	0.012462	0.014626
2	0.036639	0.051264
3	0.073277	0.124541
4	0.112114	0.236655
5	0.139918	0.376573
6	0.148313	0.524887
7	0.137296	0.662182
8	0.113269	0.775451
9	0.084574	0.860025
10	0.057849	0.917874
11	0.036602	0.954477
12	0.021595	0.976072
13	0.011961	0.988033
14	0.006254	0.994286
15	0.003102	0.997388
16	0.001466	0.998854
17	0.000662	0.999516
18	0.000287	0.999803
19	0.000120	0.999922

k = 50·0
Mean = 6·82
Variance = 7·75

n	P(n)	F(n)
0	0.001675	0.001675
1	0.010053	0.011728
2	0.030761	0.042490
3	0.063984	0.106473
4	0.101734	0.208207
5	0.131847	0.340055
6	0.145032	0.485087
7	0.139231	0.624318
8	0.119042	0.743360
9	0.092059	0.835420
10	0.065178	0.900598
11	0.042662	0.943260
12	0.026024	0.969284
13	0.014894	0.984178
14	0.008043	0.992220
15	0.004118	0.996338
16	0.002007	0.998345
17	0.000935	0.999281
18	0.000418	0.999698
19	0.000179	0.999878
20	0.000074	0.999952

k = 0·5
Mean = 0·06
Variance = 0·06

n	P(n)	F(n)
0	0·948683	0·948683
1	0·047434	0·996117
2	0·003558	0·999675
3	0·000296	0·999971

k = 1·0
Mean = 0·11
Variance = 0·12

n	P(n)	F(n)
0	0·900000	0·900000
1	0·090000	0·990000
2	0·009000	0·999000
3	0·000900	0·999900
4	0·000090	0·999990

k = 1·5
Mean = 0·17
Variance = 0·19

n	P(n)	F(n)
0	0·853815	0·853815
1	0·128072	0·981887
2	0·016009	0·997896
3	0·001868	0·999764
4	0·000210	0·999974

k = 2·0
Mean = 0·22
Variance = 0·25

n	P(n)	F(n)
0	0·810000	0·810000
1	0·162000	0·972000
2	0·024300	0·996300
3	0·003240	0·999540
4	0·000405	0·999945

k = 2·5
Mean = 0·28
Variance = 0·31

n	P(n)	F(n)
0	0·768433	0·768433
1	0·192108	0·960542
2	0·033619	0·994161
3	0·005043	0·999204
4	0·000693	0·999897
5	0·000090	0·999987

k = 3·0
Mean = 0·33
Variance = 0·37

n	P(n)	F(n)
0	0·729000	0·729000
1	0·218700	0·947700
2	0·043740	0·991440
3	0·007290	0·998730
4	0·001094	0·999823
5	0·000153	0·999977

k = 3·5
Mean = 0·39
Variance = 0·43

n	P(n)	F(n)
0	0·691590	0·691590
1	0·242057	0·933647
2	0·054463	0·988109
3	0·009985	0·998094
4	0·001623	0·999717
5	0·000243	0·999960

k = 4·0
Mean = 0·44
Variance = 0·49

n	P(n)	F(n)
0	0·656100	0·656100
1	0·262440	0·918540
2	0·065610	0·984150
3	0·013122	0·997272
4	0·002296	0·999568
5	0·000367	0·999936

k = 4·5
Mean = 0·50
Variance = 0·56

n	P(n)	F(n)
0	0·622431	0·622431
1	0·280094	0·902525
2	0·077026	0·979551
3	0·016689	0·996240
4	0·003129	0·999369
5	0·000532	0·999901

k = 5·0
Mean = 0·56
Variance = 0·62

n	P(n)	F(n)
0	0·590490	0·590490
1	0·295245	0·885735
2	0·088574	0·974308
3	0·020667	0·994976
4	0·004133	0·999109
5	0·000744	0·999853
6	0·000124	0·999977

k = 5·5
Mean = 0·61
Variance = 0·68

n	P(n)	F(n)
0	0·560188	0·560188
1	0·308103	0·868291
2	0·100134	0·968425
3	0·025033	0·993458
4	0·005320	0·998778
5	0·001011	0·999789
6	0·000177	0·999966

k = 6·0
Mean = 0·67
Variance = 0·74

n	P(n)	F(n)
0	0·531441	0·531441
1	0·318865	0·850306
2	0·111603	0·961908
3	0·029761	0·991669
4	0·006696	0·998365
5	0·001339	0·999704
6	0·000246	0·999950

k = 6·5
Mean = 0·72
Variance = 0·80

n	P(n)	F(n)
0	0·504169	0·504169
1	0·327710	0·831879
2	0·122891	0·954770
3	0·034819	0·989590
4	0·008270	0·997859
5	0·001737	0·999596
6	0·000333	0·999929

k = 7·0
Mean = 0·78
Variance = 0·86

n	P(n)	F(n)
0	0.478297	0.478297
1	0.334808	0.813105
2	0.133923	0.947028
3	0.040177	0.987205
4	0.010044	0.997249
5	0.002210	0.999459
6	0.000442	0.999901

k = 7·5
Mean = 0·83
Variance = 0·93

n	P(n)	F(n)
0	0.453752	0.453752
1	0.340314	0.794066
2	0.144634	0.938700
3	0.045801	0.984501
4	0.012023	0.996523
5	0.002765	0.999289
6	0.000576	0.999865
7	0.000111	0.999976

k = 8·0
Mean = 0·89
Variance = 0·99

n	P(n)	F(n)
0	0.430467	0.430467
1	0.344374	0.774841
2	0.154968	0.929809
3	0.051656	0.981465
4	0.014205	0.995671
5	0.003409	0.999080
6	0.000739	0.999819
7	0.000148	0.999966

k = 8·5
Mean = 0·94
Variance = 1·05

n	P(n)	F(n)
0	0.408377	0.408377
1	0.347120	0.755498
2	0.164882	0.920380
3	0.057709	0.978089
4	0.016591	0.994680
5	0.004148	0.998828
6	0.000933	0.999761
7	0.000193	0.999954

k = 9·0
Mean = 1·00
Variance = 1·11

n	P(n)	F(n)
0	0.387420	0.387420
1	0.348678	0.736099
2	0.174339	0.910438
3	0.063924	0.974363
4	0.019177	0.993540
5	0.004986	0.998526
6	0.001163	0.999689
7	0.000249	0.999939

k = 9·5
Mean = 1·06
Variance = 1·17

n	P(n)	F(n)
0	0.367539	0.367539
1	0.349162	0.716702
2	0.183310	0.900012
3	0.070269	0.970281
4	0.021959	0.992240
5	0.005929	0.998169
6	0.001433	0.999602
7	0.000317	0.999919

k = 10·0
Mean = 1·11
Variance = 1·23

n	P(n)	F(n)
0	0.348678	0.348678
1	0.348678	0.697357
2	0.191773	0.889130
3	0.076709	0.965839
4	0.024931	0.990770
5	0.006981	0.997750
6	0.001745	0.999495
7	0.000399	0.999894
8	0.000085	0.999979

k = 12·0
Mean = 1·33
Variance = 1·48

n	P(n)	F(n)
0	0.282430	0.282430
1	0.338915	0.621345
2	0.220295	0.841640
3	0.102804	0.944444
4	0.038552	0.982996
5	0.012337	0.995333
6	0.003495	0.998828
7	0.000899	0.999727
8	0.000213	0.999940

k = 14·0
Mean = 1·56
Variance = 1·73

n	P(n)	F(n)
0	0.228768	0.228768
1	0.320275	0.549043
2	0.240206	0.789249
3	0.128110	0.917359
4	0.054447	0.971806
5	0.019601	0.991407
6	0.006207	0.997614
7	0.001773	0.999387
8	0.000466	0.999853
9	0.000114	0.999967

k = 16·0
Mean = 1·78
Variance = 1·98

n	P(n)	F(n)
0	0.185302	0.185302
1	0.296483	0.481785
2	0.252011	0.733796
3	0.151206	0.885002
4	0.071823	0.956826
5	0.028729	0.985555
6	0.010055	0.995610
7	0.003160	0.998770
8	0.000909	0.999679
9	0.000242	0.999921

k = 18·0
Mean = 2·00
Variance = 2·22

n	P(n)	F(n)
0	0.150095	0.150095
1	0.270170	0.420265
2	0.256662	0.676927
3	0.171108	0.848035
4	0.089832	0.937866
5	0.039526	0.977392
6	0.015152	0.992544
7	0.005195	0.997739
8	0.001623	0.999362
9	0.000469	0.999831
10	0.000127	0.999958

k = 20·0
Mean = 2·22
Variance = 2·47

n	P(n)	F(n)
0	0.121577	0.121577
1	0.243153	0.364730
2	0.255311	0.620041
3	0.187228	0.807269
4	0.107656	0.914925

n	P(n)	F(n)
5	0.051675	0.966600
6	0.021531	0.988131
7	0.007997	0.996129
8	0.002699	0.998828
9	0.000840	0.999667
10	0.000244	0.999911

n	P(n)	F(n)
5	0.092074	0.916579
6	0.047572	0.964151
7	0.021747	0.985898
8	0.008971	0.994869
9	0.003389	0.998258
10	0.001186	0.999444
11	0.000388	0.999832
12	0.000120	0.999952

n	P(n)	F(n)
5	0.129447	0.840220
6	0.079826	0.920045
7	0.043334	0.963379
8	0.021125	0.984505
9	0.009389	0.993894
10	0.003850	0.997743
11	0.001470	0.999213
12	0.000527	0.999740
13	0.000178	0.999918

k=22.0
Mean=2.44
Variance=2.72

n	P(n)	F(n)
0	0.098477	0.098477
1	0.216650	0.315127
2	0.249147	0.564274
3	0.199318	0.763591
4	0.124574	0.888165
5	0.064778	0.952943
6	0.029150	0.982093
7	0.011660	0.993753
8	0.004227	0.997980
9	0.001409	0.999389
10	0.000437	0.999826
11	0.000127	0.999953

k=28.0
Mean=3.11
Variance=3.46

n	P(n)	F(n)
0	0.052335	0.052335
1	0.146537	0.198872
2	0.212479	0.411351
3	0.212479	0.623830
4	0.164671	0.788502
5	0.105390	0.893891
6	0.057964	0.951856
7	0.028154	0.980010
8	0.012317	0.992327
9	0.004927	0.997254
10	0.001823	0.999077
11	0.000630	0.999707
12	0.000205	0.999912

k=34.0
Mean=3.78
Variance=4.20

n	P(n)	F(n)
0	0.027813	0.027813
1	0.094564	0.122376
2	0.165486	0.287863
3	0.198584	0.486447
4	0.183690	0.670136
5	0.139604	0.809741
6	0.090743	0.900484
7	0.051853	0.952337
8	0.026575	0.978911
9	0.012402	0.991313
10	0.005333	0.996645
11	0.002133	0.998779
12	0.000800	0.999578
13	0.000283	0.999861
14	0.000095	0.999956

k=24.0
Mean=2.67
Variance=2.96

n	P(n)	F(n)
0	0.079766	0.079766
1	0.191439	0.271206
2	0.239299	0.510505
3	0.207393	0.717898
4	0.139990	0.857888
5	0.078394	0.936283
6	0.037891	0.974173
7	0.016239	0.990412
8	0.006293	0.996705
9	0.002237	0.998942
10	0.000738	0.999680
11	0.000228	0.999909

k=30.0
Mean=3.33
Variance=3.70

n	P(n)	F(n)
0	0.042391	0.042391
1	0.127173	0.169565
2	0.197119	0.366684
3	0.210260	0.576944
4	0.173465	0.750408
5	0.117956	0.868364
6	0.068808	0.937172
7	0.035387	0.972559
8	0.016366	0.988925
9	0.006910	0.995835
10	0.002695	0.998530
11	0.000980	0.999510
12	0.000335	0.999845
13	0.000108	0.999953

k=36.0
Mean=4.00
Variance=4.44

n	P(n)	F(n)
0	0.022528	0.022528
1	0.081102	0.103631
2	0.150039	0.253670
3	0.190050	0.443719
4	0.185298	0.629018
5	0.148239	0.777256
6	0.101296	0.878553
7	0.060778	0.939331
8	0.032668	0.971999
9	0.015971	0.987970
10	0.007187	0.995157
11	0.003005	0.998162
12	0.001177	0.999339
13	0.000435	0.999774
14	0.000152	0.999926

k=26.0
Mean=2.89
Variance=3.21

n	P(n)	F(n)
0	0.064611	0.064611
1	0.167988	0.232599
2	0.226784	0.459383
3	0.211665	0.671048
4	0.153457	0.824505

k=32.0
Mean=3.56
Variance=3.95

n	P(n)	F(n)
0	0.034337	0.034337
1	0.109878	0.144215
2	0.181299	0.325513
3	0.205472	0.530985
4	0.179788	0.710773

k=38.0
Mean=4.22
Variance=4.69

n	P(n)	F(n)
0	0.018248	0.018248
1	0.069342	0.087590
2	0.135218	0.222808
3	0.180290	0.403098
4	0.184798	0.587896

5	0.155230	0.743126
6	0.111248	0.854374
7	0.069927	0.924301
8	0.039334	0.963636
9	0.020104	0.983740
10	0.009449	0.993189
11	0.004123	0.997312
12	0.001684	0.998995
13	0.000648	0.999643
14	0.000236	0.999879
15	0.000082	0.999961

k = 40.0
Mean = 4.44
Variance = 4.94

n	P(n)	F(n)
0	0.014781	0.014781
1	0.059124	0.073904
2	0.121203	0.195108
3	0.169685	0.364792
4	0.182411	0.547203
5	0.160522	0.707725
6	0.120391	0.828116
7	0.079114	0.907230
8	0.046480	0.953710
9	0.024789	0.978499
10	0.012147	0.990645
11	0.005521	0.996167
12	0.002347	0.998513
13	0.000939	0.999452
14	0.000355	0.999807
15	0.000128	0.999935

k = 42.0
Mean = 4.67
Variance = 5.19

n	P(n)	F(n)
0	0.011973	0.011973
1	0.050285	0.062257
2	0.108112	0.170369
3	0.158564	0.328933
4	0.178384	0.507317
5	0.164114	0.671431
6	0.128556	0.799987
7	0.088153	0.888139
8	0.053993	0.942133
9	0.029996	0.972129
10	0.015298	0.987427
11	0.007232	0.994659
12	0.003194	0.997853
13	0.001327	0.999180
14	0.000521	0.999701

15	0.000195	0.999896
16	0.000069	0.999965

k = 44.0
Mean = 4.89
Variance = 5.43

n	P(n)	F(n)
0	0.009698	0.009698
1	0.042670	0.052368
2	0.096008	0.148375
3	0.147212	0.295587
4	0.172974	0.468561
5	0.166055	0.634615
6	0.135611	0.770227
7	0.096865	0.867092
8	0.061752	0.928844
9	0.035679	0.964522
10	0.018910	0.983432
11	0.009283	0.992715
12	0.004255	0.996970
13	0.001833	0.998803
14	0.000746	0.999549
15	0.000289	0.999837
16	0.000106	0.999944

k = 46.0
Mean = 5.11
Variance = 5.68

n	P(n)	F(n)
0	0.007855	0.007855
1	0.036134	0.043989
2	0.084914	0.128903
3	0.135863	0.264766
4	0.166432	0.431198
5	0.166432	0.597631
6	0.141467	0.739098
7	0.105090	0.844188
8	0.069622	0.913810
9	0.041773	0.955583
10	0.022975	0.978559
11	0.011697	0.990255
12	0.005556	0.995811
13	0.002479	0.998290
14	0.001045	0.999334
15	0.000418	0.999752
16	0.000159	0.999912

k = 48.0
Mean = 5.33
Variance = 5.93

n	P(n)	F(n)
0	0.006363	0.006363
1	0.030541	0.036904
2	0.074825	0.111729
3	0.124709	0.236437
4	0.159004	0.395441
5	0.165364	0.560805
6	0.146071	0.706876
7	0.112684	0.819559
8	0.077470	0.897029
9	0.048204	0.945233
10	0.027476	0.972709
11	0.014487	0.987196
12	0.007123	0.994319
13	0.003288	0.997607
14	0.001432	0.999039
15	0.000592	0.999631
16	0.000233	0.999864
17	0.000088	0.999952

k = 50.0
Mean = 5.56
Variance = 6.17

n	P(n)	F(n)
0	0.005154	0.005154
1	0.025769	0.030923
2	0.065711	0.096633
3	0.113898	0.210532
4	0.150915	0.361447
5	0.162989	0.524436
6	0.149406	0.673842
7	0.119525	0.793367
8	0.085162	0.878529
9	0.054882	0.933411
10	0.032380	0.965791
11	0.017662	0.983453
12	0.008978	0.992431
13	0.004282	0.996713
14	0.001927	0.998640
15	0.000822	0.999462
16	0.000334	0.999796
17	0.000130	0.999926

k=2·0
Mean=0·11
Variance=0·11

n	P(n)	F(n)
0	0.902500	0.902500
1	0.090250	0.992750
2	0.006769	0.999519
3	0.000451	0.999970

k=4·0
Mean=0·21
Variance=0·22

n	P(n)	F(n)
0	0.814506	0.814506
1	0.162901	0.977407
2	0.020363	0.997770
3	0.002036	0.999806
4	0.000178	0.999985

k=6·0
Mean=0·32
Variance=0·33

n	P(n)	F(n)
0	0.735092	0.735092
1	0.220528	0.955619
2	0.038592	0.994212
3	0.005146	0.999357
4	0.000579	0.999936

k=8·0
Mean=0·42
Variance=0·44

n	P(n)	F(n)
0	0.663420	0.663420
1	0.265368	0.928789
2	0.059708	0.988496
3	0.009951	0.998448
4	0.001368	0.999816
5	0.000164	0.999980

k=10·0
Mean=0·53
Variance=0·55

n	P(n)	F(n)
0	0.598737	0.598737
1	0.299368	0.898105
2	0.082326	0.980432
3	0.016465	0.996897
4	0.002676	0.999573
5	0.000375	0.999947

k=12·0
Mean=0·63
Variance=0·66

n	P(n)	F(n)
0	0.540360	0.540360
1	0.324216	0.864576
2	0.105370	0.969946
3	0.024586	0.994533
4	0.004610	0.999143
5	0.000738	0.999880
6	0.000104	0.999985

k=14·0
Mean=0·74
Variance=0·78

n	P(n)	F(n)
0	0.487675	0.487675
1	0.341372	0.829047
2	0.128015	0.957062
3	0.034137	0.991199
4	0.007254	0.998454
5	0.001306	0.999759
6	0.000207	0.999966

k=16·0
Mean=0·84
Variance=0·89

n	P(n)	F(n)
0	0.440127	0.440127
1	0.352101	0.792228
2	0.149643	0.941871
3	0.044893	0.986764
4	0.010662	0.997426
5	0.002132	0.999558
6	0.000373	0.999932

k=18·0
Mean=0·95
Variance=1·00

n	P(n)	F(n)
0	0.397214	0.397214
1	0.357493	0.754707
2	0.169809	0.924516
3	0.056603	0.981119
4	0.014858	0.995978
5	0.003269	0.999246
6	0.000627	0.999873
7	0.000107	0.999980

k=20·0
Mean=1·05
Variance=1·11

n	P(n)	F(n)
0	0.358486	0.358486
1	0.358486	0.716972
2	0.188205	0.905177
3	0.069009	0.974185
4	0.019840	0.994025
5	0.004762	0.998787
6	0.000992	0.999779
7	0.000184	0.999963

k=22·0
Mean=1·16
Variance=1·22

n	P(n)	F(n)
0	0.323534	0.323534
1	0.355887	0.679420
2	0.204635	0.884055
3	0.081854	0.965909
4	0.025579	0.991489
5	0.006651	0.998139
6	0.001496	0.999636
7	0.000299	0.999935

k=24·0
Mean=1·26
Variance=1·33

n	P(n)	F(n)
0	0.291989	0.291989
1	0.350387	0.642376
2	0.218992	0.861368
3	0.094896	0.956264
4	0.032028	0.988292
5	0.008968	0.997259
6	0.002167	0.999427
7	0.000464	0.999891
8	0.000090	0.999981

k=26·0
Mean=1·37
Variance=1·44

n	P(n)	F(n)
0	0.263520	0.263520
1	0.342576	0.606096
2	0.231239	0.837335
3	0.107911	0.945247
4	0.039118	0.984364
5	0.011735	0.996100
6	0.003032	0.999132
7	0.000693	0.999824
8	0.000143	0.999967

k = 28·0
Mean = 1·47
Variance = 1·55

n	P(n)	F(n)
0	0.237827	0.237827
1	0.332958	0.570785
2	0.241394	0.812179
3	0.120697	0.932876
4	0.046770	0.979646
5	0.014966	0.994613
6	0.004116	0.998728
7	0.001000	0.999728
8	0.000219	0.999947

k = 30·0
Mean = 1·58
Variance = 1·66

n	P(n)	F(n)
0	0.214639	0.214639
1	0.321958	0.536597
2	0.249518	0.786114
3	0.133076	0.919191
4	0.054894	0.974084
5	0.018664	0.992748
6	0.005444	0.998192
7	0.001400	0.999592
8	0.000324	0.999915

k = 32·0
Mean = 1·68
Variance = 1·77

n	P(n)	F(n)
0	0.193711	0.193711
1	0.309938	0.503650
2	0.255699	0.759349
3	0.144896	0.904245
4	0.063392	0.967637
5	0.022821	0.990458
6	0.007037	0.997495
7	0.001910	0.999405
8	0.000466	0.999870
9	0.000103	0.999974

k = 34·0
Mean = 1·79
Variance = 1·88

n	P(n)	F(n)
0	0.174825	0.174825
1	0.297202	0.472026
2	0.260052	0.732078
3	0.156031	0.888109
4	0.072164	0.960273
5	0.027422	0.987696
6	0.008912	0.996608
7	0.002546	0.999154
8	0.000653	0.999807
9	0.000152	0.999959

k = 36·0
Mean = 1·89
Variance = 1·99

n	P(n)	F(n)
0	0.157779	0.157779
1	0.284003	0.441782
2	0.262702	0.704484
3	0.166378	0.870862
4	0.081109	0.951972
5	0.032444	0.984415
6	0.011085	0.995500
7	0.003325	0.998826
8	0.000894	0.999720
9	0.000218	0.999938

k = 38·0
Mean = 2·00
Variance = 2·11

n	P(n)	F(ṅ)
0	0.142396	0.142396
1	0.270552	0.412948
2	0.263788	0.676736
3	0.175859	0.852594
4	0.090128	0.942722
5	0.037854	0.980576
6	0.013564	0.994140
7	0.004263	0.998403
8	0.001199	0.999602
9	0.000306	0.999908

k = 40·0
Mean = 2·11
Variance = 2·22

n	P(n)	F(n)
0	0.128512	0.128512
1	0.257024	0.385536
2	0.263450	0.648986
3	0.184415	0.833401
4	0.099123	0.932524
5	0.043614	0.976138
6	0.016355	0.992494
7	0.005374	0.997868
8	0.001579	0.999446
9	0.000421	0.999867
10	0.000103	0.999970

k = 42·0
Mean = 2·21
Variance = 2·33

n	P(n)	F(n)
0	0.115982	0.115982
1	0.243563	0.359545
2	0.261830	0.621375
3	0.192009	0.813383
4	0.108005	0.921388

5	0.049682	0.971070
6	0.019459	0.990529
7	0.006672	0.997201
8	0.002043	0.999244
9	0.000568	0.999812
10	0.000145	0.999956

k = 44·0
Mean = 2·32
Variance = 2·44

n	P(n)	F(n)
0	0.104674	0.104674
1	0.230283	0.334957
2	0.259068	0.594025
3	0.198619	0.792644
4	0.116689	0.909332
5	0.056011	0.965343
6	0.022871	0.988214
7	0.008168	0.996382
8	0.002604	0.998985
9	0.000752	0.999738
10	0.000199	0.999937

k = 46·0
Mean = 2·42
Variance = 2·55

n	P(n)	F(n)
0	0.094468	0.094468
1	0.217277	0.311745
2	0.255300	0.567046
3	0.204240	0.771286
4	0.125097	0.896383
5	0.062549	0.958932
6	0.026583	0.985515
7	0.009874	0.995389
8	0.003271	0.998659
9	0.000981	0.999641
10	0.000270	0.999910

k = 48·0
Mean = 2·53
Variance = 2·66

n	P(n)	F(n)
0	0.085258	0.085258
1	0.204618	0.289876
2	0.250657	0.540533
3	0.208881	0.749414
4	0.133162	0.882576

n	P(n)	F(n)
5	0.069244	0.951820
6	0.030583	0.982403
7	0.011796	0.994199
8	0.004055	0.998254
9	0.001262	0.999516
10	0.000360	0.999875
11	0.000095	0.999970

k = 50·0
Mean = 2·63
Variance = 2·77

n	P(n)	F(n)
0	0.076945	0.076945
1	0.192362	0.269307
2	0.245262	0.514570
3	0.212560	0.727130
4	0.140821	0.867951
5	0.076044	0.943995
6	0.034853	0.978848
7	0.013941	0.992789
8	0.004967	0.997756
9	0.001600	0.999356
10	0.000472	0.999828
11	0.000129	0.999957

k = 60·0
Mean = 3·16
Variance = 3·32

n	P(n)	F(n)
0	0.046070	0.046070
1	0.138209	0.184279
2	0.210769	0.395049
3	0.217795	0.612843
4	0.171514	0.784357
5	0.109769	0.894126
6	0.059458	0.953584
7	0.028030	0.981614
8	0.011738	0.993352
9	0.004434	0.997786
10	0.001530	0.999316
11	0.000487	0.999802
12	0.000144	0.999946

k = 70·0
Mean = 3·68
Variance = 3·88

n	P(n)	F(n)
0	0.027584	0.027584
1	0.096543	0.124127
2	0.171364	0.295490
3	0.205636	0.501127
4	0.187643	0.688770

n	P(n)	F(n)
5	0.138856	0.827626
6	0.086785	0.914411
7	0.047112	0.961523
8	0.022673	0.984195
9	0.009825	0.994020
10	0.003881	0.997901
11	0.001411	0.999312
12	0.000476	0.999788
13	0.000150	0.999939

k = 80·0
Mean = 4·21
Variance = 4·43

n	P(n)	F(n)
0	0.016515	0.016515
1	0.066061	0.082577
2	0.133775	0.216351
3	0.182825	0.399177
4	0.189681	0.588858
5	0.159332	0.748190
6	0.112860	0.861050
7	0.069328	0.930379
8	0.037697	0.968076
9	0.018430	0.986506
10	0.008201	0.994707
11	0.003355	0.998062
12	0.001272	0.999334
13	0.000450	0.999784
14	0.000150	0.999934

k = 90·0
Mean = 4·74
Variance = 4·99

n	P(n)	F(n)
0	0.009888	0.009888
1	0.044498	0.054386
2	0.101232	0.155618
3	0.155223	0.310841
4	0.180446	0.491287
5	0.169620	0.660907
6	0.134282	0.795189
7	0.092079	0.887268
8	0.055823	0.943091
9	0.030393	0.973483
10	0.015044	0.988528
11	0.006838	0.995366
12	0.002878	0.998244
13	0.001129	0.999373
14	0.000415	0.999788
15	0.000144	0.999932

k = 100·0
Mean = 5·26
Variance = 5·54

n	P(n)	F(n)
0	0.005921	0.005921
1	0.029603	0.035523
2	0.074747	0.110270
3	0.127069	0.237339
4	0.163602	0.400941
5	0.170146	0.571087
6	0.148878	0.719965
7	0.112722	0.832686
8	0.075383	0.908069
9	0.045230	0.953298
10	0.024650	0.977948
11	0.012325	0.990273
12	0.005700	0.995974
13	0.002456	0.998429
14	0.000991	0.999420
15	0.000377	0.999797
16	0.000135	0.999932

k = 110·0
Mean = 5·79
Variance = 6·09

n	P(n)	F(n)
0	0.003545	0.003545
1	0.019497	0.023041
2	0.054103	0.077145
3	0.100992	0.178137
4	0.142652	0.320789
5	0.162623	0.483412
6	0.155847	0.639259
7	0.129131	0.768390
8	0.094427	0.862816
9	0.061902	0.924718
10	0.036832	0.961550
11	0.020090	0.981640
12	0.010129	0.991769
13	0.004753	0.996521
14	0.002088	0.998609
15	0.000863	0.999472
16	0.000337	0.999809
17	0.000125	0.999934

k = 120·0
Mean = 6·32
Variance = 6·65

n	P(n)	F(n)
0	0.002122	0.002122
1	0.012735	0.014857
2	0.038522	0.053379
3	0.078328	0.131707
4	0.120430	0.252137

n	P(n)	F(n)
5	0.149333	0.401469
6	0.155555	0.557024
7	0.139999	0.697023
8	0.111124	0.808148
9	0.079022	0.887170
10	0.050969	0.938139
11	0.030118	0.968257
12	0.016439	0.984696
13	0.008346	0.993043
14	0.003964	0.997007
15	0.001771	0.998778
16	0.000747	0.999525
17	0.000299	0.999824
18	0.000114	0.999937

k = 130.0
Mean = 6.84
Variance = 7.20

n	P(n)	F(n)
0	0.001271	0.001271
1	0.008260	0.009531
2	0.027052	0.036582
3	0.059514	0.096096
4	0.098941	0.195037
5	0.132581	0.327619
6	0.149154	0.476773
7	0.144892	0.621665
8	0.124064	0.745729
9	0.095116	0.840845
10	0.066106	0.906951
11	0.042067	0.949018
12	0.024714	0.973732
13	0.013498	0.987230
14	0.006894	0.994124
15	0.003309	0.997433
16	0.001499	0.998932
17	0.000644	0.999576
18	0.000263	0.999839
19	0.000102	0.999941

k = 140.0
Mean = 7.37
Variance = 7.76

n	P(n)	F(n)
0	0.000761	0.000761
1	0.005326	0.006087
2	0.018774	0.024861
3	0.044432	0.069293
4	0.079423	0.148716
5	0.114369	0.263085
6	0.138196	0.401281
7	0.144118	0.545399
8	0.132409	0.677808
9	0.108869	0.786677
10	0.081108	0.867785
11	0.055301	0.923085
12	0.034793	0.957879
13	0.020341	0.978219
14	0.011115	0.989334

n	P(n)	F(n)
15	0.005706	0.995040
16	0.002764	0.997803
17	0.001268	0.999071
18	0.000553	0.999624
19	0.000230	0.999854
20	0.000091	0.999946

k = 150.0
Mean = 7.89
Variance = 8.31

n	P(n)	F(n)
0	0.000456	0.000456
1	0.003417	0.003872
2	0.012898	0.016770
3	0.032675	0.049445
4	0.062490	0.111935
5	0.096235	0.208170
6	0.124304	0.332474
7	0.138510	0.470984
8	0.135913	0.606896
9	0.119301	0.726198
10	0.094844	0.821042
11	0.068978	0.890020
12	0.046273	0.936292
13	0.028831	0.965124
14	0.016784	0.981908
15	0.009175	0.991083
16	0.004731	0.995814
17	0.002310	0.998124
18	0.001072	0.999195
19	0.000474	0.999669
20	0.000200	0.999869
21	0.000081	0.999950

k = 160.0
Mean = 8.42
Variance = 8.86

n	P(n)	F(n)
0	0.000273	0.000273
1	0.002182	0.002455
2	0.008783	0.011238
3	0.023714	0.034951
4	0.048316	0.083267
5	0.079239	0.162506
6	0.108953	0.271460
7	0.129188	0.400647
8	0.134839	0.535487
9	0.125850	0.661337
10	0.106343	0.767680
11	0.082174	0.849855
12	0.058549	0.908404
13	0.038733	0.947137
14	0.023931	0.971068

n	P(n)	F(n)
15	0.013880	0.984948
16	0.007591	0.992539
17	0.003929	0.996468
18	0.001932	0.998400
19	0.000905	0.999305
20	0.000405	0.999710
21	0.000174	0.999883
22	0.000071	0.999955

k = 170.0
Mean = 8.95
Variance = 9.42

n	P(n)	F(n)
0	0.000163	0.000163
1	0.001388	0.001551
2	0.005934	0.007486
3	0.017012	0.024497
4	0.036788	0.061285
5	0.064010	0.125295
6	0.093348	0.218644
7	0.117352	0.335996
8	0.129821	0.465817
9	0.128379	0.594196
10	0.114899	0.709094
11	0.094008	0.803103
12	0.070898	0.874000
13	0.049628	0.923629
14	0.032436	0.956065
15	0.019894	0.975959
16	0.011501	0.987460
17	0.006292	0.993752
18	0.003268	0.997020
19	0.001617	0.998637
20	0.000764	0.999401
21	0.000346	0.999746
22	0.000150	0.999896
23	0.000063	0.999959

k = 180.0
Mean = 9.47
Variance = 9.97

n	P(n)	F(n)
0	0.000098	0.000098
1	0.000880	0.000978
2	0.003982	0.004960
3	0.012079	0.017039
4	0.027631	0.044669
5	0.050840	0.095510
6	0.078379	0.173889
7	0.104132	0.278021
8	0.121704	0.399725
9	0.127113	0.526839
10	0.120122	0.646961
11	0.103742	0.750703
12	0.082561	0.833264
13	0.060968	0.894232
14	0.042025	0.936257

n	P(n)	F(n)
15	0.027176	0.963433
16	0.016560	0.979993
17	0.009547	0.989539
18	0.005224	0.994763
19	0.002722	0.997485
20	0.001354	0.998840
21	0.000645	0.999485
22	0.000295	0.999779
23	0.000129	0.999908

k = 190·0
Mean = 10·00
Variance = 10·53

n	P(n)	F(n)
0	0.000059	0.000059
1	0.000556	0.000615
2	0.002656	0.003270
3	0.008498	0.011769
4	0.020502	0.032271
5	0.039774	0.072045
6	0.064633	0.136678
7	0.090486	0.227164
8	0.111411	0.338575
9	0.122552	0.461127
10	0.121939	0.583067
11	0.110854	0.693921
12	0.092840	0.786761
13	0.072130	0.858891
14	0.052294	0.911185
15	0.035560	0.946745
16	0.022781	0.969526
17	0.013802	0.983328
18	0.007936	0.991264
19	0.004344	0.995608
20	0.002270	0.997878
21	0.001135	0.999013
22	0.000544	0.999557
23	0.000251	0.999808
24	0.000111	0.999919

k = 200·0
Mean = 10·53
Variance = 11·08

n	P(n)	F(n)
0	0.000035	0.000035
1	0.000351	0.000386
2	0.001761	0.002147
3	0.005930	0.008077
4	0.015047	0.023124
5	0.030697	0.053821
6	0.052440	0.106262
7	0.077162	0.183424
8	0.099829	0.283253
9	0.115358	0.398610
10	0.120549	0.519159
11	0.115069	0.634228
12	0.101165	0.735393
13	0.082488	0.817882
14	0.062750	0.880632
15	0.044762	0.925394
16	0.030074	0.955468
17	0.019106	0.974574
18	0.011517	0.986091
19	0.006607	0.992698
20	0.003617	0.996315
21	0.001895	0.998210
22	0.000952	0.999161
23	0.000459	0.999621
24	0.000213	0.999834
25	0.000096	0.999930